COURSE OF THEORETICAL PHYSICS

Volume 8

ELECTRODYNAMICS OF CONTINUOUS MEDIA

COURSE OF THEORETICAL PHYSICS

Vol. 1. *Mechanics*

Vol. 2. *The Classical Theory of Fields*

Vol. 3. *Quantum Mechanics—Non-relativistic Theory*

Vol. 4. *Relativistic Quantum Theory*

Vol. 5. *Statistical Physics*

Vol. 6. *Fluid Mechanics*

Vol. 7. *Theory of Elasticity*

Vol. 9. *Physical Kinetics*

ELECTRODYNAMICS OF CONTINUOUS MEDIA

by

L. D. LANDAU AND E. M. LIFSHITZ

INSTITUTE OF PHYSICAL PROBLEMS, U.S.S.R. ACADEMY OF SCIENCES

Volume 8 of *Course of Theoretical Physics*

Translated from the Russian by

J. B. SYKES AND J. S. BELL

PERGAMON PRESS

Oxford · London · New York · Paris

1960

ADDISON-WESLEY PUBLISHING COMPANY, INC.

Reading, Massachusetts

PERGAMON PRESS LTD.
Headington Hill Hall, Oxford
4 and 5 Fitzroy Square, London W.1

PERGAMON PRESS S.A.R.L.
24 Rue des Écoles, Paris Ve

First published in English 1960

SOLE DISTRIBUTORS IN THE UNITED STATES
Addison-Wesley Publishing Company, Inc.
Reading, Massachusetts, U.S.A.

Library of Congress Card Number 60-14731

Printed in Great Britain by J. W. Arrowsmith Ltd., Bristol

CONTENTS

PREFACE

THE present volume in the *Course of Theoretical Physics* deals with the theory of electromagnetic fields in matter and with the theory of the macroscopic electric and magnetic properties of matter. These theories include a very wide range of topics, as may be seen from the Contents.

In writing this book we have experienced considerable difficulties, partly because of the need to make a selection from the extensive existing material, and partly because the customary exposition of many topics to be included does not possess the necessary physical clarity, and sometimes is actually wrong. We realise that our own treatment still has many defects, which we hope to correct in future editions.

We are grateful to Professor V. L. GINZBURG, who read the book in manuscript and made some useful comments. I. E. DZYALOSHINSKIĬ and L. P. PITAEVSKIĬ gave great help in reading the proofs of the Russian edition. Thanks are due also to Dr SYKES and Dr BELL, who not only carried out excellently the arduous task of translating the book, but also made some useful comments concerning its contents.

L. D. LANDAU
E. M. LIFSHITZ

Moscow
June, 1959

NOTATION

Electric field **E**

Electric induction **D**

Magnetic field **H**

Magnetic induction **B**

External electric field $\mathfrak{E}$

External magnetic field $\mathfrak{H}$

Dielectric polarisation **P**

Magnetisation **M**

Total electric moment of a body $\mathscr{P}$

Total magnetic moment of a body $\mathscr{M}$

Dielectric permeability ϵ

Magnetic permeability μ

Current density **j**

Conductivity σ

Absolute temperature (in energy units) T

Thermodynamic quantities:	per unit volume	for a body
entropy	S	$\mathscr{S}$
internal energy	U	$\mathscr{U}$
free energy	F	$\mathscr{F}$
thermodynamic potential	Φ	$\wp$

Chemical potential ζ

A complex periodic time factor is always taken as $e^{-i\omega t}$.

The summation convention always applies to three-dimensional (Latin) and two-dimensional (Greek) suffixes occurring twice in vector and tensor expressions.

CHAPTER I

ELECTROSTATICS OF CONDUCTORS

§1. The electrostatic field of conductors

LIKE all macroscopic theories, the theory of electromagnetic fields in matter deals with physical quantities averaged over elements of volume which are "physically infinitesimal", ignoring the microscopic variations of the quantities which result from the molecular structure of matter. For example, instead of the actual "microscopic" value of the electric field **e**, we discuss its averaged value, denoted by **E**:

$$\bar{\mathbf{e}} = \mathbf{E}. \tag{1.1}$$

The fundamental equations of the electrodynamics of continuous media are obtained by averaging the equations for the electromagnetic field in a vacuum. This method of obtaining the macroscopic equations from the microscopic was first used by H. A. LORENTZ.

The form of the equations of macroscopic electrodynamics and the significance of the quantities appearing in them depend essentially on the physical nature of the medium, and on the way in which the field varies with time. It is therefore reasonable to derive and investigate these equations separately for each type of physical object.

It is well known that all bodies can be divided, as regards their electric properties, into two classes, *conductors* and *dielectrics*, differing in that any electric field causes in a conductor, but not in a dielectric, the motion of charges, i.e. an *electric current.*†

Let us begin by studying the constant electric fields produced by charged conductors, that is, the *electrostatics of conductors*. First of all, it follows from the fundamental property of conductors that, in the electrostatic case, the electric field inside a conductor must be zero. For a field **E** which was not zero would cause a current; the propagation of a current in a conductor involves a dissipation of energy, and hence cannot occur in a stationary state (with no external sources of energy).

Hence it follows, in turn, that any charges in a conductor must be located on its surface. The presence of charges inside a conductor would necessarily cause an electric field in it;‡ they can be distributed on its surface, however,

---

† It should be mentioned that the conductor is here assumed to be homogeneous (in composition, temperature, etc.). In an inhomogeneous conductor, as we shall see later, there may be fields which cause no motion of charges.

‡ This is clearly seen from equation (1.8) below.

in such a way that the fields which they produce in its interior are mutually balanced.

Thus the problem of the electrostatics of conductors amounts to determining the electric field in the vacuum outside the conductors and the distribution of charges on their surfaces.

At any point far from the surface of the body, the mean field **E** in the vacuum is almost the same as the actual field **e**. The two fields differ only in the immediate neighbourhood of the body, where the effect of the irregular molecular fields is noticeable, and this difference does not affect the averaged field equations. The exact microscopic Maxwell's equations in the vacuum are

$$\mathrm{div}\,\mathbf{e} = 0. \tag{1.2}$$

$$\mathbf{curl}\,\mathbf{e} = -(1/c)\partial\mathbf{h}/\partial t, \tag{1.3}$$

where **h** is the microscopic magnetic field. Since the mean magnetic field is assumed to be zero, the derivative $\partial\mathbf{h}/\partial t$ also vanishes on averaging, and we find that the constant electric field in the vacuum satisfies the usual equations

$$\mathrm{div}\,\mathbf{E} = 0, \qquad \mathbf{curl}\,\mathbf{E} = 0, \tag{1.4}$$

i.e. it is a potential field with a potential ϕ such that

$$\mathbf{E} = -\mathbf{grad}\,\phi, \tag{1.5}$$

and ϕ satisfies Laplace's equation

$$\triangle\phi = 0. \tag{1.6}$$

The boundary conditions on the field **E** at the surface of a conductor follow from the equation $\mathbf{curl}\,\mathbf{E} = 0$, which, like the original equation (1.3), is valid both outside and inside the body. Let us take the z-axis in the direction of the normal to the surface at some point on the conductor. The component E_z of the field takes very large values in the immediate neighbourhood of the surface (because there is a finite potential difference over a very small distance). This large field pertains to the surface itself and depends on the physical properties of the surface, but is not involved in our electrostatic problem, because it falls off over distances comparable with the distances between atoms. It is important to note, however, that, if the surface is homogeneous, the derivatives $\partial E_z/\partial x$, $\partial E_z/\partial y$ along the surface remain finite, even though E_z itself becomes very large. Hence, since $(\mathbf{curl}\,\mathbf{E})_x = \partial E_z/\partial y - \partial E_y/\partial z = 0$, we find that $\partial E_y/\partial z$ is finite. This means that E_y is continuous at the surface, since a discontinuity in E_y would mean an infinity of the derivative $\partial E_y/\partial z$. The same applies to E_x, and since $\mathbf{E} = 0$ inside the conductor, we reach the conclusion that the tangential components of the external field at the surface must be zero:

$$\mathbf{E}_t = 0. \tag{1.7}$$

Thus the electrostatic field must be normal to the surface of the conductor at every point. Since $\mathbf{E} = -\mathbf{grad}\,\phi$, this means that the field potential must be constant on the surface on any particular conductor. In other words, the surface of a homogeneous conductor is an equipotential surface of the electrostatic field.

The component of the field normal to the surface is very simply related to the charge density on the surface. The relation is obtained from the general electrostatic equation $\operatorname{div} \mathbf{e} = 4\pi\rho$, which on averaging gives

$$\operatorname{div} \mathbf{E} = 4\pi\bar{\rho}, \tag{1.8}$$

$\bar{\rho}$ being the mean charge density. The meaning of the integrated form of this equation is well known: the flux of the electric field through a closed surface is equal to the total charge inside that surface, multiplied by 4π. Applying this theorem to a volume element lying between two infinitesimally close unit areas, one on each side of the surface of the conductor, and using the fact that $\mathbf{E} = 0$ on the inner area, we find that $E_n = 4\pi\sigma$, where σ is the surface charge density, i.e. the charge per unit area of the surface of the conductor. Thus the distribution of charges over the surface of the conductor is given by the formula

$$4\pi\sigma = E_n = -\partial\phi/\partial n, \tag{1.9}$$

the derivative of the potential being taken along the outward normal to the surface. The total charge on the conductor is

$$e = -\frac{1}{4\pi}\oint \frac{\partial\phi}{\partial n}\,\mathrm{d}f, \tag{1.10}$$

the integral being taken over the whole surface.

The potential distribution in the electrostatic field has the following remarkable property: the function $\phi(x, y, z)$ can take maximum and minimum values only at boundaries of regions where there is a field. This theorem can also be formulated thus: a test charge e introduced into the field cannot be in stable equilibrium, since there is no point at which its potential energy $e\phi$ would have a minimum.

The proof of the theorem is very simple. Let us suppose, for example, that the potential has a maximum at some point A not on the boundary of a region where there is a field. Then the point A can be surrounded by a small closed surface on which the normal derivative $\partial\phi/\partial n < 0$ everywhere. Consequently, the integral over this surface $\oint(\partial\phi/\partial n)\,\mathrm{d}f < 0$. But by Laplace's equation $\oint(\partial\phi/\partial n)\,\mathrm{d}f = \int \triangle\phi\,\mathrm{d}V = 0$, giving a contradiction.

§2. The energy of the electrostatic field of conductors

Let us calculate the total energy $\mathscr{U}$ of the electrostatic field of charged conductors,†

$$\mathscr{U} = \frac{1}{8\pi}\int E^2\,\mathrm{d}V, \tag{2.1}$$

† The square E^2 is not the same as the mean square $\overline{e^2}$ of the actual field near the surface of a conductor or inside it (where $E = 0$ but, of course, $\overline{e^2} \neq 0$). By calculating the integral (2.1) we ignore the internal energy of the conductor as such, which is here of no interest, and the affinity of the charges for the surface.

where the integral is taken over all space outside the conductors. We transform this integral as follows:

$$\mathscr{U} = -\frac{1}{8\pi}\int \mathbf{E}\cdot\mathbf{grad}\,\phi\,\mathrm{d}V = -\frac{1}{8\pi}\int \mathrm{div}\,(\phi\mathbf{E})\,\mathrm{d}V + \frac{1}{8\pi}\int \phi\,\mathrm{div}\,\mathbf{E}\,\mathrm{d}V.$$

The second integral vanishes by (1.4), and the first can be transformed into integrals over the surfaces of the conductors which bound the field and over an infinitely remote surface. The latter of these vanishes, because the field diminishes sufficiently rapidly at infinity. Denoting by ϕ_a the constant value of the potential on the ath conductor, we have†

$$\mathscr{U} = \frac{1}{8\pi}\sum_a \oint \phi E_n\,\mathrm{d}f = \frac{1}{8\pi}\sum_a \phi_a \oint E_n\,\mathrm{d}f.$$

Finally, since the total charges e_a on the conductors are given by (1.10) we obtain

$$\mathscr{U} = \tfrac{1}{2}\sum_a e_a\,\phi_a, \tag{2.2}$$

which is analogous to the expression for the energy of a system of point charges.

The charges and potentials of the conductors cannot both be arbitrarily prescribed; there are certain relations between them. Since the field equations in a vacuum are linear and homogeneous, these relations must also be linear, i.e. they must be given by equations of the form

$$e_a = \sum_b C_{ab}\,\phi_b, \qquad (2.3$$

where the quantities C_{aa}, C_{ab} have the dimensions of length and depend on the shape and relative position of the conductors. The quantities C_{aa} are called *capacity coefficients*, and the quantities C_{ab} ($a \neq b$) are called *electrostatic induction coefficients*. In particular, if there is only one conductor, we have $e = C\phi$, where C is the *capacity*, which in order of magnitude is equal to the linear dimension of the body. The converse relations, giving the potentials in terms of the charges, are

$$\phi_a = \sum_b C^{-1}{}_{ab}\,e_b, \tag{2.4}$$

where the coefficients $C^{-1}{}_{ab}$ form a matrix which is the inverse of the matrix C_{ab}.

Let us calculate the change in the energy of a system of conductors caused by an infinitesimal change in their charges or potentials. Varying the original

† In transforming volume integrals into surface integrals, both here and later, it must be borne in mind that E_n is the component of the field along the outward normal to the conductor. This direction is opposite to that of the outward normal to the region of the volume integration, namely the space outside the conductors. The sign of the integral is therefore changed in the transformation.

expression (2.1), we have $\delta\mathscr{U} = (1/4\pi)\int \mathbf{E}\cdot\delta\mathbf{E}\,\mathrm{d}V$. This can be further transformed by two equivalent methods. Putting $\mathbf{E} = -\mathbf{grad}\,\phi$ and using the fact that the varied field, like the original field, satisfies equations (1.4) (so that div $\delta\mathbf{E} = 0$), we can write

$$\delta\mathscr{U} = -\frac{1}{4\pi}\int \mathbf{grad}\,\phi\cdot\delta\mathbf{E}\,\mathrm{d}V = -\frac{1}{4\pi}\int \operatorname{div}(\phi\,\delta\mathbf{E})\,\mathrm{d}V$$
$$= \frac{1}{4\pi}\sum_a \phi_a \oint \delta E_n\,\mathrm{d}f,$$

that is

$$\delta\mathscr{U} = \sum_a \phi_a\,\delta e_a, \tag{2.5}$$

which gives the change in energy due to a change in the charges. This result is obvious; it is the work required to bring infinitesimal charges δe_a to the various conductors from infinity, where the field potential is zero.

On the other hand, we can write

$$\delta\mathscr{U} = -\frac{1}{4\pi}\int \mathbf{E}\cdot\mathbf{grad}\,\delta\phi\,\mathrm{d}V = -\frac{1}{4\pi}\int \operatorname{div}(\mathbf{E}\,\delta\phi)\,\mathrm{d}V$$
$$= \frac{1}{4\pi}\sum_a \delta\phi_a \oint E_n\,\mathrm{d}f,$$

that is

$$\delta\mathscr{U} = \sum_a e_a\,\delta\phi_a, \tag{2.6}$$

which expresses the change in energy in terms of the change in the potentials of the conductors.

Formulae (2.5) and (2.6) show that, by differentiating the energy $\mathscr{U}$ with respect to the charges, we obtain the potentials of the conductors, and the derivatives of $\mathscr{U}$ with respect to the potentials are the charges:

$$\partial\mathscr{U}/\partial e_a = \phi_a, \qquad \partial\mathscr{U}/\partial\phi_a = e_a. \tag{2.7}$$

But the potentials and charges are linear functions of each other. Using (2.3) we have $\partial^2\mathscr{U}/\partial\phi_a\partial\phi_b = \partial e_b/\partial\phi_a = C_{ba}$, and by reversing the order of differentiation we get C_{ab}. Hence it follows that

$$C_{ab} = C_{ba}, \tag{2.8}$$

and similarly $C^{-1}{}_{ab} = C^{-1}{}_{ba}$. The energy $\mathscr{U}$ can be written as a quadratic form in either the potentials or the charges:

$$\mathscr{U} = \tfrac{1}{2}\sum_{a,b} C_{ab}\,\phi_a\phi_b = \tfrac{1}{2}\sum_{a,b} C^{-1}{}_{ab}\,e_a e_b. \tag{2.9}$$

This quadratic form must be positive definite, like the original expression (2.1). From this condition we can derive various inequalities which the coefficients C_{ab} must satisfy. In particular, all the capacity coefficients are positive:

$$C_{aa} > 0 \tag{2.10}$$

(and also $C^{-1}{}_{aa} > 0$).†

All the electrostatic induction coefficients, on the other hand, are negative:

$$C_{ab} < 0 \quad (a \neq b). \tag{2.11}$$

That this must be so is seen from the following simple arguments. Let us suppose that every conductor except the ath is earthed, i.e. their potentials are zero. Then the charge induced by the charged ath conductor on another (the bth, say) is $e_b = C_{ba}\phi_a$. It is obvious that the sign of the induced charge must be opposite to that of the inducing potential, and therefore $C_{ab} < 0$. This can be more rigorously shown from the fact that the potential of the electrostatic field cannot reach a maximum or minimum outside the conductors. For example, let the potential ϕ_a of the only conductor not earthed be positive. Then the potential is positive in all space, its least value (zero) being attained only on the earthed conductors. Hence it follows that the normal derivative $\partial\phi/\partial n$ of the potential on the surfaces of these conductors is positive, and their charges are therefore negative, by (1.10). Similar arguments show that $C^{-1}{}_{ab} > 0$.

The energy of the electrostatic field of conductors has a certain extremum property, though this property is more formal than physical. To derive it, let us suppose that the charge distribution on the conductors undergoes an infinitesimal change (the total charge on each conductor remaining unaltered), in which the charges may penetrate into the conductors; we ignore the fact that such a charge distribution cannot in reality be stationary. We consider the change in the integral $\mathscr{U} = (1/8\pi)\int E^2 \mathrm{d}V$, which must now be extended over all space, including the volumes of the conductors themselves (since after the displacement of the charges the field $\mathbf{E}$ may not be zero inside the conductors). We write

$$\begin{aligned}\delta\mathscr{U} &= -\frac{1}{4\pi}\int \mathbf{grad}\,\phi\cdot\delta\mathbf{E}\,\mathrm{d}V \\ &= -\frac{1}{4\pi}\int \operatorname{div}(\phi\delta\mathbf{E})\,\mathrm{d}V + \frac{1}{4\pi}\int \phi\operatorname{div}\delta\mathbf{E}\,\mathrm{d}V.\end{aligned}$$

The first integral vanishes, being equivalent to one over an infinitely remote surface. In the second integral, we have by (1.8) $\operatorname{div}\delta\mathbf{E} = 4\pi\delta\bar{\rho}$, so that $\delta\mathscr{U} = \int \phi\delta\bar{\rho}\,\mathrm{d}V$. This integral vanishes if ϕ is the potential of the true electrostatic field, since then ϕ is constant inside each conductor, and the integral $\int \delta\bar{\rho}\,\mathrm{d}V$ over the volume of each conductor is zero, since its total charge remains unaltered.

† We may also mention that another inequality which must be satisfied if the form (2.9) is positive is $C_{aa}C_{bb} > C_{ab}{}^2$.

Thus the energy of the actual electrostatic field is a minimum† relative to the energies of fields which could be produced by any other distribution of the charges on or in the conductors (*Thomson's theorem*).

From this theorem it follows, in particular, that the introduction of an uncharged conductor into the field of given charges (charged conductors) reduces the total energy of the field. To prove this, it is sufficient to compare the energy of the actual field resulting from the introduction of the uncharged conductor with the energy of the fictitious field in which there are no induced charges on that conductor. The former energy, since it has the least possible value, is less than the latter energy, which is also the energy of the original field (since, in the absence of induced charges, the field would penetrate into the conductor, remaining unaltered). This result can also be formulated thus: an uncharged conductor remote from a system of given charges is attracted towards the system.

Finally, it can be shown that a conductor (charged or not) brought into an electrostatic field cannot be in stable equilibrium under electric forces alone. This assertion generalises the theorem for a point charge proved at the end of §1, and can be derived by combining the latter theorem with Thomson's theorem. We shall not pause to give the derivation in detail.

Formulae (2.9) are useful for calculating the energy of a system of conductors at finite distances apart. The energy of an uncharged conductor in a uniform external field $\mathfrak{E}$, which may be imagined as due to charges at infinity, requires special consideration. According to (2.2), this energy is $\mathscr{U} = \frac{1}{2}e\phi$, where e is the remote charge which causes the field, and ϕ is the potential at this charge due to the conductor. $\mathscr{U}$ does not include the energy of the charge e in its own field, since we are interested only in the energy of the conductor. The charge on the conductor is zero, but the external field causes it to acquire a dipole electric moment, which we denote by $\mathscr{P}$. The potential of the electric dipole field at a large distance $\mathbf{r}$ from it is $\phi = \mathscr{P}\cdot\mathbf{r}/r^3$. Hence $\mathscr{U} = e\mathscr{P}\cdot\mathbf{r}/2r^3$. But $-e\mathbf{r}/r^3$ is just the field $\mathfrak{E}$ due to the charge e. Thus

$$\mathscr{U} = -\tfrac{1}{2}\,\mathscr{P}\cdot\mathfrak{E}. \tag{2.12}$$

Since all the field equations are linear, it is evident that the components of the dipole moment $\mathscr{P}$ are linear functions of the components of the field $\mathfrak{E}$. The coefficients of proportionality between $\mathscr{P}$ and $\mathfrak{E}$ have the dimensions of length cubed, and are therefore proportional to the volume of the conductor:

$$\mathscr{P}_i = V\alpha_{ik}\mathfrak{E}_k, \tag{2.13}$$

where the coefficients α_{ik} depend only on the shape of the body. The quantities $V\alpha_{ik}$ form a tensor, which may be called the *polarisability tensor* of the body.

† We shall not give here the simple arguments which demonstrate that the extremum is a minimum.

This tensor is symmetrical: $\alpha_{ik} = \alpha_{ki}$, a statement which will be proved in §11. Accordingly, the energy (2.12) is

$$\mathscr{U} = -\tfrac{1}{2}V\alpha_{ik}\mathfrak{E}_i\mathfrak{E}_k. \tag{2.14}$$

PROBLEMS

PROBLEM 1. Express the mutual capacity C of two conductors (with charges $\pm e$) in terms of the coefficients C_{ab}.

SOLUTION. The *mutual capacity* of two conductors is defined as the coefficient C in the relation $e = C(\phi_2-\phi_1)$, and the energy of the system is given in terms of C by $\mathscr{U} = \frac{1}{2}e^2/C$. Comparing with (2.9), we obtain

$$\begin{aligned} 1/C &= C^{-1}{}_{11}-2C^{-1}{}_{12}+C^{-1}{}_{22} \\ &= (C_{11}+2C_{12}+C_{22})/(C_{11}C_{22}-C_{12}^2). \end{aligned}$$

PROBLEM 2. A point charge e is situated at O, near a system of earthed conductors, and induces on them charges e_a. If the charge e were absent, and the ath conductor were at potential ϕ'_a, the remainder being earthed, the field potential at O would be ϕ'_0. Express the charges e_a in terms of ϕ'_a and ϕ'_0.

SOLUTION. If charges e_a on the conductors give them potentials ϕ_a, and similarly for e'_a and ϕ'_a, it follows from (2.3) that

$$\sum_a \phi_a e'_a = \sum_{a,b} \phi_a C_{ab}\phi'_b = \sum_a \phi'_a e_a.$$

We apply this relation to two states of the system formed by all the conductors and the charge e (regarding the latter as a very small conductor). In one state the charge e is present, the charges on the conductors are e_a, and their potentials are zero. In the other state the charge e is zero, and one of the conductors has a potential $\phi'_a \neq 0$. Then we have $e\phi'_0+e_a\phi'_a = 0$, whence $e_a = -e\phi'_0/\phi'_a$.

For example, if a charge e is at a distance r from the centre of an earthed conducting sphere of radius $a(< r)$, then $\phi'_0 = \phi'_a a/r$, and the charge induced on the sphere is $e_a = -ea/r$.

As a second example, let us consider a charge e placed between two concentric conducting spheres of radii a and b, at a distance r from the centre such that $a < r < b$. If the outer sphere is earthed and the inner one is charged to potential ϕ'_a, the potential at distance r is

$$\phi'_0 = \phi'_a\frac{1/r-1/b}{1/a-1/b}.$$

Hence the charge induced on the inner sphere by the charge e is $e_a = -ea(b-r)/r(b-a)$. Similarly the charge induced on the outer sphere is $e_b = -eb(r-a)/r(b-a)$.

PROBLEM 3. Two conductors, of capacities C_1 and C_2, are placed at a distance r apart which is large compared with their dimensions. Determine the coefficients C_{ab}.

SOLUTION. If conductor 1 has a charge e_1, and conductor 2 is uncharged, then in the first approximation $\phi_1 = e_1/C_1$, $\phi_2 = e_1/r$; here we neglect the variation of the field over conductor 2 and its polarisation. Thus $C^{-1}{}_{11} = 1/C_1$, $C^{-1}{}_{12} = 1/r$, and similarly $C^{-1}{}_{22} = 1/C_2$. Hence we find†

$$C_{11} = C_1\left(1+\frac{C_1C_2}{r^2}\right), \qquad C_{12} = -\frac{C_1C_2}{r}, \qquad C_{22} = C_2\left(1+\frac{C_1C_2}{r^2}\right).$$

† The subsequent terms in the expansion are in general of order (in $1/r$) one higher than those given. If, however, r is taken as the distance between the "centres of charge" of the two bodies (for spheres, between the geometrical centres), then the order of the subsequent terms is two higher.

PROBLEM 4. Determine the capacity of a ring (radius b) of thin conducting wire of circular cross-section (radius $a \ll b$).

SOLUTION. Since the wire is thin, the field at the surface of the ring is almost the same as that of charges distributed along the axis of the wire (for a right cylinder, it would be exactly the same). Hence the potential of the ring is

$$\phi_a = \frac{e}{2\pi b}\oint \frac{dl}{r},$$

where r is the distance from a point on the surface of the ring to an element dl of the axis of the wire, the integration being over all such elements. We divide the integral into two parts corresponding to $r < \Delta$ and $r > \Delta$, Δ being a distance such that $a \ll \Delta \ll b$. Then for $r < \Delta$ the segment of the ring concerned may be regarded as straight, and therefore

$$\oint\limits_{\Delta>r} \frac{dl}{r} = \int\limits_{-\Delta}^{\Delta} \frac{dl}{\sqrt{(l^2+a^2)}} \cong 2\log(2\Delta/a).$$

In the range $r > \Delta$ the thickness of the wire may be neglected, i.e. r may be taken as the distance between two points on its axis. Then

$$\oint\limits_{r>\Delta} \frac{dl}{r} = 2\int\limits_{\varphi_0}^{\pi} \frac{b\,d\phi}{2b\sin\frac{1}{2}\phi} = -2\log\tan\tfrac{1}{4}\phi_0,$$

where ϕ is the angle subtended at the centre of the ring by the chord r, and the lower limit of integration is such that $2b\sin\frac{1}{2}\phi_0 = \Delta$, whence $\phi_0 \cong \Delta/b$. When the two parts of the integral are added, Δ cancels, and the capacity of the ring is

$$C = \frac{e}{\phi_a} = \frac{\pi b}{\log(8b/a)}.$$

§3. Methods of solving problems in electrostatics

The general methods of solving Laplace's equation for given boundary conditions on certain surfaces are studied in mathematical physics, and we shall not give a detailed description of them here. We shall merely mention some of the more elementary procedures and solve various problems of intrinsic interest.†

(1) *The method of images.* The simplest example of the use of this method is to determine the field due to a point charge e outside a conducting medium which occupies a half-space. The principle of the method is to find fictitious point charges which, together with the given charge or charges, produce a field such that the surface of the conductor is an equipotential surface. In the case just mentioned, this is achieved by placing a fictitious charge $e' = -e$ at a point which is the image of e in the plane which bounds the conducting medium. The potential of the field due to the charge e and its image e' is

$$\phi = e\left(\frac{1}{r} - \frac{1}{r}\right), \tag{3.1}$$

† The solutions of many more complex problems are given by W. R. SMYTHE, *Static and Dynamic Electricity*, 2nd ed., McGraw-Hill, New York, 1950; G. A. GRINBERG, *Selected Problems in the Mathematical Theory of Electric and Magnetic Phenomena* (*Izbrannye voprosy matematicheskoĭ teorii élektricheskikh i magnitnykh yavleniĭ*), Moscow, 1948.

where r and r' are the distances of a point from the charges e and e'. On the bounding plane, $r = r'$ and the potential has the constant value zero, so that the necessary boundary condition is satisfied and (3.1) gives the solution of the problem. It may be noted that the charge e is attracted to the conductor by a force $e^2/(2a)^2$ (the *image force*; a is the distance of the charge from the conductor), and the energy of their interaction is $-e^2/4a$.

The distribution of surface charge induced on the bounding plane by the point charge e is given by

$$\sigma = -\frac{1}{4\pi}\left[\frac{\partial\phi}{\partial n}\right]_{r=r'} = -\frac{e}{2\pi}\frac{a}{r^3}. \tag{3.2}$$

It is easy to see that the total charge on the plane is $\int \sigma \mathrm{d}f = -e$, as it should be.

The total charge induced on an originally uncharged insulated conductor by other charges is, of course, zero. Hence, if in the present case the conducting medium (in reality a large conductor) is insulated, we must suppose that, besides the charge $-e$, a charge $+e$ is also induced, which, however, has no finite density, being distributed over the large surface of the conductor.

Next, let us consider a more difficult problem, that of the field due to a point charge e near a spherical conductor. To solve this problem, we use the following result, which can easily be proved by direct calculation. The potential of the field due to two point charges e and $-e'$, namely $\phi = e/r - e'/r'$, vanishes on the surface of a sphere whose centre is on the line joining the charges (but not between them). If the radius of the sphere is R and its centre is distant l and l' from the two charges, then $l/l' = (e/e')^2$, $R^2 = ll'$.

Let us first suppose that the spherical conductor is maintained at a constant potential $\phi = 0$, i.e. it is earthed. Then the field outside the sphere due to the point charge e at A (Fig. 1), at a distance l from the centre of the sphere, is the same as the field due to two charges, namely the given charge e and a fictitious charge $-e'$ at A' inside the sphere, at a distance l' from its centre, where

$$l' = R^2/l, \qquad e' = eR/l. \tag{3.3}$$

The potential of this field is

$$\phi = \frac{e}{r} - \frac{eR}{lr'}, \tag{3.4}$$

r and r' being as shown in Fig. 1. A non-zero total charge $-e'$ is induced on the surface of the sphere. The energy of the interaction between the charge and the sphere is

$$\mathscr{U} = -\tfrac{1}{2}ee'/(l-l') = -\tfrac{1}{2}e^2R/(l^2-R^2), \tag{3.5}$$

and the charge is attracted to the sphere by a force $F = -\partial\mathscr{U}/\partial l = -e^2lR/(l^2-R^2)^2$.

If the total charge on the spherical conductor is kept equal to zero (an insulated uncharged sphere), a further fictitious charge must be introduced, such that the total charge induced on the surface of the sphere is zero, and the potential on that surface is still constant. This is done by placing a charge $+e'$ at the centre of the sphere. The potential of the required field is then given by the formula

$$\phi = \frac{e}{r} - \frac{e'}{r'} + \frac{e'}{r_0}. \tag{3.6}$$

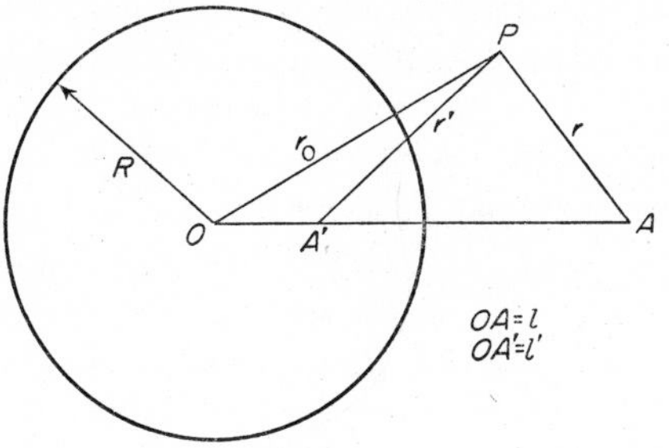

FIG. 1

The energy of interaction in this case is

$$\mathscr{U} = \tfrac{1}{2} ee'\left(\frac{1}{l} - \frac{1}{l-l'}\right) = -\frac{e^2R^3}{2l^2(l^2-R^2)}. \tag{3.7}$$

Finally, if the charge e is at A' (Fig. 1) in a spherical cavity in a conducting medium, the field inside the cavity must be the same as the field due to the charge e at A' and its image at A outside the sphere, regardless of whether the conductor is earthed or insulated:

$$\phi = \frac{e}{r'} - \frac{eR}{l'r}. \tag{3.8}$$

(2) *The method of inversion.* There is a simple method whereby in some cases a known solution of one electrostatic problem gives the solution of another problem. This method is based on the invariance of Laplace's equation with respect to a certain transformation of the variables.

In spherical co-ordinates Laplace's equation has the form

$$\frac{1}{r^2}\frac{\partial}{\partial r}\left(r^2\frac{\partial\phi}{\partial r}\right) + \frac{1}{r^2}\triangle_\Omega\phi = 0,$$

where $\triangle_\Omega$ denotes the angular part of the Laplacian operator. It is easy to see that this equation is unaltered in form if the variable r is replaced by a new variable r' such that

$$r = R^2/r' \tag{3.9}$$

(the *inversion transformation*) and at the same time the unknown function ϕ is replaced by ϕ' such that

$$\phi = r'\phi'/R. \tag{3.10}$$

Here R is some constant having the dimensions of length (the *radius of inversion*). Thus, if the function $\phi(\mathbf{r})$ satisfies Laplace's equation, then so does the function

$$\phi'(\mathbf{r}') = R\phi(R^2\mathbf{r}'/r'^2)/r'. \tag{3.11}$$

Let us assume that we know the electrostatic field due to some system of conductors, all at the same potential ϕ_0, and point charges. The potential $\phi(\mathbf{r})$ is usually defined so as to vanish at infinity. Here, however, we shall define $\phi(\mathbf{r})$ so that it tends to $-\phi_0$ at infinity. Then $\phi = 0$ on the conductors.

We may now ascertain what problem of electrostatics will be solved by the transformed function (3.11). First of all, the shapes and relative positions of all the conductors of finite size will be changed. The boundary condition of constant potential on their surfaces will be automatically satisfied, since $\phi' = 0$ if $\phi = 0$. Furthermore, the positions and magnitudes of all the point charges will be changed. A charge e at a point $\mathbf{r}_0$ moves to $\mathbf{r}'_0 = R^2\mathbf{r}_0/r_0^2$ and takes a value e' which can be determined as follows. As $\mathbf{r} \to \mathbf{r}_0$ the potential $\phi(\mathbf{r})$ tends to infinity as $e/|\delta\mathbf{r}|$, where $\delta\mathbf{r} = \mathbf{r}-\mathbf{r}_0$. Differentiating the relation $\mathbf{r} = R^2\mathbf{r}'/r'^2$, we find that the magnitudes of the small differences $\delta\mathbf{r}$ and $\delta\mathbf{r}' = \mathbf{r}'-\mathbf{r}'_0$ are related by $(\delta\mathbf{r})^2 = R^4(\delta\mathbf{r}')^2/r'^4_0$. Hence, as $\mathbf{r}' \to \mathbf{r}'_0$, the function ϕ' tends to infinity as $eR/r'_0|\delta\mathbf{r}| = er'_0/R|\delta\mathbf{r}'|$, corresponding to a charge

$$e' = er'_0/R = eR/r_0. \tag{3.12}$$

Finally, let us examine the behaviour of the function $\phi'(\mathbf{r}')$ near the origin. For $\mathbf{r}' = 0$ we have $\mathbf{r} \to \infty$ and $\phi(\mathbf{r}) \to -\phi_0$. Hence, as $\mathbf{r}' \to 0$, the function ϕ' tends to infinity as $-R\phi_0/r'$. This means that there is a charge $e_0 = -R\phi_0$ at the point $\mathbf{r}' = 0$.

We shall give, for reference, the way in which certain geometrical figures are transformed by inversion. A spherical surface of radius a and centre $\mathbf{r}_0$ is given by the equation $(\mathbf{r}-\mathbf{r}_0)^2 = a^2$. On inversion, this becomes $([R^2\mathbf{r}'/r'^2]-\mathbf{r}_0)^2 = a^2$, which, on multiplying by r'^2 and rearranging, can be written $(\mathbf{r}'-\mathbf{r}'_0)^2 = a'^2$, where

$$\mathbf{r}'_0 = -R^2\mathbf{r}_0/(a^2-r_0^2), \qquad a' = aR^2/|a^2-r_0^2|. \tag{3.13}$$

Thus we have another sphere, of radius a' and centre $\mathbf{r}'_0$. If the original sphere passes through the origin ($a = r_0$), then $a' = \infty$. In this case the sphere is transformed into a plane perpendicular to the vector $\mathbf{r}_0$ and distant $r'_0-a' = R^2/(a+r_0) = R^2/2a$ from the origin.

(3) *The method of conformal mapping*. A field which depends on only two Cartesian co-ordinates (x and y, say) is said to be *two-dimensional*.

The theory of functions of a complex variable is a powerful means of solving two-dimensional problems of electrostatics. The theoretical basis of the method is as follows.

An electrostatic field in a vacuum satisfies two equations: $\mathbf{curl}\,\mathbf{E} = 0$, $\operatorname{div}\mathbf{E} = 0$. The first of these makes it possible to introduce the field potential, defined by $\mathbf{E} = -\mathbf{grad}\,\phi$. The second equation shows that we can also define a *vector potential* $\mathbf{A}$ of the field, such that $\mathbf{E} = \mathbf{curl}\,\mathbf{A}$. In the two-dimensional case, the vector $\mathbf{E}$ lies in the xy-plane, and depends only on x and y. Accordingly, the vector $\mathbf{A}$ can be chosen so that it is perpendicular to the xy-plane. Then the field components are given in terms of the derivatives of ϕ and $\mathbf{A}$ by

$$E_x = -\partial\phi/\partial x = \partial A/\partial y, \qquad E_y = -\partial\phi/\partial y = -\partial A/\partial x. \tag{3.14}$$

These relations between the derivatives of ϕ and A are, mathematically, just the well-known Cauchy–Riemann conditions, which express the fact that the complex quantity

$$w = \phi - iA \tag{3.15}$$

is an analytic function of the complex argument $z = x+iy$. This means that the function $w(z)$ has a definite derivative at every point, independent of the direction in which the derivative is taken. For example, differentiating along the x-axis, we find $\mathrm{d}w/\mathrm{d}z = \partial\phi/\partial x - i\partial A/\partial x$, or

$$\mathrm{d}w/\mathrm{d}z = -E_x + iE_y. \tag{3.16}$$

The function w is called the *complex potential.*

The lines of force are defined by the equation $\mathrm{d}x/E_x = \mathrm{d}y/E_y$. Expressing E_x and E_y as derivatives of A, we can write this as $(\partial A/\partial x)\mathrm{d}x + (\partial A/\partial y)\mathrm{d}y = \mathrm{d}A = 0$, whence $A(x, y) = \text{constant}$. Thus the lines on which the imaginary part of the function $w(z)$ is constant are the lines of force. The lines on which its real part is constant are the equipotential lines. The orthogonality of these families of lines is ensured by the relations (3.14), according to which

$$\frac{\partial\phi}{\partial x}\frac{\partial A}{\partial x} + \frac{\partial\phi}{\partial y}\frac{\partial A}{\partial y} = 0.$$

Both the real and the imaginary part of an analytic function $w(z)$ satisfy Laplace's equation. We could therefore equally well take $\operatorname{im} w$ as the field potential. The lines of force would then be given by $\operatorname{re} w = \text{constant}$. Instead of (3.15) we should have $w = A + i\phi$.

The flux of the electric field through any section of an equipotential line is given by the integral $\oint E_n \mathrm{d}l = -\oint (\partial\phi/\partial n)\mathrm{d}l$, where $\mathrm{d}l$ is an element of length of the equipotential line and $\mathbf{n}$ the direction of the normal to it. According to (3.14) we have $\partial\phi/\partial n = -\partial A/\partial l$, the choice of sign denoting that l is measured to the left when one looks along $\mathbf{n}$. Thus $\oint E_n \mathrm{d}l = \oint (\partial A/\partial l)\mathrm{d}l = A_2 - A_1$, where A_2 and A_1 are the values of A at the ends of the section. In particular, since the flux of the electric field through a closed contour is $4\pi e$, where e is the total charge enclosed by the contour (per unit length of conductors perpendicular to the plane), it follows that

$$e = (1/4\pi)\Delta A, \tag{3.17}$$

where ΔA is the change in A on passing counterclockwise round the closed equipotential line.

The simplest example of the complex potential is that of the field of a charged straight wire passing through the origin and perpendicular to the plane. The field is given by $E_r = 2e/r$, $E_\theta = 0$, where r,θ are polar co-ordinates in the xy-plane, and e is the charge per unit length of the wire. The corresponding complex potential is

$$w = -2e \log z = -2e \log r - 2ie\theta. \tag{3.18}$$

If the charged wire passes through the point (x_0, y_0) instead of the origin, the complex potential is

$$w = -2e \log(z - z_0), \tag{3.19}$$

where $z_0 = x_0 + iy_0$.

Mathematically, the functional relation $w = w(z)$ constitutes a *conformal mapping* of the plane of the complex variable z on the plane of the complex variable w. Let C be the cross-sectional contour of a conductor in the xy-plane, and ϕ_0 its potential. It is clear from the above discussion that the problem of determining the field due to this conductor amounts to finding a function $w(z)$ which maps the contour C in the z-plane on the line $w = \phi_0$, parallel to the axis of ordinates, in the w-plane. Then $\operatorname{re} w$ gives the potential of the field. (If the function $w(z)$ maps the contour C on a line parallel to the axis of abscissae, then the potential is $\operatorname{im} w$.)

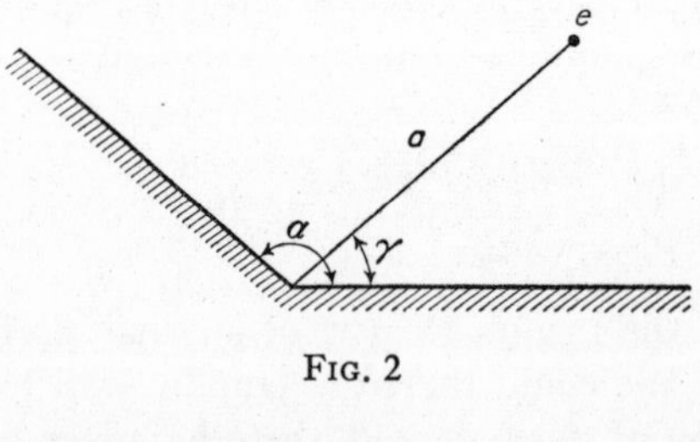

FIG. 2

(4) *The wedge problem.* We shall give here, for reference, formulae for the field due to a point charge e placed between two intersecting conducting half-planes. Let the z-axis of a system of cylindrical co-ordinates (r, θ, z) be along the apex of the wedge, the angle θ being measured from one of the planes, and let the position of the charge e be $(a, \gamma, 0)$ (Fig. 2). The angle α between the planes may be either less or greater than π; in the latter case we have a charge outside a conducting wedge.

The field potential is given by†

$$\phi = \frac{e}{\alpha\sqrt{(2ar)}}\int_{\eta}^{\infty}\left\{\frac{\sinh(\pi\zeta/\alpha)}{\cosh(\pi\zeta/\alpha)-\cos[\pi(\theta-\gamma)/\alpha]}-\frac{\sinh(\pi\zeta/\alpha)}{\cosh(\pi\zeta/\alpha)-\cos[\pi(\theta+\gamma)/\alpha]}\right\}\times$$
$$\times\frac{d\zeta}{\sqrt{(\cosh\zeta-\cosh\eta)}},\quad \cosh\eta = (a^2+r^2+z^2)/2ar,\quad \eta > 0. \tag{3.20}$$

The potential $\phi = 0$ on the surface of the conductors, i.e. for $\theta = 0$ or α.

In particular, for $\alpha = 2\pi$ we have a conducting half-plane in the field of a point charge. In this case the integral in (3.20) can be evaluated explicitly, giving

$$\left.\begin{aligned}\phi &= \frac{e}{\pi}\left\{\frac{1}{R}\cos^{-1}\left(\frac{-\cos\frac{1}{2}(\theta-\gamma)}{\cosh\frac{1}{2}\eta}\right)-\frac{1}{R'}\cos^{-1}\left(\frac{-\cos\frac{1}{2}(\theta+\gamma)}{\cosh\frac{1}{2}\eta}\right)\right\},\\ R^2 &= a^2+r^2+z^2-2ar\cos(\gamma-\theta),\\ R'^2 &= a^2+r^2+z^2-2ar\cos(\gamma+\theta).\end{aligned}\right\} \tag{3.21}$$

In the limit as the point (r, θ, z) tends to the position of the charge e, the potential (3.21) becomes

$$\phi = \phi'+e/R,\quad \text{where } \phi' = -\frac{e}{2\pi a}\left[1+\frac{\pi-\gamma}{\sin\gamma}\right]. \tag{3.22}$$

The second term is just the Coulomb potential, which becomes infinite as $R \to 0$, while ϕ' is the change caused by the conductor in the potential at the position of the charge. The energy of the interaction between the charge and the conducting half-plane is

$$\mathscr{U} = \tfrac{1}{2}e\phi' = -\frac{e^2}{4\pi a}\left[1+\frac{\pi-\gamma}{\sin\gamma}\right]. \tag{3.23}$$

PROBLEMS

PROBLEM 1. Determine the field near an uncharged conducting sphere of radius R placed in a uniform external electric field $\mathfrak{E}$.

SOLUTION. We write the potential in the form $\phi = \phi_0+\phi_1$, where $\phi_0 = -\mathfrak{E}\cdot\mathbf{r}$ is the potential of the external field and ϕ_1 is the required change in potential due to the sphere. By symmetry, the function ϕ_1 can depend only on the constant vector $\mathfrak{E}$. The only such solution of Laplace's equation which vanishes at infinity is

$$\phi_1 = -\text{constant}\times\mathfrak{E}\cdot\mathbf{grad}\,(1/r) = \text{constant}\times\mathfrak{E}\cdot\mathbf{r}/r^3,$$

the origin being taken at the centre of the sphere. On the surface of the sphere ϕ must be constant, and so the constant in ϕ_1 is R^3, whence

$$\phi = -\mathfrak{E}\cdot\mathbf{r}\left(1-\frac{R^3}{r^3}\right) = -\mathfrak{E}r\cos\theta\left(1-\frac{R^3}{r^3}\right),$$

where θ is the angle between $\mathfrak{E}$ and $\mathbf{r}$. The distribution of charge on the surface of the sphere is given by

$$\sigma = -(1/4\pi)[\partial\phi/\partial r]_{r=R} = (3\mathfrak{E}/4\pi)\cos\theta.$$

† This formula was first given by H. M. MACDONALD (1895). Its derivation is given by him in *Electromagnetism*, Bell, London, 1934, p. 79.

The total charge $e = 0$. The dipole moment of the sphere is most easily found by comparing ϕ_1 with the potential $\mathscr{P}\cdot\mathbf{r}/r^3$ of an electric dipole field, whence $\mathscr{P} = R^3\mathfrak{E}$.

PROBLEM 2. The same as Problem 1, but for an infinite cylinder in a uniform transverse field.

SOLUTION. We use polar co-ordinates in a plane perpendicular to the axis of the cylinder. The solution of the two-dimensional Laplace's equation which depends only on a constant vector is

$$\phi_1 = \text{constant}\times\mathfrak{E}\cdot\mathbf{grad}\,(\log r) = \text{constant}\times\mathfrak{E}\cdot\mathbf{r}/r^2.$$

Adding $\phi_0 = -\mathfrak{E}\cdot\mathbf{r}$ and putting the constant equal to R^2, we have

$$\phi = -\mathfrak{E}r\cos\theta\left(1-\frac{R^2}{r^2}\right).$$

The surface charge density is $\sigma = (\mathfrak{E}/2\pi)\cos\theta$. The dipole moment per unit length of the cylinder can be found by comparing ϕ with the potential of a two-dimensional dipole field, namely $2\mathscr{P}\cdot\mathbf{grad}\,(\log r) = 2\mathscr{P}\cdot\mathbf{r}/r^2$, so that $\mathscr{P} = \frac{1}{2}R^2\mathfrak{E}$.

PROBLEM 3. Determine the field near a wedge-shaped projection on a conductor.

SOLUTION. We take polar co-ordinates r, θ in a plane perpendicular to the apex of the wedge, the origin being at the vertex of the angle θ_0 of the wedge. The angle θ is measured from one face of the wedge, the region outside the conductor being $0 \leqslant \theta \leqslant 2\pi-\theta_0$. Near the apex of the wedge, the potential can be expanded in powers of r, and we shall be interested in the first term of the expansion (after the constant term), which contains the lowest power of r. The solutions of the two-dimensional Laplace's equation which are proportional to r^n are $r^n\cos n\theta$ and $r^n\sin n\theta$. The solution having the smallest n which satisfies the condition $\phi = \text{constant}$ for $\theta = 0$ and $\theta = 2\pi-\theta_0$ (i.e. on the surface of the conductor) is

$$\phi = \text{constant}\times r^n\sin n\theta, \qquad n = \pi/(2\pi-\theta_0).$$

The value of the constant can be determined only by solving the problem for the whole field. The field varies as r^{n-1}. For $\theta_0 < \pi$ $(n < 1)$, therefore, the field becomes infinite at the apex of the wedge. In particular, for a very sharp wedge ($\theta_0 \ll 1$, $n \cong \frac{1}{2}$) E increases as $r^{-\frac{1}{2}}$ as $r \to 0$. Near a wedge-shaped concavity in a conductor ($\theta_0 > \pi$, $n > 1$) the field tends to zero.

PROBLEM 4. Determine the field near the end of a sharp conical point on the surface of a conductor.

SOLUTION. We take spherical co-ordinates, with the origin at the vertex of the cone and the polar axis along the axis of the cone. Let the angle of the cone be $2\theta_0 \ll 1$, so that the region outside the conductor corresponds to polar angles in the range $\theta_0 \leqslant \theta \leqslant \pi$. We seek a solution for the variable part of the potential, which is symmetrical about the axis, in the form

$$\phi = r^n f(\theta), \tag{1}$$

with the smallest possible value of n. Laplace's equation

$$\frac{1}{r^2}\frac{\partial}{\partial r}\left(r^2\frac{\partial\phi}{\partial r}\right)+\frac{1}{r^2\sin\theta}\frac{\partial}{\partial\theta}\left(\sin\theta\frac{\partial\phi}{\partial\theta}\right) = 0,$$

after substitution of (1), gives

$$\frac{1}{\sin\theta}\frac{\mathrm{d}}{\mathrm{d}\theta}\left(\sin\theta\frac{\mathrm{d}f}{\mathrm{d}\theta}\right)+n(n+1)f = 0. \tag{2}$$

The condition of constant potential on the surface of the cone means that we must have $f(\theta_0) = 0$.

For small θ_0 we seek a solution by assuming that $n \ll 1$ and $f(\theta)$ is of the form $\text{constant}\times[1+\psi(\theta)]$, where $\psi \ll 1$. (For $\theta_0 \to 0$, i.e. an infinitely sharp point, we should expect that ϕ tends to a constant almost everywhere near the cone.) The equation for ψ is

$$\frac{1}{\sin\theta}\frac{\mathrm{d}}{\mathrm{d}\theta}\left(\sin\theta\frac{\mathrm{d}\psi}{\mathrm{d}\theta}\right) = -n. \tag{3}$$

The solution having no singularities outside the cone (in particular, at $\theta = \pi$) is $\psi(\theta) = 2n \log \sin \frac{1}{2}\theta$.

For $\theta \sim \theta_0 \ll 1$, ψ is no longer small. Nevertheless, this expression remains valid, since the second term in equation (2) may be neglected because θ is small. To determine the constant n in the first approximation we must require that the function $f = 1+\psi$ vanishes for $\theta = \theta_0$. Thus† $n = -1/2 \log \theta_0$. The field increases to infinity as $r^{-(1-n)}$ in the neighbourhood of the vertex, i.e. essentially as $1/r$.

PROBLEM 5. The same as Problem 4, but for a sharp conical depression on the surface of a conductor.

SOLUTION. The region outside the conductor now corresponds to the range $0 \leqslant \theta \leqslant \theta_0$. As in Problem 4, we seek ϕ in the form (1), but now $n \gg 1$. Since $\theta \ll 1$ for all points in the field, equation (2) of Problem 4 becomes

$$\frac{1}{\theta}\frac{d}{d\theta}\left(\theta\frac{df}{d\theta}\right)+n^2 f = 0.$$

This is Bessel's equation, and the solution having no singularities in the field is $J_0(n\theta)$. The value of n is determined as the smallest root of the equation $J_0(n\theta_0) = 0$, whence $n = 2{\cdot}4/\theta_0$.

PROBLEM 6. Determine the energy of the attraction between an electric dipole and a plane conducting surface.

SOLUTION. We take the x-axis perpendicular to the surface of the conductor, and passing through the dipole; let the dipole moment vector $\mathscr{P}$ lie in the xy-plane. The image of the dipole is at the point $-x$ and has a moment $\mathscr{P}'_x = \mathscr{P}_x$, $\mathscr{P}'_y = -\mathscr{P}_y$. The required energy of attraction is half the energy of the interaction between the dipole and its image, and is $\mathscr{U} = -(2\mathscr{P}_x^2+\mathscr{P}_y^2)/16x^3$.

PROBLEM 7. Determine the mutual capacity per unit length of two parallel infinite conducting cylinders of radii a and b, their axes being at a distance c apart.‡

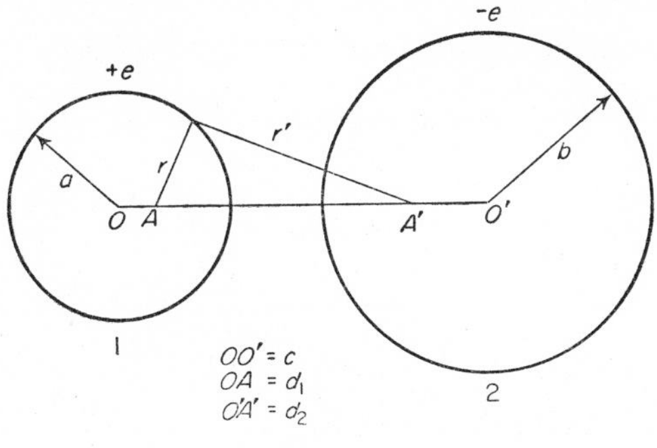

FIG. 3

SOLUTION. The field due to the two cylinders is the same as that which would be produced (in the region outside the cylinders) by two charged wires passing through certain points A and A' (Fig. 3). The wires have charges $\pm e'$ per unit length, equal to the charges on the cylinders, and the points A and A' lie on OO' in such a way that the surfaces of the cylinders are equipotential surfaces. For this to be so, the distances OA and $O'A'$ must be such

† A more rigorous calculation gives the formula $n = 1/2 \log (2/\theta_0)$, containing a coefficient in the (large) logarithm, which cannot really be obtained by the simple method given here.

‡ The corresponding problem for two spheres cannot be solved in closed form. The difference arises because, in the field of two parallel wires bearing equal and opposite charges, all the equipotential surfaces are circular cylinders, whereas in the field of two equal and opposite point charges the equipotential surfaces are not spheres.

that $OA \cdot OA' = a^2$, $O'A' \cdot O'A = b^2$, i.e. $d_1(c-d_2) = a^2$, $d_2(c-d_1) = b^2$. Then, for each cylinder, the ratio r/r' of the distances from A and A' is constant. On cylinder 1, $r/r' = a/OA' = a/(c-d_2) = d_1/a$, and on cylinder 2, $r'/r = d_2/b$. Accordingly, the potentials of the cylinders are $\phi_1 = -2e \log (r/r') = -2e \log (d_1/a)$, $\phi_2 = 2e \log (d_2/b)$, $\phi_2 - \phi_1 = 2e \log (d_1 d_2/ab)$. Hence we find the required mutual capacity $C = e/(\phi_2-\phi_1)$:

$$1/C = 2 \log (d_1 d_2/ab) = 2 \cosh^{-1} [(c^2-a^2-b^2)/2ab].$$

In particular, for a cylinder of radius a at a distance h ($> a$) from a conducting plane, we put $c = b+h$ and take the limit as $b \to \infty$, obtaining $1/C = 2 \cosh^{-1} (h/a)$.

If two hollow cylinders are placed one inside the other ($c < b-a$), there is no field outside, while the field between the cylinders is the same as that due to two wires of charges $\pm e$ passing through A and A' (Fig. 4). The same method gives

$$1/C = 2 \cosh^{-1} [(a^2+b^2-c^2)/2ab].$$

PROBLEM 8. The boundary of a conductor is an infinite plane with a hemispherical projection. Determine the charge distribution on the surface.

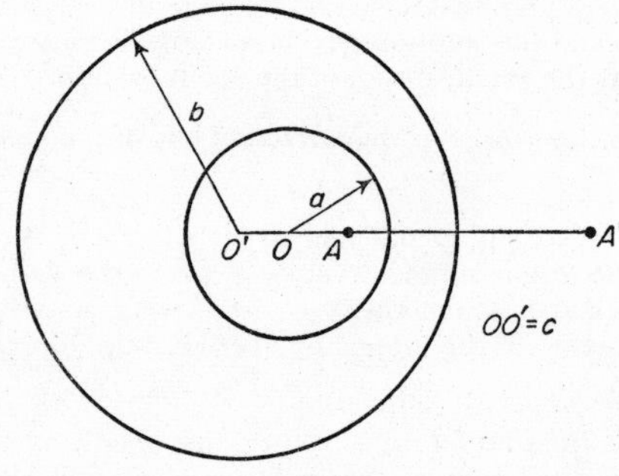

FIG. 4

SOLUTION. In the field determined in Problem 1, whose potential is

$$\phi = \text{constant} \times z\left(1 - \frac{R^3}{r^3}\right),$$

the plane $z = 0$ with a projection $r = R$ is an equipotential surface, on which $\phi = 0$. Hence it can be the surface of a conductor, and the above formula gives the field outside the conductor. The charge distribution on the plane part of the surface is given by

$$\sigma = -\frac{1}{4\pi}\left[\frac{\partial\phi}{\partial z}\right]_{z=0} = \sigma_0\left(1 - \frac{R^3}{r^3}\right);$$

we have taken the constant in ϕ as $-4\pi\sigma_0$, so that σ_0 is the charge density far from the projection. On the surface of the projection we have

$$\sigma = -\frac{1}{4\pi}\left[\frac{\partial\phi}{\partial r}\right]_{r=R} = 3\sigma_0\frac{z}{R}.$$

PROBLEM 9. Determine the dipole moment of a thin conducting cylindrical rod, of length $2l$ and radius $a \ll l$, in an electric field $\mathfrak{E}$ parallel to its axis.

SOLUTION. Let $\tau(z)$ be the charge per unit length induced on the surface of the rod, and z the co-ordinate along the axis of the rod, measured from its midpoint. The condition of constant potential on the surface of the conductor is

$$-\mathfrak{E}z + \frac{1}{2\pi}\int_0^{2\pi}\int_{-l}^{l} \frac{\tau(z')\,dz'\,d\phi}{R} = 0,$$

$$R^2 = (z'-z)^2 + 4a^2 \sin^2 \tfrac{1}{2}\phi,$$

where ϕ is the angle between planes passing through the axis of the cylinder and through two points on its surface at a distance R apart. We divide the integral into two parts, putting $\tau(z') \equiv \tau(z)+[\tau(z')-\tau(z)]$. Since $l \gg a$, we have for points not too near the ends of the rod

$$\frac{\tau(z)}{2\pi}\iint \frac{dz'\,d\phi}{R} \cong \frac{\tau(z)}{2\pi}\int_0^{2\pi} \log\frac{l^2-z^2}{a^2\sin^2\frac{1}{2}\phi}\,d\phi = \tau(z)\log\frac{4(l^2-z^2)}{a^2},$$

using the result that $\int_0^{\pi} \log\sin\phi\,d\phi = -\pi\log 2$. In the integral which contains the difference $\tau(z')-\tau(z)$, we can neglect the a^2 term in R, since it no longer causes the integral to diverge. Thus

$$\mathfrak{E}z = \tau(z)\log\frac{4(l^2-z^2)}{a^2} + \int_{-l}^{l}\frac{\tau(z')-\tau(z)}{|z'-z|}\,dz'.$$

The quantity τ is almost proportional to z, and in this approximation the integral gives $-2\tau(z)$, the result being

$$\tau(z) = \frac{\mathfrak{E}z}{\log[4(l^2-z^2)/a^2]-2}.$$

This expression is invalid near the ends of the rod, but in calculating the dipole moment that region is unimportant. In the above approximation we have

$$\mathscr{P} = \int_{-l}^{l}\tau(z)z\,dz = \frac{\mathfrak{E}}{L}\int_0^l\left\{z^2-\frac{z^2}{2L}\log\left(1-\frac{z^2}{l^2}\right)\right\}dz$$

$$= \frac{\mathfrak{E}l^3}{3L}\left\{1+\frac{1}{L}\left(\frac{4}{3}-\log 2\right)\right\},$$

where $L = \log(2l/a)-1$ is large, or (with the same accuracy)

$$\mathscr{P} = \frac{\mathfrak{E}l^3}{3\log(4l/a)-7}.$$

PROBLEM 10. Determine the capacity of a hollow conducting cap of a sphere.

SOLUTION. We take the origin O at a point on the rim of the cap (Fig. 5), and carry out the inversion transformation $r = l^2/r'$, where l is the diameter of the cap. The cap then becomes the half-plane shown by the dashed line in Fig. 5, which is perpendicular to the radius AO of the cap and passes through the point B on its rim. The angle $\gamma = \pi-\theta$, where 2θ is the angle subtended by the diameter of the cap at the centre of the sphere.

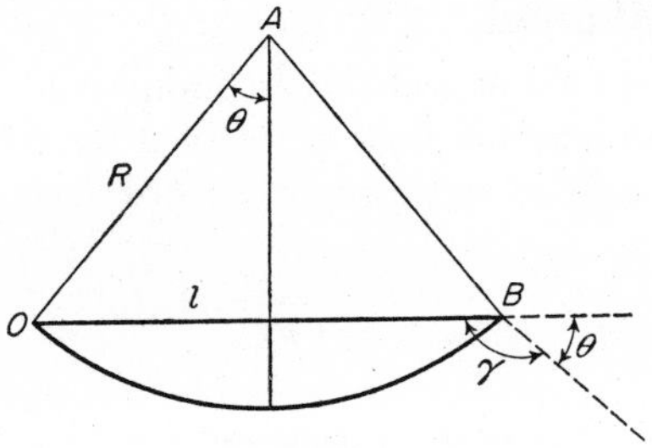

FIG. 5

If the charge on the cap is e and its potential is taken as zero, then as $r \to \infty$ the potential $\phi \to -\phi_0+e/r$. Accordingly, in the transformed problem, as $r' \to 0$ the potential is $\phi' \to l\phi/r' \cong -l\phi_0/r'+e/l$, where the first term corresponds to a charge $e' = -l\phi_0$ at the origin.

According to formula (3.22), we have

$$\phi' = \frac{e'}{r'} - \frac{e'}{2\pi l}\left(1+\frac{\theta}{\sin\theta}\right)$$

(the potential near a charge e' at a distance l from the edge of a conducting half-plane at zero potential). Comparing the two expressions, we have for the required capacity $C = e/\phi_0$

$$C = \frac{l}{2\pi}\left(1+\frac{\theta}{\sin\theta}\right) = \frac{R}{\pi}(\sin\theta+\theta),$$

where R is the radius of the cap.

PROBLEM 11. Determine the correction due to edge effects on the value $C = S/4\pi d$ for the capacity of a plane condenser (S being the area of the plates, and $d \ll \sqrt{S}$ the distance between them).

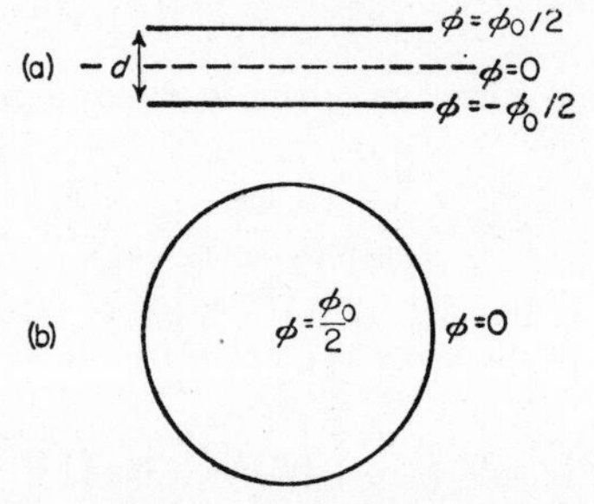

FIG. 6

SOLUTION. Since the plates have free edges, the distribution of charge over them is not uniform. To determine the required correction in a first approximation, we consider points which are at distances x from the edge such that $d \ll x \ll \sqrt{S}$. For example, taking the upper layer (at potential $\phi = \frac{1}{2}\phi_0$, Fig. 6a) and neglecting its distance $\frac{1}{2}d$ from the mid-plane (the equipotential surface $\phi = 0$), we have the problem of the field near the boundary between two parts of a plane having different potentials (Fig. 6b). The solution is elementary†, and the excess charge (relative to the value of σ far from the edge) is $\Delta\sigma = E_n/4\pi = \phi_0/8\pi^2 x$, so that the total excess charge is $L\int \Delta\sigma \, dx = (\phi_0 L/8\pi^2)\log(\sqrt{S}/d)$, where L is the perimeter of the plate. In calculating the logarithmically divergent integral, we have taken the limits as those of the region $d \ll x \ll \sqrt{S}$. Hence we find the capacity‡

$$C = \frac{S}{4\pi d} + \frac{L}{8\pi^2}\log\frac{\sqrt{S}}{d}.$$

§4. A conducting ellipsoid

The problem of the field of a charged conducting ellipsoid and that of an ellipsoid in a uniform external field are solved by the use of *ellipsoidal co-ordinates*. These are related to Cartesian co-ordinates by the equation

$$\frac{x^2}{a^2+u} + \frac{y^2}{b^2+u} + \frac{z^2}{c^2+u} = 1 \quad (a > b > c). \tag{4.1}$$

† See §22. In formula (22.2) for the potential we must here put $\phi_{ab} = \frac{1}{2}\phi_0$, $\alpha = \pi$.

‡ A more exact calculation (determining the coefficient in the argument of the logarithm) demands considerably more elaborate methods, and the result depends on the shape of the plates. If these are circular, of radius R, we obtain *Kirchhoff's formula*

$$C = \frac{R^2}{4d} + \frac{R}{4\pi}\left(\log\frac{16\pi R}{d} - 1\right).$$

This equation, a cubic in u, has three different real roots ξ, η, ζ, which lie in the following ranges:

$$\xi \geqslant -c^2, \quad -c^2 \geqslant \eta \geqslant -b^2, \quad -b^2 \geqslant \zeta \geqslant -a^2. \tag{4.2}$$

These three roots are the ellipsoidal co-ordinates of the point x, y, z. Their geometrical significance is seen from the fact that the surfaces of constant ξ, η and ζ are respectively ellipsoids and hyperboloids of one and two sheets, all confocal with the ellipsoid

$$x^2/a^2+y^2/b^2+z^2/c^2 = 1. \tag{4.3}$$

One surface of each of the three families passes through each point in space, and the three surfaces are orthogonal. The formulae for transformation from ellipsoidal to Cartesian co-ordinates are given by solving three simultaneous equations of the type (4.1), and are†

$$\left.\begin{aligned} x &= \pm\sqrt{\left[\frac{(\xi+a^2)(\eta+a^2)(\zeta+a^2)}{(b^2-a^2)(c^2-a^2)}\right]}, \\ y &= \pm\sqrt{\left[\frac{(\xi+b^2)(\eta+b^2)(\zeta+b^2)}{(c^2-b^2)(a^2-b^2)}\right]}, \\ z &= \pm\sqrt{\left[\frac{(\xi+c^2)(\eta+c^2)(\zeta+c^2)}{(a^2-c^2)(b^2-c^2)}\right]}. \end{aligned}\right\} \tag{4.4}$$

The element of length in ellipsoidal co-ordinates is

$$\left.\begin{gathered} \mathrm{d}l^2 = h_1{}^2\mathrm{d}\xi^2+h_2{}^2\,\mathrm{d}\eta^2+h_3{}^2\,\mathrm{d}\zeta^2, \\ h_1 = \sqrt{[(\xi-\eta)(\xi-\zeta)]}/2R_\xi, \quad h_2 = \sqrt{[(\eta-\zeta)(\eta-\xi)]}/2R_\eta, \\ h_3 = \sqrt{[(\zeta-\xi)(\zeta-\eta)]}/2R_\zeta, \quad R_u{}^2 = (u+a^2)(u+b^2)(u+c^2), \\ u = \xi, \eta, \zeta. \end{gathered}\right\} \tag{4.5}$$

Accordingly, Laplace's equation in these co-ordinates is

$$\begin{aligned} \triangle\phi = \frac{4}{(\xi-\eta)(\zeta-\xi)(\eta-\zeta)} \times \\ \times\left[(\eta-\zeta)\,R_\xi\frac{\partial}{\partial\xi}\left(R_\xi\frac{\partial\phi}{\partial\xi}\right)+(\zeta-\xi)\,R_\eta\frac{\partial}{\partial\eta}\left(R_\eta\frac{\partial\phi}{\partial\eta}\right)+(\xi-\eta)\,R_\zeta\frac{\partial}{\partial\zeta}\left(R_\zeta\frac{\partial\phi}{\partial\zeta}\right)\right] = 0. \end{aligned} \tag{4.6}$$

If two of the semiaxes a, b, c become equal, the system of ellipsoidal co-ordinates degenerates. Let $a = b > c$. Then the cubic equation (4.1) becomes a quadratic,

$$\frac{\rho^2}{a^2+u}+\frac{z^2}{c^2+u} = 1, \qquad \rho^2 = x^2+y^2, \tag{4.7}$$

† Strictly speaking, the ellipsoidal co-ordinates should be taken not as ξ, η, ζ themselves but as $\sqrt{(a^2+\zeta)}$, $\sqrt{(b^2+\eta)}$, $\sqrt{(c^2+\xi)}$. Then the double signs would not appear in (4.4), and the two systems of co-ordinates would be in one-to-one correspondence, as they should be.

with two roots whose values lie in the ranges $\xi \geqslant -c^2$, $-c^2 \geqslant \eta \geqslant -a^2$. The co-ordinate surfaces of constant ξ and η become respectively confocal oblate spheroids and confocal hyperboloids of revolution of one sheet (Fig. 7). As the third co-ordinate we can take the polar angle ϕ in the xy-plane ($x = \rho\cos\phi$, $y = \rho\sin\phi$). For $a = b$ the ellipsoidal co-ordinate ζ degenerates to a constant, $-a^2$. Its relation to the angle ϕ is given by the way in which it tends to $-a^2$ as b tends to a, namely

$$\cos\phi = \sqrt{[(a^2+\zeta)/(a^2-b^2)]} \quad \text{as} \quad b \to a. \tag{4.8}$$

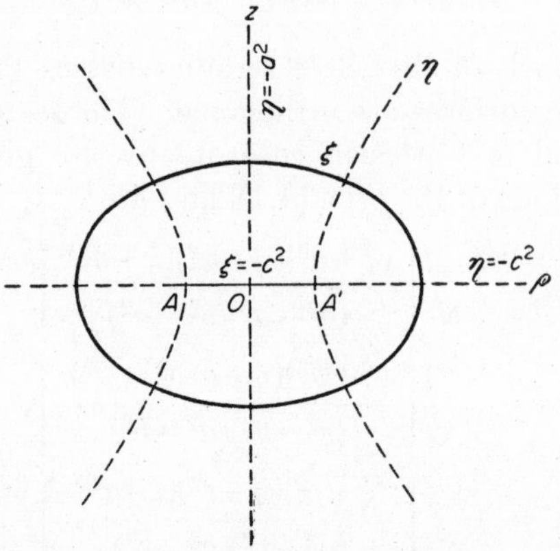

FIG. 7

This is easily seen from (4.4) or directly from (4.1). The relation between the co-ordinates z, ρ and ξ, η is given, according to (4.4), by

$$z = \pm\sqrt{\left[\frac{(\xi+c^2)(\eta+c^2)}{c^2-a^2}\right]}, \qquad \rho = \sqrt{\left[\frac{(\xi+a^2)(\eta+a^2)}{a^2-c^2}\right]}. \tag{4.9}$$

The co-ordinates ξ, η, ϕ are called *oblate spheroidal co-ordinates.*†

Similarly, for $a > b = c$ ellipsoidal co-ordinates become *prolate spheroidal co-ordinates.* Two co-ordinates ξ and ζ are roots of the equation

$$\frac{x^2}{a^2+u}+\frac{\rho^2}{b^2+u} = 1, \qquad \rho^2 = y^2+z^2, \tag{4.10}$$

where $\xi \geqslant -b^2$, $-b^2 \geqslant \zeta \geqslant -a^2$. The surfaces of constant ξ and ζ are prolate spheroids and hyperboloids of revolution of two sheets (Fig. 8). The co-ordinate η degenerates to a constant, $-b^2$, for $c \to b$, and we have

$$\cos\phi = \sqrt{[(b^2+\eta)/(b^2-c^2)]}, \tag{4.11}$$

where ϕ is the polar angle in the yz-plane. The relation between the co-ordinates x, ρ and ξ, ζ is given by

$$x = \pm\sqrt{\left[\frac{(\xi+a^2)(\zeta+a^2)}{a^2-b^2}\right]}, \qquad \rho = \sqrt{\left[\frac{(\xi+b^2)(\zeta+b^2)}{b^2-a^2}\right]}. \tag{4.12}$$

† We here use the definition of spheroidal co-ordinates such that they are the limit of ellipsoidal co-ordinates. Other definitions are used in the literature, but are easily related to ours.

The upper limit of integration is taken so that the field is zero at infinity. The constant A is most simply determined from the condition that at large distances r the field must become a Coulomb field and $\phi \cong e/r$, where e is the total charge on the conductor. When $r \to \infty$, $\xi \to \infty$, and $\xi \cong r^2$, as we see from equation (4.1) with $u = \xi$. For large ξ we have $R_\xi \cong \xi^{3/2}$, and $\phi \cong 2A/\sqrt{\xi} = 2A/r$. Hence $2A = e$, and therefore

$$\phi(\xi) = \tfrac{1}{2}e\int_{\xi}^{\infty}\frac{d\xi}{R_\xi}. \tag{4.14}$$

The integral is an elliptic integral of the first kind. The surface of the conductor corresponds to $\xi = 0$, and so the capacity of the conductor is given by

$$\frac{1}{C} = \tfrac{1}{2}\int_{0}^{\infty}\frac{d\xi}{R_\xi}. \tag{4.15}$$

The distribution of charge on the surface of the ellipsoid is determined by the normal derivative of the potential:

$$\sigma = -\frac{1}{4\pi}\left[\frac{\partial\phi}{\partial n}\right]_{\xi=0} = -\frac{1}{4\pi}\left[\frac{1}{h_1}\frac{\partial\phi}{\partial\xi}\right]_{\xi=0} = \frac{e}{4\pi}\frac{1}{\sqrt{(\eta\zeta)}}.$$

From equations (4.4) we easily see that for $\xi = 0$

$$\frac{x^2}{a^4}+\frac{y^2}{b^4}+\frac{z^2}{c^4} = \frac{\eta\zeta}{a^2b^2c^2}.$$

Hence

$$\sigma = \frac{e}{4\pi abc}\left(\frac{x^2}{a^4}+\frac{y^2}{b^4}+\frac{z^2}{c^4}\right)^{-\frac{1}{2}} \tag{4.16}$$

For a spheroid the integrals (4.14), (4.15) degenerate and can be expressed in terms of elementary functions. For a prolate spheroid ($a > b = c$) the field potential is

$$\phi = \frac{e}{\sqrt{(a^2-b^2)}}\tanh^{-1}\sqrt{\frac{a^2-b^2}{\xi+a^2}}, \tag{4.17}$$

and the capacity is

$$C = \frac{\sqrt{(a^2-b^2)}}{\cosh^{-1}(a/b)}. \tag{4.18}$$

For an oblate spheroid ($a = b > c$) we have

$$\phi = \frac{e}{\sqrt{(a^2-c^2)}}\tan^{-1}\sqrt{\frac{a^2-c^2}{\xi+c^2}}, \qquad C = \frac{\sqrt{(a^2-c^2)}}{\cos^{-1}(c/a)}. \tag{4.19}$$

In a system of oblate spheroidal co-ordinates the foci of the spheroids and hyperboloids lie on a circle of radius $\sqrt{(a^2-c^2)}$ in the xy-plane; in Fig. 7 AA' is a diameter of this circle. Let us draw a plane passing through the z-axis and some point P. It intersects the focal circle at two points; let their distances from P be r_1, r_2. If the co-ordinates of P are ρ, z, then

$$r_1^2 = [\rho-\sqrt{(a^2-c^2)}]^2+z^2, \qquad r_2^2 = [\rho+\sqrt{(a^2-c^2)}]^2+z^2.$$

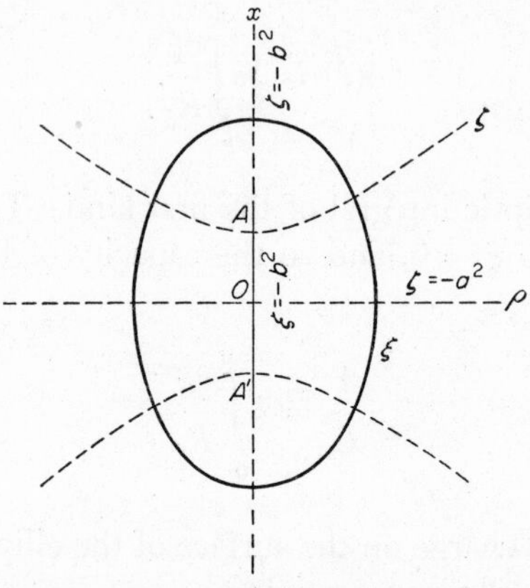

FIG. 8

The spheroidal co-ordinates ξ, η are given in terms of r_1, r_2 by

$$\xi = \tfrac{1}{4}(r_1+r_2)^2-a^2, \qquad \eta = \tfrac{1}{4}(r_2-r_1)^2-a^2. \tag{4.13}$$

In a system of prolate spheroidal co-ordinates the foci are the points $x = \pm\sqrt{(a^2-b^2)}$ on the x-axis (the points A, A' in Fig. 8). If r_1 and r_2 are the distances of these foci from P, then

$$r_1^2 = \rho^2+[z-\sqrt{(a^2-b^2)}]^2, \quad r_2^2 = \rho^2+[z+\sqrt{(a^2-b^2)}]^2,$$

and the spheroidal co-ordinates ξ, ζ are given in terms of r_1, r_2 by the same formulae (4.13), with ζ in place of η.

Let us now turn to the problem of the field of a charged ellipsoid whose surface is given by the equation (4.3). In ellipsoidal co-ordinates this is the surface $\xi = 0$. It is therefore clear that, if we seek the field potential as a function of ξ only, all the ellipsoidal surfaces $\xi =$ constant, and in particular the surface of the conductor, will be equipotential surfaces. Laplace's equation (4.6) then becomes

$$\frac{d}{d\xi}\left(R_\xi \frac{d\phi}{d\xi}\right) = 0,$$

whence

$$\phi(\xi) = A\int_\xi^\infty \frac{d\xi}{R_\xi}.$$

In particular, for a circular disc ($a = b$, $c = 0$)

$$C = 2a/\pi. \tag{4.20}$$

Let us now consider the problem of an uncharged conducting ellipsoid in a uniform external electric field $\mathfrak{E}$. Without loss of generality we may take the field $\mathfrak{E}$ to be along one of the axes of the ellipsoid. In any other case this field may be resolved into components along the three axes, and the resultant field is a superposition of those arising from each component separately.

The potential of a uniform field $\mathfrak{E}$ along the x-axis (the a-axis of the ellipsoid) is, in ellipsoidal co-ordinates,

$$\phi_0 = -\mathfrak{E}x = -\mathfrak{E}\sqrt{[(\xi+a^2)(\eta+a^2)(\zeta+a^2)/(b^2-a^2)(c^2-a^2)]}. \tag{4.21}$$

We write the field potential outside the ellipsoid as $\phi = \phi_0+\phi'$, where ϕ' gives the required perturbation of the external field by the ellipsoid, and seek ϕ' in the form

$$\phi' = \phi_0 F(\xi). \tag{4.22}$$

In this function the factors depending on η and ζ are the same as in ϕ_0; this enables us to satisfy the boundary condition at $\xi = 0$ for arbitrary η, ζ (i.e. on the surface of the ellipsoid). Substituting (4.22) in Laplace's equation (4.6), we obtain for $F(\xi)$ the equation

$$\frac{\mathrm{d}^2F}{\mathrm{d}\xi^2}+\frac{\mathrm{d}F}{\mathrm{d}\xi}\frac{\mathrm{d}}{\mathrm{d}\xi}\log[R_\xi(\xi+a^2)] = 0.$$

One solution of this equation is $F =$ constant, and the other is

$$F(\xi) = A\int_\xi^\infty \frac{\mathrm{d}\xi}{(\xi+a^2)R_\xi}. \tag{4.23}$$

The upper limit of integration is taken so that $\phi' \to 0$ for $\xi \to \infty$. The integral is an elliptic integral of the second kind.

We must have $\phi =$ constant on the surface of the ellipsoid. For this condition to be satisfied with $\xi = 0$ and arbitrary η, ζ, the constant value of ϕ must be zero. Determining the coefficient A in $F(\xi)$ so that $F(0) = -1$, we obtain the following final expression for the field potential:

$$\phi = \phi_0\left\{1-\int_\xi^\infty \frac{\mathrm{d}s}{(s+a^2)R_s}\Big/\int_0^\infty \frac{\mathrm{d}s}{(s+a^2)R_s}\right\}. \tag{4.24}$$

Let us find the form of the potential ϕ' at large distances r from the ellipsoid. For large r, the co-ordinate ξ is large, and $\xi \cong r^2$, as follows at once from equation (4.1). Hence

$$\int_\xi^\infty \frac{\mathrm{d}s}{(s+a^2)R_s} \cong \int_{r^2}^\infty \frac{\mathrm{d}s}{s^{5/2}} = \frac{2}{3r^3},$$

and the potential $\phi' = \mathfrak{E}\, xV/4\pi n^{(x)}r^3$, where $V = \frac{4}{3}\pi abc$ is the volume of the ellipsoid and $n^{(x)}$, $n^{(y)}$, $n^{(z)}$ are defined by

$$n^{(x)} = \tfrac{1}{2}abc\int_0^\infty \frac{ds}{(s+a^2)R_s}, \quad n^{(y)} = \tfrac{1}{2}abc\int_0^\infty \frac{ds}{(s+b^2)R_s},$$

$$n^{(z)} = \tfrac{1}{2}abc\int_0^\infty \frac{ds}{(s+c^2)R_s}. \tag{4.25}$$

The expression for ϕ' is, as we should expect, the potential of an electric dipole: $\phi' = x\mathscr{P}_x/r^3$, where the dipole moment of the ellipsoid is

$$\mathscr{P}_x = \mathfrak{E}_x V/4\pi n^{(x)}. \tag{4.26}$$

Analogous expressions give the dipole moment when the field $\mathfrak{E}$ is along the y or z axis.

The positive constants $n^{(x)}$, $n^{(y)}$, $n^{(z)}$ depend only on the shape of the ellipsoid, and not on its volume; they are called the *depolarisation coefficients.*† If the co-ordinate axes do not necessarily coincide with those of the ellipsoid, formula (4.26) must be written in the tensor form

$$(4\pi/V)n_{ik}\mathscr{P}_k = \mathfrak{E}_i. \tag{4.27}$$

The quantities $n^{(x)}$, $n^{(y)}$, $n^{(z)}$ are the principal values of the symmetrical tensor n_{ik} of rank two.

In the general case of arbitrary a, b, c, it follows from the definitions of $n^{(x)}$, $n^{(y)}$, $n^{(z)}$ that

$$n^{(x)} < n^{(y)} < n^{(z)} \text{ if } a > b > c. \tag{4.28}$$

Further, by adding the integrals for $n^{(x)}$, $n^{(y)}$, $n^{(z)}$ and using as the variable of integration $u = R_s^2$, we find

$$n^{(x)}+n^{(y)}+n^{(z)} = \tfrac{1}{2}abc \int_{(abc)^2}^\infty \frac{du}{u^{3/2}},$$

whence

$$n^{(x)}+n^{(y)}+n^{(z)} = 1. \tag{4.29}$$

The sum of the three depolarisation coefficients is thus unity; in tensor notation, $n_{ii} = 1$. Since these coefficients are positive, none can exceed unity.

For a sphere ($a = b = c$) it is evident from symmetry that

$$n^{(x)} = n^{(y)} = n^{(z)} = \tfrac{1}{3}. \tag{4.30}$$

For a cylinder with its axis in the x-direction ($a \to \infty$), we have‡

$$n^{(x)} = 0, \quad n^{(y)} = n^{(z)} = \tfrac{1}{2}. \tag{4.31}$$

---

† Useful tables of these coefficients have been given by E. C. Stoner (*Philosophical Magazine* [7] **36**, 803, 1945).

‡ These values for a sphere and a cylinder agree, of course, with those found in §3, Problems 1 and 2.

The elliptic integrals (4.25) can be expressed in terms of elementary functions if the ellipsoid is a spheroid. For a prolate spheroid ($a > b = c$) of eccentricity $e = \sqrt{(1-b^2/a^2)}$,

$$n^{(x)} = \frac{1-e^2}{2e^3}\left(\log\frac{1+e}{1-e}-2e\right), \quad n^{(y)} = n^{(z)} = \tfrac{1}{2}(1-n^{(x)}). \tag{4.32}$$

If the spheroid is nearly spherical ($e \ll 1$) we have approximately

$$n^{(x)} = \tfrac{1}{3}-\tfrac{2}{15}e^2, \quad n^{(y)} = n^{(z)} = \tfrac{1}{3}+\tfrac{1}{15}e^2. \tag{4.33}$$

For an oblate spheroid ($a = b > c$)

$$n^{(z)} = \frac{1+e^2}{e^3}(e-\tan^{-1}e), \quad n^{(x)} = n^{(y)} = \tfrac{1}{2}(1-n^{(z)}), \tag{4.34}$$

where $e = \sqrt{(a^2/c^2-1)}$. If $e \ll 1$, then

$$n^{(z)} = \tfrac{1}{3}+\tfrac{2}{15}e^2, \quad n^{(x)} = n^{(y)} = \tfrac{1}{3}-\tfrac{1}{15}e^2. \tag{4.35}$$

PROBLEMS

PROBLEM 1. Find the field of a charged conducting circular disc of radius a, expressing it in cylindrical co-ordinates. Find the distribution of charge on the disc.

SOLUTION. The charge distribution is obtained by taking the limit of formula (4.16) as $c \to 0$, $z \to 0$, with $z/c = \sqrt{(1-r^2/a^2)}$ (where $r^2 = x^2+y^2$), in accordance with (4.3). This gives

$$\sigma = \frac{e}{4\pi a^2}\left(1-\frac{r^2}{a^2}\right)^{-\frac{1}{2}}.$$

The field potential is given in all space by formula (4.19), where we put $c = 0$ and express ξ in terms of r and z by means of equation (4.1) with $c = 0$, $u = \xi$, $a = b$:

$$\phi = \frac{e}{a}\tan^{-1}\left[\frac{2a^2}{r^2+z^2-a^2+\sqrt{[(r^2+z^2-a^2)^2+4a^2z^2]}}\right]^{\frac{1}{2}}.$$

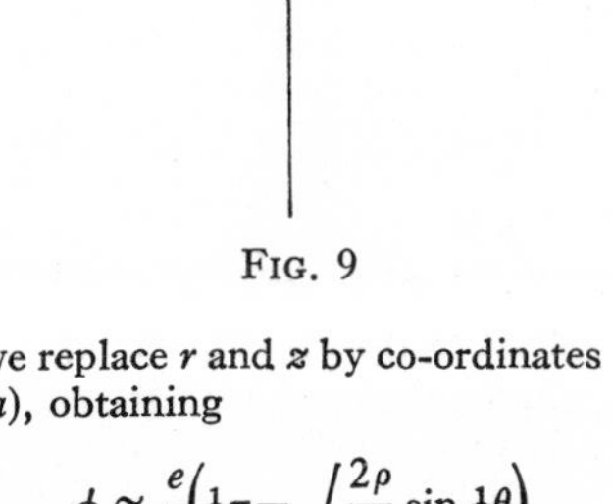

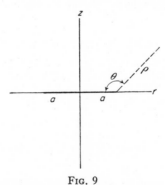

FIG. 9

Near the edge of the disc, we replace r and z by co-ordinates ρ and θ such that $z = \rho\sin\theta$, $r = a-\rho\cos\theta$ (Fig. 9; $\rho \ll a$), obtaining

$$\phi \cong \frac{e}{a}\left(\tfrac{1}{2}\pi-\sqrt{\frac{2\rho}{a}}\sin\tfrac{1}{2}\theta\right),$$

in agreement with the general result derived in §3, Problem 3.

PROBLEM 2. Determine the electric quadrupole moment of a charged ellipsoid.

SOLUTION. The *quadrupole moment tensor* of a charged conductor is defined as $D_{ik} = e(3\overline{x_i x_k} - \overline{r^2}\delta_{ik})$, where e is the total charge, and the bar denotes an average such as

$$\overline{x_i x_k} = \frac{1}{e}\oint x_i x_k \sigma \, \mathrm{d}f.$$

It is evident that the axes of the ellipsoid are also the principal axes of the tensor D_{ik}. Using formula (4.16) for σ, and for the element of surface of the ellipsoid the expression

$$\mathrm{d}f = \frac{\mathrm{d}x\,\mathrm{d}y}{\nu_z} = \frac{\mathrm{d}x\,\mathrm{d}y}{z/c^2}\sqrt{\left[\frac{x^2}{a^4}+\frac{y^2}{b^4}+\frac{z^2}{c^4}\right]},$$

we obtain

$$\overline{z^2} = \frac{c}{4\pi ab}\int z\,\mathrm{d}x\,\mathrm{d}y = \tfrac{1}{3}c^2;$$

the integration over x and y covers twice the area of the cross-section of the ellipsoid by the xy-plane. Thus

$$D_{xx} = \tfrac{1}{5}e(2a^2-b^2-c^2), \quad D_{yy} = \tfrac{1}{5}e(2b^2-c^2-a^2), \quad D_{zz} = \tfrac{1}{5}e(2c^2-a^2-b^2).$$

PROBLEM 3. Determine the distribution of charge on the surface of an uncharged conducting ellipsoid placed in a uniform external field.

SOLUTION. According to formula (1.9) we have

$$\sigma = -\frac{1}{4\pi}\left[\frac{\partial\phi}{\partial n}\right]_{\xi=0} = -\left[\frac{1}{4\pi h_1}\frac{\partial\phi}{\partial\xi}\right]_{\xi=0};$$

by (4.5) the element of length along the normal to the surface of the ellipsoid is $h_1\mathrm{d}\xi$. Substituting (4.24) and using the fact that

$$\nu_x = \left[\frac{1}{h_1}\frac{\partial x}{\partial\xi}\right]_{\xi=0} = \left[\frac{x}{2a^2h_1}\right]_{\xi=0}$$

(where $\boldsymbol{\nu}$ is a unit vector along the normal to the surface), we have $\sigma = \mathfrak{E}\nu_x/4\pi n^{(x)}$ when the external field is in the x-direction. When the direction of the external field is arbitrary this becomes

$$\sigma = \frac{1}{4\pi}\nu_i n^{-1}{}_{ik}\mathfrak{E}_k = \frac{1}{4\pi}\left[\frac{\nu_x}{n^{(x)}}\mathfrak{E}_x + \frac{\nu_y}{n^{(y)}}\mathfrak{E}_y + \frac{\nu_z}{n^{(z)}}\mathfrak{E}_z\right].$$

PROBLEM 4. The same as Problem 3, but for a plane circular disc of radius a lying parallel to the field.† Determine also the dipole moment of the disc.

SOLUTION. Let us regard the disc as the limit of a spheroid when the semiaxis c tends to zero. The depolarisation coefficient along this axis (the z-axis) tends to 1, and those along the x and y axes tend to zero: $n^{(z)} = 1-\pi c/2a$, $n^{(x)} = n^{(y)} = \pi c/4a$, by (4.34). The component ν_x of the unit vector along the normal to the surface of the spheroid tends to zero:

$$\nu_x = \frac{x}{a^2}\left(\frac{x^2+y^2}{a^4}+\frac{z^2}{c^4}\right)^{-\frac{1}{2}} \to \frac{x}{a^2}\frac{c^2}{z} = \frac{xc}{a^2}\left(1-\frac{x^2+y^2}{a^2}\right)^{-\frac{1}{2}}.$$

Hence the charge density is

$$\sigma = \frac{\mathfrak{E}}{4\pi}\frac{\nu_x}{n^{(x)}} = \frac{\mathfrak{E}\rho\cos\phi}{\pi^2\sqrt{(a^2-\rho^2)}},$$

where ρ and ϕ are polar co-ordinates in the plane of the disc.

The dipole moment of the disc is obtained from formula (4.26), and is $\mathscr{P} = 4a^3\mathfrak{E}/3\pi$. Thus it is proportional to a^3, and not to the "volume" a^2c of the disc.

---

† The problem for a disc lying perpendicular to the field is trivial: the field remain uniform in all space, and charges $\sigma = \pm\mathfrak{E}/4\pi$ are induced on the two sides of the disc.

PROBLEM 5. Determine the field potential outside a conducting spheroid with its axis of symmetry parallel to a uniform external field.

SOLUTION. For a prolate spheroid ($a > b = c$, with the field $\mathfrak{E}$ in the x-direction) we find, on calculating the integral in formula (4.24),

$$\phi = -\mathfrak{E}x\left\{1 - \frac{\tanh^{-1}\sqrt{[(a^2-b^2)/(\xi+a^2)]} - \sqrt{[(a^2-b^2)/(\xi+a^2)]}}{\tanh^{-1}\sqrt{(1-b^2/a^2)} - \sqrt{(1-b^2/a^2)}}\right\}.$$

The co-ordinate ξ is related to x and $\rho = \sqrt{(y^2+z^2)}$ by

$$\frac{\rho^2}{b^2+\xi} + \frac{x^2}{a^2+\xi} = 1,$$

with $0 \leqslant \xi \leqslant \infty$ in the space outside the ellipsoid.

For an oblate spheroid ($a = b > c$) the field $\mathfrak{E}$ is along the z-axis. We must therefore replace $s+a^2$ by $s+c^2$ and put $\phi_0 = -\mathfrak{E}z$ in the integrals in (4.24). Then

$$\phi = -\mathfrak{E}z\left\{1 - \frac{\sqrt{[(a^2-c^2)/(\xi+c^2)]} - \tan^{-1}\sqrt{[(a^2-c^2)/(\xi+c^2)}}{\sqrt{(a^2/c^2-1)} - \tan^{-1}\sqrt{(a^2/c^2-1)}}\right\},$$

where the co-ordinate ξ is related to z and $\rho = \sqrt{(x^2+y^2)}$ by

$$\frac{\rho^2}{a^2+\xi} + \frac{z^2}{c^2+\xi} = 1.$$

PROBLEM 6. The same as Problem 5, but with the axis of symmetry perpendicular to the external field.

SOLUTION. For a prolate spheroid (with the field along the z-axis)

$$\phi = -\mathfrak{E}z\left\{1 - \frac{\sqrt{(\xi+a^2)/(\xi+b^2)} - (a^2-b^2)^{-\frac{1}{2}}\tanh^{-1}\sqrt{[(a^2-b^2)/(\xi+a^2)]}}{a/b^2 - (a^2-b^2)^{-\frac{1}{2}}\tanh^{-1}\sqrt{(1-b^2/a^2)}}\right\}.$$

For an oblate spheroid (with the field along the x-axis)

$$\phi = -\mathfrak{E}x\left\{1 - \frac{(a^2-c^2)^{-\frac{1}{2}}\tan^{-1}\sqrt{[(a^2-c^2)/(\xi+c^2)]} - \sqrt{(\xi+c^2)/(\xi+a^2)}}{(a^2-c^2)^{-\frac{1}{2}}\tan^{-1}\sqrt{(a^2/c^2-1)} - c/a^2}\right\}.$$

PROBLEM 7. A uniform field $\mathfrak{E}$ in the z-direction (in the half-space $z < 0$) is bounded by an earthed conducting plane at $z = 0$, containing a circular aperture. Determine the field and charge distribution on the plane.

SOLUTION. The xy-plane with a circular aperture of radius a and centre at the origin may be regarded as the limit of the hyperboloids of revolution of one sheet

$$\frac{\rho^2}{a^2-|\eta|} - \frac{z^2}{|\eta|} = 1, \qquad \rho^2 = x^2+y^2,$$

as $|\eta| \to 0$. These hyperboloids are one of the families of co-ordinate surfaces in a system of oblate spheroidal co-ordinates with $c = 0$. The Cartesian co-ordinate z, according to (4.9), is given in terms of ξ and η by $z = \sqrt{(\xi|\eta|)}/a$, and $\sqrt{\xi}$ must be taken with the positive and negative sign in the upper and lower half-space respectively.

Let us seek a solution in the form $\phi = -\mathfrak{E}z\,F(\xi)$. For the function $F(\xi)$ we obtain

$$F(\xi) = \text{constant} \times \int \frac{d\xi}{\xi^{\frac{3}{2}}(\xi+a^2)} = \text{constant} \times \left[\frac{a}{\sqrt{\xi}} - \tan^{-1}\frac{a}{\sqrt{\xi}}\right];$$

the constant of integration is put equal to zero in accordance with the condition $\phi = 0$ for $z \to +\infty$, i.e. $\sqrt{\xi} \to +\infty$. The inverse tangent of a negative quantity must be taken as $\tan^{-1}(a/-\sqrt{\xi}) = \pi - \tan^{-1}(a/\sqrt{\xi})$, and not as $-\tan^{-1}(a/\sqrt{\xi})$ since the potential would then be discontinuous at the aperture ($\xi = 0$). The constant coefficient is chosen so that, for $z \to -\infty$ (i.e. for $\sqrt{\xi} \to -\infty$ and $\tan^{-1}(a/\sqrt{\xi}) \to \pi$), $\phi \to -\mathfrak{E}z$, and so we finally have

$$\phi = -\frac{\mathfrak{E}z}{\pi}\left[\tan^{-1}\frac{a}{\sqrt{\xi}} - \frac{a}{\sqrt{\xi}}\right] = -\frac{\mathfrak{E}}{\pi}\sqrt{|\eta|}\left[\frac{\sqrt{\xi}}{a}\tan^{-1}\frac{a}{\sqrt{\xi}} - 1\right].$$

On the conducting plane $\eta = 0$ and the potential is zero, as it should be.

At large distances $r = \sqrt{(z^2+\rho^2)}$ from the aperture we have $\xi \cong r^2$, and the potential (in the upper half-plane) is

$$\phi \cong \frac{\mathfrak{E}a^2}{3\pi}\frac{\sqrt{-\eta}}{\xi} = \mathfrak{E}a^3 z/3\pi r^3,$$

i.e. we have a dipole field, the moment of the dipole being $\mathscr{P} = \mathfrak{E}a^3/3\pi$.

The field decreases as $1/r^3$, and therefore the flux of the field through an infinitely remote surface (in the half-space $z > 0$) is zero. This means that all the lines of force passing through the aperture reach the upper side of the conducting plane.

The distribution of charge on the conducting plane is given by

$$\sigma = \mp\frac{1}{4\pi}\left[\frac{\partial\phi}{\partial z}\right]_{z=0} = \mp\frac{a}{4\pi\sqrt{\xi}}\frac{\partial\phi}{\partial\sqrt{-\eta}} = \pm\frac{\mathfrak{E}}{4\pi^2}\left[\tan^{-1}\frac{a}{\sqrt{\xi}} - \frac{a}{\sqrt{\xi}}\right],$$

where the $\mp$ signs refer to the upper and lower sides of the plane respectively. According to the formula

$$\frac{\rho^2}{a^2+\xi} + \frac{z^2}{\xi} = 1,$$

which relates ξ to ρ, z, we have $\sqrt{\xi} = \pm\sqrt{(\rho^2-a^2)}$ on the plane $z = 0$. Thus the charge distribution on the lower side of the conducting plane is given by the formula

$$\sigma = -\frac{\mathfrak{E}}{4\pi^2}\left(\pi - \sin^{-1}\frac{a}{\rho} + \frac{a}{\sqrt{(\rho^2-a^2)}}\right).$$

As $\rho \to \infty$ we have $\sigma = -\mathfrak{E}/4\pi$, as we should expect. On the upper side

$$\sigma = -\frac{\mathfrak{E}}{4\pi^2}\left(\frac{a}{\sqrt{(\rho^2-a^2)}} - \sin^{-1}\frac{a}{\rho}\right).$$

PROBLEM 8. The same as Problem 7, but for a plane with a slit of width $2b$.

SOLUTION. The xy-plane with a slit along the x-axis may be regarded as the limit of the hyperbolic cylinders

$$\frac{y^2}{b^2-|\eta|} - \frac{z^2}{|\eta|} = 1$$

as $|\eta| \to 0$. These hyperbolic cylinders are one of the families of co-ordinate surfaces in a system of ellipsoidal co-ordinates with $a \to \infty$, $c \to 0$. The Cartesian co-ordinate $z = \sqrt{(\xi|\eta|)}/b$.

As in Problem 7, we seek a solution in the form $\phi = -\mathfrak{E}zF(\xi)$, obtaining for the function F

$$F = \text{constant} \times \int \frac{d\xi}{\xi^{3/2}\sqrt{(\xi+b^2)}}.$$

Here the coefficient and the constant of integration are determined by the conditions that $F = 0$ and 1 for $z \to +\infty$ and $-\infty$ respectively (i.e. for $\sqrt{\xi} \to +\infty$ and $-\infty$), and the final result is

$$\phi = \frac{\mathfrak{E}}{2b}[\sqrt{(\xi+b^2)} \mp \sqrt{\xi}]\sqrt{|\eta|},$$

where we now take $\sqrt{\xi}$ positive and the two signs $\mp$ correspond to the regions $z > 0$ and $z < 0$.

At large distances from the slit we have in the upper half-space $\xi \cong y^2+z^2 = r^2$, and the potential is $\phi \cong \frac{1}{4}b\mathfrak{E}\sqrt{(|\eta|\,\xi)} = \frac{1}{4}\mathfrak{E}b^2 z/r^2$, i.e. the field of a two-dimensional dipole of moment $\frac{1}{8}\mathfrak{E}b^2$ per unit length of the slit (see the formula in §3, Problem 2).

The distribution of charge on the conducting plane is given by

$$\sigma = -\frac{\mathfrak{E}}{8\pi}\left(\frac{y}{\sqrt{(y^2-b^2)}} \mp 1\right).$$

§5. The forces on a conductor

In an electric field certain forces act on the surface of a conductor. These forces are easily calculated as follows.

The momentum flux density in an electric field in a vacuum is given by the *Maxwell stress tensor*:†

$$-\sigma_{ik} = \frac{1}{4\pi}(\tfrac{1}{2}E^2\delta_{ik} - E_i E_k).$$

The force on an element $\mathbf{df}$ of the surface of the body is just the "flux" of momentum through it from outside, and is therefore $\sigma_{ik}\mathrm{d}f_k = \sigma_{ik}n_k\mathrm{d}f$ (the sign is changed because the normal vector $\mathbf{n}$ is outwards and not inwards). The quantity $\sigma_{ik}n_k$ is thus the force $\mathbf{F}_s$ per unit area of the surface. Since, at the surface of a conductor, the field $\mathbf{E}$ has no tangential component, we obtain

$$\mathbf{F}_s = \mathbf{n}E^2/8\pi, \tag{5.1}$$

or, introducing the surface charge density σ,

$$\mathbf{F}_s = 2\pi\sigma^2\mathbf{n} = \tfrac{1}{2}\sigma\mathbf{E}.$$

We therefore conclude that a "negative pressure" acts on the surface of a conductor; it is directed along the outward normal to the surface, and its magnitude is equal to the energy density in the field.

The total force $\mathbf{F}$ on the conductor is obtained by integrating the force (5.1) over the whole surface:

$$\mathbf{F} = \oint (E^2/8\pi)\,\mathbf{df}. \tag{5.2}$$

Usually, however, it is more convenient to calculate this quantity from the general laws of mechanics, by differentiating the energy $\mathscr{U}$. The force, in the direction of a co-ordinate q, acting on a conductor is $-\partial\mathscr{U}/\partial q$, where the derivative signifies the rate of change of energy when the body is translated in the q-direction. The energy must be expressed in terms of the charges on the conductors (which give rise to the field), and the differentiation is performed with the charges constant. Denoting this by the suffix e, we write

$$F_q = -(\partial\mathscr{U}/\partial q)_e. \tag{5.3}$$

Similarly, the projection, on any axis, of the total moment of the forces on the conductor is

$$K = -(\partial\mathscr{U}/\partial\psi)_e, \tag{5.4}$$

where ψ is the angle of rotation of the body about that axis.

---

† See *The Classical Theory of Fields*, §4–8, Addison-Wesley Press, Cambridge (Mass.), 1951; Pergamon Press, London, 1959. $-\sigma_{ik}$ is there denoted by $T_{\alpha\beta}$.

In the present case we are applying this formula to a surface which does not precisely coincide with that of the body, but is some distance away, in order to exclude the effect of the field structure near the surface (see §1).

If, however, the energy is expressed as a function of the potentials of the conductors, and not of their charges, the calculation of the forces from the energy requires special consideration. The reason is that, to maintain constant the potential of a moving conductor, it is necessary to use other bodies. For example, the potential of a conductor can be kept constant by connecting it to another conductor of very large capacity, a "charge reservoir". On receiving a charge e_a, the conductor takes it from the reservoir, whose potential ϕ_a is unchanged on account of its large capacity, although its energy is reduced by $e_a\phi_a$. When the whole system of conductors receives charges e_a, the energy of the reservoirs connected to them changes by a total of $-\Sigma e_a\phi_a$. Only the energy of the conductors, and not that of the reservoirs, appears in $\mathcal{U}$. In this sense we can say that $\mathcal{U}$ pertains to a system which is not energetically closed. Thus, for a system of conductors whose potentials are kept constant, the part of the mechanical energy is played not by $\mathcal{U}$, but by

$$\tilde{\mathcal{U}} = \mathcal{U} - \sum_a e_a\phi_a. \tag{5.5}$$

Substituting (2.2), we find that $\mathcal{U}$ and $\tilde{\mathcal{U}}$ differ only in sign:

$$\tilde{\mathcal{U}} = -\mathcal{U}. \tag{5.6}$$

The force F_q is obtained by differentiating $\tilde{\mathcal{U}}$ with respect to q for constant potentials, i.e.

$$F_q = -(\partial\tilde{\mathcal{U}}/\partial q)_\phi = (\partial\mathcal{U}/\partial q)_\phi. \tag{5.7}$$

Thus the forces acting on a conductor can be obtained by differentiating $\mathcal{U}$ either for constant charges or for constant potentials, the only difference being that the derivative must be taken with the minus sign in the first case and with the plus sign in the second.

The same result could be obtained more formally by starting from the differential identity

$$\mathrm{d}\mathcal{U} = \sum_a \phi_a\,\mathrm{d}e_a - F_q\,\mathrm{d}q, \tag{5.8}$$

in which $\mathcal{U}$ is regarded as a function of the charges on the conductors and the co-ordinate q. This identity states that $\partial\mathcal{U}/\partial e_a = \phi_a$ and $\partial\mathcal{U}/\partial q = -F_q$. Using the variables ϕ_a instead of e_a, we have

$$\mathrm{d}\tilde{\mathcal{U}} = -\sum_a e_a\,\mathrm{d}\phi_a - F_q\,\mathrm{d}q, \tag{5.9}$$

which gives (5.7).

At the end of §2 we have discussed the energy of a conductor in a uniform external electric field. The total force on a conductor in a uniform field is, of course, zero. The expression for the energy (2.14) can, however, be used to determine the force acting on a conductor in a quasi-uniform field

$\mathfrak{E}$, i.e. a field which varies only slightly over the dimensions of the conductor. In such a field the energy can still be calculated, to a first approximation, from formula (2.14), and the force **F** is the gradient of this energy:

$$\mathbf{F} = -\mathbf{grad}\,\mathscr{U} = \tfrac{1}{2}\alpha_{ik}V\,\mathbf{grad}\,(\mathfrak{E}_i\mathfrak{E}_k). \tag{5.10}$$

The total torque **K** is in general non-zero even in a uniform external field. By the general laws of mechanics **K** can be determined by considering an infinitesimal virtual rotation of the body. The change in energy in such a rotation is related to **K** by $\delta\mathscr{U} = -\mathbf{K}\cdot\delta\boldsymbol{\psi}$, $\delta\boldsymbol{\psi}$ being the angle of the rotation. A rotation through an angle $\delta\boldsymbol{\psi}$ in a uniform field is equivalent to a rotation of the field through an angle $-\delta\boldsymbol{\psi}$ relative to the body. The change in the field is $\delta\mathfrak{E} = -\delta\boldsymbol{\psi}\times\mathfrak{E}$, and the change in energy is

$$\delta\mathscr{U} = (\partial\mathscr{U}/\partial\mathfrak{E})\cdot\delta\mathfrak{E} = -\delta\boldsymbol{\psi}\cdot\mathfrak{E}\times\partial\mathscr{U}/\partial\mathfrak{E}.$$

But $\partial\mathscr{U}/\partial\mathfrak{E} = -\mathscr{P}$, as we see from a comparison of formulae (2.13) and (2.14). Hence $\delta\mathscr{U} = -\mathscr{P}\times\mathfrak{E}\cdot\delta\boldsymbol{\psi}$, whence

$$\mathbf{K} = \mathscr{P}\times\mathfrak{E}, \tag{5.11}$$

in accordance with the usual expression given by the theory of fields in a vacuum.

If the total force and torque on a conductor are zero, the conductor remains at rest in the field, and effects involving the deformation of the body (called *electrostriction*) become important. The forces (5.1) on the surface of the conductor result in changes in its shape and volume. Because the force is an extending one, the volume of the body increases. A complete determination of the deformation requires a solution of the equations of the theory of elasticity, with the given distribution of forces (5.1) on the surface of the body. If, however, we are interested only in the change in volume, the problem can be solved very simply.

To do so, we must bear in mind that, if the deformation is slight (as in fact is true for electrostriction), the effect of the change of shape on the change of volume is of the second order of smallness. In the first approximation, therefore, the change in volume can be regarded as the result of deformation without change in shape, i.e. as a volume expansion under the action of some effective excess pressure Δp which is uniformly distributed over the surface of the body and replaces the exact distribution given by (5.1). The relative change in volume is obtained by multiplying Δp by the coefficient of uniform expansion of the substance. The pressure Δp is given, according to a well-known formula, by the derivative of the electric energy $\mathscr{U}$ of the body with respect to its volume: $\Delta p = -\partial\mathscr{U}/\partial V$.†

Let the deforming field be due to the charged conductor itself. Then the energy $\mathscr{U} = \frac{1}{2}e^2/C$, and the pressure is $\Delta p = -\frac{1}{2}e^2\partial C^{-1}/\partial V$. For a given

† The quantity thus determined is the pressure exerted on the surface by the body itself; the pressure acting on the surface from outside is obtained by changing the sign.

shape, the capacity of the body (having the dimensions of length) is proportional to the linear dimension, i.e. to $V^{1/3}$. Hence

$$\Delta p = e^2/6CV = e\phi/6V. \tag{5.12}$$

If an uncharged conductor is situated in a uniform external field $\mathfrak{E}$, its energy is given by formula (2.14). The extending pressure is therefore

$$\Delta p = \tfrac{1}{2}\alpha_{ik}\mathfrak{E}_i\mathfrak{E}_k. \tag{5.13}$$

PROBLEMS

PROBLEM 1. A small conductor of capacity c (equal in order of magnitude to its dimension) is at a distance r from the centre of a spherical conductor of large radius a ($\gg c$). The distance $r-a$ from the conductor to the surface of the sphere is supposed large compared with c, but not large compared with a. The two conductors are joined by a thin wire, so that they are at the same potential ϕ. Determine the force of their mutual repulsion.

SOLUTION. Since the conductor c is small, we can suppose that its potential is the sum of the potential $\phi a/r$ at a distance r from the centre of the large sphere and the potential e/c due to the charge e on the conductor itself. Hence $\phi = \phi a/r + e/c$, or $e = c\phi\,(1-a/r)$. The required force of interaction F is the Coulomb repulsion between the charge e on the conductor and the charge $a\phi$ on the sphere:

$$F = \frac{ac\phi^2}{r^2}\left(1-\frac{a}{r}\right).$$

This expression is correct to within terms of higher order in c. Thus the small conductor is repelled from the sphere with a force which decreases as it approaches the surface.

PROBLEM 2. A charged conducting sphere is cut in half. Determine the force of repulsion between the hemispheres.†

SOLUTION. We imagine the hemispheres separated by an infinitely narrow slit, and determine the force F on each of them by integrating over the surface the force $(E^2/8\pi)\cos\theta$, which is the projection of (5.1) on a direction perpendicular to the plane of separation of the hemispheres. In the slit $E = 0$, and on the outer surface $E = e/a^2$, where a is the radius of the sphere and e the total charge on it. The result is $F = e^2/8a^2$.

PROBLEM 3. The same as Problem 2, but for an uncharged sphere in a uniform external field $\mathfrak{E}$ perpendicular to the plane of separation.

SOLUTION. As in Problem 2, except that the field on the surface of the sphere is $E = 3\,\mathfrak{E}\cos\theta$ (§3, Problem 1). The required force is $F = 9a^2\mathfrak{E}^2/16$.

PROBLEM 4. Determine the change in volume and in shape of a conducting sphere in a uniform external electric field.

SOLUTION. The change in volume $\Delta V/V = \Delta p/K$, where K is the modulus of volume expansion of the material, and Δp is given by formula (5.13). For a sphere, $\alpha_{ik} = \delta_{ik}\alpha = 3\delta_{ik}/4\pi$ (§3, Problem 1), so that $\Delta V/V = 3\mathfrak{E}^2/8\pi K$.

As a result of the deformation, the sphere is changed into a prolate spheroid. To determine the eccentricity, we may regard the deformation as a uniform pure shear in the volume of the body, just as, to determine the change in the total volume, we regarded it as a uniform volume expansion.

The condition of equilibrium for a deformed body may be formulated as requiring that the sum of the electrostatic and elastic energies should be a minimum. The former is, by (2.12) and (4.26),

$$\mathcal{U}_{\text{es}} = -\frac{V}{8\pi n}\mathfrak{E}^2 \cong -\frac{3V\mathfrak{E}^2}{8\pi} - \frac{3V}{10\pi}\frac{a-b}{R}\mathfrak{E}^2,$$

† In Problems 2 and 3 we assume that the hemispheres are at the same potential.

where R is the original radius of the sphere, a and b the semiaxes of the spheroid, and $n \cong \frac{1}{3} - 4(a-b)/15R$ is the depolarisation coefficient (see (4.33).)

Since the deformation is axially symmetrical about the direction of the field (the x-axis), only the components u_{xx} and $u_{yy} = u_{zz}$ of the strain tensor are non-zero. Since we are considering equilibrium with respect to a change in shape, we can regard the volume as unchanged, i.e. $u_{ii} = 0$. Hence the elastic energy may be written†

$$\mathscr{U}_{\mathrm{el}} = \tfrac{1}{2} u_{ik} \sigma_{ik} V = \tfrac{1}{3}(\sigma_{xx} - \sigma_{yy})(u_{xx} - u_{yy}) V,$$

where σ_{ik} is the elastic stress tensor. We have $\sigma_{xx} - \sigma_{yy} = 2\mu(u_{xx} - u_{yy})$, where μ is the modulus of rigidity of the material, and $u_{xx} - u_{yy} = (a-b)/R$. Hence

$$\mathscr{U}_{\mathrm{el}} = \tfrac{2}{3}\mu(a-b)^2 V/R^2.$$

Making the sum $\mathscr{U}_{\mathrm{es}} + \mathscr{U}_{\mathrm{el}}$ a minimum, we have $(a-b)/R = 9\mathfrak{E}^2/40\pi\mu$.

PROBLEM 5. Find the relation between frequency and wavelength for waves propagated on a charged plane surface of a liquid conductor (in a gravitational field). Obtain the condition for this surface to be stable (YA. I. FRENKEL', 1935).

SOLUTION. Let the wave be propagated along the x-axis, with the z-axis vertically upwards. The vertical displacement of points on the surface of the liquid is $\zeta = a e^{i(kx - \omega t)}$. When the surface is at rest, the field above it is $E_z = E = 4\pi\sigma_0$, and its potential $\phi = -4\pi\sigma_0 z$, where σ_0 is the surface charge density. The potential of the field above the oscillating surface can be written as $\phi = -4\pi\sigma_0 z + \phi_1$, with $\phi_1 = \text{constant} \times e^{i(kx-\omega t)} e^{-kz}$, ϕ_1 being a small correction which satisfies the equation $\triangle \phi_1 = 0$ and vanishes for $z \to \infty$. On the surface itself, the potential must have a constant value, which we take to be zero, and so $\phi_1 = 4\pi\sigma_0\zeta$ for $z = 0$.

According to (5.1), an additional negative pressure acts on the charged surface of the liquid; this pressure is, as far as terms of the first order in ϕ_1, $E^2/8\pi \cong E_z^2/8\pi \cong 2\pi\sigma_0^2 + [k\sigma_0\phi_1]_{z=0} = 2\pi\sigma_0^2 + 4\pi\sigma_0^2 k\zeta$. The constant term $2\pi\sigma_0^2$ is of no importance, since it can be included in the constant external pressure.

The consideration of the hydrodynamical motion in the wave is entirely analogous to the theory of capillary waves‡, differing only by the presence of the additional pressure mentioned above. At the surface of the liquid we have the boundary condition $\rho g\zeta + \rho[\partial\Phi/\partial t]_{z=0} - \alpha\partial^2\zeta/\partial x^2 - 4\pi\sigma_0^2 k\zeta = 0$, where α is the surface-tension coefficient, ρ the density of the liquid, and Φ its velocity potential. Φ and ζ are also related by $\partial\zeta/\partial t = [\partial\Phi/\partial z]_{z=0}$. Substituting in these two relations $\zeta = a e^{i(kx-\omega t)}$ and $\Phi = A e^{i(kx-\omega t)}$ and eliminating a and A, we find the required relation between k and ω:

$$\omega^2 = k(g\rho - 4\pi\sigma_0^2 k + \alpha k^2)/\rho. \tag{1}$$

If the surface of the liquid is to be stable, the frequency ω must be real for all values of k (since otherwise there would be complex ω with a positive imaginary part, and the factor $e^{-i\omega t}$ would increase indefinitely). The condition for the right-hand side of (1) to be positive is $(4\pi\sigma_0^2)^2 - 4g\rho\alpha < 0$, or $\sigma_0^4 < g\rho\alpha/4\pi^2$. This is the condition for stability.

PROBLEM 6. Find the condition of stability for a charged spherical drop (RAYLEIGH, 1882).

SOLUTION. The sum of the electrostatic and surface energies of the drop is $\mathscr{U} = e^2/2C + \alpha S$, where α is the surface-tension coefficient of the liquid, C the capacity of the drop and S its surface area. Instability occurs (with increasing e) with respect to deformation of the sphere into a spheroid, and does so when $\mathscr{U}$ becomes a decreasing function of the eccentricity (for a given volume). The spherical shape always corresponds to an extremum of $\mathscr{U}$; the stability condition is therefore $[\partial^2\mathscr{U}/\partial(a-b)^2]_{a=b} > 0$, where a and b are the semiaxes of the spheroid, and the differentiation is carried out with $ab^2 = \text{constant}$. Using the formula for the surface of a spheroid and (4.18) for its capacity, we find after a somewhat lengthy calculation $e^2 < 16\pi a^3\alpha$.

---

† See *Theory of Elasticity*, §4, Pergamon Press, London, 1959.
‡ See *Fluid Mechanics*, §61, Pergamon Press, London, 1959.

CHAPTER II

ELECTROSTATICS OF DIELECTRICS

§6. The electric field in dielectrics

WE SHALL now go on to consider a constant electric field in another class of substances, namely dielectrics. The fundamental property of dielectrics is that a constant current cannot flow in them. Hence the constant electric field need not be zero, as in conductors, and we have to derive the equations which describe this field. One equation is obtained by averaging equation (1.3), and is again

$$\textbf{curl}\,\mathbf{E} = 0. \tag{6.1}$$

A second equation is obtained by averaging the equation div $\mathbf{e} = 4\pi\rho$:

$$\operatorname{div}\mathbf{E} = 4\pi\bar{\rho}. \tag{6.2}$$

Let us suppose that no charges are brought into the dielectric from outside, which is the most usual and important case. Then the total charge in the volume of the dielectric is zero; even if it is placed in an electric field we have $\int \bar{\rho}\mathrm{d}V = 0$. This integral equation, which must be valid for a body of any shape, means that the average charge density can be written as the divergence of a certain vector, which is usually denoted by $-\mathbf{P}$:

$$\bar{\rho} = -\operatorname{div}\mathbf{P}, \tag{6.3}$$

while outside the body $\mathbf{P} = 0$. For, on integrating over the volume bounded by a surface which encloses the body but nowhere enters it, we find $\int\bar{\rho}\mathrm{d}V = -\int \operatorname{div}\mathbf{P}\,\mathrm{d}V = -\oint \mathbf{P}\cdot\mathrm{d}\mathbf{f} = 0$. $\mathbf{P}$ is called the *dielectric polarisation*, or simply the *polarisation*, of the body. A dielectric in which $\mathbf{P}$ differs from zero is said to be *polarised*. The vector $\mathbf{P}$ determines not only the volume charge density (6.3), but also the density σ of the charges on the surface of the polarised dielectric. If we integrate formula (6.3) over an element of volume lying between two neighbouring unit areas, one on each side of the dielectric surface, we have, since $\mathbf{P} = 0$ on the outer area (cf. the derivation of formula (1.9)),

$$\sigma = P_n, \tag{6.4}$$

where P_n is the component of the vector $\mathbf{P}$ along the outward normal to the surface.

To see the physical significance of the quantity $\mathbf{P}$ itself, let us consider the total dipole moment of all the charges within the dielectric; unlike the total charge, the total dipole moment need not be zero. By definition, it is the integral $\int \mathbf{r}\bar{\rho}\,\mathrm{d}V$. Substituting $\bar{\rho}$ from (6.3) and again integrating over a volume which includes the whole body we have

$$\int \mathbf{r}\bar{\rho}\,\mathrm{d}V = -\int \mathbf{r}\ \mathrm{div}\ \mathbf{P}\,\mathrm{d}V = -\oint \mathbf{r}(\mathbf{df}\cdot\mathbf{P})+\int (\mathbf{P}\cdot\mathbf{grad})\mathbf{r}\,\mathrm{d}V.$$

The integral over the surface is zero, and in the second term we have $(\mathbf{P}\cdot\mathbf{grad})\mathbf{r} = \mathbf{P}$, so that

$$\int \mathbf{r}\bar{\rho}\,\mathrm{d}V = \int \mathbf{P}\,\mathrm{d}V. \tag{6.5}$$

Thus the polarisation vector is the dipole moment (or *electric moment*) per unit volume of the dielectric.†

Substituting (6.3) in (6.2), we obtain the second equation of the electrostatic field in the form

$$\mathrm{div}\,\mathbf{D} = 0, \tag{6.6}$$

where we have introduced a quantity **D** defined by

$$\mathbf{D} = \mathbf{E}+4\pi\mathbf{P}, \tag{6.7}$$

called the *electric induction.*‡ The equation (6.6) has been derived by averaging the density of charges in the dielectric. If, however, charges not belonging to the dielectric are brought in from outside (we shall call these *extraneous charges*), then their density must be added to the right-hand side of equation (6.6):

$$\mathrm{div}\,\mathbf{D} = 4\pi\rho_{\mathrm{ex}}. \tag{6.8}$$

On the surface of separation between two different dielectrics, certain boundary conditions must be satisfied. One of these follows from the equation $\mathbf{curl}\,\mathbf{E} = 0$. If the surface of separation is uniform as regards physical properties,|| this condition requires the continuity of the tangential component of the field:

$$\mathbf{E}_{1t} = \mathbf{E}_{2t}; \tag{6.9}$$

cf. the derivation of the condition (1.7). The second condition follows from the equation $\mathrm{div}\,\mathbf{D} = 0$, and requires the continuity of the normal component of the induction:

$$D_{1n} = D_{2n}. \tag{6.10}$$

† It should be noticed that the relation (6.3) inside the dielectric and the condition $\mathbf{P} = 0$ outside do not in themselves determine **P** uniquely; inside the dielectric we could add to **P** any vector of the form **curl f**. **P** can be completely determined only by establishing its connection with the dipole moment.

‡ Sometimes the *electric displacement*, a term due to MAXWELL, but one which is obsolete.

|| That is, as regards composition of the adjoining media, temperature, etc. If the dielectric is a crystal, the crystallographic direction of the surface must be constant, i.e. the surface must be a plane.

For a discontinuity in the normal component $D_n = D_z$ would involve an infinity of the derivative $\partial D_z/\partial z$, and therefore of div **D**.

At a boundary between a dielectric and a conductor, $\mathbf{E}_t = 0$, and the condition on the normal component is obtained from (6.8):

$$\mathbf{E}_t = 0, \quad D_n = 4\pi\sigma, \tag{6.11}$$

where σ is the charge density on the surface of the conductor.

§7. The dielectric permeability

In order that equations (6.1) and (6.6) should form a complete set of equations determining the electrostatic field, they must be supplemented by a relation between the induction **D** and the field **E**. In the great majority of cases this relation may be supposed linear. It corresponds to the first terms in an expansion of **D** in powers of **E**, and its correctness is due to the smallness of the external electric fields in comparison with the internal molecular fields.

The linear relation between **D** and **E** is especially simple in the most important case, that of an isotropic dielectric. It is evident that, in an isotropic dielectric, the vectors **D** and **E** must be in the same direction. The linear relation between them is therefore a simple proportionality:†

$$\mathbf{D} = \epsilon\mathbf{E}. \tag{7.1}$$

The coefficient ϵ is the *dielectric permeability* or *dielectric constant* of the substance and is a function of its thermodynamic state.

As well as the induction, the polarisation also is proportional to the field:

$$\mathbf{P} = \kappa\mathbf{E} \equiv (\epsilon - 1)\mathbf{E}/4\pi. \tag{7.2}$$

The quantity κ is called the *polarisation coefficient* of the substance, or its *dielectric susceptibility*. Later (§14) we shall show that the dielectric permeability always exceeds unity; the polarisability, accordingly, is always positive. The polarisability of a rarefied medium (a gas) may be regarded as proportional to its density.

The boundary conditions (6.9) and (6.10) on the surface separating two isotropic dielectrics become

$$\mathbf{E}_{t1} = \mathbf{E}_{t2}, \quad \epsilon_1 E_{n1} = \epsilon_2 E_{n2}. \tag{7.3}$$

Thus the normal component of the field is discontinuous, changing in inverse proportion to the dielectric permeability of the medium.

---

† It should be mentioned, however, that this relation, which assumes that **D** and **E** vanish simultaneously, is, strictly speaking, valid only in dielectrics which are homogeneous as regards physical properties (composition, temperature, etc.). In inhomogeneous bodies **D** may be non-zero even when $\mathbf{E} = 0$, and is determined by the gradients of thermodynamic quantities which vary through the body. The corresponding terms, however, are very small, and in practice are of no importance. We shall therefore use the relation (7.1) in what follows, even for inhomogeneous bodies.

In a homogeneous dielectric, $\epsilon =$ constant, and then it follows from $\operatorname{div} \mathbf{D} = 0$ that $\operatorname{div} \mathbf{P} = 0$. By the definition (6.3) this means that the volume charge density in such a body is zero (but the surface density (6.4) is in general not zero). On the other hand, in an inhomogeneous dielectric we have a non-zero volume charge density

$$\bar{\rho} = -\operatorname{div} \mathbf{P} = -\operatorname{div}\frac{\epsilon-1}{4\pi\epsilon}\mathbf{D} = -\frac{1}{4\pi}\mathbf{D}\cdot\mathbf{grad}\frac{\epsilon-1}{\epsilon} = -\frac{1}{4\pi\epsilon}\mathbf{E}\cdot\mathbf{grad}\,\epsilon.$$

If we introduce the electric field potential by $\mathbf{E} = -\mathbf{grad}\,\phi$, then equation (6.1) is automatically satisfied, and the equation $\operatorname{div} \mathbf{D} = \operatorname{div} \epsilon\mathbf{E} = 0$ gives

$$\operatorname{div}(\epsilon\,\mathbf{grad}\,\phi) = 0. \tag{7.4}$$

This equation becomes the ordinary Laplace's equation only in a homogeneous dielectric medium. The boundary conditions (7.3) can be rewritten as the following conditions on the potential:

$$\begin{aligned} \phi_1 &= \phi_2, \\ \epsilon_1 \partial\phi_1/\partial n &= \epsilon_2 \partial\phi_2/\partial n; \end{aligned} \tag{7.5}$$

the continuity of the tangential derivatives of the potential is equivalent to the continuity of ϕ itself.

In a dielectric medium which is piecewise homogeneous, equation (7.4) reduces in each homogeneous region to Laplace's equation $\triangle\phi = 0$, so that the dielectric permeability appears in the solution of the problem only through the conditions (7.5). These conditions, however, involve only the ratio of the dielectric permeabilities of two adjoining media. In particular, the solution of an electrostatic problem for a dielectric body of permeability ϵ_2, surrounded by a medium of permeability ϵ_1, is the same as for a body of permeability ϵ_2/ϵ_1, surrounded by a vacuum.

Let us consider how the results obtained in Chapter I for the electrostatic field of conductors will be modified if these conductors are not in a vacuum but in a homogeneous and isotropic dielectric medium. In both cases the potential distribution satisfies the equation $\triangle\phi = 0$, with the boundary condition that ϕ is constant on the surface of the conductor, and the only difference is that, instead of $E_n = -\partial\phi/\partial n = 4\pi\sigma$, we have

$$D_n = -\epsilon\,\partial\phi/\partial n = 4\pi\sigma, \tag{7.6}$$

giving the relation between the potential and the surface charge. Hence it is clear that the solution of the problem of the field of a charged conductor in a vacuum gives the solution of the same problem with a dielectric in place of the vacuum if we make the formal substitution $\phi \to \epsilon\phi$, $e \to e$ or $\phi \to \phi$, $e \to e/\epsilon$. For given charges on the conductors, the potential and the field are reduced by a factor ϵ in comparison with their values in a vacuum. This reduction in the field can be explained as the result of a partial "screening" of the charge on the conductor by the surface charges on the adjoining polarised dielectric. If, on the other hand, the potentials of the conductors are maintained, then the field is unchanged but the charges are increased by a factor ϵ.

Finally, it may be noted that in electrostatics we may formally regard a conductor (uncharged) as a body of infinite dielectric permeability, in the sense that its effect on an external electric field is the same as that of a dielectric (of the same form) as $\epsilon \to \infty$. For, since the boundary condition on the induction **D** is finite, **D** must remain finite in the body even for $\epsilon \to \infty$. This means that $\mathbf{E} \to 0$, in accordance with the properties of conductors.

PROBLEMS

PROBLEM 1. Determine the field due to a point charge e at a distance h from a plane boundary separating two different dielectric media.

SOLUTION. Let O be the position of the charge e in medium 1, and O' its image in the plane of separation, situated in medium 2 (Fig. 10). We shall seek the field in medium 1 in the form of the field of two point charges, e and a fictitious charge e' at O' (cf. the method of images, §3): $\phi_1 = e/\epsilon_1 r + e'/\epsilon_1 r'$, where r and r' are the distances from O and O' respectively. In medium 2 we seek the field as that of a fictitious charge e'' at O: $\phi_2 = e''/\epsilon_2 r$. On the boundary plane ($r = r'$) the conditions (7.5) must hold, leading to the equations $e - e' = e''$, $(e+e')/\epsilon_1 = e''/\epsilon_2$, whence

$$e' = e(\epsilon_1 - \epsilon_2)/(\epsilon_1 + \epsilon_2), \qquad e'' = 2\epsilon_2 e/(\epsilon_1 + \epsilon_2). \tag{1}$$

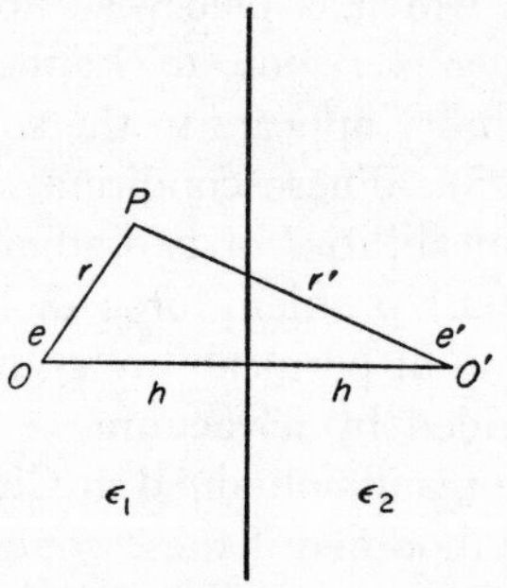

FIG. 10

For $\epsilon_2 \to \infty$ we have $e' = -e$, $\phi_2 = 0$, i.e. the result obtained in §3 for the field of a point charge near a conducting plane.

The force acting on the charge e (the "image force") is

$$F = \frac{ee'}{(2h)^2 \epsilon_1} = \left(\frac{e}{2h}\right)^2 \frac{\epsilon_1 - \epsilon_2}{\epsilon_1(\epsilon_1 + \epsilon_2)};$$

$F > 0$ corresponds to repulsion.

PROBLEM 2. The same as Problem 1, but for an infinite charged straight wire parallel to a plane boundary surface at a distance h.

SOLUTION. As in Problem 1, except that the field potentials in the two media are $\phi_1 = -(2e/\epsilon_1)\log r - (2e'/\epsilon_1)\log r'$, $\phi_2 = -(2e''/\epsilon_2)\log r$, where e, e', e'' are the charges per unit length of the wire and of its images, and r, r' are the distances in a plane perpendicular to the wire. The same expressions (1) are obtained for e', e'', and the force on unit length of the wire is $F = 2ee'/2h\epsilon_1 = e^2(\epsilon_1 - \epsilon_2)/h\epsilon_1(\epsilon_1 + \epsilon_2)$.

PROBLEM 3. Determine the field due to an infinite charged straight wire in a medium with dielectric constant ϵ_1, lying parallel to a cylinder of radius a and dielectric constant ϵ_2, at a distance b ($> a$) from its axis.†

SOLUTION. We seek the field in medium 1 as that produced in a homogeneous dielectric (with constant ϵ_1) by the actual wire (passing through O in Fig. 11), with charge e per unit length, and two fictitious wires with charges e' and $-e'$ per unit length, passing through A and O' respectively. The point A is at a distance a^2/b from the axis of the cylinder. Then, for all points on the circumference, the distances r and r' from O and A are in a constant ratio $r'/r = a/b$, and so it is possible to satisfy the boundary conditions on this circumference. In medium 2 we seek the field as that produced in a homogeneous medium (with constant ϵ_2) by a fictitious charge e'' on the wire passing through O.

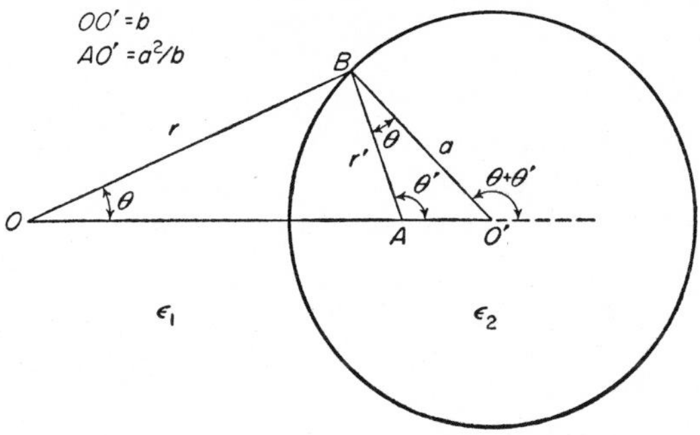

FIG. 11

The boundary conditions on the surface of separation are conveniently formulated in terms of the potential ϕ ($\mathbf{E} = -\mathbf{grad}\,\phi$) and the vector potential $\mathbf{A}$ (cf. §3), defined by $\mathbf{D} = \mathbf{curl}\,\mathbf{A}$ (in accordance with the equation $\operatorname{div}\mathbf{D} = 0$). In a two-dimensional problem, $\mathbf{A}$ is in the z-direction (perpendicular to the plane of the figure). The conditions of continuity for the tangential components of $\mathbf{E}$ and the normal component of $\mathbf{D}$ are equivalent to $\phi_1 = \phi_2$, $A_1 = A_2$.

For the field of a charged wire we have in polar co-ordinates r, θ: $\phi = -(2e/\epsilon)\log r +$ constant, $A = 2e\theta +$constant; cf. (3.18). Hence the boundary conditions are

$$\frac{2}{\epsilon_1}(-e\log r - e\log r' + e'\log a) = -\frac{2e''}{\epsilon_2}\log r + \text{constant},$$

$$2[e\theta + e'\theta' - e'(\theta+\theta')] = 2e''\theta,$$

where the angles are as shown in Fig. 11, and we have used the fact that $OO'B$ and $BO'A$ are similar triangles. Hence $\epsilon_2(e+e') = \epsilon_1 e''$, $e - e' = e''$, and the expressions for e' and e'' are again formulae (1) of Problem 1.

The force acting on unit length of the charged wire is parallel to OO', and is

$$F = eE = \frac{2ee'}{\epsilon_1}\left(\frac{1}{OA} - \frac{1}{OO'}\right) = \frac{2e^2(\epsilon_1-\epsilon_2)a^2}{\epsilon_1(\epsilon_1+\epsilon_2)b(b^2-a^2)};$$

$F > 0$ corresponds to repulsion.

PROBLEM 4. The same as Problem 3, but for the case where the wire is inside a cylinder of dielectric permeability ϵ_2 ($b < a$).

† The corresponding problem of a point charge near a dielectric sphere cannot be solved in closed form.

SOLUTION. We seek the field in medium 2 as that due to the actual wire, of charge e per unit length (O in Fig. 12), and a fictitious wire of charge e' per unit length passing through A, which is now outside the cylinder. In medium 1 we seek the field as that of wires with charges e'' and $e-e''$ passing through O and O' respectively. By the same method as in the preceding problem we find $e' = -e(\epsilon_1-\epsilon_2)/(\epsilon_1+\epsilon_2)$, $e'' = 2\epsilon_1 e/(\epsilon_1+\epsilon_2)$. For $\epsilon_2 > \epsilon_1$ the wire is repelled from the surface of the cylinder by a force

$$F = \frac{2ee'}{\epsilon_2}\frac{1}{OA} = \frac{2e^2(\epsilon_2-\epsilon_1)b}{\epsilon_2(\epsilon_1+\epsilon_2)(a^2-b^2)}.$$

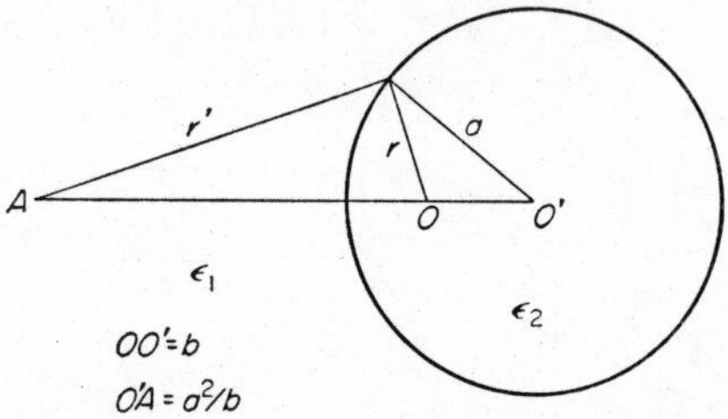

FIG. 12

PROBLEM 5. Show that the field potential $\phi_A(\mathbf{r}_B)$ at a point $\mathbf{r}_B$ in an arbitrary inhomogeneous dielectric medium, due to a point charge e at $\mathbf{r}_A$, is equal to the potential $\phi_B(\mathbf{r}_A)$ at $\mathbf{r}_A$ due to the same charge at $\mathbf{r}_B$.

SOLUTION. The potentials $\phi_A(\mathbf{r})$ and $\phi_B(\mathbf{r})$ satisfy the equations

$$\operatorname{div}(\epsilon\,\mathbf{grad}\,\phi_A) = -4\pi e\delta(\mathbf{r}-\mathbf{r}_A),\quad \operatorname{div}(\epsilon\,\mathbf{grad}\,\phi_B) = -4\pi e\delta(\mathbf{r}-\mathbf{r}_B).$$

Multiplying the first by ϕ_B and the latter by ϕ_A and subtracting, we have

$$\operatorname{div}(\phi_B\,\epsilon\,\mathbf{grad}\,\phi_A)-\operatorname{div}(\phi_A\,\epsilon\,\mathbf{grad}\,\phi_B) = -4\pi e\delta(\mathbf{r}-\mathbf{r}_A)\phi_B(\mathbf{r})+4\pi e\delta(\mathbf{r}-\mathbf{r}_B)\phi_A(\mathbf{r}).$$

Integration of this equation over all space gives the required relation:

$$\phi_A(\mathbf{r}_B) = \phi_B(\mathbf{r}_A).$$

§8. A dielectric ellipsoid

The polarisation of a dielectric ellipsoid in a uniform external electric field has some unusual properties which render this example particularly interesting.

Let us consider first a simple special case, that of a dielectric sphere in an external field $\mathfrak{E}$. We denote its dielectric constant by $\epsilon^{(i)}$, and that of the medium surrounding it by $\epsilon^{(e)}$. We take the origin of spherical co-ordinates at the centre of the sphere, and the direction of $\mathfrak{E}$ as the polar axis, and seek the field potential outside the sphere in the form $\phi^{(e)} = \mathfrak{E}\cdot\mathbf{r}+A\mathfrak{E}\cdot\mathbf{r}/r^3$; the first term is the potential of the external field imposed, and the second, which vanishes at infinity, gives the required change in potential due to the sphere (cf. §3, Problem 1, solution). Inside the sphere, we seek the field potential to the form $\phi^{(i)} = -B\mathfrak{E}\cdot\mathbf{r}$, the only function which satisfies Laplace's equation, remains finite at the centre of the sphere, and depends only on the constant vector $\mathfrak{E}$ (which is the only parameter of the problem).

The constants A and B are determined by the boundary conditions on the surface of the sphere. It may be seen at once, however, that the field in the sphere $\mathbf{E}^{(i)} = B\mathfrak{E}$ is uniform and differs only in magnitude from the applied field $\mathfrak{E}$.

The boundary condition of continuity of the potential gives $\mathbf{E}^{(i)} = \mathfrak{E}(1-A/R^3)$, where R is the radius of the sphere, and the condition of continuity of the normal component of the induction gives

$$\mathbf{D}^{(i)} = \epsilon^{(e)}\mathfrak{E}(1+2A/R^3).$$

Eliminating A from these two equations, we obtain

$$\tfrac{1}{3}(\mathbf{D}^{(i)}+2\epsilon^{(e)}\mathbf{E}^{(i)}) = \epsilon^{(e)}\mathfrak{E} \tag{8.1}$$

or, substituting $\mathbf{D}^{(i)} = \epsilon^{(i)}\mathbf{E}^{(i)}$,

$$\mathbf{E}^{(i)} = 3\epsilon^{(e)}\mathfrak{E}/(2\epsilon^{(e)}+\epsilon^{(i)}). \tag{8.2}$$

The problem of an infinite dielectric cylinder in an external field perpendicular to its axis is solved in an entirely similar manner (cf. §3, Problem 2). The field inside the cylinder, like that inside the sphere in the above example, is uniform. It satisfies the relation

$$\tfrac{1}{2}(\mathbf{D}^{(i)}+\epsilon^{(e)}\mathbf{E}^{(i)}) = \epsilon^{(e)}\mathfrak{E}, \tag{8.3}$$

or

$$\mathbf{E}^{(i)} = 2\epsilon^{(e)}\mathfrak{E}/(\epsilon^{(e)}+\epsilon^{(i)}). \tag{8.4}$$

The relations (8.1) and (8.3), in which the dielectric constant $\epsilon^{(i)}$ of the sphere or cylinder does not appear explicitly, are particularly important because their validity does not depend on a linear relation between **E** and **D** within the body; they hold whatever the form of this relation (e.g. for anisotropic bodies). The analogous relations

$$\mathbf{E}^{(i)} = \mathfrak{E} \tag{8.5}$$

for a cylinder in a longitudinal field and

$$\mathbf{D}^{(i)} = \epsilon^{(e)}\mathfrak{E} \tag{8.6}$$

for a flat plate in a field perpendicular to it are similarly valid; these relations are evident at once from the boundary conditions.

The property of causing a uniform field within itself on being placed in a uniform external field is found to pertain to any ellipsoid, whatever the ratio of the semiaxes a, b, c. The problem of the polarisation of a dielectric ellipsoid is solved by the use of ellipsoidal co-ordinates, in the same way as the corresponding problem for a conducting ellipsoid in §4.

Let the external field be again in the x-direction. The field potential outside the ellipsoid may again be sought in the form (4.22): $\phi'_e = \phi_0 F(\xi)$, with the function $F(\xi)$ given by (4.23). Such a function cannot, however, appear in the field potential ϕ_i inside the sphere, since it does not satisfy the condition that the field must be finite everywhere inside the ellipsoid. For let us consider the surface $\xi = -c^2$, which is an ellipse in the xy-plane, lying within the ellipsoid. For $\xi \to -c^2$, the integral (4.23) behaves as $\sqrt{(\xi+c^2)}$.

The field, i.e. the potential gradient, therefore behaves as $1/\sqrt{(\xi+c^2)}$, and becomes infinite at $\xi = -c^2$. Thus the only solution suitable for the field inside the ellipsoid is $F(\xi) = \text{constant}$, so that ϕ_i must be sought in the form $\phi_i = B\phi_0$. We see that the potential ϕ_i differs only by a constant factor from the potential ϕ_0 of the uniform field. In other words, the field inside the ellipsoid is also uniform.

We shall not pause to write out the formulae for the field outside the ellipsoid, which are of little interest. The uniform field inside the ellipsoid can be found without actually writing out the boundary conditions, by using some results already known.

Let us first suppose that the ellipsoid is in a vacuum ($\epsilon^{(e)} = 1$). Then there must be a linear relation between the vectors $\mathbf{E}^{(i)}$, $\mathbf{D}^{(i)}$ and $\mathfrak{E}$ (which are all in the x-direction), of the form $aE_x + bD_x = \mathfrak{E}_x$, where the coefficients a, b depend only on the shape of the ellipsoid, and not on its dielectric permeability $\epsilon^{(i)}$. The existence of such a relation follows from the form of the boundary conditions, as we saw above in the examples of the sphere and the cylinder.

To determine a and b we notice that, in the trivial particular case $\epsilon^{(i)} = 1$, we have simply $\mathbf{E} = \mathbf{D} = \mathfrak{E}$, and so $a+b = 1$. Another particular case for which the solution is known is that of a conducting ellipsoid. In a conductor $\mathbf{E}^{(i)} = 0$, and the induction $\mathbf{D}^{(i)}$, though it has no direct physical significance, may be regarded formally as being related to the total dipole moment of the ellipsoid by $\mathbf{D} = 4\pi\mathbf{P} = 4\pi\mathscr{P}/V$. According to (4.26) we then have $D_x = \mathfrak{E}_x/n^{(x)}$, i.e. $b = n^{(x)}$, and so $a = 1-n^{(x)}$. Thus we conclude that†

$$(1-n^{(x)})E^{(i)}{}_x + n^{(x)}D^{(i)}{}_x = \mathfrak{E}_x. \tag{8.7}$$

Similar relations, but with other coefficients, hold for the fields in the y and z directions. Like the particular formulae (8.1) and (8.3), they are valid whatever the relation between $\mathbf{E}$ and $\mathbf{D}$ inside the ellipsoid.

The field inside the ellipsoid, when $\mathfrak{E}$ is in the x-direction, is found from (8.7) by putting $D^{(i)}{}_x = \epsilon^{(i)}E^{(i)}{}_x$:

$$E^{(i)}{}_x = \mathfrak{E}_x/[1+(\epsilon^{(i)}-1)n^{(x)}], \tag{8.8}$$

and the total dipole moment of the ellipsoid is

$$\mathscr{P}_x = VP_x = (\epsilon^{(i)}-1)VE^{(i)}{}_x/4\pi = \tfrac{1}{3}abc(\epsilon^{(i)}-1)\mathfrak{E}_x/[1+(\epsilon^{(i)}-1)n^{(x)}]. \tag{8.9}$$

If the field $\mathfrak{E}$ has components along all three axes, then the field inside the ellipsoid is still uniform, but in general not parallel to $\mathfrak{E}$. For an arbitrary choice of co-ordinate axes we can write the relation (8.7) in the general form

$$E^{(i)}{}_i + n_{ik}(D^{(i)}{}_k - E^{(i)}{}_k) = \mathfrak{E}_i. \tag{8.10}$$

† This result can also be written $E^{(i)}{}_x = \mathfrak{E}_x - 4\pi n^{(x)}P_x$. The quantity $4\pi n^{(x)}P_x$ is sometimes called the *depolarising field*. A similar formula holds for a magnetised ellipsoid in a uniform external magnetic field (see §27). In this case $n^{(x)}$, $n^{(y)}$, $n^{(z)}$ are called *demagnetisation coefficients*.

The transition to the case where the dielectric permeability of the medium differs from unity is effected by simply replacing $\epsilon^{(i)}$ by $\epsilon^{(i)}/\epsilon^{(e)}$. Then formula (8.7) becomes

$$(1-n^{(x)})\epsilon^{(e)}E^{(i)}{}_x + n^{(x)}D^{(i)}{}_x = \epsilon^{(e)}\mathfrak{E}_x. \qquad (8.11)$$

This formula can be applied, in particular, to the field inside an ellipsoidal cavity in an infinite dielectric medium. In this case $\epsilon^{(i)} = 1$.

PROBLEMS†

PROBLEM 1. Determine the torque on a spheroid in a uniform electric field.

SOLUTION. According to the general formula (16.13), the torque on an ellipsoid is $\mathbf{K} = \mathscr{P} \times \mathfrak{E}$, where $\mathscr{P}$ is the dipole moment of the ellipsoid. In a spheroid, the vector $\mathscr{P}$ is in a plane passing through the axis of symmetry and the direction of $\mathfrak{E}$. The torque is perpendicular to this plane, and a calculation of its magnitude from formulae (8.9) gives

$$K = \frac{(\epsilon-1)^2|1-3n|\mathfrak{E}^2 V \sin 2\alpha}{8\pi[n\epsilon+1-n][(1-n)\epsilon+1+n]},$$

where α is the angle between the direction of $\mathfrak{E}$ and the axis of symmetry of the spheroid, and n is the depolarisation coefficient along the axis (so that the depolarisation coefficients in the directions perpendicular to the axis are $\frac{1}{2}(1-n)$). The torque is directed so that it tends to turn the axis of symmetry of a prolate ($n < \frac{1}{3}$) or oblate ($n > \frac{1}{3}$) ellipsoid parallel or perpendicular to the field respectively.

For a conducting ellipsoid ($\epsilon \to \infty$) we have

$$K = \frac{|1-3n|}{8\pi n(1-n)} V\mathfrak{E}^2 \sin 2\alpha.$$

PROBLEM 2. A hollow dielectric sphere (of dielectric constant ϵ and internal and external radii b and a) is in a uniform external field $\mathfrak{E}$. Determine the field in the cavity.

SOLUTION. As above in the problem of a continuous sphere, we seek the field potentials in the vacuum outside the sphere (region 1) and in the cavity (region 3) in the forms $\phi_1 = -\mathfrak{E}\cos\theta\,(r-A/r^2)$, $\phi_3 = -B\mathfrak{E}r\cos\theta$, and that in the dielectric (region 2) as $\phi_2 = -C\mathfrak{E}\cos\theta\,(r-D/r^2)$, where A, B, C, D are constants determined from the conditions of continuity of ϕ and $\epsilon\,\partial\phi/\partial r$ at the boundaries 1–2 and 2–3. Thus the field $\mathbf{E}_3 = B\mathfrak{E}$ in the cavity is uniform, but the field $\mathbf{E}_2$ in the sphere is not. A calculation of the constant gives the result

$$\mathbf{E}_3 = 9\epsilon\mathfrak{E}/[(\epsilon+2)(2\epsilon+1)-2(\epsilon-1)^2(b/a)^3].$$

PROBLEM 3. The same as Problem 2, but for a hollow cylinder in a uniform transverse field.‡

SOLUTION. As in Problem 2, with the result

$$\mathbf{E}_3 = 4\epsilon\mathfrak{E}/[(\epsilon+1)^2-(\epsilon-1)^2(b/a)^2].$$

§9. The dielectric permeability of a mixture

If a substance is a finely dispersed mixture (an emulsion, powder mixture, etc.), we can consider the electric field averaged over volumes which are large compared with the scale of the inhomogeneities. The mixture is a homogeneous and isotropic medium with respect to such an average field,

† In these three Problems the body is assumed to be in a vacuum.

‡ In a longitudinal field the solution is clearly $\mathbf{E}_3 = \mathfrak{E}$.

and so may be characterised by an effective dielectric permeability, which we denote by ϵ_{mix}. If $\bar{\mathbf{E}}$ and $\bar{\mathbf{D}}$ are the field and induction averaged in this way, then, by the definition of ϵ_{mix},

$$\bar{\mathbf{D}} = \epsilon_{\mathrm{mix}}\bar{\mathbf{E}}. \tag{9.1}$$

If all the particles in the mixture are isotropic, and the differences in their dielectric permeabilities are small in comparison with ϵ itself, it is possible to calculate ϵ_{mix} in a general form which is correct as far as terms of the second order in these differences.

We write the local field as $\mathbf{E} = \bar{\mathbf{E}} + \delta\mathbf{E}$, and the local dielectric permeability as $\bar{\epsilon} + \delta\epsilon$, where

$$\bar{\epsilon} = (1/V)\int \epsilon \, \mathrm{d}V \tag{9.2}$$

is obtained by averaging over the volume. Then the mean induction is

$$\bar{\mathbf{D}} = \overline{(\bar{\epsilon} + \delta\epsilon)(\bar{\mathbf{E}} + \delta\mathbf{E})} = \bar{\epsilon}\bar{\mathbf{E}} + \overline{\delta\epsilon\delta\mathbf{E}}, \tag{9.3}$$

since the mean values of $\delta\epsilon$ and $\delta\mathbf{E}$ are zero by definition. In the zero-order approximation $\epsilon_{\mathrm{mix}} = \bar{\epsilon}$; the first non-zero correction term will, of course, be of the second order in $\delta\epsilon$, as we see from (9.3).

From the non-averaged equation $\operatorname{div}\mathbf{D} = 0$ we have, as far as small terms of the first order,

$$\operatorname{div}[(\bar{\epsilon} + \delta\epsilon)(\bar{\mathbf{E}} + \delta\mathbf{E})] = \bar{\epsilon}\operatorname{div}\delta\mathbf{E} + \bar{\mathbf{E}}\cdot\mathbf{grad}\,\delta\epsilon = 0,$$

or, substituting $\delta\mathbf{E} = -\mathbf{grad}\,\delta\phi$, $\bar{\epsilon}\triangle\delta\phi = \bar{\mathbf{E}}\cdot\mathbf{grad}\,\delta\epsilon$. Taking the gradient, we have

$$\triangle\delta\mathbf{E} = -(1/\bar{\epsilon})(\bar{\mathbf{E}}\cdot\mathbf{grad})\,\mathbf{grad}\,\delta\epsilon. \tag{9.4}$$

The averaging of the product $\delta\epsilon\delta\mathbf{E}$ in (9.3) is done in two stages. We first average over the volume of particles of a given kind, i.e. for a given $\delta\epsilon$. The value of $\delta\mathbf{E}$ thus averaged is easily obtained from equation (9.4): on account of the isotropy of the mixture as a whole, the operator $\partial^2/\partial x_j \partial x_k$ on the right-hand side of (9.4) becomes, after averaging, $\frac{1}{3}\delta_{ik}\triangle$, so that we have $\triangle\overline{\delta\mathbf{E}} = -(1/3\bar{\epsilon})\bar{\mathbf{E}}\triangle\delta\epsilon$, whence $\overline{\delta\mathbf{E}} = -(1/3\bar{\epsilon})\bar{\mathbf{E}}\delta\epsilon$. Multiplying by $\delta\epsilon$ and effecting the final averaging over all components of the mixture, we obtain $\overline{\delta\epsilon\delta\mathbf{E}} = -(1/3\bar{\epsilon})\bar{\mathbf{E}}\overline{(\delta\epsilon)^2}$. Finally, substituting this expression in (9.3) and comparing with (9.1), we have the required result:

$$\epsilon_{\mathrm{mix}} = \bar{\epsilon} - (1/3\bar{\epsilon})\overline{(\delta\epsilon)^2}. \tag{9.5}$$

This formula can be written in another manner if we put

$$\overline{\epsilon^{\frac{1}{3}}} = \overline{(\bar{\epsilon} + \delta\epsilon)^{\frac{1}{3}}} = \bar{\epsilon}^{\frac{1}{3}}\left(1 - \frac{\overline{(\delta\epsilon)^2}}{9\bar{\epsilon}^2}\right);$$

this is accurate to terms of the second order. Then

$$\epsilon_{\mathrm{mix}}^{\frac{1}{3}} = \overline{\epsilon^{\frac{1}{3}}}. \tag{9.6}$$

Thus we can say that, in this approximation, the cube root of ϵ is additive.

PROBLEM

Determine the dielectric permeability of an emulsion of low concentration but with an arbitrary difference between the dielectric permeabilities of the medium (ϵ_1) and the disperse phase (ϵ_2).

SOLUTION. In the integral

$$\frac{1}{V}\int (\mathbf{D}-\epsilon_1\mathbf{E})\,dV \equiv \overline{\mathbf{D}}-\epsilon_1\overline{\mathbf{E}}$$

the integrand is zero except within particles of the emulsion. It is therefore proportional to the volume concentration c of the emulsion, and in calculating it we can assume that the particles are in an external field which equals the mean field $\overline{\mathbf{E}}$. Assuming the particles spherical and using formula (8.2), we obtain for the proportionality coefficient between $\overline{\mathbf{D}}$ and $\overline{\mathbf{E}}$

$$\epsilon_{\text{mix}} = \epsilon_1+3c\epsilon_1(\epsilon_2-\epsilon_1)/(\epsilon_2+2\epsilon_1).$$

This formula is correct to terms of the first order in c. When ϵ_1 and ϵ_2 are nearly equal it is the same (to the first order in c and the second in $\epsilon_2-\epsilon_1$) as the result given by formula (9.6) for small c.

§10. Thermodynamic relations for dielectrics in an electric field

The question of the change in thermodynamic properties owing to the presence of an electric field does not arise for conductors. Since there is no electric field inside a conductor, any change in its thermodynamic properties amounts simply to an increase in its total energy by the energy of the field which it produces in the surrounding space.† This quantity is quite independent of the thermodynamic state (and, in particular, of the temperature) of the body, and so does not affect the entropy, for example.

On the other hand, an electric field penetrates into a dielectric and so has a great effect on its thermodynamic properties. To investigate this effect, let us first determine the work done on a thermally insulated dielectric when the field in it undergoes an infinitesimal change.

The electric field in which the dielectric is placed must be imagined as due to various external charged conductors, and the change in the field can then be regarded as resulting from changes in the charges on these conductors.‡ Let us suppose for simplicity that there is only one conductor, of charge e and potential ϕ. The work which must be done to increase its charge by an infinitesimal amount δe is

$$\delta R = \phi\delta e; \tag{10.1}$$

this is the mechanical work done by the given field on a charge δe brought from infinity (where the field potential is zero) to the surface of the conductor,

† We here neglect the energy of the attachment of the charge to the substance of the conductor; this will be discussed in §22.

‡ The final results which we shall obtain involve only the values of the field inside the dielectric, and therefore are independent of the origin of the field. For this reason there is no need for special discussion of the case where the field is produced, not by charged conductors, but (for instance) by extraneous charges placed in the dielectric itself or by pyroelectric polarisation of it (§13).

i.e. through a potential difference of ϕ. We shall put δR in a form which is expressed in terms of the field in the space filled with dielectric which surrounds the conductor.

If D_n is the component of the electric induction vector in the direction of the normal to the surface of the conductor (out of the dielectric and into the conductor), then the surface charge density on the conductor is $-D_n/4\pi$, so that

$$e = -\frac{1}{4\pi}\oint D_n \,\mathrm{d}f = -\frac{1}{4\pi}\oint \mathbf{D}\cdot\mathrm{d}\mathbf{f}.$$

Since the potential ϕ is constant on the surface of the conductor, we can write

$$\delta R = \phi\delta e = -\frac{1}{4\pi}\oint \phi\delta\mathbf{D}\cdot\mathrm{d}\mathbf{f} = -\frac{1}{4\pi}\int \operatorname{div}(\phi\delta\mathbf{D})\,\mathrm{d}V.$$

The last integral is taken over the whole volume outside the conductor. Since the varied field, like the original field, must satisfy the field equations, we have $\operatorname{div}\delta\mathbf{D} = 0$, and so $\operatorname{div}(\phi\delta\mathbf{D}) = \phi \operatorname{div}\delta\mathbf{D}+\delta\mathbf{D}\cdot\mathbf{grad}\,\phi = -\mathbf{E}\cdot\delta\mathbf{D}$. Thus the following important formula is obtained:

$$\delta R = \int (\mathbf{E}\cdot\delta\mathbf{D}/4\pi)\,\mathrm{d}V. \tag{10.2}$$

It should be emphasised that the integration in (10.2) is over the whole field, including the vacuum if the dielectric does not occupy all space outside the conductor.

The work done on a thermally insulated body is just the change in its energy at constant entropy. Hence the expression (10.2) must be included in the thermodynamic relation which gives the infinitesimal change in the total energy of the body; the latter contains also the energy of the electric field. Denoting the total energy by $\mathscr{U}$, we therefore have

$$\delta\mathscr{U} = T\delta\mathscr{S}+\frac{1}{4\pi}\int \mathbf{E}\cdot\delta\mathbf{D}\,\mathrm{d}V, \tag{10.3}$$

where T is the temperature of the body and $\mathscr{S}$ its entropy.†

Accordingly we have for the total free energy‡ $\mathscr{F} = \mathscr{U}-T\mathscr{S}$

$$\delta\mathscr{F} = -\mathscr{S}\delta T+\frac{1}{4\pi}\int \mathbf{E}\cdot\delta\mathbf{D}\,\mathrm{d}V. \tag{10.4}$$

Similar thermodynamic relations can be obtained for the quantities pertaining to unit volume of the body. Let U, S and ρ be the internal energy,

† The body in general becomes inhomogeneous in an electric field, and so the volume (whose differential is usually included in the expression for $\delta\mathscr{U}$) no longer characterises the state of the body.

‡ This quantity is meaningful only when the temperature is constant throughout the body.

entropy and mass of unit volume. It is well known that the ordinary thermodynamic relation (in the absence of a field) for the internal energy of unit volume is $dU = TdS + \zeta d\rho$, where ζ is the chemical potential of the substance.† In the presence of a field in a dielectric, there must be added the integrand in (10.3):

$$dU = T\,dS + \zeta\,d\rho + \mathbf{E}\cdot d\mathbf{D}/4\pi. \tag{10.5}$$

For the free energy per unit volume of the dielectric, $F = U - TS$, we therefore have

$$dF = -S\,dT + \zeta\,d\rho + \mathbf{E}\cdot d\mathbf{D}/4\pi. \tag{10.6}$$

These relations are the basis of the thermodynamics of dielectrics.

We see that U and F are the thermodynamic potentials with respect to S, ρ, $\mathbf{D}$ and T, ρ, $\mathbf{D}$ respectively. In particular, we can obtain the field by differentiating these potentials with respect to the components of the vector $\mathbf{D}$:

$$\mathbf{E} = 4\pi(\partial U/\partial \mathbf{D})_{S,\rho} = 4\pi(\partial F/\partial \mathbf{D})_{T,\rho}. \tag{10.7}$$

The free energy is more convenient in this respect, since it is to be differentiated at constant temperature, whereas the internal energy must be expressed in terms of the entropy, which is less easy.

Together with U and F, it is convenient to introduce thermodynamic potentials in which the components of the vector $\mathbf{E}$, instead of $\mathbf{D}$, are the independent variables. Such are

$$\tilde{U} = U - \mathbf{E}\cdot\mathbf{D}/4\pi, \quad \tilde{F} = F - \mathbf{E}\cdot\mathbf{D}/4\pi. \tag{10.8}$$

On differentiating these we have

$$\begin{aligned} d\tilde{U} &= T\,dS + \zeta\,d\rho - \mathbf{D}\cdot d\mathbf{E}/4\pi, \\ d\tilde{F} &= -S\,dT + \zeta\,d\rho - \mathbf{D}\cdot d\mathbf{E}/4\pi. \end{aligned} \tag{10.9}$$

Hence, in particular,

$$\mathbf{D} = -4\pi(\partial \tilde{U}/\partial \mathbf{E})_{S,\rho} = -4\pi(\partial \tilde{F}/\partial \mathbf{E})_{T,\rho}. \tag{10.10}$$

It should be noticed that the relation between the thermodynamic quantities with and without the tilde is exactly that which occurs in §5 for the energy of the electrostatic field of conductors in a vacuum. For the integral $\int \mathbf{E}\cdot\mathbf{D}\,dV$ can be transformed in an exactly similar manner to the one at the

† See *Statistical Physics*, §24, Pergamon Press, London, 1958. Instead of the mass density we there use the number of particles N per unit volume, which is related to the density by $\rho = Nm$, where m is the mass of one particle. For this reason the chemical potentials as defined here and in *Statistical Physics* differ by a constant factor (the potential here being referred to unit mass, and there to one particle).

We here denote the chemical potential by ζ instead of the more usual letter μ. The use of the letter ρ for the mass density as well as the charge density cannot lead to any misunderstanding, because the two quantities never appear together.

beginning of §2, with the equation $\operatorname{div}\mathbf{D} = 0$ inside the dielectric and the boundary condition $D_n = 4\pi\sigma$ on the surfaces of conductors :

$$\frac{1}{4\pi}\int \mathbf{E}\cdot\mathbf{D}\,\mathrm{d}V = -\frac{1}{4\pi}\int \mathbf{grad}\,\phi\cdot\mathbf{D}\,\mathrm{d}V$$

$$= \frac{1}{4\pi}\sum_a \int \phi_a D_n\,\mathrm{d}f = \sum_a \phi_a e_a. \qquad (10.11)$$

Hence we have for the internal energy, for example,

$$\tilde{\mathscr{U}} = \mathscr{U} - \int \frac{\mathbf{E}\cdot\mathbf{D}}{4\pi}\mathrm{d}V = \mathscr{U} - \sum_a \phi_a e_a, \qquad (10.12)$$

in agreement with the definition (5.5).

It is useful to derive also the formulae for infinitesimal changes in these quantities, expressed in terms of the charges and potentials of the conductors (the sources of the field). For example, the variation in the free energy (for a given temperature) is

$$(\delta\mathscr{F})_T = \delta R = \sum_a \phi_a \delta e_a. \qquad (10.13)$$

For the variation of $\tilde{\mathscr{F}}$ we have

$$(\delta\tilde{\mathscr{F}})_T = (\delta\mathscr{F})_T - \delta\sum_a \phi_a e_a = -\sum_a e_a \delta\phi_a. \qquad (10.14)$$

We can say that the quantities without the tilde are the thermodynamic potentials with respect to the charges on the conductors, while those with it are thermodynamic potentials with respect to their potentials.

It is known from thermodynamics† that the various thermodynamic potentials have the property of being minima in a state of thermodynamic equilibrium, relative to various changes in the state of the body. In formulating these conditions of equilibrium in an electric field, it is necessary to state whether changes of state with constant charges on the conductors (the field sources) or those with constant potentials are being considered. For example, in equilibrium $\mathscr{F}$ and $\tilde{\mathscr{F}}$ are minima with respect to changes in state occurring at constant temperature and (respectively) constant charges and potentials of the conductors (the same is true for $\mathscr{U}$ and $\tilde{\mathscr{U}}$ at constant entropy).

If any processes (such as chemical reactions) which are not directly related to the electric field can occur in the body, the condition of equilibrium with respect to these processes is that F is a minimum for given density, temperature and induction $\mathbf{D}$, or that $\tilde{F}$ is a minimum for constant density, temperature and field $\mathbf{E}$.

Hitherto we have made no assumptions concerning the dependence of $\mathbf{D}$ on $\mathbf{E}$, so that all the thermodynamic relations derived above are valid

---

† See *Statistical Physics*, §15.

whatever the nature of this dependence. Let us now apply them to an isotropic dielectric, where a linear relation $\mathbf{D} = \epsilon\mathbf{E}$ holds. In this case integration of (10.5) and (10.6) gives

$$U = U_0(S, \rho) + D^2/8\pi\epsilon,$$
$$F = F_0(T, \rho) + D^2/8\pi\epsilon, \tag{10.15}$$

where U_0 and F_0 pertain to the dielectric in the absence of the field. Thus in this case the quantity $D^2/8\pi\epsilon = \epsilon E^2/8\pi = ED/8\pi$ is the change in the internal energy (for given entropy and density) or in the free energy (for given temperature and density), per unit volume of the dielectric medium, resulting from the presence of the field.

The expressions for the potentials $\tilde{U}$ and $\tilde{F}$ are similarly

$$\tilde{U} = U_0(S, \rho) - \epsilon E^2/8\pi,$$
$$\tilde{F} = F_0(T, \rho) - \epsilon E^2/8\pi. \tag{10.16}$$

We see that the differences $U - U_0$ and $\tilde{U} - U_0$ in this case differ only in sign, as they did for an electric field in a vacuum (§5). In a dielectric medium, however, this simple result holds good only when there is a linear relation between **D** and **E**.

We shall write out also, for future reference, formulae for the entropy density S and the chemical potential ζ, which follow from (10.15):

$$S = -\left(\frac{\partial F}{\partial T}\right)_{\rho\,\mathbf{D}} = S_0(T, \rho) + \frac{D^2}{8\pi\epsilon^2}\left(\frac{\partial \epsilon}{\partial T}\right)_{\rho}$$
$$= S_0(T, \rho) + \frac{E^2}{8\pi}\left(\frac{\partial \epsilon}{\partial T}\right)_{\rho}, \tag{10.17}$$

$$\zeta = \left(\frac{\partial F}{\partial \rho}\right)_{T,\mathbf{D}} = \zeta_0(T, \rho) - \frac{E^2}{8\pi}\left(\frac{\partial \epsilon}{\partial \rho}\right)_{T}. \tag{10.18}$$

These quantities, of course, differ from zero only inside the dielectric.

The total free energy is obtained by integrating (10.15) over all space. By (10.11) we have

$$\mathscr{F} - \mathscr{F}_0 = \int \mathbf{E}\cdot\mathbf{D}\,\mathrm{d}V/8\pi = \tfrac{1}{2}\Sigma e_a\phi_a. \tag{10.19}$$

This last expression is formally identical with the energy of the electrostatic field of conductors in a vacuum. The same result can be obtained directly by starting from the variation $\delta\mathscr{F}$ (10.13) for an infinitesimal change in the charges on the conductors. In the present case, when **D** and **E** are linearly related, all the field equations and their boundary conditions are also linear. Hence the potentials of the conductors must (as for the field in a vacuum) be linear functions of their charges, and integration of equation (10.13) gives (10.19).

It should be emphasised that these arguments do not presuppose the dielectric to fill all space outside the conductors. If, however, this is so, we can go further and use the results at the end of §7 to draw the following conclusion. For given charges on the conductors, the presence of the dielectric medium reduces by a factor ϵ both the potentials of the conductors and the field energy, as compared with the values for a field in a vacuum. If, on the other hand, the potentials of the conductors are maintained constant, then their charges and the field energy are increased by a factor ϵ.

PROBLEM

Determine the height h to which a liquid rises in a vertical plane condenser.

SOLUTION. For given potentials on the condenser plates, $\mathscr{F}$ must be a minimum. $\mathscr{F}$ includes the energy $\frac{1}{2}\rho g h^2$ of the liquid under gravity. From this condition we easily obtain $h = (\epsilon-1)E^2/8\pi\rho g$.

§11. The total free energy of a dielectric

The total free energy $\mathscr{F}$ (or the total internal energy $\mathscr{U}$), as defined in §10, includes the energy of the external electric field which polarises the dielectric. It is also meaningful to consider the total free energy less the energy of the field which would be present in all space if the body were absent. We denote this field by $\mathfrak{E}$. Then the total free energy in this sense is

$$\int (F - \mathfrak{E}^2/8\pi)\,\mathrm{d}V, \qquad (11.1)$$

where F is the free energy density. Here we shall denote this quantity by the letter $\mathscr{F}$, which in §10 signified $\int F\mathrm{d}V$. It should be emphasised that the difference between the two definitions of $\mathscr{F}$ is a quantity independent of the thermodynamic state and properties of the dielectric, and hence it has no effect on the fundamental differential relations of thermodynamics pertaining to this quantity.†

Let us calculate the change in $\mathscr{F}$ resulting from an infinitesimal change in the field which occurs at constant temperature and does not destroy the thermodynamic equilibrium of the medium. Since $\delta F = \mathbf{E}\cdot\delta\mathbf{D}/4\pi$, we have $\delta\mathscr{F} = \int (\mathbf{E}\cdot\delta\mathbf{D} - \mathfrak{E}\cdot\delta\mathfrak{E})\mathrm{d}V/4\pi$. This expression is identically equal to

$$\delta\mathscr{F} = \int (\mathbf{D}-\mathfrak{E})\cdot\delta\mathfrak{E}\,\mathrm{d}V/4\pi + \int \mathbf{E}\cdot(\delta\mathbf{D}-\delta\mathfrak{E})\,\mathrm{d}V/4\pi - \int (\mathbf{D}-\mathbf{E})\cdot\delta\mathfrak{E}\,\mathrm{d}V/4\pi. \qquad (11.2)$$

In the first integral we write $\delta\mathfrak{E} = -\mathbf{grad}\,\delta\phi_0$ (where ϕ_0 is the potential of the field $\mathfrak{E}$) and integrate by parts:

$$\int \mathbf{grad}\,\delta\phi_0\cdot(\mathbf{D}-\mathfrak{E})\,\mathrm{d}V = \oint \delta\phi_0(\mathbf{D}-\mathfrak{E})\cdot\mathbf{df} - \int \delta\phi_0\,\mathrm{div}\,(\mathbf{D}-\mathfrak{E})\,\mathrm{d}V.$$

† It may be noted that there would be no sense in subtracting $E^2/8\pi$ from F, because $\mathbf{E}$ is the field as modified by the presence of the dielectric, and so the difference $F - E^2/8\pi$ could not be regarded as the free energy density of the dielectric as such.

It is easy to see that both the integrals on the right-hand side are zero. For the volume integral this follows at once from the equations div $\mathbf{D} = 0$ and div $\mathfrak{E} = 0$ which the induction in the dielectric and the field in the vacuum must respectively satisfy. The surface integral is taken over the surfaces of the conductors which produce the field and over an infinitely distant surface. The latter of these is, as usual, zero, and for each of the conductors $\delta\phi_0 =$ constant, so that $\oint \delta\phi_0(\mathbf{D}-\mathfrak{E})\cdot d\mathbf{f} = \delta\phi_0 \oint (\mathbf{D}-\mathfrak{E})\cdot d\mathbf{f}$. The field $\mathfrak{E}$, by definition, is produced by the same sources as the field **E** and induction **D** (i.e. by the same conductors with given total charges e). Hence the two integrals $\oint D_n df$ and $\oint \mathfrak{E}_n df$ are both equal to $4\pi e$, and their difference is zero.

Similarly, we can see that the second term in (11.2) is also zero, by putting $\mathbf{E} = -\mathbf{grad}\, \phi$ and using the same transformation. Finally, we have

$$\delta\mathscr{F} = -\int (\mathbf{D}-\mathbf{E})\cdot\delta\mathfrak{E}\, dV/4\pi = -\int \mathbf{P}\cdot\delta\mathfrak{E}\, dV. \tag{11.3}$$

It should be noticed that the integral in this expression need be taken only over the volume of the dielectric medium, since outside it $\mathbf{P} = 0$.

However, we must emphasise that the integrand $\mathbf{P}\cdot\delta\mathfrak{E}$ cannot be interpreted as the variation of the free energy density in the same way as was done with formulae (10.3), (10.4). First of all, this density must exist outside the body, which modifies the field in the surrounding space also. It is clear, moreover, that the energy density at any point in the body can depend only on the field actually present there, and not on the field which would be present if the body were removed.

If the external field $\mathfrak{E}$ is uniform, then

$$\delta\mathscr{F} = -\delta\mathfrak{E}\cdot\int \mathbf{P}\, dV = -\mathscr{P}\cdot\delta\mathfrak{E}, \tag{11.4}$$

where $\mathscr{P}$ is the total electric dipole moment of the body. Hence the thermodynamic identity for the free energy can be written in this case as

$$d\mathscr{F} = -\mathscr{S}dT - \mathscr{P}\cdot d\mathfrak{E}. \tag{11.5}$$

The total electric moment of the body can therefore be obtained by differentiating the total free energy:

$$\mathscr{P} = -(\partial\mathscr{F}/\partial\mathfrak{E})_T. \tag{11.6}$$

The latter formula can also be obtained directly from the general statistical formula

$$\overline{\partial\hat{\mathscr{H}}/\partial\lambda} = (\partial\mathscr{F}/\partial\lambda)_T,$$

where $\hat{\mathscr{H}}$ is the Hamiltonian of the body as the system of its component particles, and λ is any parameter characterising the external conditions in which the body is placed.† For a body in a uniform external field $\mathfrak{E}$, the

† See *Statistical Physics*, §§11, 15.

Hamiltonian contains a term $-\mathfrak{E}\cdot\hat{\mathscr{P}}$, where $\hat{\mathscr{P}}$ is the dipole moment operator. Taking $\mathfrak{E}$ as the parameter λ, we obtain the required formula.

If **D** and **E** are connected by the linear relation $\mathbf{D} = \epsilon\mathbf{E}$, we can similarly calculate explicitly not only the variation $\delta\mathscr{F}$ but $\mathscr{F}$ itself. We have

$$\mathscr{F} - \mathscr{F}_0 = \int (\mathbf{E}\cdot\mathbf{D} - \mathfrak{E}^2)\,\mathrm{d}V/8\pi.$$

This can be identically transformed into

$$\mathscr{F} - \mathscr{F}_0 = \int (\mathbf{E}+\mathfrak{E})\cdot(\mathbf{D}-\mathfrak{E})\,\mathrm{d}V/8\pi - \int \mathfrak{E}\cdot(\mathbf{D}-\mathbf{E})\,\mathrm{d}V/8\pi.$$

The first term on the right is zero, as we see by putting

$$\mathbf{E}+\mathfrak{E} = -\mathbf{grad}\,(\phi+\phi_0)$$

and again using the same transformation. Hence we have

$$\mathscr{F} - \mathscr{F}_0(V, T) = -\tfrac{1}{2}\int \mathfrak{E}\cdot\mathbf{P}\,\mathrm{d}V. \tag{11.7}$$

In particular, in a uniform external field

$$\mathscr{F} - \mathscr{F}_0(V, T) = -\tfrac{1}{2}\mathfrak{E}\cdot\mathscr{P}. \tag{11.8}$$

This last equation can also be obtained by direct integration of the relation (11.3) if we notice that, since all the field equations are linear when $\mathbf{D} = \epsilon\mathbf{E}$, the electric moment $\mathscr{P}$ must be a linear function of $\mathfrak{E}$.

The linear relation between the components of $\mathscr{P}$ and $\mathfrak{E}$ can be written

$$\mathscr{P}_i = V\alpha_{ik}\mathfrak{E}_k, \tag{11.9}$$

as for conductors (§2). For a dielectric, however, the polarisability depends not only on the shape but also on the dielectric constant. The symmetry of the tensor α_{ik}, mentioned in §2, follows at once from the relation (11.6); it is sufficient to notice that the second derivative $\partial^2\mathscr{F}/\partial\mathfrak{E}_k\partial\mathfrak{E}_i = -\partial\mathscr{P}_i/\partial\mathfrak{E}_k = -V\alpha_{ik}$ is independent of the order of differentiation.

Formula (11.7) becomes still simpler in the important case where ϵ is close to 1, i.e. the dielectric susceptibility $\kappa = (\epsilon-1)/4\pi$ is small. In this case, in calculating the energy, we can neglect the modification of the field due to the presence of the body, putting $\mathbf{P} = \kappa\mathbf{E} \cong \kappa\mathfrak{E}$. Then

$$\mathscr{F} - \mathscr{F}_0 = -\tfrac{1}{2}\kappa\int \mathfrak{E}^2\,\mathrm{d}V, \tag{11.10}$$

the integral being taken over the volume of the body. In a uniform field, the dipole moment $\mathscr{P} = V\kappa\mathfrak{E}$, and the free energy is

$$\mathscr{F} - \mathscr{F}_0 = -\tfrac{1}{2}\kappa V\mathfrak{E}^2. \tag{11.11}$$

In the general case of an arbitrary relation between **D** and **E**, the simple formulae (11.7) and (11.8) do not hold. Here the formula

$$\mathscr{F} = \int\left(F-\frac{\mathfrak{E}^2}{8\pi}\right)\mathrm{d}V = \int\left[F-\frac{\mathbf{E}\cdot\mathbf{D}}{8\pi}-\tfrac{1}{2}\mathbf{P}\cdot\mathfrak{E}\right]\mathrm{d}V \tag{11.12}$$

may be useful in calculating $\mathscr{F}$; its derivation is obvious after the above discussion. Here also the integrand in the latter integral is zero outside the body, so that the integration is taken only over the volume of the body.

PROBLEM

Derive the formula which replaces (11.7) when the body is not in a vacuum but in a medium of dielectric permeability $\epsilon^{(e)}$.

SOLUTION. Using the same transformations as before, we find

$$\mathscr{F}-\mathscr{F}_0 = -\frac{1}{8\pi}\int \mathfrak{E}\cdot(\mathbf{D}-\epsilon^{(e)}\mathbf{E})\,\mathrm{d}V.$$

§12. Electrostriction of isotropic dielectrics

For a solid dielectric in an electric field the concept of pressure cannot be defined as for an isotropic body in the absence of a field, because the forces acting on a dielectric (which we shall determine in §§15, 16) vary over the body, and are anisotropic even if the body itself is isotropic. An exact determination of the deformation (*electrostriction*) of such a body involves the solution of a complex problem of the theory of elasticity.

However, matters are much simpler if we are interested only in the change in the total volume of the body. As we saw in §5, the shape of the body may then be regarded as unchanged, i.e. the deformation may be regarded as a uniform volume compression or expansion.

We shall neglect the dielectric properties of the external medium (the atmosphere, for instance) in which the body is situated, i.e. we suppose that $\epsilon = 1$. This medium thus serves merely to exert a uniform pressure on the surface of the body, which we shall denote by p. If $\mathscr{F}$ is the total free energy of the body, then we have the thermodynamic relation $p = -(\partial\mathscr{F}/\partial V)_T$, and accordingly the expression for the differential $\mathrm{d}\mathscr{F}$ contains a term $-p\mathrm{d}V$. For example, in a uniform external field, (11.5) becomes

$$\mathrm{d}\mathscr{F} = -\mathscr{S}\mathrm{d}T-p\,\mathrm{d}V-\mathscr{P}\cdot\mathrm{d}\mathfrak{E}.$$

We introduce the total thermodynamic potential of the body in accordance with the usual thermodynamic relation

$$\mathscr{G} = \mathscr{F}+pV. \tag{12.1}$$

The differential of this quantity in a uniform external field is

$$\mathrm{d}\mathscr{G} = -\mathscr{S}\,\mathrm{d}T+V\,\mathrm{d}p-\mathscr{P}\cdot\mathrm{d}\mathfrak{E}. \tag{12.2}$$

The change in the thermodynamic quantities in an external electric field is usually a relatively small quantity. It is known† that a small change in the free energy (for given T and V) is equal to the small change in the thermodynamic potential (for given T and p). Hence, besides (11.8), we can write analogously

$$\mathscr{G} = \mathscr{G}_0 - \tfrac{1}{2}\mathfrak{E}\cdot\mathscr{P} \tag{12.3}$$

for the thermodynamic potential of a body in a uniform external field. Here $\mathscr{G}_0$ is the value for the body in the absence of the field and for given values of p and T, while $\mathscr{F}_0$ in (11.8) is the free energy in the absence of the field and for given values of V and T.

Making explicit the dependence of the dipole moment on V and $\mathfrak{E}$ according to (11.9), we can rewrite (12.3) as

$$\mathscr{G} = \mathscr{G}_0(p, T) - \tfrac{1}{2}V\alpha_{ik}\mathfrak{E}_i\mathfrak{E}_k, \tag{12.4}$$

where the correction term must be expressed as a function of temperature and pressure by means of the equation of state for the body in the absence of the field. In particular, for a substance of small dielectric susceptibility this formula becomes simply

$$\mathscr{G} = \mathscr{G}_0(p, T) - \tfrac{1}{2}\kappa V\mathfrak{E}^2; \tag{12.5}$$

cf. (11.11).

The required change in volume $V - V_0$ in the external field can now be obtained immediately by differentiating $\mathscr{G}$ with respect to pressure for constant T and $\mathfrak{E}$. For example, from (12.5) we have

$$V - V_0 = -\tfrac{1}{2}\mathfrak{E}^2[\partial(\kappa V)/\partial p]_T. \tag{12.6}$$

This quantity may be either positive or negative (whereas, in electrostriction of conductors, the volume is always greater in the presence of the field).

Similarly, we can calculate the amount of heat Q absorbed in a dielectric when an external electric field is isothermally applied (the external pressure being constant).‡ Differentiation of $\mathscr{G} - \mathscr{G}_0$ with respect to temperature gives the change in the entropy of the body, and by multiplying this by T we obtain the required quantity of heat. For example, from (12.5) we obtain

$$Q = \tfrac{1}{2}\mathfrak{E}^2 T[\partial(\kappa V)/\partial T]_p. \tag{12.7}$$

Positive values of Q correspond to absorption of heat.

PROBLEMS

Problem 1. Determine the change in volume and the electrocaloric effect for a dielectric ellipsoid in a uniform electric field parallel to one of its axes.

---

† See *Statistical Physics*, §15.

‡ If the body is thermally insulated, the application of the field results in a change of temperature $\Delta T = -Q/C_p$, where C_p is the specific heat at constant pressure.

SOLUTION. From formulae (12.3) and (8.9) we have

$$\mathscr{G} = \mathscr{G}_0 - \frac{V}{8\pi}\frac{\epsilon-1}{n\epsilon+1-n}\mathfrak{E}^2.$$

The relative change in volume is found to be

$$\frac{V-V_0}{V} = \frac{\mathfrak{E}^2}{8\pi}\left[\frac{\epsilon-1}{n\epsilon+1-n}\frac{1}{K} - \frac{1}{(n\epsilon+1-n)^2}\left(\frac{\partial\epsilon}{\partial p}\right)_T\right],$$

and the electrocaloric effect

$$Q = \frac{TV\mathfrak{E}^2}{8\pi}\left[\frac{\epsilon-1}{n\epsilon+1-n}\alpha + \frac{1}{(n\epsilon+1-n)^2}\left(\frac{\partial\epsilon}{\partial T}\right)_p\right],$$

where $1/K = -(1/V)(\partial V/\partial p)_T$ is the compressibility of the body, and $\alpha = (1/V)(\partial V/\partial T)_p$ the thermal expansion coefficient.

In particular, for a plane disc in a field perpendicular to it, $n = 1$, so that

$$\frac{V-V_0}{V} = \frac{\mathfrak{E}^2}{8\pi}\left[\frac{\epsilon-1}{\epsilon}\frac{1}{K} - \frac{1}{\epsilon^2}\left(\frac{\partial\epsilon}{\partial p}\right)_T\right],$$

$$Q = \frac{TV\mathfrak{E}^2}{8\pi}\left[\frac{\epsilon-1}{\epsilon}\alpha + \frac{1}{\epsilon^2}\left(\frac{\partial\epsilon}{\partial T}\right)_p\right].$$

For a similar disc (or any cylinder) in a longitudinal field, $n = 0$, and

$$\frac{V-V_0}{V} = \frac{\mathfrak{E}^2}{8\pi}\left[\frac{\epsilon-1}{K} - \left(\frac{\partial\epsilon}{\partial p}\right)_T\right], \quad Q = \frac{TV\mathfrak{E}^2}{8\pi}\left[(\epsilon-1)\alpha + \left(\frac{\partial\epsilon}{\partial T}\right)_p\right].$$

PROBLEM 2. Determine the difference between the heat capacity $\mathscr{C}_\phi$ of a plane disc in a field perpendicular to it, with a constant potential difference between its faces, and the heat capacity $\mathscr{C}_D$ at constant induction, the external pressure being maintained constant in each case.†

SOLUTION. According to the results of Problem 1, the entropy of the disc is

$$\mathscr{S} = -\left(\frac{\partial\mathscr{G}}{\partial T}\right)_{p,\mathfrak{E}} = \mathscr{S}_0(p, T) + \frac{V\mathfrak{E}^2}{8\pi}\left[\frac{\epsilon-1}{\epsilon}\alpha + \frac{1}{\epsilon^2}\left(\frac{\partial\epsilon}{\partial T}\right)_p\right].$$

The induction inside the disc is the same as the external field: $D = \mathfrak{E}$. Hence, to calculate the heat capacity $\mathscr{C}_D$, we must differentiate $\mathscr{S}$ for constant $\mathfrak{E}$. The potential difference between the faces of the disc is $\phi = El = \mathfrak{E}\, l/\epsilon$, where l is its thickness. For a uniform compression or expansion of a body, l is proportional to $V^{1/3}$. Hence, to calculate the heat capacity $\mathscr{C}_\phi$, we must differentiate $\mathscr{S}$ for constant $\mathfrak{E}V^{1/3}/\epsilon$. The required difference is found to be

$$\mathscr{C}_\phi - \mathscr{C}_D = \frac{TV\mathfrak{E}^2}{4\pi\epsilon}\left[(\epsilon-1)\alpha + \frac{1}{\epsilon}\left(\frac{\partial\epsilon}{\partial T}\right)_p\right]\left[\frac{1}{\epsilon}\left(\frac{\partial\epsilon}{\partial T}\right)_p - \tfrac{1}{3}\alpha\right].$$

PROBLEM 3. Determine the electrocaloric effect in a homogeneous dielectric whose total volume is kept constant.

SOLUTION. Strictly speaking, when an external field is applied the density of the body changes (and ceases to be uniform), even if the total volume is kept constant. In calculating the change in the total entropy, however, we can ignore this and assume the density ρ constant at every point.‡

---

† $\mathscr{C}_\phi$ is the heat capacity of a disc between the plates of a plane condenser in circuit with a constant e.m.f. In an unconnected condenser with constant charges on the plates, the heat capacity of the disc is $\mathscr{C}_D$.

‡ The change in density $\delta\rho$ is of the second order with respect to the field ($\sim E^2$), and the consequent change in the total entropy is of the fourth order: the term in the change of total entropy which is linear in $\delta\rho$ is $(\partial S_0/\partial\rho)\int\delta\rho\,dV$, and the integral is zero because the total mass of the body is unaltered.

According to (10.17) the total entropy of the body is

$$\mathscr{S} = \mathscr{S}_0(\rho, T) + \frac{1}{8\pi}\left(\frac{\partial \epsilon}{\partial T}\right)_\rho \int E^2 \,\mathrm{d}V,$$

where the integration is over the volume of the body. The amount of heat absorbed is

$$Q = \frac{T}{8\pi}\left(\frac{\partial \epsilon}{\partial T}\right)_\rho \int E^2 \,\mathrm{d}V.$$

PROBLEM 4. Determine the difference $\mathscr{C}_\phi - \mathscr{C}_D$ (see Problem 2) when the total volume of the disc is kept constant.

SOLUTION. When the volume, and therefore the thickness, of the disc are constant, differentiation for constant potential difference is equivalent to differentiation for constant field E. Using the formula of Problem 3 for the entropy we have

$$\mathscr{C}_E - \mathscr{C}_D = \frac{TVE^2}{4\pi\epsilon}\left(\frac{\partial \epsilon}{\partial T}\right)_p^2.$$

PROBLEM 5. A condenser consists of two conducting surfaces at a distance h apart which is small compared with their dimensions; the space between them is filled with a substance of dielectric permeability ϵ_1. A sphere of radius $a \ll h$ and dielectric permeability ϵ_2 is placed in the condenser. Determine the change in capacity.

SOLUTION. Let the sphere be placed in the condenser in such a way that the potential difference ϕ between the plates remains unchanged. The free energy for constant potentials of the conductors is $\tilde{\mathscr{F}}$. In the absence of the sphere, $\tilde{\mathscr{F}} = -\frac{1}{2}C_0\phi^2$, where C_0 is the original capacity of the condenser. Since the sphere is small, we may imagine it to be brought into a uniform field $\mathfrak{E} = \phi/h$, and the change in $\tilde{\mathscr{F}}$ is small. The small change in $\tilde{\mathscr{F}}$ at constant potentials is equal to the small change in $\mathscr{F}$ at constant charges on the sources of the field. Using the formula derived in §11, Problem, and (8.2), we have

$$\tilde{\mathscr{F}} = -\tfrac{1}{2}C_0\phi^2 - \tfrac{1}{2}a^3\epsilon^{(e)}(\epsilon^{(i)} - \epsilon^{(e)})\phi^2/(2\epsilon^{(e)} + \epsilon^{(i)})h^2,$$

whence the required capacity is

$$C = C_0 + a^3\epsilon^{(e)}(\epsilon^{(i)} - \epsilon^{(e)})/(2\epsilon^{(e)} + \epsilon^{(i)})h^2.$$

§13. Dielectric properties of crystals

In an anisotropic dielectric medium (a crystal) the linear relation between the electric induction and the electric field is less simple, and does not reduce to a simple proportionality.

The most general form of such a relation is

$$D_i = D_{0i} + \epsilon_{ik}E_k, \tag{13.1}$$

where $\mathbf{D}_0$ is a constant vector, and the quantities ϵ_{ik} form a tensor of rank two, called the *dielectric permeability tensor* (or simply the *dielectric tensor*). The inhomogeneous term $\mathbf{D}_0$ in (13.1) does not, however, appear for all crystals. The majority of the types of crystal symmetry do not admit this constant vector (see below), and we then have simply

$$D_i = \epsilon_{ik}E_k. \tag{13.2}$$

The tensor ϵ_{ik} is symmetrical:

$$\epsilon_{ik} = \epsilon_{ki}. \tag{13.3}$$

In order to prove this, it is sufficient to use the thermodynamic relation (10.10) and to observe that the second derivative $-4\pi\partial^2\tilde{F}/\partial E_k\partial E_i = \partial D_i/\partial E_k = \epsilon_{ik}$ is independent of the order of differentiation.

For $\tilde{F}$ itself we have (when (13.2) holds) the expression

$$\tilde{F} = F_0 - \epsilon_{ik}E_iE_k/8\pi. \tag{13.4}$$

The free energy F is

$$F = \tilde{F} + E_iD_i/4\pi = F_0 + \epsilon^{-1}{}_{ik}D_iD_k/8\pi. \tag{13.5}$$

Like every symmetrical tensor of rank two, the tensor ϵ_{ik} can be brought to diagonal form by a suitable choice of the co-ordinate axes. In general, therefore, the tensor ϵ is determined by three independent quantities, namely the three principal values $\epsilon^{(1)}$, $\epsilon^{(2)}$, $\epsilon^{(3)}$. All these are necessarily greater than unity, just as $\epsilon > 1$ for an isotropic body (see §14).

The number of different principal values of the tensor ϵ_{ik} may be less than three for certain symmetries of the crystal.†

In crystals of the triclinic, monoclinic and rhombic systems, all three principal values are different; such crystals are said to be *biaxial*.‡ In crystals of the triclinic system, the directions of the principal axes of the tensor ϵ_{ik} are not uniquely related to any directions in the crystal. In those of the monoclinic system, one of the principal axes must coincide with the axis of symmetry of the second order or be perpendicular to the plane of symmetry of the crystal. In crystals of the rhombic system, all three principal axes of the tensor ϵ_{ik} are crystallographically fixed.

Next, in crystals of the tetragonal, rhombohedral and hexagonal systems, two of the three principal values are equal, so that there are only two independent quantities; such crystals are said to be *uniaxial*. One of the principal axes coincides with the axis of crystal symmetry of the fourth, third or sixth order, but the directions of the other two principal axes can be chosen arbitrarily.||

Finally, in crystals of the cubic system all three principal values of the tensor ϵ_{ik} are the same, and the directions of the principal axes are entirely arbitrary.†† This means that the tensor ϵ_{ik} is of the form $\epsilon\delta_{ik}$, i.e. it is determined by a single scalar ϵ. In other words, as regards their dielectric properties, crystals of the cubic system are no different from isotropic bodies.

---

† The fairly obvious symmetry properties of the tensor ϵ_{ik} that are given below can be very simply obtained by using a result of tensor algebra: to every symmetrical tensor of rank two there corresponds a *tensor ellipsoid*, the lengths of whose semiaxes are proportional to the principal values of the tensor. The symmetry of the ellipsoid corresponds to that of the crystal.

‡ This name refers to the optical properties of the crystals; see §§78, 79.

|| In this case the tensor ellipsoid degenerates into a spheroid, completely symmetrical about the longitudinal axis. It should be emphasised that, as regards the physical properties of the crystal which are determined by a symmetrical tensor of rank two, the presence of an axis of symmetry of the third or higher order is equivalent to complete isotropy in the plane perpendicular to this axis.

†† The tensor ellipsoid here degenerates into a sphere.

Let us now examine the dielectric properties of crystals for which the constant term $\mathbf{D}_0$ appears in (13.1). The presence of this term signifies that the dielectric is spontaneously polarised even in the absence of an external electric field. Such bodies are said to be *pyroelectric*. The magnitude of this spontaneous polarisation is, however, in practice always very small (in comparison with the molecular fields). This is because large values of $\mathbf{D}_0$ would lead to strong fields within the body, which is energetically unfavourable and therefore could not correspond to thermodynamic equilibrium. The smallness of $\mathbf{D}_0$ also ensures the legitimacy of an expansion of $\mathbf{D}$ in powers of $\mathbf{E}$, of which (13.1) represents the first two terms.

The thermodynamic quantities for a pyroelectric body are found by integrating the relation $-4\pi\partial\tilde{F}/\partial E_i = D_i = D_{0i}+\epsilon_{ik}E_k$, whence

$$\tilde{F} = F_0-\epsilon_{ik}E_iE_k/8\pi-E_iD_{0i}/4\pi. \tag{13.6}$$

The free energy is

$$\begin{aligned} F = \tilde{F}+E_iD_i/4\pi &= F_0+\epsilon_{ik}E_iE_k/8\pi \\ &= F_0+\epsilon^{-1}{}_{ik}(D_i-D_{0i})(D_k-D_{0k})/8\pi. \end{aligned} \tag{13.7}$$

It should be noted that the term in $\tilde{F}$ linear in E_i does not appear in F.†

The total free energy of a pyroelectric can be calculated from formula (11.12) by substituting (13.7) and (13.1). If there is no external field, $\mathfrak{E} = 0$, and we have simply

$$F = \int[F_0-(\mathbf{E}\cdot\mathbf{D}_0/8\pi)]\,dV. \tag{13.8}$$

It is remarkable that the free energy of a pyroelectric in the absence of an external field depends, like the field $\mathbf{E}$, not only on the volume of the body but also on its shape.

As has already been pointed out, the phenomenon of pyroelectricity is not possible for every crystal symmetry. Since, in any symmetry transformation, all the properties of the crystal must remain unchanged, it is clear that the only crystals which can be pyroelectric are those in which there is a direction which is unchanged (and, in particular, not reversed) in all symmetry transformations, and that this will be the direction of the constant vector $\mathbf{D}_0$.

This condition is satisfied only by those symmetry groups which consist of a single axis together with planes of symmetry which pass through the axis. In particular, crystals having a centre of symmetry certainly cannot be

† It should also be noted that in these formulae we neglect the *piezoelectric effect*, i.e. the effect of internal stresses on the electric properties of a body; see §17. The formulae given here are therefore, strictly speaking, applicable only when the fields are uniform throughout the body, and internal stresses do not arise.

pyroelectric. We may enumerate those out of the 32 crystal classes in which pyroelectricity occurs:

triclinic system: C_1
monoclinic system: C_s, C_2
rhombic system: C_{2v}
tetragonal system: C_4, C_{4v}
rhombohedral system: C_3, C_{3v}
hexagonal system: C_6, C_{6v}.

There are, of course, no pyroelectric cubic crystals. In a crystal of class C_1 the direction of the pyroelectric vector $\mathbf{D}_0$ is not related to any direction fixed in the crystal; in one of class C_s, it must lie in the plane of symmetry. In all the remaining classes listed above the direction of $\mathbf{D}_0$ is that of the axis of symmetry.

It should be mentioned that, under ordinary conditions, pyroelectric crystals have zero total electric dipole moment, although their polarisation is not zero. The reason is that there is a non-zero field $\mathbf{E}$ inside a spontaneously polarised dielectric. Since a body usually has a small but non-zero conductivity, the presence of a field gives rise to a current, which flows until the free charges formed on the surface of the body annihilate the field inside it. The same effect is produced by ions deposited on the surface from the air. Experimentally, pyroelectric properties are observed when a body is heated and a change in its spontaneous polarisation is detected.

PROBLEMS

PROBLEM 1. Determine the field of a pyroelectric sphere in a vacuum.

SOLUTION. The field inside the sphere is uniform, and the field and induction are related by $2\mathbf{E} = -\mathbf{D}$ (as follows from (8.1) when $\mathfrak{E} = 0$, i.e. when there is no applied external field). Substituting in (13.1), we obtain the equation $2E_i + \epsilon_{ik}E_k = -D_{0i}$. We take the co-ordinate axes to be the principal axes of the tensor ϵ_{ik}. Then this equation gives $E_i = -D_{0i}/(2+\epsilon^{(i)})$. The polarisation of the sphere is $P_i = (D_i - E_i)/4\pi = 3D_{0i}/4\pi(2+\epsilon^{(i)})$. The field outside the sphere is that of an electric dipole of moment $\mathscr{P} = \mathbf{P}V$.

PROBLEM 2. Determine the field of a point charge in a homogeneous anisotropic medium.†

SOLUTION. The field of a point charge is given by the equation $\operatorname{div}\mathbf{D} = 4\pi e\delta(\mathbf{r})$ (the charge being at the origin). In an anisotropic medium $D_i = \epsilon_{ik}E_k = -\epsilon_{ik}\,\partial\phi/\partial x_k$; taking the co-ordinate axes x, y, z along the principal axes of the tensor ϵ_{ik}, we obtain for the potential the equation

$$\epsilon^{(x)}\partial^2\phi/\partial x^2 + \epsilon^{(y)}\partial^2\phi/\partial y^2 + \epsilon^{(z)}\partial^2\phi/\partial z^2 = -4\pi e\delta(x)\,\delta(y)\,\delta(z).$$

By the introduction of new variables

$$x' = x/\sqrt{\epsilon^{(x)}}, \qquad y' = y/\sqrt{\epsilon^{(y)}}, \qquad z' = z/\sqrt{\epsilon^{(z)}}, \tag{1}$$

this becomes

$$\frac{\partial^2\phi}{\partial x'^2} + \frac{\partial^2\phi}{\partial y'^2} + \frac{\partial^2\phi}{\partial z'^2} = -\frac{4\pi e}{\sqrt{(\epsilon^{(x)}\epsilon^{(y)}\epsilon^{(z)})}}\,\delta(x')\,\delta(y')\,\delta(z'),$$

† In Problems 2–5 the anisotropic dielectric is assumed not to be pyroelectric.

which formally differs from the equation for the field in a vacuum only in that e is replaced by $e/\sqrt{(\epsilon^{(x)}\epsilon^{(y)}\epsilon^{(z)})}$. Hence

$$\phi = \frac{e'}{r'} = \frac{e}{\sqrt{(\epsilon^{(x)}\epsilon^{(y)}\epsilon^{(z)})}}\left[\frac{x^2}{\epsilon^{(x)}}+\frac{y^2}{\epsilon^{(y)}}+\frac{z^2}{\epsilon^{(z)}}\right]^{-\frac{1}{2}}.$$

In tensor notation, independent of the system of co-ordinates chosen, we have

$$\phi = e/\sqrt{(|\epsilon|\epsilon^{-1}{}_{ik}x_ix_k)},$$

where $|\epsilon|$ is the determinant of the tensor ϵ_{ik}.

PROBLEM 3. Determine the capacity of a conducting sphere, of radius a, in an anisotropic dielectric medium.

SOLUTION. By the transformation shown in Problem 2, the determination of the field of a sphere with charge e in an anisotropic medium reduces to the determination of the field in a vacuum due to a charge e' distributed over the surface of the ellipsoid $\epsilon_{ik}x'_ix'_k = \epsilon^{(x)}x'^2 + \epsilon^{(y)}y'^2+\epsilon^{(z)}z'^2 = a^2$. Using formula (4.14) for the potential due to an ellipsoid, we find the required capacity to be given by

$$\frac{1}{C} = \frac{1}{2\sqrt{(\epsilon^{(x)}\epsilon^{(y)}\epsilon^{(z)})}}\int_0^\infty\left[\left(\xi+\frac{a^2}{\epsilon^{(x)}}\right)\left(\xi+\frac{a^2}{\epsilon^{(y)}}\right)\left(\xi+\frac{a^2}{\epsilon^{(z)}}\right)\right]^{-\frac{1}{2}}\mathrm{d}\xi.$$

PROBLEM 4. Determine the field in a flat anisotropic plate in a uniform external field $\mathfrak{E}$.

SOLUTION. From the condition of continuity of the tangential component of the field it follows that $\mathbf{E} = \mathfrak{E}+A\mathbf{n}$, where $\mathfrak{E}$ is the uniform field outside the plate, $\mathbf{n}$ a unit vector normal to its surface, and A a constant. The constant is determined from the condition of continuity of the normal component of the induction, $\mathbf{n}\cdot\mathbf{D} = \mathbf{n}\cdot\mathfrak{E}$, or $n_i\epsilon_{ik}E_k = n_i\epsilon_{ik}\mathfrak{E}_k + A\epsilon_{ik}n_in_k = \mathfrak{E}_in_i$. Hence $A = -(\epsilon_{ik}-\delta_{ik})n_i\mathfrak{E}_k/\epsilon_{lm}n_ln_m$.

PROBLEM 5. Determine the torque on an anisotropic dielectric sphere, of radius a, in a uniform external field $\mathfrak{E}$ in a vacuum.

SOLUTION. According to (8.2) we have for the field inside the sphere $E_x = 3\mathfrak{E}_x/(\epsilon^{(x)}+2)$, and similarly for E_y, E_z. Here the axes of x, y, z are taken to be the principal axes of the tensor ϵ_{ik}. Hence the components of the dipole moment of the sphere are

$$\mathscr{P}_x = \frac{4}{3}\pi a^3 P_x = \frac{\epsilon^{(x)}-1}{\epsilon^{(x)}+2}a^3\mathfrak{E}_x, \text{ etc.}$$

The components of the torque on the sphere are

$$K_z = (\mathscr{P}\times\mathfrak{E})_z = 3a^3\mathfrak{E}_x\mathfrak{E}_y(\epsilon^{(x)}-\epsilon^{(y)})/(\epsilon^{(x)}+2)(\epsilon^{(y)}+2),$$

and similarly for K_x, K_y.

PROBLEM 6. An infinite anisotropic medium contains a spherical cavity of radius a. Express the field in the cavity in terms of the uniform field $E^{(e)}$ far from the cavity.

SOLUTION. The transformation (1) of Problem 2 reduces the equation for the field potential in the medium to Laplace's equation for the field in a vacuum. The equation for the field in the cavity is transformed into that for the field in a medium with dielectric constants $1/\epsilon^{(x)}$, $1/\epsilon^{(y)}$, $1/\epsilon^{(z)}$. Moreover, the sphere is transformed into an ellipsoid with semiaxes $a/\sqrt{\epsilon^{(x)}}$, $a/\sqrt{\epsilon^{(y)}}$, $a/\sqrt{\epsilon^{(z)}}$. Let $n^{(x)}$, $n^{(y)}$, $n^{(z)}$ be the depolarisation coefficients of such an ellipsoid (given by formulae (4.25)). Applying formula (8.7) to the field of this ellipsoid, we obtain the relation

$$(1-n^{(x)})\frac{\partial\phi^{(i)}}{\partial x'}+\frac{n^{(x)}}{\epsilon^{(x)}}\frac{\partial\phi^{(i)}}{\partial x'} = \frac{\partial\phi^{(e)}}{\partial x'},$$

and similarly for the y and z directions. Returning to the original co-ordinates, we have $\partial\phi/\partial x' = \sqrt{\epsilon^{(x)}}\,\partial\phi/\partial x = \sqrt{\epsilon^{(x)}}E_x$, so that the field in the cavity is

$$E^{(i)}{}_x = \frac{\epsilon^{(x)}}{\epsilon^{(x)}-n^{(x)}(\epsilon^{(x)}-1)}E^{(e)}{}_x.$$

§14. The sign of the dielectric susceptibility

To elucidate the way in which the thermodynamic quantities for a dielectric in a field depend on its dielectric constant, let us consider the formal problem of the change in the electric component of the total free energy of the body when ϵ undergoes an infinitesimal change.

For an isotropic (not necessarily homogeneous) body we have by (10.19) $\mathscr{F}-\mathscr{F}_0 = \int(D^2/8\pi\epsilon)\mathrm{d}V$. When ϵ changes, so does the induction, and the variation in the free energy is therefore

$$\delta\mathscr{F} = \int\frac{\mathbf{D}\cdot\delta\mathbf{D}}{4\pi\epsilon}\mathrm{d}V - \int\frac{D^2}{8\pi\epsilon^2}\delta\epsilon\,\mathrm{d}V = \int\frac{\mathbf{E}\cdot\delta\mathbf{D}}{4\pi}\mathrm{d}V - \int\frac{E^2}{8\pi}\delta\epsilon\,\mathrm{d}V.$$

The first term in the last member is the same as (10.2), which gives the work done in an infinitesimal change in the field sources (i.e. charges on conductors). In the present case, however, we are considering a change in the field but no change in the sources. This term therefore vanishes, leaving

$$\delta\mathscr{F} = -\int\delta\epsilon(E^2/8\pi)\,\mathrm{d}V. \qquad (14.1)$$

From this formula there follows, first of all, an important result: any increase in the dielectric constant of the medium, even if in only a part of it (the sources of the field remaining unchanged), reduces the total free energy. In particular, we can say that the free energy is always reduced when uncharged conductors are brought into a dielectric medium, since these conductors may (in electrostatics) be regarded as bodies whose dielectric constant is infinite. This conclusion generalises the theorem (§2) that the energy of the electrostatic field in a vacuum is diminished when an uncharged conductor is placed in it.

Formula (14.1) can also be used to prove the statement in §7 that the dielectric constant of any body exceeds unity, i.e. the dielectric susceptibility $(\epsilon-1)/4\pi$ is positive. To show this, we must first show independently that the total change in the free energy of a dielectric when it is placed in an electric field is negative.† This can be done by the use of thermodynamic perturbation theory, the change in the free energy of the body being regarded as the result of a perturbation of its quantum energy levels by the electric field. According to this theory we have‡

$$\mathscr{F}-\mathscr{F}_0 = \bar{V}_{nn} - \frac{1}{2}\sum_n\sum_m{}' \frac{|V_{nm}|^2(w_m-w_n)}{E_n^{(0)}-E_m^{(0)}} - \frac{1}{2kT}\overline{(V_{nn}-\bar{V}_{nn})^2}. \qquad (14.2)$$

† The change proportional to the square of the field is meant. It may be recalled that, in pyroelectric bodies, the change in the free energy contains also a term linear in the field, which is of no interest here.

‡ See *Statistical Physics*, §32, formulae (32.5), (32.6). The formulae given here differ from those in *Statistical Physics* only in form.

Here $E_n^{(0)}$ are the unperturbed levels, V_{mn} the matrix elements of the perturbing energy, and the bar denotes a statistical averaging with respect to the Gibbs distribution $w_n = \exp\{(\mathscr{F}_0 - E_n^{(0)})/kT\}$.

The term $\bar{V}_{nn}$ in formula (14.2), which is linear in the field, is zero except in pyroelectric bodies. The quadratic change in the free energy, which is of interest here, is given by the remaining terms. It is evident from the form in which they are written here that they are negative.

If we formally consider the change in the free energy as the result of a gradual change in the dielectric constant of the body from 1 to a given value ϵ, it follows from formula (14.1) that $\mathscr{F} - \mathscr{F}_0$ is negative only if $\epsilon > 1$. This completes the proof.

In the same way we can prove the inequalities $\epsilon^{(i)} > 1$ for the principal values of the tensor ϵ_{ik} in an anisotropic dielectric medium. To do so, it is evidently sufficient to consider the energy of a field parallel to each of the three principal axes in turn.

The total free energy is diminished, in particular, when any charge is brought up to a dielectric body from infinity (a process which may be regarded as an increase of ϵ in a certain volume of the field round the charge). In order to conclude from this that any charge is attracted to a dielectric, we should, strictly speaking, prove also that F cannot attain a minimum for any finite distance between the charge and the body. We shall not pause here to prove this statement, especially as the presence of an attractive force between a charge and a dielectric may be regarded as a fairly evident consequence of the interaction between the charge and the dipole moment of the dielectric, which it polarises.

We can deduce immediately from formula (14.1) the direction of motion of a dielectric body in an almost uniform electric field, i.e. one which may be regarded as uniform over the dimensions of the body. In this case E^2 is taken outside the integral, and the difference $\mathscr{F} - \mathscr{F}_0$ is a negative quantity, proportional to E^2. In order to take a position in which its free energy is a minimum, the body will therefore move in the direction of E increasing.

§15. Electric forces in a fluid dielectric

The problem of calculating the forces (called *ponderomotive* forces) which act on a dielectric in an arbitrary non-uniform electric field is fairly complicated and requires separate consideration for fluids (liquids or gases) and for solids. We shall take first the simpler case, that of fluid dielectrics. We denote by $\mathbf{f}dV$ the force on a volume element dV, and call the vector $\mathbf{f}$ the *force density*.

It is well known that the forces acting on any finite volume in a body can be reduced to forces applied to the surface of that volume.† This is a consequence of the law of conservation of momentum. The force acting on the

† See *Theory of Elasticity*, §2, Pergamon Press, London, 1959.

matter in a volume dV is the change in its momentum per unit time. This change must be equal to the amount of momentum entering the volume through its surface per unit time. If we denote the momentum flux tensor by $-\sigma_{ik}$, then

$$\int f_i \,\mathrm{d}V = \oint \sigma_{ik}\,\mathrm{d}f_k, \tag{15.1}$$

where the integration on the right is over the surface of the volume V. The tensor σ_{ik} is called the *stress tensor*. It is evident that $\sigma_{ik}\mathrm{d}f_k = \sigma_{ik}n_k\mathrm{d}f$ is the ith component of the force on a surface element df ($\mathbf{n}$ being a unit vector along the normal to the surface outwards from the volume under consideration).

Similarly, the total torque acting on a given volume also reduces to a surface integral, by virtue of the law of conservation of angular momentum. This reduction is possible because of the symmetry of the stress tensor ($\sigma_{ik} = \sigma_{ki}$), which thus expresses the conservation law mentioned.

On transforming the surface integral in (15.1) into a volume integral, we obtain $\int f_i \mathrm{d}V = \int (\partial\sigma_{ik}/\partial x_k)\mathrm{d}V$, whence, since the volume of integration is arbitrary,

$$f_i = \partial\sigma_{ik}/\partial x_k. \tag{15.2}$$

This is a well-known formula giving the body forces in terms of the stress tensor.

Let us now calculate the stress tensor. Any small region of the surface may be regarded as plane, and the properties of the body and the electric field near it as uniform. Hence, to simplify the derivation, we can with no loss of generality consider a plane-parallel layer of material (of thickness h and uniform composition, density and temperature) in an electric field which is uniform but whose direction is arbitrary.† This field may be imagined to be due to conducting planes, bearing appropriate charge distributions, applied to the surfaces of the layer.

Following the general method for determining forces, we subject one of the conducting planes (the upper one, say) to a virtual translation over an infinitesimal distance $\boldsymbol{\xi}$, whose direction is arbitrary and need not be that of the normal $\mathbf{n}$. We shall suppose that the potential of the conductor remains unchanged at every point, and that the homogeneous deformation of the dielectric layer, resulting from the translation, is isothermal.

A force $-\sigma_{ik}n_k$ is exerted by the layer on unit area of the surface. In the virtual displacement this force does work $-\sigma_{ik}n_k\xi_i$. The work done in an isothermal deformation at constant potential is equal to the decrease in $\int \tilde{F}\mathrm{d}V$, i.e. in $h\tilde{F}$ per unit surface area. Thus

$$\sigma_{ik}\xi_i n_k = \delta(h\tilde{F}) = h\delta\tilde{F} + \tilde{F}\delta h. \tag{15.3}$$

† We thus ignore any terms in the stress tensor depending on the gradients of temperature, field, etc. These terms, however, are vanishingly small in comparison with terms which do not contain derivatives, in the same way as any terms containing derivatives which might appear in the relation between **D** and **E**.

The thermodynamic quantities for the fluid depend (for given temperature and field) only on its density; deformations which do not change the density (i.e. pure shears) do not affect the thermodynamic state. We can therefore write for an isothermal variation $\delta\tilde{F}$ in a fluid

$$\begin{aligned}\delta\tilde{F} &= \left(\frac{\partial\tilde{F}}{\partial\mathbf{E}}\right)_{T,\rho}\cdot\delta\mathbf{E}+\left(\frac{\partial\tilde{F}}{\partial\rho}\right)_{\mathbf{E},T}\delta\rho \\ &= -\frac{\mathbf{D}\cdot\delta\mathbf{E}}{4\pi}+\left(\frac{\partial\tilde{F}}{\partial\rho}\right)_{\mathbf{E},T}\delta\rho.\end{aligned} \tag{15.4}$$

The change in the density of the layer is related to the change in its thickness by $\delta\rho = -\rho\delta h/h$. The variation of the field is calculated as follows. At a given point in space (with radius vector $\mathbf{r}$) there appears matter which was originally at $\mathbf{r}-\mathbf{u}$, where $\mathbf{u}$ is the particle displacement vector in the layer. Since, under the conditions stated (homogeneous deformation, and constant potential on the conducting planes), each particle carries its potential with it, the change in the potential at a given point in space is $\delta\phi = \phi(\mathbf{r}-\mathbf{u})-\phi(\mathbf{r}) = -\mathbf{u}\cdot\mathbf{grad}\,\phi = \mathbf{u}\cdot\mathbf{E}$, where $\mathbf{E}$ is the uniform field in the undeformed layer. Since the deformation is homogeneous, however, we have

$$\mathbf{u} = z\boldsymbol{\xi}/h, \tag{15.5}$$

where z is the distance from the lower surface. Hence the variation of the field is

$$\delta\mathbf{E} = -\mathbf{n}(\mathbf{E}\cdot\boldsymbol{\xi})/h. \tag{15.6}$$

Substituting the above expressions in (15.4) and using also the fact that $\delta h = \xi_z = \boldsymbol{\xi}\cdot\mathbf{n}$, we obtain

$$\begin{aligned}\sigma_{ik}\xi_i n_k &= \frac{1}{4\pi}(\mathbf{n}\cdot\mathbf{D})(\boldsymbol{\xi}\cdot\mathbf{E})-\boldsymbol{\xi}\cdot\mathbf{n}\,\rho\frac{\partial\tilde{F}}{\partial\rho}+\boldsymbol{\xi}\cdot\mathbf{n}\tilde{F} \\ &= \left\{\frac{E_iD_k}{4\pi}-\rho\frac{\partial\tilde{F}}{\partial\rho}\delta_{ik}+\tilde{F}\delta_{ik}\right\}\xi_i n_k.\end{aligned}$$

Hence we have finally the following expression for the stress tensor:

$$\sigma_{ik} = [\tilde{F}-\rho(\partial\tilde{F}/\partial\rho)_{\mathbf{E},T}]\delta_{ik}+E_iD_k/4\pi. \tag{15.7}$$

In isotropic media, which are those here considered, $\mathbf{E}$ and $\mathbf{D}$ are parallel. Hence $E_iD_k = E_kD_i$, and the tensor (15.7) is symmetrical, as it should be.

If the linear relation $\mathbf{D} = \epsilon\mathbf{E}$ holds, then

$$\tilde{F} = F_0(\rho, T)-\epsilon E^2/8\pi; \tag{15.8}$$

see (10.16). F_0 is the free energy per unit volume in the absence of the field.

According to a well-known thermodynamic relation, the derivative of the free energy per unit mass with respect to the specific volume is the pressure:

$$\left[\frac{\partial}{\partial(1/\rho)}\left(\frac{F_0}{\rho}\right)\right]_T = F_0-\rho\left(\frac{\partial F_0}{\partial\rho}\right)_T = -p_0;$$

$p_0 = p_0(\rho, T)$ is the pressure which would be found in the medium in the absence of a field and for given values of ρ and T. Hence, substituting (15.8) in (15.7), we have

$$\sigma_{ik} = -p_0(\rho, T)\delta_{ik}-\frac{E^2}{8\pi}\left[\epsilon-\rho\left(\frac{\partial\epsilon}{\partial\rho}\right)_T\right]\delta_{ik}+\frac{\epsilon E_iE_k}{4\pi}. \tag{15.9}$$

In a vacuum, this expression becomes the familiar Maxwell stress tensor of the electric field:†

$$\sigma_{ik} = (E_iE_k-\tfrac{1}{2}E^2\delta_{ik})/4\pi.$$

The forces exerted on the surface of separation by two adjoining media must be equal and opposite: $\sigma_{ik}n_k = -\sigma'_{ik}n'_k$, where the quantities with and without the prime refer to the two media. The normal vectors **n** and **n**′ are in opposite directions, so that

$$\sigma_{ik}n_k = \sigma'_{ik}n_k. \tag{15.10}$$

At the boundary of two isotropic media the condition of equality of the tangential forces is satisfied identically. For, substituting (15.7) in (15.10) and taking the tangential component, we obtain $\mathbf{E}_tD_n = \mathbf{E}'_tD'_n$. This equation is satisfied by virtue of the boundary conditions of continuity on $\mathbf{E}_t$ and D_n. The condition of equality of the normal forces is, however, a non-trivial condition on the pressure difference between the two media.

For example, let us consider a boundary between a liquid and the atmosphere (for which we can put $\epsilon = 1$). Denoting by a prime quantities pertaining to the atmosphere, and using formula (15.9) for σ_{ik}, we have

$$-p_0(\rho, T)+\frac{E^2}{8\pi}\rho\left(\frac{\partial\epsilon}{\partial\rho}\right)_T+\frac{\epsilon}{8\pi}(E_n{}^2-E_t{}^2)$$
$$= -p_{\text{atm}}+\frac{1}{8\pi}(E'_n{}^2-E'_t{}^2).$$

Using the boundary conditions $E_t = E'_t$, $D_n = \epsilon E_n = D'_n = E'_n$, we can rewrite this equation as

$$p_0(\rho, T)-p_{\text{atm}} = \frac{\rho E^2}{8\pi}\left(\frac{\partial\epsilon}{\partial\rho}\right)_T-\frac{\epsilon-1}{8\pi}(\epsilon E_n{}^2+E_t{}^2). \tag{15.11}$$

This relation is to be taken as determining the density ρ of the liquid near its surface from the electric field in it.

† See *The Classical Theory of Fields*, §4–8, Addison-Wesley Press, Cambridge (Mass.), 1951; Pergamon Press, London, 1959.

Let us now determine the body forces acting in a dielectric medium. Differentiating (15.9) in accordance with (15.2) gives

$$f_i = \frac{\partial}{\partial x_i}\left[-p_0+\frac{E^2}{8\pi}\rho\left(\frac{\partial\epsilon}{\partial\rho}\right)_T\right]-\frac{E^2}{8\pi}\frac{\partial\epsilon}{\partial x_i}+\frac{1}{4\pi}\left[-\tfrac{1}{2}\epsilon\frac{\partial}{\partial x_i}E^2+\frac{\partial}{\partial x_k}(E_iD_k)\right].$$

On using the equation div $\mathbf{D} \equiv \partial D_k/\partial x_k = 0$, the expression in the brackets in the last term can be reduced to

$$-\epsilon E_k\frac{\partial E_k}{\partial x_i}+D_k\frac{\partial E_i}{\partial x_k} = -D_k\left(\frac{\partial E_k}{\partial x_i}-\frac{\partial E_i}{\partial x_k}\right),$$

which is zero, since **curl** $\mathbf{E} = 0$. Thus we have

$$\mathbf{f} = -\mathbf{grad}\,p_0(\rho, T)+\frac{1}{8\pi}\mathbf{grad}\left[E^2\rho\left(\frac{\partial\epsilon}{\partial\rho}\right)_T\right]-\frac{E^2}{8\pi}\mathbf{grad}\,\epsilon. \tag{15.12}$$

If the dielectric contains extraneous charges of density ρ_{ex}, the force $\mathbf{f}$ contains a further term $\mathbf{E}$ div $\mathbf{D}/4\pi$, or, since div $\mathbf{D} = 4\pi\rho_{ex}$,

$$\rho_{ex}\mathbf{E}; \tag{15.13}$$

however, it should not be supposed that this result is obvious (cf. §16, Problem 3).

In a gas, as already mentioned in §7, we can assume the difference $\epsilon-1$ to be proportional to the density. Then $\rho\,\partial\epsilon/\partial\rho = \epsilon-1$, and formula (15.12) takes the simpler form

$$\mathbf{f} = -\mathbf{grad}\,p_0+\frac{\epsilon-1}{8\pi}\mathbf{grad}\,E^2. \tag{15.14}$$

Formula (15.12) is valid for media of both uniform and non-uniform composition. In the latter case ϵ is a function not only of ρ and T but also of the concentration of the mixture, which varies through the medium. In a body of uniform composition, on the other hand, ϵ is a function only of ρ and T, and **grad** ϵ can be written as

$$\mathbf{grad}\,\epsilon = (\partial\epsilon/\partial T)_\rho\,\mathbf{grad}\,T+(\partial\epsilon/\partial\rho)_T\,\mathbf{grad}\,\rho.$$

Then (15.12) becomes

$$\mathbf{f} = -\mathbf{grad}\,p_0(\rho, T)+\frac{\rho}{8\pi}\mathbf{grad}\left[E^2\left(\frac{\partial\epsilon}{\partial\rho}\right)_T\right]-\frac{E^2}{8\pi}\left(\frac{\partial\epsilon}{\partial T}\right)_\rho\mathbf{grad}\,T. \tag{15.15}$$

If the temperature also is constant through the body, the third term on the right is zero, and in the first term **grad** p_0 can be replaced by ρ **grad** ζ_0, in accordance with the thermodynamic identity for the chemical potential in the absence of a field, $\rho\mathrm{d}\zeta_0 = \mathrm{d}p_0-S_0\mathrm{d}T$. Thus

$$\mathbf{f} = -\rho\,\mathbf{grad}\left[\zeta_0-\frac{E^2}{8\pi}\left(\frac{\partial\epsilon}{\partial\rho}\right)_T\right]. \tag{15.16}$$

The expression in the brackets is just the chemical potential ζ in an electric field (see (10.18)), and therefore $\mathbf{f} = -\rho\, \mathbf{grad}\, \zeta$.

In particular, the condition of mechanical equilibrium $\mathbf{f} = 0$ is, for constant temperature,

$$\zeta = \zeta_0 - (E^2/8\pi)(\partial\epsilon/\partial\rho)_T = \text{constant}, \tag{15.17}$$

in accordance with the thermodynamic condition of equilibrium.† This condition can usually be written still more simply. The change in density of the medium due to the field is proportional to E^2. Hence, if the medium is of uniform density in the absence of the field, we can put $\rho = \text{constant}$ in the last two terms in (15.15) when the field is present; an allowance for the change in ρ is beyond the accuracy of formulae which assume the linear relation $\mathbf{D} = \epsilon\mathbf{E}$. Then, equating to zero $\mathbf{f}$ from (15.15), we obtain the equilibrium condition at constant temperature in the form

$$p_0(\rho, T) - (\rho E^2/8\pi)(\partial\epsilon/\partial\rho)_T = \text{constant}, \tag{15.18}$$

which differs from (15.17) in that ζ is replaced by p_0/ρ.

§16. Electric forces in solids

The dielectric properties of a solid body change not only when its density changes (as with liquids) but also under deformations (pure shears) which do not affect the density. Let us first consider bodies which are isotropic in the absence of the field. In general, the deformed body is no longer isotropic; in consequence, its dielectric properties also become anisotropic, and the scalar dielectric permeability ϵ is replaced by the dielectric tensor ϵ_{ik}.

The state of a slightly deformed body is described by the strain tensor

$$u_{ik} = \frac{1}{2}\left(\frac{\partial u_i}{\partial x_k} + \frac{\partial u_k}{\partial x_i}\right),$$

where $\mathbf{u}(x,y,z)$ is the displacement vector for points in the body. Since these quantities are small, only the first-order terms in u_{ik} need be retained in the variation of the components ϵ_{ik}. Accordingly, we represent the dielectric tensor of the deformed body as

$$\epsilon_{ik} = \epsilon_0\delta_{ik} + a_1 u_{ik} + a_2 u_{ll}\delta_{ik}. \tag{16.1}$$

Here ϵ_0 is the dielectric permeability of the undeformed body, and the other two terms, which contain the scalar constants a_1, a_2, form the most general tensor of rank two which can be constructed linearly from the components u_{ik}.

Let us now see where the derivation given in §15 must be modified. Since, in a solid body, $\tilde{F}$ depends on all the components of the strain tensor, we must replace (15.4) by $\delta\tilde{F} = -\mathbf{D}\cdot\delta\mathbf{E}/4\pi + (\partial\tilde{F}/\partial u_{ik})\delta u_{ik}$. For the virtual

† See *Statistical Physics*, §25.

displacement considered, the vector **u** is given by formula (15.5), so that the strain tensor is $u_{ik} = (\xi_i n_k + \xi_k n_i)/2h$. Substituting this in $\delta\tilde{F}$ and using the symmetry of the tensor u_{ik}, and therefore of the derivatives $\partial\tilde{F}/\partial u_{ik}$, we obtain

$$\delta\tilde{F} = -\mathbf{D}\cdot\delta\mathbf{E}/4\pi + (\xi_i n_k/h)\partial\tilde{F}/\partial u_{ik}. \tag{16.2}$$

It is now evident that we find, instead of (15.7), the following expression for the stress tensor:†

$$\sigma_{ik} = \tilde{F}\delta_{ik} + (\partial\tilde{F}/\partial u_{ik})_{T\,\mathbf{E}} + E_i D_k/4\pi. \tag{16.3}$$

Formula (16.3) is valid whatever the relation between **D** and **E**. For a body which is neither pyroelectric nor piezoelectric, so that $D_i = \epsilon_{ik}E_k$, $\tilde{F}$ is given by formula (13.4) and the required derivatives are $\partial\tilde{F}/\partial u_{ik} = \partial F_0/\partial u_{ik} - (a_1 E_i E_k + a_2 E^2\delta_{ik})/8\pi$. We then put $\epsilon_{ik} = \epsilon_0\delta_{ik}$ everywhere in (16.3) and obtain the following formula for the stress tensor:

$$\sigma_{ik} = \sigma^{(0)}{}_{ik} + (2\epsilon_0 - a_1)E_i E_k/8\pi - (\epsilon_0 + a_2)E^2\delta_{ik}/8\pi. \tag{16.4}$$

$\sigma^{(0)}{}_{ik}$ is the stress tensor in the absence of an electric field, determined by the moduli of rigidity and compression according to the ordinary formulae of the theory of elasticity.

Let us now make similar calculations for anisotropic solids.‡ The necessary modification of the above argument is as follows. When the layer undergoes a virtual deformation, its crystallographic axes are rotated, and their orientation relative to the electric field is therefore changed. On account of the anisotropy of the dielectric properties of the crystal, this leads to an additional change in $\tilde{F}$ not shown in (16.2). To calculate this change we can equally well suppose that the crystal axes rotate through some angle $\delta\boldsymbol{\phi}$ relative to the field **E**, or that the field rotates through an angle $-\delta\boldsymbol{\phi}$ relative to the axes, and the latter approach is the more convenient.

Thus the variation of the field (15.6) considered above must be augmented by the change in **E** on rotation through an angle $-\delta\boldsymbol{\phi}$: $\delta\mathbf{E} = -\mathbf{n}(\mathbf{E}\cdot\boldsymbol{\xi})/h - \delta\boldsymbol{\phi}\times\mathbf{E}$. The angle $\delta\boldsymbol{\phi}$ is related to the displacement vector **u** in the deformation by $\delta\boldsymbol{\phi} = \frac{1}{2}\,\mathbf{curl}\,\mathbf{u}$; this equation is easily obtained by noticing that, when the body rotates through an angle $\delta\boldsymbol{\phi}$, its points are displaced by $\mathbf{u} = \delta\boldsymbol{\phi}\times\mathbf{r}$. Substituting **u** from (15.5), we find $\delta\boldsymbol{\phi} = \mathbf{curl}\, z\boldsymbol{\xi}/2h = \mathbf{n}\times\boldsymbol{\xi}/2h$,

† The quantity $\tilde{F}$ in this formula, and in all preceding formulae, is the free energy per unit volume. In the theory of elasticity, however, a somewhat different definition is usual: the thermodynamic quantities are referred to the amount of matter contained in unit volume of the undeformed body, which may after deformation occupy some other volume. It is easy to go from one definition to the other by expressing the relative volume change in the deformation in terms of the tensor u_{ik}; on account of the presence of the derivative with respect to u_{ik} in (16.3), this must be done with allowance for second-order terms. As a result, the first two terms on the right of (16.3) combine into one of the form $\partial\tilde{F}/\partial u_{ik}$, in accordance with the usual formula of elasticity theory.

‡ We shall see in §17 that the phenomenon of electrostriction in crystals may, for some types of symmetry, differ markedly from that in isotropic bodies. Such crystals are said to be *piezoelectric*. Here, however, we discuss only electrostriction in non-piezoelectric bodies.

and $\delta\mathbf{E} = -\mathbf{n}(\mathbf{E}\cdot\boldsymbol{\xi})/h + \mathbf{E}\times(\mathbf{n}\times\boldsymbol{\xi})/2h = -[\mathbf{n}(\mathbf{E}\cdot\boldsymbol{\xi}) + \boldsymbol{\xi}(\mathbf{n}\cdot\mathbf{E})]/2h$. The first term in (16.2) becomes

$$-\frac{1}{4\pi}\mathbf{D}\cdot\delta\mathbf{E} = \frac{1}{8\pi h}[(\mathbf{n}\cdot\mathbf{D})(\boldsymbol{\xi}\cdot\mathbf{E}) + (\boldsymbol{\xi}\cdot\mathbf{D})(\mathbf{n}\cdot\mathbf{E})] = \frac{1}{4\pi h}\xi_i n_k\,.\,\tfrac{1}{2}(E_i D_k + E_k D_i).$$

Hence we see that the product $E_i D_k$ in (16.3) must be replaced by the second factor in the last expression:

$$\sigma_{ik} = \tilde{F}\delta_{ik} + \frac{\partial\tilde{F}}{\partial u_{ik}} + \frac{1}{8\pi}(E_i D_k + E_k D_i). \tag{16.5}$$

This expression is symmetrical in the suffixes i and k, as it should be.

The expression (16.1) for the dielectric tensor, involving two scalar constants, must be replaced in the case of a dielectric crystal by

$$\epsilon_{ik} = \epsilon^{(0)}{}_{ik} + a_{iklm}u_{lm}, \tag{16.6}$$

where a_{iklm} is a constant tensor of rank four, symmetrical with respect to the pairs of suffixes i, k and l, m (but not with respect to an interchange of these pairs). The number of independent non-zero components of this tensor depends on the crystal class.

We shall not pause to write out here the formula for the stress tensor (analogous to (16.4)) which is obtained by using (16.6).

The formulae which we have obtained give the stresses inside a solid dielectric. They are not needed, however, if we wish to determine the total force $\mathbf{F}$ or the total torque $\mathbf{K}$ exerted on the body by the external field. Let us consider a body immersed in a fluid medium and kept at rest there. The total force on it is equal to the integral $\oint \sigma_{ik}n_k \mathrm{d}f$, taken over the surface. Since the force $\sigma_{ik}n_k$ is continuous, it does not matter whether this integral is calculated from the values of σ_{ik} given by (16.4) or from formula (15.9), which relates to the medium surrounding the body. Let us suppose that this medium is in mechanical and thermal equilibrium. Then the calculation is further simplified if we use the condition of equilibrium (15.18). From this condition, part of the stress tensor (15.9) is constant through the body, being a uniform compressing or expanding pressure and making no contribution to the total force $\mathbf{F}$ and torque $\mathbf{K}$ acting on the body. These can therefore be calculated by writing σ_{ik} as

$$\sigma_{ik} = (\epsilon/4\pi)(E_i E_k - \tfrac{1}{2}E^2\delta_{ik}) \tag{16.7}$$

simply, where $\mathbf{E}$ is the field in the fluid and ϵ its dielectric permeability; this expression differs only by a factor ϵ from the Maxwell stress tensor of the electric field in a vacuum. Thus

$$\mathbf{F} = (\epsilon/4\pi)\oint[\mathbf{E}(\mathbf{n}\cdot\mathbf{E}) - \tfrac{1}{2}E^2\mathbf{n}]\,\mathrm{d}f, \tag{16.8}$$

$$\mathbf{K} = (\epsilon/4\pi)\oint[\mathbf{r}\times\mathbf{E}(\mathbf{n}\cdot\mathbf{E}) - \tfrac{1}{2}E^2\mathbf{r}\times\mathbf{n}]\,\mathrm{d}f. \tag{16.9}$$

It may also be noted that, since the fluid is in equilibrium, we can take these integrals over any closed surface which surrounds the body in question (but, of course, does not enclose any of the charged bodies which are sources of the field).

The calculation of the total force on a dielectric in an electric field in a vacuum can also be approached in another way by expressing this force, not in terms of the actual field, but in terms of the field $\mathfrak{E}$ which would be produced by the given sources in the absence of the dielectric; this is the "external field" in which the body is placed. Here it is assumed that the distribution of charges producing the field is unchanged when the body is brought in. This condition may not be fulfilled in practice—for example, if the charges are distributed over the surface of an extended conductor and the dielectric is brought to a finite distance from it.

In a virtual translation of the body over an infinitesimal distance $\mathbf{u}$, the total free energy of the body varies, according to (11.3), by $\delta\mathcal{F} = -\int \mathbf{P}\cdot\delta\mathfrak{E}\,\mathrm{d}V$, where $\delta\mathfrak{E} = \mathfrak{E}(\mathbf{r}+\mathbf{u})-\mathfrak{E}(\mathbf{r}) = (\mathbf{u}\cdot\mathbf{grad})\mathfrak{E}$ is the change in the field at any given point in the body. Since $\mathbf{u}$ = constant and $\mathbf{curl}\,\mathfrak{E} = 0$, we have $\mathbf{P}\cdot(\mathbf{u}\cdot\mathbf{grad})\mathfrak{E} = \mathbf{P}\cdot\mathbf{grad}(\mathbf{u}\cdot\mathfrak{E}) = \mathbf{u}\cdot(\mathbf{P}\cdot\mathbf{grad})\mathfrak{E}$, so that

$$\delta\mathcal{F} = -\mathbf{u}\cdot\int(\mathbf{P}\cdot\mathbf{grad})\mathfrak{E}\,\mathrm{d}V.$$

But $\delta\mathcal{F} = -\mathbf{u}\cdot\mathbf{F}$, and we therefore have for the required force†

$$\mathbf{F} = \int(\mathbf{P}\cdot\mathbf{grad})\mathfrak{E}\,\mathrm{d}V. \tag{16.10}$$

Similarly, the total torque on the body can be determined. We shall not go through the calculation, but merely give the result:

$$\mathbf{K} = \int\mathbf{P}\times\mathfrak{E}\,\mathrm{d}V+\int\mathbf{r}\times(\mathbf{P}\cdot\mathbf{grad})\mathfrak{E}\,\mathrm{d}V. \tag{16.11}$$

In an almost uniform field, which may be regarded as constant over the dimensions of the body, formula (16.10) gives to a first approximation

$$\mathbf{F} = \left(\int\mathbf{P}\,\mathrm{d}V\cdot\mathbf{grad}\right)\mathfrak{E} = (\mathcal{P}\cdot\mathbf{grad})\mathfrak{E}, \tag{16.12}$$

where $\mathcal{P}$ is the total dipole moment of the polarised dielectric; this result, of course, could have been obtained by direct differentiation of $\mathcal{F}$ from (11.8). In formula (16.11) we neglect the second term in the first approximation and reach the natural conclusion that

$$\mathbf{K} = \mathcal{P}\times\mathfrak{E}. \tag{16.13}$$

† It should be emphasised, however, that the integrand in (16.10) cannot be interpreted as the force density. The reason is that the local forces in the dielectric arise not only from the field $\mathfrak{E}$ but also from the internal fields which, by Newton's third law, contribute nothing to the total force, though they modify the distribution of forces over the volume of the body.

PROBLEMS

PROBLEM 1. A dielectric sphere of radius a in a uniform external field $\mathfrak{E}$ is cut in half by a plane perpendicular to the field. Determine the force of attraction between the hemispheres.

SOLUTION. We imagine the hemispheres separated by an infinitely narrow slit and determine the force from formula (16.8) with $\epsilon = 1$, integrating over the surface of a hemisphere; $\mathbf{E}$ is the field in the vacuum near the surface. According to (8.2) the field $\mathbf{E}^{(i)}$ inside the sphere is uniform and equal to $3\mathfrak{E}/(2+\epsilon)$, where ϵ is the dielectric constant of the sphere. The field in the slit is perpendicular to the surface and is $\mathbf{E} = \mathbf{D}^{(i)} = 3\epsilon\mathfrak{E}/(2+\epsilon)$. On the outer surface of the sphere we have

$$E_r = D^{(i)}{}_r = \frac{3\epsilon}{2+\epsilon}\,\mathfrak{E}\cos\theta, \qquad E_\theta = E^{(i)}{}_\theta = -\frac{3}{\epsilon+2}\,\mathfrak{E}\sin\theta,$$

where θ is the angle between the radius vector and the direction of $\mathfrak{E}$. A calculation of the integral gives an attractive force†

$$F = 9(\epsilon-1)^2\, a^2\, \mathfrak{E}^2/16(\epsilon+2)^2.$$

PROBLEM 2. Determine the change in shape of a dielectric sphere in a uniform external electric field.

SOLUTION. As in §5, Problem 4. In determining the change in shape, we assume the volume of the sphere to be unchanged.‡ The elastic part of the free energy is given by the same expression as in §5, Problem 4. The electric part is given by

$$-\tfrac{1}{2}\mathscr{P}\cdot\mathfrak{E} = -\frac{V}{8\pi}\frac{\epsilon^{(x)}-1}{1+n(\epsilon^{(x)}-1)}\mathfrak{E}^2,$$

and the dielectric permeability in the x-direction is, by (16.1), $\epsilon^{(x)} = \epsilon_0+a_1u_{xx} = \epsilon_0+ +\tfrac{2}{3}a_1(u_{xx}-u_{yy}) = \epsilon_0+\tfrac{2}{3}a_1(a-b)/R$. From the condition that the total free energy is a minimum we find

$$\frac{a-b}{R} = \frac{9\mathfrak{E}^2}{40\pi\mu}\frac{(\epsilon_0-1)^2+5a_1}{(\epsilon_0+2)^2}.$$

For $\epsilon_0 \to \infty$ this tends to the value for a conducting sphere.

PROBLEM 3. Determine the body forces in an isotropic solid dielectric, assumed homogeneous, when extraneous charges are present in it.

SOLUTION. Assuming ϵ_0, a_1, a_2 constant and using the equations $\mathbf{curl}\,\mathbf{E} = 0$, $\operatorname{div}\mathbf{D} \cong \epsilon_0 \operatorname{div}\mathbf{E} = 4\pi\rho_{\text{ex}}$, we have from (16.4)

$$f_i = \frac{\partial\sigma_{ik}}{\partial x_k} = \frac{\partial\sigma^{(0)}{}_{ik}}{\partial x_k} - \frac{1}{8\pi}(\tfrac{1}{2}a_1+a_2)\frac{\partial E^2}{\partial x_i} + \left(1-\frac{a_1}{2\epsilon_0}\right)\rho_{\text{ex}}E_i.$$

§17. Piezoelectrics

The internal stresses which occur in an isotropic dielectric in an electric field are proportional to the square of the field. The effect is similar in crystals belonging to some of the crystal classes. For certain types of symmetry, however, the electrostriction properties of the crystals are quite different. The internal stresses in these *piezoelectric* bodies resulting from

† It is by chance that, in the limit $\epsilon \to \infty$, this expression tends to the result obtained in §5, Problem 3, for a conducting sphere (indeed, the forces are in opposite directions). The two cases are evidently not physically equivalent, because there is no field in the slit between two conducting hemispheres at the same potential, whereas in this problem there is a field in the slit.

‡ The change in volume is determined in §12, Problem 1.

an electric field are proportional to the field itself. The converse effect also occurs: the deformation of a piezoelectric is accompanied by the appearance in it of a field proportional to the deformation.

Since in a piezoelectric only the principal (linear) effect is of interest, we can neglect the terms quadratic in the field in the general formula (16.5). Then $\sigma_{ik} = \tilde{F}\delta_{ik} + (\partial\tilde{F}/\partial u_{ik})_{T,\mathbf{E}}$. In this section we shall use the thermodynamic quantities referred to the matter in unit volume of the undeformed body (see the first footnote to §16). Taking $\tilde{F}$ in this sense, we have simply

$$\sigma_{ik} = (\partial\tilde{F}/\partial u_{ik})_{T,\mathbf{E}}. \tag{17.1}$$

Accordingly, the thermodynamic relation for the differential $\mathrm{d}\tilde{F}$ is

$$\mathrm{d}\tilde{F} = -S\,\mathrm{d}T + \sigma_{ik}\,\mathrm{d}u_{ik} - \mathbf{D}\cdot\mathrm{d}\mathbf{E}/4\pi. \tag{17.2}$$

The following remark should be made concerning the last term. In the form given here, this term (taken from (10.9)) pertains, strictly speaking, to unit volume of the deformed body. By ignoring this fact, we commit an error which, in the case of a piezoelectric, is of a higher order of smallness than the remaining terms in (17.2).

The independent variables in (17.2) include the components of the tensor u_{ik}. It is sometimes convenient to use instead the components σ_{ik}. To do so, we must introduce the thermodynamic potential, defined as

$$\tilde{\Phi} = \tilde{F} - u_{ik}\sigma_{ik}. \tag{17.3}$$

For the differential of this quantity we have

$$\mathrm{d}\tilde{\Phi} = -S\,\mathrm{d}T - u_{ik}\,\mathrm{d}\sigma_{ik} - \mathbf{D}\cdot\mathrm{d}\mathbf{E}/4\pi. \tag{17.4}$$

It must be emphasised that the use of the thermodynamic potential $\tilde{\Phi}$ in electrodynamics in accordance with formulae (17.3) and (17.4) rests on the validity of (17.1) and so is possible only for piezoelectric bodies.

Having thus defined the necessary thermodynamic quantities, let us now ascertain the piezoelectric properties of crystals. If σ_{ik} and E_k are taken as independent variables, the induction $\mathbf{D}$ must be regarded as a function of them, and an expansion of this function must include the linear terms in them. The linear terms in the expansion of the components of a vector in powers of the components of a tensor of rank two can be written, in the most general case, as $4\pi\gamma_{i,kl}\,\sigma_{kl}$, where the constants $\gamma_{i,kl}$ form a tensor of rank three, and the factor 4π is introduced for convenience. Since the tensor σ_{kl} is symmetrical, it is clear that the tensor $\gamma_{i,kl}$ may also be supposed to have the symmetry property

$$\gamma_{i,kl} = \gamma_{i,lk}. \tag{17.5}$$

For clarity we separate the symmetrical suffixes from the remaining one by a comma. We call $\gamma_{i,kl}$ the *piezoelectric tensor*. If it is known, the piezoelectric properties of the crystal are entirely determined.

Adding the piezoelectric terms to the expression (13.1) for the electric induction in the crystal, we have

$$D_i = D_{0i}+\epsilon_{ik}E_k+4\pi\gamma_{i,kl}\sigma_{kl}. \tag{17.6}$$

Corresponding additional terms appear in the thermodynamic quantities. The thermodynamic potential of a non-piezoelectric crystal in the absence of a field is $\tilde{\Phi} = \Phi = \Phi_0-\frac{1}{2}\mu_{iklm}\sigma_{ik}\sigma_{lm}$, where Φ_0 pertains to the undeformed body, and the second term is the ordinary elastic energy, determined by the *elastic constant tensor* μ_{iklm}.† For a piezoelectric we have

$$\tilde{\Phi} = \Phi_0-\tfrac{1}{2}\mu_{iklm}\sigma_{ik}\sigma_{lm}-\epsilon_{ik}E_iE_k/8\pi-E_iD_{0i}/4\pi-\gamma_{i,kl}E_i\sigma_{kl}. \tag{17.7}$$

The form of the last three terms is given by the fact that the derivatives of $\tilde{\Phi}$ with respect to E_i (for given temperature and internal stresses), found from the relation $D_i = -4\pi\partial\tilde{\Phi}/\partial E_i$, must accord with (17.6).

Knowing $\tilde{\Phi}$, we can obtain from (17.4) a formula giving the strain tensor in terms of the stresses σ_{ik} and the field $\mathbf{E}$:

$$u_{ik} = -(\partial\tilde{\Phi}/\partial\sigma_{ik})_{T,\mathbf{E}} = \mu_{iklm}\sigma_{lm}+\gamma_{l,ik}E_l. \tag{17.8}$$

It should be mentioned that to regard the quantities μ_{iklm} and ϵ_{ik} for a piezoelectric as elastic constants and dielectric permeability is to some extent conventional. With the definitions used here, they give respectively the strains as functions of the elastic stresses for a given field, and the induction as a function of the field for given stresses. If, however, the deformation occurs with a given value of the induction, or we consider the induction as a function of the field for given strains, the elastic constants and the dielectric permeability will be represented by other quantities, which can be expressed as somewhat complex functions of the components of the tensors μ, ϵ and γ.

The field in a piezoelectric body must be determined together with its deformation, leading to a problem in both electrostatics and elasticity theory. We must seek a simultaneous solution of the electrostatic equations

$$\operatorname{div}\mathbf{D} = 0, \qquad \mathbf{curl}\,\mathbf{E} = 0, \tag{17.9}$$

with $\mathbf{D}$ given by (17.6), and the equations of elastic equilibrium

$$\partial\sigma_{ik}/\partial x_k = 0, \tag{17.10}$$

with the appropriate boundary conditions at the surface of the body and use of the relation (17.8) between σ_{ik} and the strains. In general this problem is very complex.

---

† The tensor μ_{iklm} determines the relation between stress and strain:

$$u_{ik} = -\partial\Phi/\partial\sigma_{ik} = \mu_{iklm}\sigma_{lm}.$$

In *Theory of Elasticity*, §10, the converse relation $\sigma_{ik} = \lambda_{iklm}u_{lm}$ is used. It is evident that the symmetry properties of the tensor μ_{iklm} are exactly the same as those of λ_{iklm}.

The free energy F contains the elastic energy with the plus sign:

$$F_{\text{el}} = \tfrac{1}{2}\lambda_{iklm}u_{ik}u_{lm}.$$

The thermodynamic potential is obtained from F by subtracting $\sigma_{ik}u_{ik}$, and so

$$\Phi_{\text{el}} = F_{\text{el}}-\sigma_{ik}u_{ik} = -\tfrac{1}{2}\lambda_{iklm}u_{ik}u_{lm} = -\tfrac{1}{2}\mu_{iklm}\sigma_{ik}\sigma_{lm}.$$

The problem is much simplified for a body of ellipsoidal form with a free surface (i.e. one subject to no external mechanical forces). In this case (§8), the field inside the body is uniform; the deformation is therefore homogeneous, and the elastic stresses $\sigma_{ik} = 0$.

Finally, let us consider which types of crystal symmetry allow the existence of piezoelectricity; in other words, what are the restrictions imposed on the components of the tensor $\gamma_{i,kl}$ by the symmetry conditions. In general, this tensor (which is symmetrical in the suffixes k and l) has 18 independent non-zero components, but in reality the number of independent components is usually much smaller.

In all symmetry transformations of a given crystal, the components of the tensor $\gamma_{i,kl}$ must remain unaltered in value. Hence it follows at once that no piezoelectric body can have a centre of symmetry or, in particular, be isotropic. For, on reflection in the centre (i.e. change of sign of all three co-ordinates), the components of a tensor of rank three change sign.

Of the 32 crystal classes, only 20 allow piezoelectricity. These comprise the ten enumerated in §13 as allowing pyroelectricity (all pyroelectrics are also piezoelectrics) and the ten following classes:

rhombic system: $\boldsymbol{D}_2$
tetragonal system: $\boldsymbol{D}_4$, $\boldsymbol{D}_{2d}$, $\boldsymbol{S}_4$
rhombohedral system: $\boldsymbol{D}_3$
hexagonal system: $\boldsymbol{D}_6$, $\boldsymbol{C}_{3h}$, $\boldsymbol{D}_{3h}$
cubic system: $\boldsymbol{T}$, $\boldsymbol{T}_d$.

The non-zero components of the piezoelectric tensor for each class are given in the following Problems.

PROBLEMS

PROBLEM 1. Determine the non-zero components of the tensor $\gamma_{i,kl}$ for non-pyroelectric crystal classes which allow piezoelectricity.

SOLUTION. The class $\boldsymbol{D}_2$ has three mutually perpendicular axes of symmetry of the second order, which we take as the axes of x, y and z. Rotations through 180° about these axes change the sign of two out of the three co-ordinates. Since the components $\gamma_{i,kl}$ are transformed as the products $x_i x_k x_l$, the only non-zero components are those with three different suffixes: $\gamma_{x,yz}$, $\gamma_{z,xy}$, $\gamma_{y,zx}$. (The other non-zero components are equal to these, since $\gamma_{i,kl} = \gamma_{i,lk}$.) Accordingly, the piezoelectric part of the thermodynamic potential is†

$$\tilde{\Phi}_{\text{pie}} = -2(\gamma_{x,yz} E_x \sigma_{yz} + \gamma_{y,xz} E_y \sigma_{xz} + \gamma_{z,xy} E_z \sigma_{xy}). \tag{1}$$

The class $\boldsymbol{D}_{2d}$ is obtained by adding to the axes of class $\boldsymbol{D}_2$ two planes of symmetry passing through one axis (the z-axis, say) and bisecting the angles between the other two. Reflection in one of these planes gives the transformation $x \to y$, $y \to x$, $z \to z$. Hence the components $\gamma_{i,kl}$ which differ by interchange of x and y must be equal, so that only two out of the three coefficients in (1) are now independent: $\gamma_{z,xy}$, $\gamma_{x,yz} = \gamma_{y,xz}$.

† To avoid misunderstanding it should be recalled that, if we calculate the components of the strain tensor u_{ik} by direct differentiation of the actual expression for Φ with respect to σ_{ik}, the derivatives with respect to components σ_{ik} with $i \neq k$ give twice the corresponding components u_{ik}; see *Theory of Elasticity*, §10, Problem, footnote.

The class $\boldsymbol{T}$ is obtained from the class $\boldsymbol{D}_2$ by adding four diagonal axes of symmetry of the third order, rotations about which effect a cyclic permutation of x, y, z, e.g. $x \to z$, $y \to x$, $z \to y$. Hence all three coefficients in (1) are equal: $\gamma_{x,yz} = \gamma_{z,xy} = \gamma_{y,zx}$. The same result is obtained for the cubic class $\boldsymbol{T}_d$.

The class $\boldsymbol{D}_4$ has one axis of symmetry of the fourth order (the z-axis, say) and four of the second order lying in the xy-plane. Here the symmetry elements of the class $\boldsymbol{D}_2$ are supplemented by a rotation through 90° about the z-axis, i.e. the transformation $x \to y$, $y \to -x$, $z \to z$. Consequently, one of the coefficients in (1) must be zero ($\gamma_{z,xy} = -\gamma_{z,yx} = -\gamma_{z,xy} = 0$), and the other two are equal, but opposite in sign: $\gamma_{x,yz} = -\gamma_{y,xz}$. The same result is obtained for the class $\boldsymbol{D}_6$.

The class $\boldsymbol{S}_4$ includes the transformations $x \to y$, $y \to -x$, $z \to -z$ and $x \to -x$, $y \to -y$, $z \to z$. The non-zero components are $\gamma_{z,xy}$, $\gamma_{x,yz} = \gamma_{y,xz}$, $\gamma_{z,xx} = -\gamma_{z,yy}$, $\gamma_{x,zx} = -\gamma_{y,zy}$. One of these can be made to vanish by a suitable choice of the x and y axes.

The class $\boldsymbol{D}_3$ has one axis of symmetry of the third order (the z-axis, say), and three of the second order lying in the xy-plane; let one of these be the x-axis. To find the restrictions imposed by the presence of a third-order axis, we make a formal transformation by introducing the complex "co-ordinates" $\xi = x+iy$, $\eta = x-iy$; the co-ordinate z remains unchanged. We must also transform the tensor $\gamma_{i,kl}$ to these new co-ordinates, in which the suffixes take the values ξ, η, z. In a rotation through 120° about the z-axis these co-ordinates undergo the transformation $\xi \to \xi e^{2\pi i/3}$, $\eta \to \eta e^{-2\pi i/3}$, $z \to z$. The only components of the tensor $\gamma_{i,kl}$ which remain unchanged and so may be different from zero are $\gamma_{z,\eta\xi}$, $\gamma_{\eta,z\xi}$, $\gamma_{\xi,\xi\eta}$, $\gamma_{\xi,\xi\xi}$, $\gamma_{\eta,\eta\eta}$ and $\gamma_{z,zz}$. A rotation through 180° about the x-axis gives the transformation $x \to x$, $y \to -y$, $z \to -z$, or $\xi \to \eta$, $\eta \to \xi$, $z \to -z$; $\gamma_{z,\eta\xi}$ and $\gamma_{z,zz}$ change sign and so must be zero, while the remaining components listed above are mutually transformed in pairs, giving $\gamma_{\eta,z\xi} = -\gamma_{\xi,z\eta}$, $\gamma_{\xi,\xi\xi} = \gamma_{\eta,\eta\eta}$. In order to write an expression for $\tilde{\Phi}_{\text{pie}}$, we must form the sum $-\gamma_{i,kl}E_i\sigma_{kl}$, in which the suffixes take the values ξ, η, z:

$$\tilde{\Phi}_{\text{pie}} = -2\gamma_{\eta,z\xi}(E_\eta\sigma_{z\xi}-E_\xi\sigma_{z\eta})-\gamma_{\xi,\xi\xi}(E_\xi\sigma_{\xi\xi}+E_\eta\sigma_{\eta\eta}).$$

Here the components E_i and σ_{ik} in the co-ordinates ξ, η, z must also be expressed in terms of those in the original co-ordinates x, y, z. This is easily done by using the fact that the components of a tensor are transformed as the products of the corresponding co-ordinates. Hence, for example, from $\xi^2 = x^2-y^2+2ixy$, we have $\sigma_{\xi\xi} = \sigma_{xx}-\sigma_{yy}+2i\sigma_{xy}$. The result is

$$\tilde{\Phi}_{\text{pie}} = 2a(E_y\sigma_{zx}-E_x\sigma_{zy})+b[2E_y\sigma_{xy}-E_x(\sigma_{xx}-\sigma_{yy})], \tag{2}$$

where $a = 2i\gamma_{\eta,z\xi}$ and $b = 2\gamma_{\xi,\xi\xi}$ are real constants. The relations between the components $\gamma_{i,kl}$ in the co-ordinates x, y, z are, as we see from (2),†

$$\gamma_{y,zx} = -\gamma_{x,zy} \equiv a, \qquad \gamma_{y,xy} = -\gamma_{x,xx} = \gamma_{x,yy} \equiv b.$$

The class $\boldsymbol{D}_{3h}$ is obtained from the class $\boldsymbol{D}_3$ by adding a plane of symmetry (the xy-plane) perpendicular to the axis of the third order. Reflection in this plane changes the sign of z, and so $\gamma_{\eta,z\xi} = 0$, so that only the term with the coefficient b remains in (2).

The class $\boldsymbol{C}_{3h}$ has an axis of the third order and a plane of symmetry perpendicular to it. Reflection in this plane changes the sign of z, and so all components $\gamma_{i,kl}$ whose suffixes contain z an odd number of times must be zero. Taking into account also the restrictions derived above which are imposed by the third-order axis of symmetry, we find that only the two components $\gamma_{\eta,\eta\eta}$ and $\gamma_{\xi,\xi\xi}$ are not zero. These quantities must be complex conjugates in order that $\tilde{\Phi}$ should be real. Putting $2\gamma_{\eta,\eta\eta} = a+ib$, $2\gamma_{\xi,\xi\xi} = a-ib$, we find

$$\tilde{\Phi}_{\text{pie}} = a[2E_y\sigma_{xy}-E_x(\sigma_{xx}-\sigma_{yy})]+b[2E_x\sigma_{xy}+E_y(\sigma_{xx}-\sigma_{yy})]. \tag{3}$$

Either a or b can be made to vanish by a suitable choice of the x and y axes.

PROBLEM 2. The same as Problem 1, but for the crystal classes which allow pyroelectricity.

---

† In non-orthogonal co-ordinates such as ξ, η, z the covariant and contravariant components of tensors must be distinguished. This should have been done in returning to the original co-ordinates x, y, z. We avoid this necessity, however, by obtaining the required relations between the components $\gamma_{i,kl}$ in the co-ordinates x, y, z directly from the form of the scalar combination (2).

SOLUTION. Let the z-axis be the axis of symmetry of the second, third, fourth or sixth order, or in the class C_s be perpendicular to the plane of symmetry. In the classes C_{nv} the xz-plane is a plane of symmetry. By a suitable choice of axes three more components can be made zero in the class C_1, and one component in the classes C_s, C_n.

We give below for each class all the components $\gamma_{i,kl}$ which are not zero.

Class C_1: all $\gamma_{i,kl}$.

C_s: all those in which the suffix z appears twice or not at all.

C_{2v}: $\gamma_{z,xx}$, $\gamma_{z,yy}$, $\gamma_{z,zz}$, $\gamma_{x,xz}$, $\gamma_{y,yz}$.

C_2: the same, together with $\gamma_{x,yz}$, $\gamma_{y,xz}$, $\gamma_{z,xy}$.

C_{4v}: $\gamma_{z,xx} = \gamma_{z,yy}$, $\gamma_{z,zz}$, $\gamma_{x,xz} = \gamma_{y,yz}$.

C_4: the same, together with $\gamma_{x,yz} = -\gamma_{y,xz}$.

C_{3v}: $\gamma_{z,zz}$, $\gamma_{x,xz} = \gamma_{y,yz}$, $\gamma_{x,xx} = -\gamma_{x,yy} = -\gamma_{y,xy}$, $\gamma_{z,xx} = \gamma_{z,yy}$.

C_3: the same, together with $\gamma_{x,yz} = -\gamma_{y,zx}$, $\gamma_{y,xx} = -\gamma_{y,yy} = \gamma_{x,xy}$.

C_{6v}: $\gamma_{z,zz}$, $\gamma_{x,xz} = \gamma_{y,yz}$, $\gamma_{z,xx} = \gamma_{z,yy}$.

C_6: the same, together with $\gamma_{x,yz} = -\gamma_{y,zx}$.

PROBLEM 3. Determine Young's modulus (the coefficient of proportionality between the extending stress and the relative extension) for a flat slab of a non-pyroelectric piezoelectric in the following cases: (a) where the slab is stretched by the plates of a short-circuited condenser, (b) where it is stretched by those of an uncharged condenser, (c) where it is stretched parallel to its plane with no external field.

SOLUTION. (a) In this case the field **E** inside the slab is zero. The only non-zero component of the tensor σ_{ik} is the extending stress σ_{zz} (the z-axis being perpendicular to the slab).† From (17.8) we have $u_{zz} = \mu_{zzzz}\sigma_{zz}$, whence Young's modulus is $E = 1/\mu_{zzzz}$.

(b) In this case we have in the slab $E_x = E_y = 0$, $D_z = 0$. From (17.6) and (17.8) we have $D_z = \epsilon_{zz}E_z + 4\pi\gamma_{z,zz}\sigma_{zz} = 0$, $u_{zz} = \mu_{zzzz}\sigma_{zz} + \gamma_{z,zz}E_z$. Eliminating E_z, we obtain $1/E = \mu_{zzzz} - 4\pi\gamma_{z,zz}{}^2/\epsilon_{zz}$.

(c) In this case also, $E_x = E_y = 0$, $D_z = 0$, but the extension is along the x-axis, say. Here we have $D_z = \epsilon_{zz}E_z + 4\pi\gamma_{z,xx}\sigma_{xx} = 0$, $u_{xx} = \mu_{xxxx}\sigma_{xx} + \gamma_{z,xx}E_z$. Eliminating E_z, we obtain $1/E = \mu_{xxxx} - 4\pi\gamma_{z,xx}{}^2/\epsilon_{zz}$.

PROBLEM 4. Obtain an equation for the velocity of sound in a piezoelectric medium.

SOLUTION. In this problem it is more convenient to use u_{ik} as the independent variables, instead of σ_{ik}. We write $\tilde{F}$ in the form

$$\tilde{F} = F_0 + \tfrac{1}{2}\lambda_{iklm}\, u_{ik}\, u_{lm} - \frac{1}{8\pi}\epsilon_{ik}\, E_i E_k - \frac{1}{4\pi} E_i D_{0i} + \beta_{i,kl}\, E_i u_{kl},$$

where

$$\beta_{i,kl} = -\lambda_{klk'l'}\, \gamma_{i,k'l'},$$

whence

$$\sigma_{ik} = \partial\tilde{F}/\partial u_{ik} = \lambda_{iklm}u_{lm} + \beta_{l,ik}E_l.$$

The equations of motion from the theory of elasticity are

$$\ddot{u}_i = \frac{\partial\sigma_{ik}}{\partial x_k} = \lambda_{iklm}\frac{\partial u_{lm}}{\partial x_k} + \beta_{l,ik}\frac{\partial E_l}{\partial x_k},$$

where **u** is the displacement vector, related to u_{ik} by

$$u_{ik} = \frac{1}{2}\left(\frac{\partial u_i}{\partial x_k} + \frac{\partial u_k}{\partial x_i}\right).$$

The equation div **D** $= 0$ gives

$$\epsilon_{ik}\frac{\partial E_k}{\partial x_i} - 4\pi\beta_{i,kl}\frac{\partial u_{kl}}{\partial x_i} = 0,$$

and the field can be expressed in terms of the field potential: $E_i = -\partial\phi/\partial x_i$, which takes into account the equation **curl E** $= 0$.

† It is not assumed to coincide with any particular crystallographic direction.

In a plane sound wave, **u** and ϕ are proportional to $\exp[i(\mathbf{k}\cdot\mathbf{r}-\omega t)]$, and we find from the above equations that

$$\omega^2 u_i = \lambda_{iklm}k_k k_l u_m - \beta_{l,ik}k_k k_l \phi,$$

$$\epsilon_{ik}k_i k_k \phi + 4\pi\beta_{i,kl}k_i k_k u_l = 0.$$

Eliminating ϕ, we can write the condition of compatibility of the resulting equations for u_i as

$$|\omega^2\delta_{ik} - \lambda_{iklm}k_l k_m - 4\pi(\beta_{l,mi}k_l k_m)(\beta_{p,qk}k_p k_q)/\epsilon_{rs}k_r k_s| = 0.$$

For any given direction of the wave vector **k**, this equation determines three phase velocities of sound ω/k, which are in general different. A characteristic property of a piezoelectric medium is the involved relation between the velocity and direction of the wave.

§18. Thermodynamic inequalities

According to the formulae of §10, the total free energy can be written as the integral

$$\mathscr{F} = \int F(T, \rho, \mathbf{D})\,dV, \tag{18.1}$$

taken over all space. We shall suppose that the function $\mathbf{D}(x, y, z)$ which appears in the integrand satisfies only the equation

$$\operatorname{div}\mathbf{D} = 0 \tag{18.2}$$

inside a dielectric and the condition

$$\oint \mathbf{D}\cdot d\mathbf{f} = 4\pi e \tag{18.3}$$

on the surface of a conductor which carries a given charge. These equations establish the relation between the field and its sources. Otherwise we regard the function $\mathbf{D}(x, y, z)$ as arbitrary, and in particular we do not require it to satisfy the second field equation $\mathbf{curl}\,\mathbf{E} = 0$ (where $\mathbf{E} = 4\pi\partial F/\partial\mathbf{D}$) or the boundary condition ϕ = constant on the surface of a conductor. We shall show that these equations can then be obtained from the condition that the integral (18.1) is a minimum with respect to changes in the function $\mathbf{D}(x, y, z)$ which satisfy equations (18.2) and (18.3). It should be emphasised that the possibility of this derivation is not *a priori* evident, since the field distributions which come into consideration in determining the minimum of the integral (18.1) do not necessarily correspond to physically possible states (because they do not satisfy all the field equations), whereas, in the thermodynamic condition that the free energy is a minimum, only the various physically possible states are considered.

The problem of finding the minimum of the integral (18.1) with the subsidiary conditions (18.2) and (18.3) is solved by Lagrange's method of multipliers. We multiply the variation of the condition (18.2) by some as yet undetermined function $-\phi/4\pi$ of the co-ordinates, and that of the condition (18.3) by some undetermined constant $\phi_0/4\pi$, and then equate to zero the sum of variations

$$\int \delta F \, \mathrm{d}V - \frac{1}{4\pi}\int \phi \, \mathrm{div}\, \delta\mathbf{D} \, \mathrm{d}V + \frac{\phi_0}{4\pi}\oint \delta\mathbf{D}\cdot \mathrm{d}\mathbf{f} = 0.$$

In the first term we write†

$$\delta F = (\partial F/\partial \mathbf{D})_{T,\rho}\cdot\delta\mathbf{D} = \mathbf{E}\cdot\delta\mathbf{D}/4\pi,$$

and the second can be integrated by parts: $\int \phi \, \mathrm{div}\, \delta\mathbf{D}\, \mathrm{d}V = \oint \phi\delta\mathbf{D}\cdot\mathrm{d}\mathbf{f} - \int \delta\mathbf{D}\cdot\mathbf{grad}\,\phi\, \mathrm{d}V$. The result is

$$\int (\mathbf{E} + \mathbf{grad}\,\phi)\cdot\delta\mathbf{D}\,\mathrm{d}V + \oint (\phi_0 - \phi)\delta\mathbf{D}\cdot\mathrm{d}\mathbf{f} = 0.$$

Hence we conclude that, throughout the volume, we must have $\mathbf{E} = -\mathbf{grad}\,\phi$ (and so $\mathbf{curl}\,\mathbf{E} = 0$), and on the surface of a conductor $\phi = \phi_0 =$ constant. These are the correct equations for the field, and the Lagrangian multiplier ϕ is its potential.

Similarly it can be shown that the equations for the electric induction are obtained from the condition that the integral $\tilde{\mathscr{F}} = \int \tilde{F}\,(T, \rho, \mathbf{E})\mathrm{d}V$ is a minimum, in which the function $\mathbf{E}(x, y, z)$ is varied with the subsidiary conditions $\mathbf{E} = -\mathbf{grad}\,\phi$ and $\phi =$ constant on the surface of a conductor. For

$$\delta\tilde{\mathscr{F}} = \int (\partial\tilde{F}/\partial\mathbf{E})\cdot\delta\mathbf{E}\,\mathrm{d}V = \int \mathbf{D}\cdot\mathbf{grad}\,\delta\phi\,\mathrm{d}V/4\pi$$

$$= \oint \delta\phi\,\mathbf{D}\cdot\mathrm{d}\mathbf{f}/4\pi - \int \delta\phi\,\mathrm{div}\,\mathbf{D}\,\mathrm{d}V/4\pi = 0.$$

The first integral is zero because $\delta\phi = 0$ on the surface, and from the second we find the required equation $\mathrm{div}\,\mathbf{D} = 0$, since $\delta\phi$ is arbitrary in the volume.

If the body is not in an external electric field (in particular, if there are no charged conductors), it may be possible to formulate the condition of thermodynamic equilibrium as the condition that the total free energy (18.1) has an absolute (unconditional) minimum. This amounts to the condition that the free energy density F is a minimum as a function of the independent variable $\mathbf{D}$: $\partial F/\partial\mathbf{D} = \mathbf{E}/4\pi = 0$, i.e. the field must be zero in all space. If it is possible to find a distribution of the induction such that $\mathrm{div}\,\mathbf{D} = 0$, this state will correspond to thermodynamic equilibrium.‡

---

† The free energy is the minimum for a given temperature. The variation is with respect to two independent quantities $\mathbf{D}$ and ρ. Here we are interested only in the result of varying with respect to $\mathbf{D}$. The variation of the integral (18.1) with respect to density (with the subsidiary condition of constant mass, i.e. constant $\int \rho\,\mathrm{d}V$) gives one of the usual conditions of thermal equilibrium, namely the constancy of the chemical potential ζ.

‡ Here we are considering bodies in which $\mathbf{D}$ need not be zero even if $\mathbf{E} = 0$ (see §19). Otherwise we have simply the trivial result $\mathbf{E} = \mathbf{D} = 0$ in all space.

Equating to zero the first variation of the free energy, we find necessary but not sufficient conditions for this energy to be a minimum. The calculation of the sufficient conditions requires a discussion of the second variation. These conditions take the form of certain inequalities (called *thermodynamic inequalities*) and are the conditions which ensure the stability of the state of the body.†

When there is a linear relation between **D** and **E**, the situation is much simplified, and the thermodynamic inequality of interest here (relating to the dielectric properties of the body) becomes evident. The total free energy is $F_0 + \int (D^2/8\pi\epsilon)\mathrm{d}V$. It is clear that this can have a minimum only if $\epsilon > 0$, since otherwise the integral could be made to take any large negative value by making D^2 large enough. Thus in this case nothing new is learnt, since we know already that the dielectric permeability must in fact be not only positive but greater than unity (see §14).

In the general case of an arbitrary relation between **D** and **E**, however, it is necessary to consider the second variation of the integral (18.1), and to vary simultaneously both **D** and ρ (leaving only the temperature constant). In an isotropic body, $F(T, \rho, \mathbf{D})$ depends only on the magnitude of the vector **D**, but its three components vary independently. We take the direction of the vector **D** before variation as the z-axis. Then the change in the magnitude of **D** is given in terms of the changes in its components, as far as the second-order terms, by $\delta D = \delta D_z + (\delta D_x)^2/2D + (\delta D_y)^2/2D$. The first and second variations of the integral (18.1) are both contained in the expression

$$\int \left\{ \frac{\partial F}{\partial D}\delta D + \frac{\partial F}{\partial \rho}\delta\rho + \frac{1}{2}\frac{\partial^2 F}{\partial D^2}(\delta D)^2 + \frac{\partial^2 F}{\partial D \partial \rho}\delta D \delta\rho + \frac{1}{2}\frac{\partial^2 F}{\partial \rho^2}(\delta\rho)^2 \right\} \mathrm{d}V.$$

Substituting δD and collecting the second-order terms, we find the second variation

$$\int \frac{1}{2D}\frac{\partial F}{\partial D}[(\delta D_x)^2 + (\delta D_y)^2]\,\mathrm{d}V + \\ + \int \left\{ \frac{1}{2}\frac{\partial^2 F}{\partial D^2}(\delta D_z)^2 + \frac{\partial^2 F}{\partial D \partial \rho}\delta D_z \delta\rho + \frac{1}{2}\frac{\partial^2 F}{\partial \rho^2}(\delta\rho)^2 \right\} \mathrm{d}V. \tag{18.4}$$

These two terms are independent. The first is positive if $(1/D)\partial F/\partial D > 0$. But $\partial F/\partial \mathbf{D} = \mathbf{E}/4\pi$, so that the derivative $\partial F/\partial D$ is positive or negative according as the vectors **D** and **E** are in the same or opposite directions. Thus these vectors must be in the same direction.

The conditions for the second term in (18.4) to be positive are

$$\partial^2 F/\partial \rho^2 > 0, \tag{18.5}$$

$$\frac{\partial^2 F}{\partial \rho^2}\frac{\partial^2 F}{\partial D^2} - \left(\frac{\partial^2 F}{\partial \rho \partial D}\right)^2 > 0. \tag{18.6}$$

† See *Statistical Physics*, §21.

Since $\partial F/\partial\rho = \zeta$, $\partial F/\partial D = E/4\pi$, the first of these gives

$$(\partial\zeta/\partial\rho)_{D,T} > 0, \tag{18.7}$$

and the second can be rewritten as a Jacobian:

$$\frac{\partial(\partial F/\partial D, \partial F/\partial\rho)}{\partial(D,\rho)} = \frac{1}{4\pi}\frac{\partial(E,\zeta)}{\partial(D,\rho)} > 0.$$

Changing from the variables D, ρ to D, ζ, we have

$$\frac{\partial(E,\zeta)}{\partial(D,\rho)} = \frac{\partial(E,\zeta)}{\partial(D,\zeta)}\frac{\partial(D,\zeta)}{\partial(D,\rho)} = \left(\frac{\partial E}{\partial D}\right)_\zeta \left(\frac{\partial\zeta}{\partial\rho}\right)_D > 0;$$

by (18.7), this gives

$$(\partial E/\partial D)_{\zeta,T} > 0. \tag{18.8}$$

Thus we have derived the required thermodynamic inequalities. In the absence of a field, the inequality (18.7) becomes the usual condition that the isothermal compressibility is positive: $(\partial p/\partial\rho)_T > 0$.† The inequality (18.8) gives $\epsilon > 0$, since when $E \to 0$ the induction $D \to \epsilon E$.

Of the two inequalities (18.5), (18.6) the latter is the stronger; it may be violated while the first is not, whereas the reverse is impossible. The equation

$$\frac{\partial^2 F}{\partial\rho^2}\frac{\partial^2 F}{\partial D^2} - \left(\frac{\partial^2 F}{\partial\rho\partial D}\right)^2 = \frac{\partial(E,\zeta)}{\partial(D,\rho)} = 0$$

corresponds to what is called the *critical state*.‡ This condition is more conveniently written in a different form by multiplying it by the non-zero factor $\partial(D,\rho)/\partial(E,\rho)$:

$$\partial(E,\zeta)/\partial(E,\rho) = (\partial\zeta/\partial\rho)_{E,T} = 0. \tag{18.9}$$

The determination of further conditions for the stability of the critical state of matter requires a study of the third and fourth variations; we shall not pause to do this, but simply give the results:

$$(\partial^2\zeta/\partial\rho^2)_{E,T} = 0, \tag{18.10}$$

$$(\partial^3\zeta/\partial\rho^3)_{E,T} > 0, \tag{18.11}$$

in analogy with those found in the absence of an electric field.

---

† It should be recalled that, in the absence of a field, ζ is the thermodynamic potential of unit mass and, by the ordinary thermodynamic relations, its differential

$$d\zeta = dp/\rho - (S/\rho)\,dT,$$

so that $(\partial\zeta/\partial\rho)_T = (1/\rho)(\partial p/\partial\rho)_T$. In the above derivation the second of the ordinary thermodynamic inequalities (that the specific heat is positive) is ignored.

‡ See *Statistical Physics*, §80.

PROBLEM

Determine the displacement of the critical point of a dielectric substance in an electric field.

SOLUTION. Substituting in (18.9) the expression for ζ from (10.18), we find $(\partial\zeta_0/\partial\rho)_T - (E^2/8\pi)(\partial^2\epsilon/\partial\rho^2)_T = 0$. For the chemical potential when $E = 0$ we have $(\partial\zeta_0/\partial\rho)_T = (1/\rho)(\partial p/\partial\rho)_T$ (see the penultimate footnote to this section), where $p = p(\rho, T)$ is the equation of state in the absence of the field. Thus $(\partial p/\partial\rho)_T = (\rho E^2/8\pi)(\partial^2\epsilon/\partial\rho^2)_T$. When there is no field, the critical point is given by the equation $(\partial p/\partial\rho)_T = 0$, and if it is stable we must also have $(\partial^2 p/\partial\rho^2)_T = 0$. Hence

$$\left(\frac{\partial p}{\partial\rho}\right)_T \cong \frac{\partial^2 p}{\partial\rho^2}\Delta\rho + \frac{\partial^2 p}{\partial\rho\,\partial T}\Delta T \cong \frac{\partial^2 p}{\partial\rho\,\partial T}\Delta T,$$

where ΔT and $\Delta\rho$ are the displacements of the critical temperature and density (assumed to be of the same order of smallness, which is confirmed by the result). The temperature displacement is therefore

$$\Delta T = \frac{\rho E^2}{8\pi}\left(\frac{\partial^2\epsilon}{\partial\rho^2}\right)_T \Big/ \frac{\partial^2 p}{\partial\rho\,\partial T}.$$

The displacement of the critical pressure is $\Delta p = (\partial p/\partial T)_\rho \Delta T$. To determine the displacement $\Delta\rho$, equation (18.10) must be used in a similar manner.

§19. Ferroelectrics

The various crystalline modifications of a given substance may include some which are pyroelectric and some which are not. If the change from one to the other takes place by means of a second-order phase transition, then near the transition point the substance has a number of unusual properties which distinguish it from ordinary pyroelectrics; these are called *ferroelectric* properties.

In an ordinary pyroelectric crystal, a change in the direction of the spontaneous polarisation involves a considerable reconstruction of the crystal lattice. Even if the final result of this reconstruction is energetically favourable, its realisation may still be impossible because it would require the surmounting of very high energy barriers.

In a ferroelectric body, however, the situation is quite different because, near a second-order phase transition point (a Curie point), the arrangement of the atoms in the crystal lattice of the pyroelectric phase is only comparatively little different from the arrangement in the non-pyroelectric lattice (and so the spontaneous polarisation also is small). For this reason the change in direction of the spontaneous polarisation here requires only a relatively slight reconstruction of the lattice (a slight displacement of the atoms) and can occur quite easily.

The actual nature of the ferroelectric properties of a body depends on its crystal symmetry. The direction of the spontaneous polarisation of the pyroelectric phase (which we shall call the *ferroelectric axis*) is determined by the structure of the non-pyroelectric phase beyond the Curie point. In some cases it is uniquely determined, in the sense that the ferroelectric axis can lie in only one, crystallographically determinate, direction; the direction of the spontaneous polarisation is then determined apart from sign, since in the non-pyroelectric phase the two opposite directions parallel to the ferroelectric axis must be entirely equivalent (otherwise this form of the crystal would also be pyroelectric). In other cases, the symmetry of the non-pyroelectric phase may be such as to allow spontaneous polarisation in any of several crystallographically equivalent directions.†

The quantitative theory of ferroelectricity can be developed in terms of the general theory of second-order phase transitions;‡ this has been done by V. L. GINZBURG (1945).

The basis of the following considerations will be the thermodynamic stability of states. From this point of view the transition is characterised by the fact that, on one side of it, a state with $\mathbf{D} = 0$ can be stable, but on the other side any such state is unstable, and so there must be a non-zero induction even when the field $\mathbf{E}$ is zero. For definiteness, we shall suppose below that the pyroelectric phase ($\mathbf{D} \neq 0$) corresponds to temperatures $T < \Theta$ (where Θ is the transition point), but it should be emphasised that this disposition of the phases, though the more usual, is not obligatory, and the opposite case is also found in Nature.

Since our prime interest is in the dielectric properties of the substance, we shall first suppose that there are no internal stresses in the body. To determine the stability conditions, we can start from the condition that the total thermodynamic potential of the body is a minimum (for a given temperature and zero stresses). As we have seen in §18, this reduces to the condition that the second variation of the thermodynamic potential per unit volume Φ should be positive. For a state in which the induction is almost zero, the second variation of Φ is simply $\Phi - \Phi_0 = (1/8\pi)\epsilon^{-1}{}_{ik}D_iD_k$.

If we take the co-ordinate axes to be the principal axes of the tensor ϵ_{ik}, then

$$\Phi - \Phi_0 = \frac{1}{8\pi}\left(\frac{1}{\epsilon^{(x)}}D_x^2 + \frac{1}{\epsilon^{(y)}}D_y^2 + \frac{1}{\epsilon^{(z)}}D_z^2\right). \qquad (19.1)$$

The state with $\mathbf{D} = 0$ satisfies the stability conditions (i.e. can correspond to a minimum of Φ) so long as all three coefficients $1/\epsilon^{(i)}$ are positive. Hence the pyroelectric phase can be formed only when one of these three coefficients changes sign. The point at which the second-order phase transition takes place is determined by the vanishing of that coefficient.

---

† An instance of the first type is sodium potassium tartrate, whose non-pyroelectric phase has a rhombic symmetry. The ferroelectric axis appears in it (at the Curie point) in a completely definite crystallographic direction (one of the second-order axes), and the lattice becomes monoclinic.

An instance of the second type is barium titanate. Its non-pyroelectric modification has a cubic lattice, and any of the three cubic axes may become the ferroelectric axis. After the spontaneous polarisation has appeared at the Curie point, these three directions, of course, are no longer equivalent. The ferroelectric axis becomes the only fourth-order axis, and the lattice becomes tetragonal.

‡ See *Statistical Physics*, Chapter XIV. The discussion here following, however, is not based on the usual formulation.

The ferroelectric axis is then the one for which $1/\epsilon^{(i)}$ is zero. Here various cases can arise, depending on the symmetry of the non-pyroelectric phase. If this symmetry is such that $\epsilon^{(x)} \neq \epsilon^{(y)} \neq \epsilon^{(z)}$, only one of the coefficients in (19.1) is zero, and the position of the ferroelectric axis is uniquely defined. If $\epsilon^{(x)} = \epsilon^{(y)} = \epsilon^{(z)}$ (for which the symmetry must be cubic), all three coefficients vanish simultaneously, and the ferroelectric axis may be in one of several directions (see below). Finally, if the symmetry is such that $\epsilon^{(x)} = \epsilon^{(y)} \neq \epsilon^{(z)}$, either one or two of the coefficients in (19.1) will vanish at the transition point.

Let us consider first the case where the position of the ferroelectric axis, which we take as the z-axis, is uniquely determined. The dielectric properties of the crystal in the x and y directions then exhibit no anomalies, and to investigate the properties in the z-direction we need consider only those terms in the thermodynamic potential which contain D_z.

The expression (19.1) represents the leading terms in an expansion of Φ in powers of D. Since $1/\epsilon^{(z)}$ is small near the transition point, it is necessary to take into account the next term beyond the quadratic in the expansion in powers of D_z. There can be no odd powers in this expansion, since they would change sign with D_z (and so Φ would change), whereas here the two directions along the z-axis are equivalent. The next term after the quadratic therefore involves D_z^4:

$$\Phi = \Phi_0 + \frac{1}{8\pi\epsilon^{(z)}} D_z^2 + \frac{B}{16\pi} D_z^4.$$

In order that the state with $D_z = 0$ should be stable at the point $T = \Theta$, it is clearly necessary that the coefficient B should be positive there, and so positive in the neighbourhood of that point. Near the transition point, $1/\epsilon^{(z)}$ can be expanded in powers of the difference $T-\Theta$; the first term in the expansion is of the form $\alpha(T-\Theta)$, the coefficient α being positive (so that $1/\epsilon^{(z)} > 0$ for $T > \Theta$). Thus

$$\epsilon^{(z)} = 1/\alpha(T-\Theta), \tag{19.2}$$

and the thermodynamic potential is

$$\Phi = \Phi_0 + \frac{\alpha(T-\Theta)}{8\pi} D_z^2 + \frac{B}{16\pi} D_z^4. \tag{19.3}$$

These formulae are sufficient for the calculation of all ferroelectric properties of present interest near the transition point. First of all, from the formula $E_z = 4\pi \partial\Phi/\partial D_z$ we have

$$E_z = \alpha(T-\Theta)D_z + BD_z^3. \tag{19.4}$$

This is the fundamental relation giving the field as a function of the induction in a ferroelectric.

For $T > \Theta$ (in the non-pyroelectric phase), D_z is zero for $E_z = 0$. As E_z increases (for a given value of $T-\Theta$), the induction at first increases linearly

($D_z = E_z/\alpha(T-\Theta)$), but for sufficiently large values of E_z we have $D_z = (E_z/B)^{\frac{1}{3}}$. The proportionality coefficient $\epsilon^{(z)}$ in the linear relation is the dielectric constant of the non-pyroelectric phase. For $T \to \Theta$ it increases without limit in inverse proportion to $T-\Theta$, but the linear relation then ceases to be valid.

For $T < \Theta$ (in the pyroelectric phase), the value $D_z = 0$ cannot correspond to a stable state. For $E_z = 0$ the induction has a non-zero value, which by (19.4) is

$$D_z = D_{z0} = \pm\sqrt{[\alpha(\Theta-T)/B]}. \qquad (19.5)$$

Thus the spontaneous polarisation $P_{z0} = D_{z0}/4\pi$ of a ferroelectric decreases towards the Curie point as $\sqrt{(\Theta-T)}$.

The "dielectric constant" of the pyroelectric phase may be defined as the value of the derivative dD_z/dE_z for $E_z = 0$. From (19.4) we have $1 = [-\alpha(\Theta-T)+3BD_z^2]dD_z/dE_z$; substituting (19.5), we have $dD_z/dE_z = 1/2\alpha(\Theta-T)$ for $E_z = 0$. For sufficiently small E_z, the relation between D_z and E_z becomes

$$D_z - D_{z0} = E_z/2\alpha(\Theta-T). \qquad (19.6)$$

A comparison of (19.2) and (19.6) shows that the "dielectric constant" of the pyroelectric phase is half its value in the non-pyroelectric phase at the same distance from the Curie point.

Differentiating Φ (19.3) with respect to temperature, we can find the entropy $S = -(\partial\Phi/\partial T)_D = S_0 - \alpha D_z^2/8\pi$. Here the fourth-order term can be omitted, since the quadratic term is not zero. In the pyroelectric phase with $E_z = 0$ we have also $D_z = 0$, so that $S = S_0$. For the pyroelectric phase, substituting D_z from (19.5), we find $S = S_0 - \alpha^2(\Theta-T)/8\pi B$. Hence the specific heat of this phase at the transition point itself is

$$C_p = T\partial S/\partial T = C_{p0} + \alpha^2\Theta/8\pi B, \qquad (19.7)$$

where C_{p0} is the specific heat of the non-pyroelectric phase at this point. Thus, if the transition of the ferroelectric from one phase to the other takes place with $E_z = 0$, it is accompanied by a sudden change in the specific heat, as happens in ordinary second-order phase transitions. Moreover, $C_p > C_{p0}$, i.e. the specific heat increases when pyroelectricity appears.

Let us further investigate equation (19.4) in the pyroelectric phase (i.e. for $T < \Theta$). Figure 13 shows the approximate curve of the function $D_z(E_z)$ given by this equation. We see, first of all, that the part CC' of the curve (shown dashed in Fig. 13) does not correspond to stable states which can occur in Nature: on CC' we have $\partial E_z/\partial D_z = 4\pi\partial^2\Phi/\partial D_z^2 < 0$, whereas the condition that the second variation of the thermodynamic potential should be positive requires this derivative to be positive also. The ordinates of the points C and C' are given by the equation $\partial E_z/\partial D_z = 0$, and so we conclude that the possible values of $|D_z|$ in the pyroelectric phase are bounded below by the condition

$$D_z^2 > \alpha(\Theta-T)/3B. \qquad (19.8)$$

If we consider states of a ferroelectric with given values of E_z, there is still an ambiguity in the value of D_z, in the range of abscissae between C and C', and the question arises of the physical significance of the two values. We shall assume the ferroelectric to be a homogeneous flat slab, with the ferroelectric axis perpendicular to it, lying between the plates of a condenser, which are maintained at given potentials, i.e. which set up a given uniform field $E = E_z$.

For given potentials on the conductors, the condition of stability requires that the thermodynamic potential $\tilde{\Phi} = \Phi - \mathbf{E}\cdot\mathbf{D}/4\pi$ be a minimum. In particular, for $\mathbf{E} = 0$ there are two states in which D_z has opposite signs (the points A and A' in Fig. 13) but $\tilde{\Phi}$ $(= \Phi)$ is the same. These two states, therefore, are equally stable, i.e. they are two "phases" which can exist in contact.

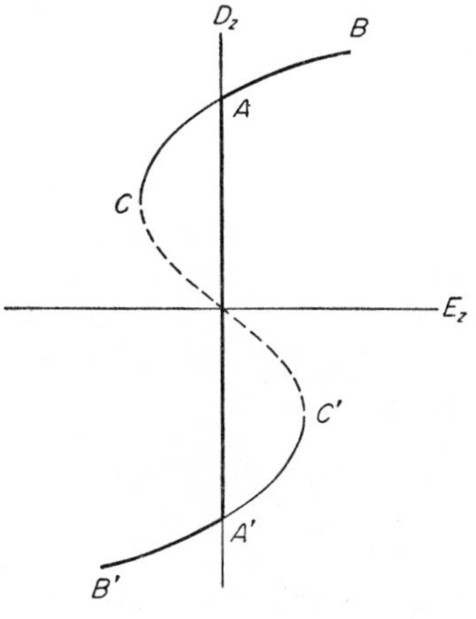

FIG. 13

Hence it is clear that the portions AC and $A'C'$ of the curve correspond to states which are metastable but not absolutely stable. It is easy to see directly that the values of $\tilde{\Phi}$ on AC and $A'C'$ are in fact greater than its values of $A'B'$ and AB for the same value of E_z. The ordinates of A and A' are given by formula (19.5). Thus the range of metastability is

$$\alpha(\Theta - T)/3B < D_z^2 < \alpha(\Theta - T)/B. \tag{19.9}$$

The existence of these two "phases" with $\mathbf{E} = 0$ is very important, since it means that a ferroelectric body can be divided into a number of separate regions or *domains* in which the polarisation is in opposite directions. On the surfaces separating these domains, the normal component of $\mathbf{D}$ and the tangential component of $\mathbf{E}$ must be continuous. The latter condition is satisfied identically, because $\mathbf{E} = 0$. From the former condition it follows that the domain boundaries must be parallel to the z-axis.

The actual shapes and sizes of the domains are determined by the condition that the total thermodynamic potential of the body should be a minimum. This subject has not yet been much studied for ferroelectrics.

If we are not interested in the details of the structure, and consider portions of the body which are large compared with the domains, we can use the induction $\bar{\mathbf{D}}$ averaged over such portions. Its component $\bar{D}_z$ can evidently take values in the range between the ordinates of A and A' in Fig. 13, i.e.

$$-\sqrt{[\alpha(\Theta - T)/B]} < \bar{D}_z < \sqrt{[\alpha(\Theta - T)/B]}. \tag{19.10}$$

In other words, if D_z in Fig. 13 is taken as the induction averaged in this way, the vertical segment AA' corresponds to the region of domain structure, and the thick curve $BAA'B'$ gives all stable states of the body.

A ferroelectric must, in particular, have a domain structure if it is not in an external electric field. For we have seen in §18 that the conditions of thermodynamic equilibrium in the absence of an external field reduce to the condition that Φ should be an absolute minimum as a function of $\mathbf{D}$, with $\mathbf{E} = 0$ everywhere.†

Let us consider ferroelectrics which belong (in the non-pyroelectric phase) to the cubic system. The cubic symmetry requires that $\epsilon^{(x)} = \epsilon^{(y)} = \epsilon^{(z)} \equiv \epsilon$, and admits two independent fourth-order invariants formed from the components of the vector $\mathbf{D}$, which may, for example, be taken as $D_x^4 + D_y^4 + D_z^4$ and $D_x^2 D_y^2 + D_x^2 D_z^2 + D_y^2 D_z^2$. Hence the expansion of the thermodynamic potential is of the form

$$\Phi = \Phi_0 + \alpha(T - \Theta)(D_x^2 + D_y^2 + D_z^2)/8\pi + B(D_x^4 + D_y^4 + D_z^4)/16\pi + \\ + C(D_x^2 D_y^2 + D_x^2 D_z^2 + D_y^2 D_z^2)/8\pi, \tag{19.11}$$

where we have again put $1/\epsilon = \alpha(T - \Theta)$, and α, B, C are constants.

It must be borne in mind, however, that cubic symmetry may admit also a third-order invariant $D_x D_y D_z$; this happens for the crystal classes $\boldsymbol{T}$ and $\boldsymbol{T_d}$, where there is no centre of symmetry. In these cases the state with $\mathbf{D} = 0$ certainly cannot satisfy the stability condition (that Φ should be a minimum), and so no Curie point can exist. Hence the ferroelectric transition can occur only in crystals of the classes $\boldsymbol{O}$, $\boldsymbol{T_h}$, $\boldsymbol{O_h}$ of the cubic system, in accordance with the expansion (19.11).

The sum of the fourth-order terms in (19.11) must be essentially positive. Hence we must have

$$B > 0, \qquad C > -B. \tag{19.12}$$

The spontaneous polarisation of a ferroelectric in the absence of an external field is determined, as already stated, by the condition that Φ should

† It should be emphasised that here we are speaking of complete thermodynamic equilibrium. This exists in ferroelectrics, but cannot do so in ordinary pyroelectrics, because of the difficulty, already mentioned, of reorienting the polarisation and so forming domains in them.

be a minimum as a function of **D**. In particular, since the second-order term in (19.11) is independent of the direction of **D**, the direction of the spontaneous polarisation is determined by the condition that the fourth-order terms are a minimum for a given absolute value of **D**. Two cases are possible. If $C > B$, the minimum of Φ corresponds to **D** being along any one of the axes x, y, z, i.e. along any of the three edges of the cube (the crystallographic directions [001], [010], [100]). If, however, $C < B$, Φ takes its minimum values when **D** is along any one of the spatial diagonals of the cube (the crystallographic directions [111], [$\bar{1}$11], etc.) i.e. when $D_x^2 = D_y^2 = D_z^2 = \frac{1}{3}D^2$. In the former case the spontaneously polarised pyroelectric phase of the ferroelectric has tetragonal symmetry, and in the latter case it has rhombohedral symmetry.

Let us consider in more detail, for example, the first case ($C > B$), and take as the z-axis the direction of the spontaneous polarisation below the Curie point. The magnitude of this polarisation is determined by the minimum of the expression $-\alpha(\Theta - T)D^2/8\pi + BD^4/16\pi$, whence

$$D_0^2 = \alpha(\Theta - T)/B. \tag{19.13}$$

The "dielectric permeability" in the z-direction below the Curie point is, of course, different from that in the x and y directions. If the field **E** is small, then D_x, D_y and $D_z - D_0$ are also small. Differentiating the expression (19.11) gives

$$E_z = 4\pi\partial\Phi/\partial D_z = -\alpha(\Theta - T)D_z + BD_z^3 \cong 2BD_0^2(D_z - D_0),$$
$$E_x = 4\pi\partial\Phi/\partial D_x \cong [CD_0^2 - \alpha(\Theta - T)]D_x, \quad \text{whence}$$
$$\left.\begin{aligned} D_z - D_0 &= E_z/2\alpha(\Theta - T),\\ D_x &= BE_x/\alpha(\Theta - T)(C - B).\end{aligned}\right\} \tag{19.14}$$

Above the Curie point the dielectric permeability of a cubic ferroelectric is the same in all directions:

$$\epsilon = 1/\alpha(T - \Theta). \tag{19.15}$$

Finally, let us briefly consider the elastic properties of ferroelectrics. According to its crystallographic class, the non-pyroelectric phase of a ferroelectric may or may not be piezoelectric.† Here particular interest attaches to piezoelectric crystals whose symmetry admits a piezoelectric relation between the deformation and the polarisation in the direction of the ferroelectric axis. These include the classes $\boldsymbol{D}_2$, $\boldsymbol{D}_{2d}$ and $\boldsymbol{S}_4$; in each case the induction D_z in the direction of the ferroelectric axis appears in the piezoelectric part of the thermodynamic potential through a term‡ $-\lambda_{z,xy}D_z\sigma_{xy}$.

---

† The non-pyroelectric phase of a ferroelectric is piezoelectric if it belongs to one of eight out of the ten classes listed at the end of §17: $\boldsymbol{D}_2$, $\boldsymbol{D}_4$, $\boldsymbol{D}_{2d}$, $\boldsymbol{S}_4$, $\boldsymbol{D}_3$, $\boldsymbol{D}_6$, $\boldsymbol{C}_{3h}$, $\boldsymbol{D}_{3h}$.

‡ Since we are using here the potential Φ, and not $\tilde{\Phi}$ as in §17, the piezoelectric tensor $\lambda_{i,kl}$ is not the same as the tensor $\gamma_{i,kl}$ introduced previously, but their symmetry properties are, of course, identical.

In the elastic energy of these crystals, the component σ_{xy} appears in a term $-\mu_{xyxy}\sigma_{xy}^2$. Thus the thermodynamic potential near the Curie point is

$$\Phi = \Phi_0+\alpha(T-T_0)D_z^2/8\pi+BD_z^4/16\pi-\lambda D_z\sigma_{xy}-\mu\sigma_{xy}^2, \quad (19.16)$$

where for brevity we have put $\lambda_{z,xy} = \lambda$, $\mu_{xyxy} = \mu$. The terms involving the other components are of no interest, since they lead to no anomaly of the piezoelectric properties near the Curie point.

Differentiating Φ with respect to D_z and σ_{xy}, we find the field E_z and the deformation u_{xy}:†

$$E_z = 4\pi\partial\Phi/\partial D_z = \alpha(T-T_0)D_z+BD_z^3-4\pi\lambda\sigma_{xy}, \quad (19.17)$$

$$u_{xy} = \tfrac{1}{2}\lambda D_z+\mu\sigma_{xy}. \quad (19.18)$$

In the non-pyroelectric region when $\mathbf{E}$ is small we can neglect the term in D_z^3 in (19.17):

$$E_z = \alpha(T-T_0)D_z-4\pi\lambda\sigma_{xy}.$$

Substituting D_z from (19.18), we find

$$u_{xy} = \frac{\lambda}{2\alpha(T-T_0)}E_z+\left[\mu+\frac{2\pi\lambda^2}{\alpha(T-T_0)}\right]\sigma_{xy}.$$

The coefficient of σ_{xy} in this formula represents the modulus of elasticity for deformations in which the field E_z is kept constant, while μ in formula (19.18) is the modulus for constant induction D_z. Hence we can write

$$\mu^{(E)} = \mu^{(D)}+2\pi\lambda^2/\alpha(T-T_0), \quad (19.19)$$

where the superscripts indicate the nature of the deformation. We see that the two coefficients behave entirely differently near the Curie point: whereas $\mu^{(D)}$ is a finite constant, $\mu^{(E)}$ increases without limit as the Curie point is approached.

In the pyroelectric region, formula (19.18) shows that the spontaneous polarisation results in a certain deformation of the body. If there are no internal stresses and the field $\mathbf{E}$ is zero, the deformation u_{xy} is proportional to D_{z0}, i.e. by (19.5) it is proportional to $\sqrt{(\Theta-T)}$.

If the symmetry (cubic, for example) of the non-pyroelectric phase of a ferroelectric does not admit a piezoelectric effect linear in $\mathbf{D}$, then the first non-vanishing terms in an expansion of the thermodynamic potential in powers of σ_{ik} and $\mathbf{D}$ are quadratic in the components D_i, i.e. they are of the form

$$-\gamma_{iklm}D_iD_k\sigma_{lm}, \quad (19.20)$$

where γ_{iklm} is a tensor of rank four, symmetrical with respect to the pairs of suffixes i, k and l, m.

† See the first footnote to §17, Problem 1, concerning differentiation with respect to the components u_{ik}.

Doubt might be cast on the legitimacy of using the expression (19.20) in the thermodynamic potential, on the grounds that, as stated in §17, this potential can be used only when quadratic effects are neglected. However, the ferroelectrics form an exception because, near the Curie point, the field **E** is small† compared with the induction **D**. The use of the thermodynamic potential involves the neglect of quantities of the order of EDu_{ik} (or, what is the same thing, $ED\sigma_{ik}$), whereas the expression (19.20) is of the order of $D^2\sigma_{ik}$.

† This is seen, for instance, from formula (19.4): the first term on the right-hand side contains the small quantity $T - \Theta$, and the second term is of the third order in **D**.

CHAPTER III

CONSTANT CURRENT

§20. The current density and the conductivity

LET US now consider the steady motion of charges in conductors, i.e. constant electric currents. We shall denote by $\mathbf{j}$ the mean charge flux density or *electric current density*.† In a constant current, the spatial distribution of $\mathbf{j}$ is independent of time, and satisfies the equation

$$\operatorname{div} \mathbf{j} = 0, \tag{20.1}$$

which states that the mean total charge in any volume of the conductor remains constant.

The electric field in the conductor in which a constant current flows is also constant, and therefore satisfies the equation

$$\mathbf{curl\,E} = 0, \tag{20.2}$$

i.e. it is a potential field.

Equations (20.1) and (20.2) must be supplemented by an equation relating $\mathbf{j}$ and $\mathbf{E}$. This equation depends on the properties of the conductor, but in the great majority of cases it may be supposed linear (*Ohm's law*). If the conductor is homogeneous and isotropic, the linear relation is a simple proportionality:

$$\mathbf{j} = \sigma \mathbf{E}. \tag{20.3}$$

The coefficient σ depends on the nature and state of the conductor; it is called the *electrical conductivity*.

In a homogeneous conductor, $\sigma =$ constant and, substituting (20.3) in (20.1), we have $\operatorname{div} \mathbf{E} = 0$. In this case the electric field potential satisfies Laplace's equation: $\triangle\phi = 0$.

At a boundary between two conducting media, the normal component of the current density must, of course, be continuous. Moreover, by the general condition that the tangential field component is continuous (which follows from $\mathbf{curl\,E} = 0$; cf. (1.7) and (6.9)), the ratio $\mathbf{j}_t/\sigma$ must be continuous. Thus the boundary conditions on the current density are

$$j_{n1} = j_{n2}, \qquad \mathbf{j}_{t1}/\sigma_1 = \mathbf{j}_{1t2}/\sigma_2, \tag{20.4}$$

or, as conditions on the field,

$$\sigma_1 E_{n1} = \sigma_2 E_{n2}, \qquad \mathbf{E}_{t1} = \mathbf{E}_{t2}. \tag{20.5}$$

† In this chapter we ignore the magnetic field due to the current, and therefore the reaction of that field on the current. If this effect is to be taken into account, the definition of the current density must be refined, which we do in §29.

At a boundary between a conductor and a non-conductor we have simply $j_n = 0$, or $E_n = 0$.†

An electric field in the presence of a current does mechanical work on the current-carrying particles moving in the conductor; the work done per unit time and volume is evidently equal to the scalar product $\mathbf{j}\cdot\mathbf{E}$. This work is dissipated into heat in the conductor. Thus the quantity of heat evolved per unit time and volume in a homogeneous conductor is

$$\mathbf{j}\cdot\mathbf{E} = \sigma E^2 = j^2/\sigma. \tag{20.6}$$

This is *Joule's law*.‡

The evolution of heat results in an increase in the entropy of the body. When an amount of heat $\mathrm{d}Q = \mathbf{j}\cdot\mathbf{E}\,\mathrm{d}V$ is evolved, the entropy of the volume element $\mathrm{d}V$ increases by $\mathrm{d}Q/T$. The rate of change of the total entropy of the body is therefore

$$\mathrm{d}\mathscr{S}/\mathrm{d}t = \int (\mathbf{j}\cdot\mathbf{E}/T)\,\mathrm{d}V. \tag{20.7}$$

Since the entropy must increase, this derivative must be positive. Putting $\mathbf{j} = \sigma\mathbf{E}$, we see that the conductivity σ must therefore be positive.

In an anisotropic body (a single crystal), the directions of the vectors $\mathbf{j}$ and $\mathbf{E}$ are in general different, and the linear relation between them is

$$j_i = \sigma_{ik}E_k, \tag{20.8}$$

where the quantities σ_{ik} form a tensor of rank two, the *conductivity tensor*, which is symmetrical (see below).

The following remark should be made here. The symmetry of the crystal would admit also an inhomogeneous term in the linear relation between $\mathbf{j}$ and $\mathbf{E}$, giving $j_i = \sigma_{ik}E_k + j_i^{(0)}$, with $\mathbf{j}^{(0)}$ a constant vector. The presence of this term would mean that the conductor was "pyroelectric", there being a non-zero field in it when $\mathbf{j} = 0$. In reality, however, this is impossible, because the entropy must increase: the term $\mathbf{j}^{(0)}\cdot\mathbf{E}$ in the integrand in (20.7) could take either sign, and so $\mathrm{d}\mathscr{S}/\mathrm{d}t$ could not be invariably positive.

Just as, for an isotropic medium, $\mathrm{d}\mathscr{S}/\mathrm{d}t > 0$ leads to $\sigma > 0$, so for an anisotropic medium this condition means that the principal values of the tensor σ_{ik} must be positive.

The dependence of the number of independent components of the tensor σ_{ik} on the symmetry of the crystal is the same as for any symmetrical tensor of rank two (see §13): for biaxial crystals, all three principal values are different, for uniaxial crystals two are equal, and for cubic crystals all three are

† It should be noticed that the equations $\mathbf{curl}\,\mathbf{E} = 0$, $\mathrm{div}\,(\sigma\mathbf{E}) = 0$ and the boundary conditions (20.5) thereon are formally identical with the equations for the electrostatic field in a dielectric, the only difference being that ϵ is replaced by σ. This enables us to solve problems of the current distribution in an infinite conductor if the solutions of the corresponding electrostatic problems are known. When the conductor is bounded by a non-conductor this analogy does not serve, because in electrostatics there is no medium for which $\epsilon = 0$.

‡ In Russian "Joule and Lenz's law".

equal, i.e. a cubic crystal behaves as an isotropic body as regards its conductivity.

The symmetry of the conductivity tensor

$$\sigma_{ik} = \sigma_{ki} \tag{20.9}$$

is a consequence of the *symmetry of the kinetic coefficients*. This general principle, due to L. ONSAGER, may be conveniently formulated, for use here and in §§25, 26, as follows.†

Let $x_1, x_2, \ldots$ be some quantities which characterise the state of the body at every point. We define also the quantities

$$X_a = -\partial S/\partial x_a, \tag{20.10}$$

where S is the entropy of unit volume of the body, and the derivative is taken at constant energy of the volume. In a state close to equilibrium, the quantities x_a are close to their equilibrium values, and the X_a are small. Processes will occur in the body which tend to bring it into equilibrium. The rates of change of the quantities x_a at each point are usually functions only of the values of the x_a (or X_a) at that point. Expanding these functions in powers of X_a and taking only the linear terms, we have

$$\partial x_a/\partial t = -\sum_b \gamma_{ab} X_b. \tag{20.11}$$

Then we can assert that the coefficients γ_{ab} (the *kinetic coefficients*) are symmetrical with respect to the suffixes a and b:

$$\gamma_{ab} = \gamma_{ba}. \tag{20.12}$$

In order to make practical use of this principle, it is necessary to choose the quantities x_a (or their derivatives $\dot{x}_a$) in some manner, and then to determine the X_a. This can usually be done very simply by means of the formula for the rate of change of the total entropy of the body

$$\frac{\mathrm{d}\mathscr{S}}{\mathrm{d}t} = -\int \sum_a X_a \frac{\partial x_a}{\partial t} \mathrm{d}V, \tag{20.13}$$

where the integration is extended over the whole volume of the body.

When a current flows in a conductor, $\mathrm{d}\mathscr{S}/\mathrm{d}t$ is given by (20.7). Comparing this with (20.13), we see that, if the components of the current density vector $\mathbf{j}$ are taken as the quantities $\dot{x}_a$, then the quantities X_a will be the components of the vector $-\mathbf{E}/T$. A comparison of formulae (20.8) and (20.11) shows that the kinetic coefficients in this case are the components of the conductivity tensor, multiplied by T. Thus the symmetry of this tensor follows immediately from the general relation (20.12).

† See *Statistical Physics*, §119, Pergamon Press, London, 1958; *Fluid Mechanics*, §58, Pergamon Press, London, 1959.

PROBLEMS

PROBLEM 1. A system of electrodes maintained at constant potentials ϕ_a is immersed in a conducting medium. A current J_a flows from each electrode. Determine the total amount of Joule heat evolved in the medium per unit time.

SOLUTION. The required amount of heat Q is given by the integral

$$Q = \int \mathbf{j}\cdot\mathbf{E}\,\mathrm{d}V = -\int \mathbf{j}\cdot\mathbf{grad}\,\phi\,\mathrm{d}V = -\int \mathrm{div}(\phi\mathbf{j})\,\mathrm{d}V,$$

taken over the volume of the medium. We transform this into a surface integral, using the fact that $j_n = 0$ at the outer boundary of the medium, while on the surfaces of the electrodes ϕ = constant = ϕ_a. The result is $Q = \Sigma\,\phi_a J_a$.

PROBLEM 2. Determine the potential distribution in a conducting sphere with a current J entering at a point O and leaving at the point O' diametrically opposite to O.

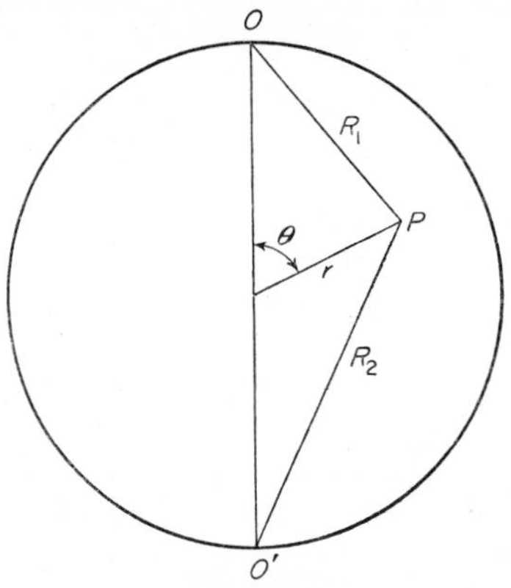

FIG. 14

SOLUTION. Near O and O' (Fig. 14) the potential must be of the forms $\phi = J/2\pi\sigma R_1$ and $\phi = -J/2\pi\sigma R_2$ respectively, R_1 and R_2 being the distances from O and O'. These functions satisfy Laplace's equation, and the integrals $-\sigma\int \mathbf{grad}\,\phi\cdot\mathbf{df}$ over infinitesimal hemispheres about O and O' are equal to $\pm J$. We seek the potential at an arbitrary point P in the sphere in the form

$$\phi = \frac{J}{2\pi\sigma}\left\{\frac{1}{R_1} - \frac{1}{R_2} + \psi\right\},$$

where ψ is a solution of Laplace's equation having no poles in or on the sphere. It is evident from symmetry that ψ, like ϕ, is a function of the spherical co-ordinates r and θ only.

On the surface of the sphere ($r = a$) we must have $\partial\phi/\partial r = 0$. Differentiating, we find the boundary condition on ψ:

$$\frac{\partial\psi}{\partial r} = \frac{1}{2a}\left(\frac{1}{R_1} - \frac{1}{R_2}\right) \text{ for } r = a.$$

If $f(r, \theta)$ is any solution of Laplace's equation, then the function

$$\int_0^r \frac{f(r, \theta)}{r}\,\mathrm{d}r$$

is also a solution.† Comparing this with the above boundary condition, we see that the

† This is easily seen either by direct calculation or from the fact that any solution $f(r, \theta)$ of Laplace's equation depending only on r and θ can be written $f = \Sigma c_n r^n P_n(\cos\theta)$, where the c_n are constants and the P_n are Legendre polynomials.

condition is met by the solution

$$\psi = \tfrac{1}{2}\int\limits_0^r \left(\frac{1}{R_1}-\frac{1}{R_2}\right)\frac{dr}{r}.$$

Substituting $R_{1,2} = \sqrt{(a^2+r^2\mp 2ar\cos\theta)}$ and effecting the integration, we have finally

$$\phi = \frac{J}{2\pi\sigma}\left\{\frac{1}{R_1}-\frac{1}{R_2}+\frac{1}{2a}\left(\sinh^{-1}\frac{a+r\cos\theta}{r\sin\theta}-\sinh^{-1}\frac{a-r\cos\theta}{r\sin\theta}\right)\right\}.$$

PROBLEM 3. Show that the current distribution in a conductor is such that the energy dissipated is a minimum.

SOLUTION. The minimum concerned is that of the intergal $\int \mathbf{j}\cdot\mathbf{E}\,dV = \int (j^2/\sigma)\,dV$, with the subsidiary condition $\operatorname{div}\mathbf{j} = 0$ (conservation of charge). Varying with respect to $\mathbf{j}$ the integral $\int[(j^2/\sigma)-2\phi\operatorname{div}\mathbf{j}]dV$, where 2ϕ is an undetermined Lagrangian multiplier, and equating the result to zero, we obtain the equation $\mathbf{j} = -\sigma\,\mathbf{grad}\,\phi$ or $\mathbf{curl}\,(\mathbf{j}/\sigma) = 0$, which is the same as (20.2) and (20.3).

§21. The Hall effect

If a conductor is in an external magnetic field $\mathbf{H}$, the relation between the current density and the electric field is again given by $j_1 = \sigma_{ik} E_k$, but the components of the conductivity tensor σ_{ik} are functions of $\mathbf{H}$ and, what is particularly important, they are no longer symmetrical with respect to the suffixes i and k. The symmetry of this tensor was proved in §20 from the symmetry of the kinetic coefficients. In a magnetic field, however, this principle must be formulated somewhat differently: when the suffixes are interchanged, the direction of the magnetic field must be reversed.† Hence we now have for the components $\sigma_{ik}(\mathbf{H})$ the relations

$$\sigma_{ik}(\mathbf{H}) = \sigma_{ki}(-\mathbf{H}). \tag{21.1}$$

The quantities $\sigma_{ik}(\mathbf{H})$ and $\sigma_{ki}(\mathbf{H})$ are not equal.

Like any tensor of rank two, σ_{ik} can be divided into symmetrical and antisymmetrical parts, which we denote by s_{ik} and a_{ik}:

$$\sigma_{ik} = s_{ik}+a_{ik}. \tag{21.2}$$

By definition

$$s_{ik}(\mathbf{H}) = s_{ki}(\mathbf{H}), \qquad a_{ik}(\mathbf{H}) = -a_{ki}(\mathbf{H}), \tag{21.3}$$

and from (21.1) it follows that

$$\begin{aligned} s_{ik}(\mathbf{H}) &= s_{ki}(-\mathbf{H}) = s_{ik}(-\mathbf{H}), \\ a_{ik}(\mathbf{H}) &= a_{ki}(-\mathbf{H}) = -a_{ik}(-\mathbf{H}). \end{aligned} \tag{21.4}$$

Thus the components of the tensor s_{ik} are even functions of the magnetic field, and those of a_{ik} are odd functions.

† See *Statistical Physics*, §119.

Any antisymmetrical tensor a_{ik} of rank two corresponds to some axial vector, whose components are

$$a_x = a_{yz}, \qquad a_y = -a_{xz}, \qquad a_z = a_{xy}. \tag{21.5}$$

In terms of this vector, the components of the product $a_{ik}E_k$ can be written as those of the vector product $\mathbf{E}\times\mathbf{a}$:

$$j_i = \sigma_{ik}E_k = s_{ik}E_k + (\mathbf{E}\times\mathbf{a})_i. \tag{21.6}$$

The Joule heat generated by the passage of the current is given by the product $\mathbf{j}\cdot\mathbf{E}$. Since the vectors $\mathbf{E}\times\mathbf{a}$ and $\mathbf{E}$ are perpendicular, their scalar product is zero identically, and so

$$\mathbf{j}\cdot\mathbf{E} = s_{ik}E_iE_k, \tag{21.7}$$

i.e. the Joule heat is determined (for a given field $\mathbf{E}$) only by the symmetrical part of the conductivity tensor.

The external magnetic field may usually be supposed weak, and the components of the conductivity tensor accordingly expanded in powers of that field. Since the function $\mathbf{a}(\mathbf{H})$ is odd, the expansion of this vector will involve only odd powers. The first terms are linear in the field, i.e. they are of the form

$$a_i = \alpha_{ik}H_k. \tag{21.8}$$

The vectors $\mathbf{a}$ and $\mathbf{H}$ are both axial, and the constants α_{ik} therefore form an ordinary (polar) tensor. The expansion of the even functions $s_{ik}(\mathbf{H})$ will involve only even powers. The first term is the conductivity $\sigma_{0,ik}$ in the absence of the field, and the next terms are quadratic in the field:

$$s_{ik} = \sigma_{0,ik} + \beta_{iklm}H_lH_m. \tag{21.9}$$

The tensor β_{iklm} is symmetrical with respect to i, k and l, m.

Thus the principal effect of the magnetic field is linear in the field and is given by the term $\mathbf{E}\times\mathbf{a}$; it is called the *Hall effect*. As we see, it gives rise to a current perpendicular to the electric field, whose magnitude is proportional to the magnetic field. It should be borne in mind, however, that, for an arbitrary anisotropic medium, the Hall current is not the only current perpendicular to $\mathbf{E}$; the current $s_{ik}E_k$ also has a component in such a direction.

The Hall effect may be differently regarded if we use the inverse formulae which express $\mathbf{E}$ in terms of the current density: $E_i = \sigma^{-1}{}_{ik}j_k$. The inverse tensor $\sigma^{-1}{}_{ik}$, like σ_{ik} itself, can be resolved into a symmetrical part ρ_{ik} and an antisymmetrical part which may be represented by an axial vector $\mathbf{b}$:

$$E_i = \rho_{ik}j_k + (\mathbf{j}\times\mathbf{b})_i. \tag{21.10}$$

The tensor ρ_{ik} and the vector $\mathbf{b}$ have the same properties as s_{ik} and $\mathbf{a}$. In particular, in weak magnetic fields the vector $\mathbf{b}$ is linear in the field. In formu-a (21.10) the Hall effect is represented by the term $\mathbf{j}\times\mathbf{b}$, i.e. by an electric field perpendicular to the current and proportional to the magnetic field and to the current **j**.

The above relations are much simplified if the conductor is isotropic. The vectors **a** and **b** must then be parallel to the magnetic field, by symmetry. The only non-zero components of the tensor ρ_{ik} are $\rho_{xx} = \rho_{yy}$ and ρ_{zz}, the field being in the z-direction. Denoting these two quantities by $\rho_\perp$ and $\rho_\parallel$ and taking the current to lie in the xz-plane, we have

$$E_x = \rho_\perp j_x, \qquad E_y = -bj_x, \qquad E_z = \rho_\parallel j_z. \tag{21.11}$$

Hence we see that, in an isotropic conductor, the Hall field is the only electric field which is perpendicular to both the current and the magnetic field.

In weak magnetic fields, the vectors **b** and **H** are related (in an isotropic body) by

$$\mathbf{b} = -R\mathbf{H} \tag{21.12}$$

simply. The constant R (called *Hall's constant*) may be either positive or negative. The form of the terms quadratic in **H** in the relation between **E** and **j**, which enter through the tensor ρ_{ik}, is easily seen from the fact that the only vectors linear in **j** and quadratic in **H** which can be constructed from **j** and **H** are $(\mathbf{j}\cdot\mathbf{H})\mathbf{H}$ and $H^2\mathbf{j}$. Hence the general form of the relation between **E** and **j** in an isotropic body, as far as the terms quadratic in **H**, is

$$\mathbf{E} = \rho_0\mathbf{j} + R\mathbf{H}\times\mathbf{j} + \beta_1 H^2\mathbf{j} + \beta_2(\mathbf{j}\cdot\mathbf{H})\mathbf{H}. \tag{21.13}$$

PROBLEM

Express the components of the inverse tensor $\sigma^{-1}{}_{ik}$ in terms of those of s_{ik} and **a**.

SOLUTION. The calculations are most simply effected by taking a system of co-ordinates in which the axes are the principal axes of the tensor s_{ik}; the form of the results in an arbitrary co-ordinate system can easily be deduced from their form in this particular case. The determinant $|\sigma|$ is

$$|\sigma| = \begin{vmatrix} s_{xx} & a_z & -a_y \\ -a_z & s_{yy} & a_x \\ a_y & -a_x & s_{zz} \end{vmatrix}$$
$$= s_{xx}s_{yy}s_{zz} + s_{xx}a_x^2 + s_{yy}a_y^2 + s_{zz}a_z^2.$$

In the general case we evidently have

$$|\sigma| = |s| + s_{ik}a_i a_k.$$

From the minors of this determinant we find the components of the inverse tensor:

$$\sigma^{-1}{}_{xx} = \rho_{xx} = (s_{yy}s_{zz} + a_x^2)/|\sigma|,$$
$$\sigma^{-1}{}_{xy} = \rho_{xy} + b_z = (a_x a_y - a_z s_{zz})/|\sigma|, \ \ldots .$$

The general expressions which give these for the particular system of co-ordinates chosen are

$$\rho_{ik} = \{s^{-1}{}_{ik}|s| + a_i a_k\}/|\sigma|, \qquad b_i = -s_{ik}a_k/|\sigma|.$$

This completes the solution.

§22. The contact potential

In order to remove a charged particle through the surface of a conductor, work must be done. The work required for a thermodynamically reversible removal of the particle is called the *work function*. This quantity is always positive; this follows immediately from the fact that a point charge is attracted to any neutral body, and therefore to any conductor (see §14). It will be more convenient to refer this work to unit (positive) charge; the sign of the work function W thus defined is the same as that of the charge on the particle removed.

The work function depends both on the nature of the conductor (and its thermodynamic state, i.e. its temperature and density) and on that of the charged particle. For example, the work function for a given metal is different for the removal of a conduction electron and for the removal of an ion from the surface. It must also be emphasised that the work function is characteristic of the surface of the conductor. It therefore depends, for instance, on the treatment of the surface and the "contamination" of it. If the conductor is a single crystal, then the work function is different for different faces.

To ascertain the physical nature of the dependence of the work function on the properties of the surface, let us establish its relation to the electric structure of the surface layer. If $\rho(x)$ is the charge density *not* averaged over physically infinitesimal segments of the x-axis (perpendicular to the layer), we can write Poisson's equation in that layer as $d^2\phi/dx^2 = -4\pi\rho$. Let the conductor occupy the region $x < 0$. Then a first integration gives

$$\frac{d\phi}{dx} = -4\pi \int_{-\infty}^{x} \rho \, dx,$$

and a second integration (by parts) gives

$$\phi - \phi(-\infty) = -4\pi x \int_{-\infty}^{x} \rho \, dx + 4\pi \int_{-\infty}^{x} x\rho \, dx.$$

For $x \to \infty$, the integral

$$\int_{-\infty}^{x} \rho \, dx$$

tends very rapidly to zero (since the surface of an uncharged conductor is electrically neutral). Hence

$$\phi(+\infty) - \phi(-\infty) = 4\pi \int_{-\infty}^{\infty} x\rho \, dx.$$

The integral on the right is the dipole moment of the charges near the surface of the body. These charges form a "double layer", in which charges of opposite sign are separated and the dipole moment is non-zero. The structure of the double layer, of course, depends on the properties of the surface (its crystallographic direction, contamination, etc.). The difference in the work function for different surfaces of a given conductor is determined by the difference in the dipole moments.

If two different conductors are placed in contact, an exchange of charged particles may occur between them. Charges pass from the body with the smaller work function to that with the greater until a potential difference between them is set up which prevents further movement of charge. This is called a *contact potential.*

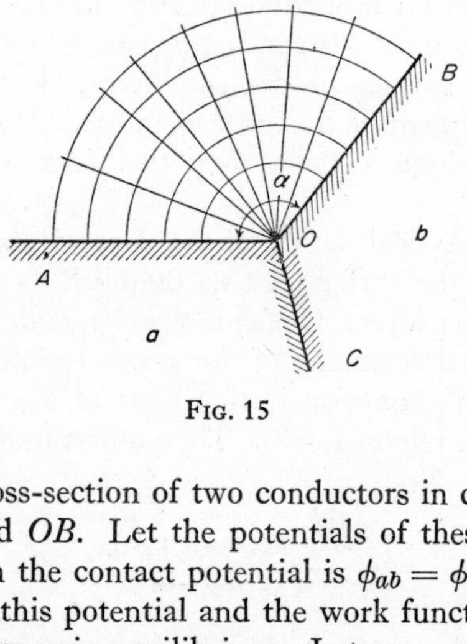

FIG. 15

Fig. 15 shows a cross-section of two conductors in contact (a and b) near their surfaces AO and OB. Let the potentials of these surfaces be ϕ_a and ϕ_b respectively. Then the contact potential is $\phi_{ab} = \phi_b - \phi_a$. The quantitative relation between this potential and the work functions is given by the condition of thermodynamic equilibrium. Let us consider the work which must be done on a particle of charge e to remove it from the conductor a through the surface AO, transfer it to the surface OB, and finally carry it into the conductor b. In a state of thermodynamic equilibrium, this work must be zero.† The work done on the particle in the three stages mentioned is eW_a, $e(\phi_b - \phi_a)$, and $-eW_b$ respectively. Putting the sum of these equal to zero, we find the required relation:

$$\phi_{ab} = W_b - W_a. \tag{22.1}$$

Thus the contact potential of the neighbouring free surfaces of two conductors in contact is equal to the difference in their work functions.

The existence of the contact potential results in the appearance of an electric field in the space outside the conductors. It is easy to determine

† Of course, in reality a particle can pass from one conductor to another only through their surface of contact, and not through the space adjoining them, but the work done is independent of the path.

this field near the line of contact of the surfaces. In a small region near this line (the point O in Fig. 15), the surfaces may be regarded as plane. The field potential outside the conductors satisfies the equation

$$\triangle\phi \equiv \frac{1}{r}\frac{\partial}{\partial r}\left(r\frac{\partial\phi}{\partial r}\right) + \frac{1}{r^2}\frac{\partial^2\phi}{\partial\theta^2} = 0,$$

where r and θ are polar co-ordinates with origin at O; on AO and OB the potential takes given constant values. We are interested in the solution which contains the lowest power of r; this is the leading term in an expansion of the potential in powers of the small distance r. The solution concerned is $\phi = \text{constant} \times \theta$. Measuring the angle θ from AO and arbitrarily taking the potential on AO as zero, we have

$$\phi = \phi_{ab}\theta/\alpha, \tag{22.2}$$

where α is the angle AOB. Thus the equipotential lines in the plane of the diagram are straight lines diverging from O. The lines of force are arcs of circles centred at O. The field is

$$E = -\frac{1}{r}\frac{\partial\phi}{\partial\theta} = -\frac{\phi_{ab}}{\alpha}\frac{1}{r}; \tag{22.3}$$

it decreases inversely as the distance from O.

As has been said above, "contact" potentials also exist between the various faces of a single crystal of metal. Hence an electric field of the kind just described must exist near the edges of the crystal.†

If several metallic conductors (at equal temperatures) are connected together, the potential between the extreme conductors is, as we easily deduce from formula (22.1), simply the difference of their work functions, as it is for two conductors in direct contact. In particular, if the metal at each end is the same, the contact potential between the ends is zero. This is evident, however, because if there were a potential difference between two like conductors, a current would flow when they were connected, in contradiction to the second law of thermodynamics.

§23. The galvanic cell

The statement at the end of §22 ceases to be valid if the circuit includes conductors in which the current is carried by different means (e.g. metals and solutions of electrolytes). Because the work function of a conductor is different for different charged particles (electrons and ions), the total contact potential in the circuit is not zero even when the conductors at each end are similar. This total potential difference is called the *electromotive force* or *e.m.f.* in the circuit; it is just the potential difference between the two like conductors before the circuit is closed. When the circuit is closed, a current flows in it; this is the basis of the operation of what are called *galvanic cells*.

† In reality, all such fields are usually compensated by the field of ions from the atmosphere which "adhere" to the surface of the crystal.

The energy which maintains the current in the circuit is supplied by chemical transformations occurring in the cell.

When we go completely round any closed circuit the field potential must, of course, return to its original value, i.e. the total change in the potential must be zero. Let us consider, for example, a contour on the surface of the conductors. When we pass from one conductor to another, the potential has a discontinuity ϕ_{ab}. The potential drop across any conductor is RJ, where J is the total current flowing through it and R is its resistance. Hence the total change in the potential round the circuit is $\Sigma\phi_{ab}-\Sigma JR$. Putting this equal to zero and using the facts that J is the same at every point in the circuit and $\Sigma\phi_{ab}$ is the electromotive force $\mathscr{E}$, we find

$$J\Sigma R = \mathscr{E}, \tag{23.1}$$

so that the current in a circuit containing a galvanic cell is equal to the e.m.f. divided by the total resistance of all the conductors in the circuit (including, of course, the internal resistance of the cell itself).

Although the e.m.f. of a galvanic cell can be expressed as a sum of contact potentials, it is very important to note that it is in reality a thermodynamic quantity, determined entirely by the states of the conductors and independent of the properties of the surfaces separating them. This is clear, because $\mathscr{E}$ is just the work per unit charge which must be done on a charged particle when it is carried reversibly along the closed circuit.

To illustrate this, let us consider a galvanic cell consisting of two electrodes of metals A and B immersed in solutions of electrolytes AX and BX, X^- being any anion. Let ζ_A and ζ_B be the chemical potentials of the metals A and B, and ζ_{AX} and ζ_{BX} those of the electrolytes in solution.† If an elementary charge e is carried along the closed circuit, an ion A^+ passes into solution from the electrode A and an ion B^+ passes out of solution to the electrode B, the change in the charges on the electrodes being compensated by the passage of an electron from A to B through the external circuit. The result is that the electrode A loses one neutral atom, the electrode B gains one, and in the electrolyte solution one molecule of BX is replaced by one of AX. Since the work done in a reversible process (at constant temperature and pressure) is equal to the change in the thermodynamic potential of the system, we have

$$e\mathscr{E}_{AB} = (\zeta_B-\zeta_{BX})-(\zeta_A-\zeta_{AX}), \tag{23.2}$$

which expresses the e.m.f. of the cell in terms of the properties of the material of the electrodes and of the electrolyte solution.

From (23.2) we can also draw the following conclusion. If the solution contains three electrolytes AX, BX, CX and three metallic electrodes A, B, C, then the e.m.f.s between each pair of them are related by

$$\mathscr{E}_{AB}+\mathscr{E}_{BC} = \mathscr{E}_{AC}. \tag{23.3}$$

† In this section we use the ordinary chemical potentials, i.e. those defined with respect to one particle.

Using the general formulae of thermodynamics, we can relate the e.m.f. of a galvanic cell to the heat evolved when a current flows, which of course is actually an irreversible phenomenon. Let Q be the amount of heat generated (both in the cell itself and in the external circuit) when the unit charge passes along the circuit; Q is just the heat of the reaction which occurs in the cell when a current flows. By a well-known formula of thermodynamics,† it is related to the work $\mathscr{E}$ by

$$Q = -T^2 \frac{\partial}{\partial T}\left(\frac{\mathscr{E}}{T}\right). \tag{23.4}$$

The definition of the partial derivative with respect to temperature depends on the conditions under which the process occurs. For example, if the current flows at constant pressure (as usually happens), then the differentiation is effected at constant pressure.

§24. Electrocapillarity

The presence of charges on the boundary between two conducting media affects the surface tension there. This phenomenon is called *electrocapillarity*. In practice, the media concerned are both liquids; usually one is a liquid metal (mercury) and the other is a solution of an electrolyte.

Let ϕ_1, ϕ_2 be the potentials of the two conductors, and e_1, e_2 the charges at the surface of separation. These charges are equal in magnitude and opposite in sign, and thus form a double layer on the surface.

The differential of the potential $\tilde{\Phi}$ of a system of two conductors at given temperature and pressure is, taking into account the surface of separation,

$$\mathrm{d}\tilde{\Phi} = \alpha\,\mathrm{d}S - e_1\,\mathrm{d}\phi_1 - e_2\,\mathrm{d}\phi_2, \tag{24.1}$$

where the term $\alpha \mathrm{d}S$ is the work done in a reversible change $\mathrm{d}S$ in the area S of the surface of separation; α is the surface-tension coefficient.‡

The thermodynamic potential $\tilde{\Phi}$ in (24.1) may be replaced by its "surface part" $\tilde{\Phi}_s$, since the volume part is constant for given temperature and pressure, and is therefore of no interest here. Putting $e_1 = -e_2 \equiv e$ and the potential difference $\phi_1 - \phi_2 = \phi$, we can write (24.1) as

$$\mathrm{d}\tilde{\Phi}_s = \alpha\,\mathrm{d}S - e\,\mathrm{d}\phi. \tag{24.2}$$

Hence

$$(\partial\tilde{\Phi}_s/\partial S)_\phi = \alpha, \tag{24.3}$$

α being expressed as a function of ϕ. Integrating, we find that $\tilde{\Phi}_s = \alpha S$.

† See *Statistical Physics*, §89.

‡ See *Statistical Physics*, §139.

Substitution in (24.2) gives $d(\alpha S) = \alpha dS - ed\phi$, or $Sd\alpha = -ed\phi$, whence

$$\sigma = -(\partial\alpha/\partial\phi)_{p,T}, \tag{24.4}$$

where $\sigma = e/S$ is the charge per unit area of the surface. The relation (24.4), first derived by G. Lippmann and J. W. Gibbs, is the fundamental formula in the theory of electrocapillarity.

In a state of equilibrium, the thermodynamic potential $\tilde{\Phi}$ must be a minimum for given values of the electric potentials on the conductors. Regarding it as a function of the surface charges e, we can write the necessary conditions for a minimum as

$$\partial\tilde{\Phi}_s/\partial e = 0, \qquad \partial^2\tilde{\Phi}_s/\partial e^2 > 0, \tag{24.5}$$

where the derivatives are taken at constant area S. To calculate these, we express $\tilde{\Phi}_s$ in terms of the thermodynamic potential $\Phi_s = \Phi_s(e)$:

$$\tilde{\Phi}_s = \Phi_s(e) - e_1\phi_1 - e_2\phi_2 = \Phi_s(e) - e\phi. \tag{24.6}$$

The vanishing of the first derivative gives

$$\frac{\partial\tilde{\Phi}_s}{\partial e} = \frac{\partial\Phi_s}{\partial e} - \phi = 0,$$

and then the condition for the second derivative to be positive becomes

$$\frac{\partial^2\tilde{\Phi}_s}{\partial e^2} = \frac{\partial^2\Phi_s}{\partial e^2} = \frac{\partial\phi}{\partial e} = \frac{1}{S}\frac{\partial\phi}{\partial\sigma} > 0,$$

or

$$\partial\sigma/\partial\phi > 0. \tag{24.7}$$

This result was to be expected, since the double layer on the surface may be regarded as a condenser of capacity $\partial e/\partial\phi$.

Differentiating equation (24.4) with respect to ϕ and using (24.7), we find that

$$\partial^2\alpha/\partial\phi^2 < 0. \tag{24.8}$$

This means that the point where $\partial\alpha/\partial\phi = -\sigma = 0$ is a maximum of α as a function of ϕ.

§25. Thermoelectric phenomena

The condition that there should be no current in a metal is that there is thermodynamic equilibrium with respect to the conduction electrons. This means not only that the temperature must be constant throughout the body, but also that the sum $e\phi + \zeta_0$ should be constant, where ζ_0 is the chemical potential of the conduction electrons in the metal (for $\phi = 0$).† If the metal

† See *Statistical Physics*, §25. Here we take ζ to be the chemical potential defined in the usual manner, viz. per unit particle (electron).

is not homogeneous, ζ_0 is not constant throughout the body even if the temperature is constant. Hence the constancy of the electric potential ϕ in this case does not mean the absence of a current in the metal, although the field $\mathbf{E} = -\mathbf{grad}\,\phi$ is zero. This makes the ordinary definition of ϕ (as the average of the true potential) inconvenient, if we wish to take inhomogeneous conductors into consideration.

It is natural to redefine the potential as $\phi+\zeta_0/e$, and we shall write this henceforward as ϕ simply.† In a homogeneous metal, the change amounts to the adding of an unimportant constant to the potential. Accordingly, the "field" $\mathbf{E} = -\mathbf{grad}\,\phi$ (which we shall use henceforward) is the same as the true mean field only in a homogeneous metal, and in general the two differ by the gradient of some function of the state.

With this definition, the current and field are both zero in a state of thermodynamic equilibrium with respect to the conduction electrons, and the relation between them is $\mathbf{j} = \sigma\mathbf{E}$ (or $j_i = \sigma_{ik}E_k$) even if the metal is not homogeneous.

Let us now consider a non-uniformly heated metal, which cannot be in thermodynamic equilibrium (with respect to the electrons). Then the field $\mathbf{E}$ is not zero even if the current is zero. In general, when both the current density $\mathbf{j}$ and the temperature gradient $\mathbf{grad}\,T$ are not zero, the relation between these quantities and the field can be written

$$\mathbf{E} = \mathbf{j}/\sigma + \alpha\,\mathbf{grad}\,T. \tag{25.1}$$

Here σ is the ordinary conductivity, and α is another quantity which is an electrical characteristic of the metal. Here we suppose for simplicity that the substance is isotropic (or of cubic symmetry), and therefore write the proportionality coefficients as scalars. The linear relation between $\mathbf{E}$ and $\mathbf{grad}\,T$ is, of course, merely the first term of an expansion, but it is sufficient in view of the smallness of the temperature gradients occurring in practice.

The same formula (25.1), in the form

$$\mathbf{j} = \sigma(\mathbf{E}-\alpha\,\mathbf{grad}\,T), \tag{25.2}$$

shows that a current can flow in a non-uniformly heated metal even if the field $\mathbf{E}$ is zero.

As well as the electric current density $\mathbf{j}$, we can consider the energy flux density $\mathbf{q}$. First of all, this quantity contains an amount $\phi\mathbf{j}$ resulting simply from the fact that each charged particle (electron) carries with it an energy $e\phi$. The difference $\mathbf{q}-\phi\mathbf{j}$, however, does not depend on the potential, and can be generally written as a linear function of the gradients $\mathbf{grad}\,\phi = -\mathbf{E}$ and $\mathbf{grad}\,T$, similarly to formula (25.2) for the current density. We shall for the present write this as

$$\mathbf{q}-\phi\mathbf{j} = \beta\mathbf{E}-\gamma\,\mathbf{grad}\,T.$$

† This definition can also be formulated as follows: the new $e\phi$ is the change in the free energy when one electron is isothermally brought into the metal. In other words, $\phi = \partial F/\partial\rho$, where F is the free energy of the metal and ρ the charge on the conduction electrons per unit volume.

The symmetry of the kinetic coefficients gives a relation between the coefficient β and the coefficient α in (25.2). To derive this, we calculate the rate of change of the total entropy of the conductor. The amount of heat evolved per unit time and volume is $-\operatorname{div}\mathbf{q}$. Hence we can put

$$\frac{\mathrm{d}\mathscr{S}}{\mathrm{d}t} = -\int\frac{\operatorname{div}\mathbf{q}}{T}\mathrm{d}V.$$

Using the equation $\operatorname{div}\mathbf{j} = 0$, we have

$$\frac{\operatorname{div}\mathbf{q}}{T} = \frac{1}{T}\{\operatorname{div}(\mathbf{q}-\phi\mathbf{j})+\operatorname{div}\phi\mathbf{j}\} = \frac{1}{T}\operatorname{div}(\mathbf{q}-\phi\mathbf{j})-\frac{\mathbf{E}\cdot\mathbf{j}}{T}.$$

The first term is integrated by parts, giving

$$\frac{\mathrm{d}\mathscr{S}}{\mathrm{d}t} = \int\frac{\mathbf{E}\cdot\mathbf{j}}{T}\mathrm{d}V-\int\frac{(\mathbf{q}-\phi\mathbf{j})\cdot\mathbf{grad}\,T}{T^2}\mathrm{d}V. \tag{25.3}$$

This formula shows that, if we take as the quantities $\partial x_a/\partial t$ (see §20) the components of the vectors $\mathbf{j}$ and $\mathbf{q}-\phi\mathbf{j}$, then the corresponding quantities X_a are the components of the vectors $-\mathbf{E}/T$ and $\mathbf{grad}\,T/T^2$. Accordingly in the relations

$$\mathbf{j} = \sigma T\frac{\mathbf{E}}{T}-\sigma\alpha T^2\frac{\mathbf{grad}\,T}{T^2},$$

$$\mathbf{q}-\phi\mathbf{j} = \beta T\frac{\mathbf{E}}{T}-\gamma T^2\frac{\mathbf{grad}\,T}{T^2},$$

the coefficients $\sigma\alpha T^2$ and βT must be equal. Thus $\beta = \sigma\alpha T$, so that $\mathbf{q}-\phi\mathbf{j} = \sigma\alpha T\mathbf{E}-\gamma\,\mathbf{grad}\,T$. Finally, expressing $\mathbf{E}$ in terms of $\mathbf{j}$ and $\mathbf{grad}\,T$ by (25.1), we have the result

$$\mathbf{q} = (\phi+\alpha T)\mathbf{j}-\kappa\,\mathbf{grad}\,T, \tag{25.4}$$

where $\kappa = \gamma - T\alpha^2\sigma$ is simply the ordinary thermal conductivity, which gives the heat flux in the absence of an electric current.

It should be pointed out that the condition that $\mathrm{d}\mathscr{S}/\mathrm{d}t$ should be positive places no new restriction on the thermoelectric coefficients. Substituting (25.1) and (25.4) in (25.3), we obtain

$$\frac{\mathrm{d}\mathscr{S}}{\mathrm{d}t} = \int\left(\frac{j^2}{\sigma T}+\frac{\kappa(\mathbf{grad}\,T)^2}{T^2}\right)\mathrm{d}V > 0, \tag{25.5}$$

whence we find only that the coefficients of thermal and electrical conductivity must be positive.

In the above formulae it was tacitly assumed that an inhomogeneity of pressure (or density) at constant temperature cannot cause a field (or current) to appear in the conductor, and consequently no term in $\mathbf{grad}\,p$ was included in (25.2) or (25.4). The existence of such terms would, in fact, contradict the law of the increase of entropy: the integrand in (25.5) would then contain terms in the products $\mathbf{j}\cdot\mathbf{grad}\,p$ and $\mathbf{grad}\,T\cdot\mathbf{grad}\,p$, which could be of either sign, and so the integral could not be necessarily positive.

The relations (25.1) and (25.4) indicate various thermoelectric effects. Let us consider the amount of heat $-\operatorname{div}\mathbf{q}$ evolved per unit time and volume in the conductor. Taking the divergence of (25.4), we have

$$\begin{aligned} Q &= -\operatorname{div}\mathbf{q} \\ &= \operatorname{div}(\kappa\,\mathbf{grad}\,T)+\mathbf{E}\cdot\mathbf{j}+\mathbf{j}\cdot\mathbf{grad}\,(\alpha T), \end{aligned}$$

or, substituting (25.1),

$$Q = \operatorname{div}(\kappa\,\mathbf{grad}\,T)+\frac{j^2}{\sigma}-T\mathbf{j}\cdot\mathbf{grad}\,\alpha. \tag{25.6}$$

The first term on the right pertains to ordinary thermal conduction, and the second term, proportional to the square of the current, is the Joule heat. The term of interest here is the third, which gives the thermoelectric effects.

Let us assume the conductor to be homogeneous. Then the change in α is due only to the temperature gradient, and $\mathbf{grad}\,\alpha = (\mathrm{d}\alpha/\mathrm{d}T)\,\mathbf{grad}\,T$; if, as usually happens, the pressure is constant through the body, $\mathrm{d}\alpha/\mathrm{d}T$ must be taken as $(\partial\alpha/\partial T)_p$. Thus the amount of heat evolved (called the *Thomson effect*) is

$$\rho\mathbf{j}\cdot\mathbf{grad}\,T, \quad \text{where } \rho = -T\,\mathrm{d}\alpha/\mathrm{d}T. \tag{25.7}$$

The coefficient ρ is called the *Thomson coefficient*. It should be noticed that this effect is proportional to the first power of the current, and not to the second power like the Joule heat. It therefore changes sign when the current is reversed. The coefficient ρ may be either positive or negative. If $\rho > 0$, the Thomson heat is positive (i.e. heat is emitted) when the current flows in the direction of increasing temperature, and heat is absorbed when it flows in the opposite direction; if $\rho < 0$ the reverse is true.

Another effect, called the *Peltier effect*, occurs when a current passes through a junction of two different metals. At the surface of contact, the temperature, the potential and the normal components of the current density and energy flux density are all continuous. Denoting by the suffixes 1 and 2 the values of quantities for the two metals and equating the normal components of $\mathbf{q}$ (25.4) on the two sides, we have, since ϕ, T and j_x are continuous,

$$[-\kappa\partial T/\partial x]_1^2 = -j_x T(\alpha_2-\alpha_1),$$

the x-axis being taken along the normal to the surface. If the positive direction of this axis is from metal 1 to metal 2, then the expression on the left-hand side of this equation is the amount of heat taken from the surface per unit time and area by thermal conduction. This heat loss is balanced by the evolution at the junction of an amount of heat given by the right-hand side of the equation. Thus the amount of heat generated per unit time and area is

$$j\Pi_{12}, \quad \text{where } \Pi_{12} = -T(\alpha_2-\alpha_1). \tag{25.8}$$

The quantity Π_{12} is called the *Peltier coefficient.* Like the Thomson effect, the Peltier effect is proportional to the first power of the current, and changes sign when the direction of the current is reversed. The Peltier coefficient is additive: $\Pi_{13} = \Pi_{12} + \Pi_{23}$, where the suffixes 1, 2, 3 refer to three different metals.

A comparison of formulae (25.7) and (25.8) shows that the Thomson and Peltier coefficients are related by

$$\rho_2 - \rho_1 = T\frac{\mathrm{d}}{\mathrm{d}T}\left(\frac{\Pi_{12}}{T}\right). \tag{25.9}$$

Next, let us consider an open circuit containing two junctions, the two end conductors being of the same metal (1 in Fig. 16). We suppose that the junctions b and c are at different temperatures T_1 and T_2, while the temperature at each end (a and d) is the same. Then there is a potential difference called a *thermoelectromotive force*, which we denote by $\mathscr{E}_T$, between the ends.

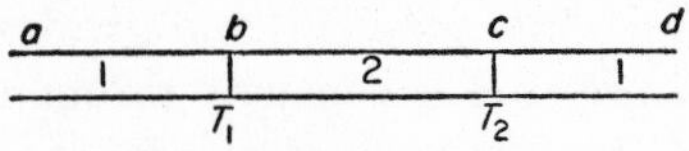

FIG. 16

To calculate this force, we put in (25.1) $\mathbf{j} = 0$ and integrate the field $\mathbf{E} = \alpha\, \mathbf{grad}\, T$ along the circuit (taken to be the x-axis):

$$\mathscr{E}_T = \int_a^d \alpha \frac{\mathrm{d}T}{\mathrm{d}x}\mathrm{d}x = \int_a^d \alpha\, \mathrm{d}T.$$

The integrations from a to b and from c to d are over temperatures from T_2 to T_1 in metal 1, and that from b to c is over temperatures from T_1 to T_2 in metal 2. Thus

$$\mathscr{E}_T = \int_{T_1}^{T_2} (\alpha_2 - \alpha_1)\,\mathrm{d}T. \tag{25.10}$$

Comparing this with (25.8), we see that the thermo-e.m.f. is related to the Peltier coefficient by

$$\mathscr{E}_T = -\int_{T_1}^{T_2} \frac{\Pi_{12}}{T}\mathrm{d}T. \tag{25.11}$$

Formulae (25.9) and (25.11) are called *Thomson's relations.*

To conclude this section, we shall give the formulae for the current and heat flux in an anisotropic conductor. These are derived from the symmetry of the kinetic coefficients in exactly the same way as formulae (25.1) and (25.4), and the results are

$$\begin{aligned} E_i &= \sigma^{-1}{}_{ik}j_k + \alpha_{ik}\partial T/\partial x_k, \\ q_i - \phi j_i &= T\alpha_{ki}j_k - \kappa_{ik}\partial T/\partial x_k. \end{aligned} \tag{25.12}$$

Here $\sigma^{-1}{}_{ik}$ is the tensor inverse to the conductivity tensor σ_{ik}, and the tensors σ_{ik} and κ_{ik} are symmetrical. The thermoelectric tensor α_{ik}, however, is in general not symmetrical.

PROBLEM

Find the relations between the coefficients of the various thermogalvanomagnetic effects, i.e., those which occur when a current flows in the simultaneous presence of an electric field, a magnetic field, and a temperature gradient.

SOLUTION. The discussion is entirely similar to that given above for thermoelectric effects. It is conveniently carried out in tensor form, so as to be applicable to both isotropic and anisotropic conductors. We write the electric current density $\mathbf{j}$ and the heat flux $\mathbf{q}$ as

$$\begin{aligned} j_i &= a_{ik}\frac{E_k}{T} + b_{ik}\frac{\partial}{\partial x_k}\left(\frac{1}{T}\right), \\ q_i - \phi j_i &= c_{ik}\frac{E_k}{T} + d_{ik}\frac{\partial}{\partial x_k}\left(\frac{1}{T}\right), \end{aligned} \tag{1}$$

where all the coefficients are functions of the magnetic field. The symmetry of the kinetic coefficients gives

$$\begin{aligned} a_{ik}(\mathbf{H}) &= a_{ki}(-\mathbf{H}), \qquad d_{ik}(\mathbf{H}) = d_{ki}(-\mathbf{H}), \\ b_{ik}(\mathbf{H}) &= c_{ki}(-\mathbf{H}). \end{aligned} \tag{2}$$

Expressing $\mathbf{E}$ and $\mathbf{q} - \phi\mathbf{j}$ in terms of $\mathbf{j}$ and $\mathbf{grad}\, T$ from (1), we have

$$\begin{aligned} E_i &= \sigma^{-1}{}_{ik}j_k + \alpha_{ik}\,\partial T/\partial x_k, \\ q_i - \phi j_i &= \beta_{ik}j_k - \kappa_{ik}\,\partial T/\partial x_k, \end{aligned} \tag{3}$$

where the tensors σ^{-1}, α, β, κ are certain functions of the tensors a, b, c, d, and have the following symmetry properties resulting from (2):

$$\begin{aligned} \sigma^{-1}{}_{ik}(\mathbf{H}) &= \sigma^{-1}{}_{ki}(-\mathbf{H}), \\ \kappa_{ik}(\mathbf{H}) &= \kappa_{ki}(-\mathbf{H}), \qquad \beta_{ik}(\mathbf{H}) = T\alpha_{ki}(-\mathbf{H}). \end{aligned} \tag{4}$$

These are the required relations in their most general form. They generalise those found in §25 for the case where there is no magnetic field and in §21 for the case where there is no temperature gradient.

For an isotropic conductor in a weak magnetic field we have, as far as the first-order terms in $\mathbf{H}$,

$$\mathbf{E} = \mathbf{j}/\sigma + \alpha\,\mathbf{grad}\,T + R\mathbf{H}\times\mathbf{j} + N\mathbf{H}\times\mathbf{grad}\,T, \tag{5}$$

$$\mathbf{q} - \phi\mathbf{j} = \alpha T\mathbf{j} - \kappa\,\mathbf{grad}\,T + NT\mathbf{H}\times\mathbf{j} + L\mathbf{H}\times\mathbf{grad}\,T. \tag{6}$$

Here σ and κ are the ordinary coefficients of electrical and thermal conductivity, α is the thermoelectric coefficient which appears in (25.1), R is the Hall coefficient, and N and L are new coefficients. The term $N\mathbf{H}\times\mathbf{grad}\,T$ may be regarded as representing the effect of the magnetic field on the thermo-e.m.f. (called the *Nernst effect*), and the term $L\mathbf{H}\times\mathbf{grad}\,T$ as representing the effect of this field on the thermal conduction (called the *Leduc-Righi effect*).

At a boundary between media, the normal components of the vectors $\mathbf{j}$ and $\mathbf{q}$ are continuous, and therefore so is that of the vector $-\kappa\,\mathbf{grad}\,T + \alpha T\mathbf{j} + NT\mathbf{H}\times\mathbf{j} + L\mathbf{H}\times\mathbf{grad}\,T$. The term $NT\mathbf{H}\times\mathbf{j}$ gives the influence of the magnetic field on the Peltier effect (called the *Ettingshausen effect*).

The amount of heat evolved in the conductor per unit time and volume is $Q = -\text{div}\,\mathbf{q}$. Here we must substitute $\mathbf{q}$ from (6) and replace $-\mathbf{grad}\,\phi = \mathbf{E}$ in accordance with (5). If the conductor is homogeneous, then the quantities α, N, L, etc. are functions of temperature alone, and so their gradients are proportional to $\mathbf{grad}\,T$. In the calculation we neglect all quantities of the second order in $\mathbf{H}$, and to the same approximation we can take $\mathbf{curl}\,(\mathbf{j}/\sigma) \cong \mathbf{curl}\,\mathbf{E} = 0$. We also note that the external field $\mathbf{H}$ (arising from sources outside the conductor under consideration) is such that $\mathbf{curl}\,\mathbf{H} = 0$.† Finally, $\text{div}\,\mathbf{j} = 0$, as for any constant current. The result is

$$Q = \frac{j^2}{\sigma} + \text{div}(\kappa\,\mathbf{grad}\,T) - T\mathbf{j}\cdot\mathbf{grad}\,\alpha + \frac{1}{\sigma T}\frac{\mathrm{d}}{\mathrm{d}T}(\sigma N T^2)\mathbf{j}\times\mathbf{H}\cdot\mathbf{grad}\,T.$$

The last term gives the change in the Thomson effect resulting from the presence of the magnetic field.

§26. Diffusion phenomena

The presence of diffusion causes certain phenomena in electrolyte solutions which do not occur in solid conductors. We shall assume, for simplicity, that the temperature is the same everywhere in the solution, and so consider only pure diffusion phenomena, uncomplicated by thermoelectric effects.

Instead of the pressure p and the concentration c, it is more convenient to take as independent variables the pressure and the chemical potential ζ. We here define ζ as the derivative of the thermodynamic potential of unit mass of the solution with respect to its concentration c (at constant p and T); by the concentration we mean the ratio of the mass of electrolyte in a volume element to the total mass of fluid in the same volume.‡ It may be recalled that the constancy of the chemical potential is (like that of the pressure and the temperature) one of the conditions of thermodynamic equilibrium.

The definition of the electric field potential given in §25 has to be somewhat modified in this case, since the current is now carried by the ions of the dissolved electrolyte, and not by the conduction electrons. A suitable definition is (cf. the second footnote to §25) $\phi = (\partial\Phi/\partial\rho)_c$, where Φ is the thermodynamic potential and ρ the sum of the ion charges in unit volume of the solution (after differentiating we put $\rho = 0$, of course, because the solution is electrically neutral). The derivative is taken at constant mass concentration, i.e. at a given sum of the masses of ions of both signs in unit volume.

---

† This neglects the very weak effect on the evolution of heat resulting from the magnetic fields of the currents themselves.

‡ The chemical potentials are usually defined as $\zeta_1 = \partial\Phi/\partial n_1$, $\zeta_2 = \partial\Phi/\partial n_2$, where Φ is the thermodynamic potential of any mass of the solution, and n_1, n_2 the numbers of particles of solute and solvent in that mass of solution. If Φ is the thermodynamic potential of unit mass, then the numbers n_1 and n_2 are related by $n_1 m_1 + n_2 m_2 = 1$ (where m_1, m_2 are the masses of the two kinds of particle), and the concentration $c = n_1 m_1$. Hence we have

$$\zeta = \frac{\partial\Phi}{\partial c} = \frac{\partial\Phi}{\partial n_1}\frac{\partial n_1}{\partial c} + \frac{\partial\Phi}{\partial n_2}\frac{\partial n_2}{\partial c} = \frac{\zeta_1}{m_1} - \frac{\zeta_2}{m_2},$$

where ζ is the chemical potential as here defined.

When a gradient of the chemical potential is present, a term proportional to it is added to the expression for the current density:

$$\mathbf{j} = \sigma(\mathbf{E} - \beta\,\mathbf{grad}\,\zeta), \tag{26.1}$$

in analogy with the added term in (25.2). We shall see below that, for a given gradient of the chemical potential (and of the temperature), **j** must be independent of the pressure gradient, and so no term in $\mathbf{grad}\,p$ appears in (26.1).†

As well as the electric current, we have to consider the transport of the mass of the electrolyte which takes place at the same time. It must be borne in mind that the passage of a current through the solution may be accompanied by a macroscopic motion of the fluid. The mass flux density of the electrolyte resulting from this motion is $\rho c\mathbf{v}$, where $\mathbf{v}$ is the velocity and ρ the density of the solution. The electrolyte is also transported by molecular diffusion. We denote the diffusion flux density by **i**, so that the total flux density is $\rho c\mathbf{v} + \mathbf{i}$. The irreversible processes of diffusion cause a further increase in entropy; the rate of change of the total entropy is‡

$$\frac{d\mathscr{S}}{dt} = \int \frac{\mathbf{E}\cdot\mathbf{j}}{T}\,dV - \int \frac{\mathbf{i}\cdot\mathbf{grad}\,\zeta}{T}\,dV. \tag{26.2}$$

Like the electric current density, the diffusion flux may be written as a linear combination of **E** and $\mathbf{grad}\,\zeta$, or of **j** and $\mathbf{grad}\,\zeta$. Using the symmetry of the kinetic coefficients, we can relate one of the coefficients in this combination to the coefficient β in (26.1), in exactly the same way as we did for **j** and $\mathbf{q} - \phi\mathbf{j}$ in §25. The result is

$$\mathbf{i} = -\frac{\rho D}{(\partial\zeta/\partial c)_{p,T}}\,\mathbf{grad}\,\zeta + \beta\mathbf{j}. \tag{26.3}$$

The coefficient of $\mathbf{grad}\,\zeta$ is here expressed in terms of the ordinary diffusion coefficient.‖

The inadmissibility in (26.1) and (26.3) of terms proportional to the pressure gradient follows, as in §25, from the law of the increase of entropy: such terms would make the derivative of the total entropy (26.2) a quantity of variable sign.

Formulae (26.1) and (26.3) give all the diffusion phenomena in electrolytes, but we shall not pause here to examine them more closely.

---

† It should be emphasised, however, that, for a given concentration gradient **j** does depend on the pressure gradient:

$$\mathbf{grad}\,\zeta = (\partial\zeta/\partial c)_{p,T}\,\mathbf{grad}\,c + (\partial\zeta/\partial p)_{c,T}\,\mathbf{grad}\,p.$$

‡ The derivation of the second term is given in *Fluid Mechanics*, §57.

‖ For $\mathbf{j} = 0$ and constant pressure and temperature we have $\mathbf{i} = -\rho D\,\mathbf{grad}\,c$.

PROBLEM

Two parallel plates of a metal A are immersed in a solution of an electrolyte AX. Find the current density as a function of the potential difference applied between the plates.

SOLUTION. When the current passes, metal is dissolved from one plate and deposited on the other. The solvent (water) remains at rest, and a mass flux of metal of density† $\rho v = jm/e$ occurs in the solution, where j is the electric current density, and m and e are the mass and charge of an ion A^+. This flux is also given by $\rho v = i + \rho v c$, where i is as shown in (26.3); assuming the pressure constant throughout the liquid,‡ we have

$$\rho D \frac{\mathrm{d}c}{\mathrm{d}x} = \left[\beta - \frac{m}{e}(1-c)\right] j, \tag{1}$$

where x is the co-ordinate in the direction of a line joining the electrodes. Since j = constant in the solution, this gives

$$jl = \int\limits_{c_1}^{c_2} \frac{\rho D \,\mathrm{d}c}{\beta - m(1-c)/e}, \tag{2}$$

where c_1, c_2 are the concentrations at the surfaces of the plates, and l is the distance between them.

The potential difference $\mathscr{E}$ between the plates is most simply found from the total amount of energy Q dissipated per unit time and unit area of the plates, which must equal $j\mathscr{E}$. By (26.1), (26.2) we have

$$Q = T\frac{\mathrm{d}\mathscr{S}}{\mathrm{d}t} = \int \left\{\frac{j^2}{\sigma} + \rho D \frac{\partial \zeta}{\partial c}\left(\frac{\mathrm{d}c}{\mathrm{d}x}\right)^2\right\} \mathrm{d}x = j\mathscr{E},$$

and therefore, using (1),

$$\mathscr{E} = \int\limits_{c_1}^{c_2} \frac{\rho D \,\mathrm{d}c}{\sigma(\beta - m(1-c)\, e)} + \int\limits_{c_1}^{c_2} \frac{\partial \zeta}{\partial c}\left[\beta - \frac{m}{e}(1-c)\right] \mathrm{d}c. \tag{3}$$

Formulae (2) and (3) implicitly solve the problem.

If the current j is small, the concentration difference $c_2 - c_1$ is also small. Replacing the integrals by $c_2 - c_1$ times the integrands, we find the effective specific resistance of the solution:

$$\frac{\mathscr{E}}{lj} = \frac{1}{\sigma} + \frac{1}{\rho D}\frac{\partial \zeta}{\partial c}\left[\beta - \frac{m}{e}(1-c)\right]^2.$$

The first term in (3) gives the potential drop ($\int (j/\sigma)\,\mathrm{d}x$) due to the passage of the current. The second term is the e.m.f. due to the concentration gradient in the solution (in a certain sense analogous to the thermo-e.m.f.). This latter expression is independent of the conditions of the particular one-dimensional problem considered, and is the general expression for the e.m.f. of a "concentration cell".

---

† It may be recalled that the hydrodynamic velocity $\mathbf{v}$ in a solution is defined so that ρ is the momentum of unit volume of the liquid; see *Fluid Mechanics*, §57. Hence the fact that in this case only the dissolved metal is moving (relative to the electrodes) does not affect the calculation of $\rho\mathbf{v}$.

‡ The change in pressure due to the motion of the liquid gives only terms of a higher order of smallness.

CHAPTER IV

CONSTANT MAGNETIC FIELD

§27. Constant magnetic field

A CONSTANT magnetic field in matter satisfies two of Maxwell's equations, obtained by averaging the microscopic equations

$$\operatorname{div} \mathbf{h} = 0, \qquad \mathbf{curl}\, \mathbf{h} = \frac{1}{c}\frac{\partial \mathbf{e}}{\partial t} + \frac{4\pi}{c}\rho \mathbf{v}. \tag{27.1}$$

The mean magnetic field is usually called the *magnetic induction* and denoted by **B**:

$$\bar{\mathbf{h}} = \mathbf{B}. \tag{27.2}$$

Hence the result of averaging the first equation (27.1) is

$$\operatorname{div} \mathbf{B} = 0. \tag{27.3}$$

In the second equation, the time derivative gives zero on averaging, since the mean field is supposed constant, and so we have

$$\mathbf{curl}\, \mathbf{B} = (4\pi/c)\overline{\rho \mathbf{v}}. \tag{27.4}$$

The mean value of the microscopic current density is in general not zero in either conductors or dielectrics. The only difference between these two classes is that in dielectrics we always have

$$\int \overline{\rho \mathbf{v}} \cdot d\mathbf{f} = 0, \tag{27.5}$$

where the integral is taken over the area of any cross-section of the body; in conductors, this integral need not be zero. Let us suppose to begin with that there is no net current in the body if it is a conductor, i.e. that (27.5) holds.

The vanishing of the integral in (27.5) for every cross-section of the body means that the vector $\overline{\rho \mathbf{v}}$ can be written as the curl of another vector, usually denoted by $c\mathbf{M}$:

$$\overline{\rho \mathbf{v}} = c\, \mathbf{curl}\, \mathbf{M}, \tag{27.6}$$

where **M** is zero outside the body; compare the similar discussion in §6. For, integrating over a surface bounded by a curve which encloses the body and nowhere enters it, we have $\int \overline{\rho \mathbf{v}} \cdot d\mathbf{f} = c \int \mathbf{curl}\, \mathbf{M} \cdot d\mathbf{f} = c \oint \mathbf{M} \cdot d\mathbf{l} = 0$.

The vector **M** is called the *magnetisation* of the body. Substituting it in (27.4), we find

$$\mathbf{curl}\,\mathbf{H} = 0, \tag{27.7}$$

where the vector **H** and the magnetic induction **B** are related by

$$\mathbf{B} = \mathbf{H} + 4\pi\mathbf{M}, \tag{27.8}$$

which is analogous to the relation between the electric field **E** and induction **D**. Although **H** is, by analogy with **E**, usually called the *magnetic field*, it must be remembered that the true mean field is really **B** and not **H**.

To see the physical significance of the quantity **M**, let us consider the total magnetic moment due to all the charged particles moving in the body. By the definition of the magnetic moment,† this is

$$\int \mathbf{r} \times \overline{\rho \mathbf{v}}\, \mathrm{d}V/2c = \tfrac{1}{2}\int \mathbf{r} \times \mathbf{curl}\,\mathbf{M}\, \mathrm{d}V.$$

Since $\rho\mathbf{v} \equiv 0$ outside the body, the integral can be taken over any volume which includes the body. We transform the integral as follows:

$$\int \mathbf{r} \times \mathbf{curl}\,\mathbf{M}\, \mathrm{d}V = -\oint \mathbf{r} \times (\mathbf{M} \times \mathrm{d}\mathbf{f}) - \int (\mathbf{M} \times \mathbf{grad}) \times \mathbf{r}\, \mathrm{d}V.$$

The integral over the surface outside the body is zero. In the second term we have $(\mathbf{M} \times \mathbf{grad}) \times \mathbf{r} = -\mathbf{M}\, \mathrm{div}\, \mathbf{r} + \mathbf{M} = -2\mathbf{M}$. Thus we obtain

$$\frac{1}{2c}\int \mathbf{r} \times \overline{\rho \mathbf{v}}\, \mathrm{d}V = \int \mathbf{M}\, \mathrm{d}V. \tag{27.9}$$

We see that the magnetisation vector is the magnetic moment per unit volume.‡

The equations (27.3) and (27.7) must be supplemented by a relation between **H** and **B** in order to complete the system of equations. For example, in non-ferromagnetic bodies in fairly weak magnetic fields, **B** and **H** are linearly related. In isotropic bodies, this linear relation becomes a simple proportionality:

$$\mathbf{B} = \mu\mathbf{H}. \tag{27.10}$$

The coefficient μ is called the *magnetic permeability*. We also have $\mathbf{M} = \chi\mathbf{H}$, where the coefficient

$$\chi = (\mu - 1)/4\pi \tag{27.11}$$

is called the *magnetic susceptibility*.

† See *The Classical Theory of Fields*, §5–9, Addison-Wesley Press, Cambridge (Mass.), 1951; Pergamon Press, London, 1959.

‡ The quantity **M** is completely determined only when this relation is established. The relation (27.6) inside the body, and $\mathbf{M} = 0$ outside it, do not uniquely define **M**: the gradient of any scalar could be added to **M** inside the body without affecting (27.6) (cf. the similar remark in the first footnote to §6).

Unlike the dielectric constant ϵ, which always exceeds unity, the magnetic permeability may be either greater or less than unity. (It is, however, always positive, as we shall prove in §30. The reason for the differing behaviour of μ and ϵ is discussed in §31.) The magnetic susceptibility χ may correspondingly be either positive or negative.

Another, quantitative, difference is that the magnetic susceptibility of the great majority of bodies is very small in comparison with the dielectric susceptibility. This difference arises because the magnetisation of a (non-ferromagnetic) body is a relativistic effect, of order v^2/c^2, where v is the velocity of the electrons in the atoms.†

From the equations div $\mathbf{B} = 0$, $\mathbf{curl}\,\mathbf{H} = 0$ it follows (cf. §6) that at a boundary between two different media we must have

$$B_{1n} = B_{2n}, \qquad \mathbf{H}_{1t} = \mathbf{H}_{2t}. \tag{27.12}$$

This system of equations and boundary conditions is formally identical with those for the electrostatic field in a dielectric in the absence of free charges, differing only in that **E** and **D** are replaced by **H** and **B** respectively. Since $\mathbf{curl}\,\mathbf{H} = 0$, we can put $\mathbf{H} = -\mathbf{grad}\,\psi$; the equations for the potential ψ are the same as those for the electrostatic potential. Thus the solutions of the various problems of electrostatics discussed in Chapter II can be immediately applied to problems with a constant magnetic field. In particular, the formulae derived in §8 for a dielectric ellipsoid in a uniform electric field hold also, with appropriate substitutions, for a magnetic ellipsoid in a uniform magnetic field.

The tangential component of the magnetic induction, unlike its normal component, is discontinuous at a surface separating two media. The magnitude of the discontinuity can be related to the current density on the surface. To do this, we integrate both sides of equation (27.4) over a small interval Δl crossing the surface along the normal. We then let Δl tend to zero; the integral $\int \overline{\rho \mathbf{v}}\, \mathrm{d}l$ may tend to some finite limit. The quantity

$$\mathbf{g} = \int \overline{\rho \mathbf{v}}\, \mathrm{d}l \tag{27.13}$$

may be called the *surface current density*; it gives the charge passing per unit time across unit length of a line in the surface. We take the direction of **g** at a given point on the surface as the y-axis, and the direction of the normal from medium 1 to medium 2 as the x-axis. Then the integration of equation (27.4) gives

$$\int \left(\frac{\partial B_x}{\partial z} - \frac{\partial B_z}{\partial x} \right) \mathrm{d}x = \frac{4\pi}{c} g_y = \frac{4\pi}{c} g.$$

Since B_x is continuous, the derivative $\partial B_x/\partial z$ is finite, and so its integral tends to zero with Δl. The integral of $\partial B_z/\partial x$ gives the difference in the

† The ratio v/c appears with **H** in the Hamiltonian of the interaction of the body with the magnetic field, and again in the magnetic moments of the atoms or molecules.

values of B_z on the two sides of the surface. Thus $B_{2z} - B_{1z} = -4\pi g/c$. This can be written in vector form:

$$4\pi\mathbf{g}/c = \mathbf{n}\times(\mathbf{B}_2 - \mathbf{B}_1) = 4\pi\mathbf{n}\times(\mathbf{M}_2 - \mathbf{M}_1), \qquad (27.14)$$

where $\mathbf{n}$ is a unit vector along the normal into region 2; the last member of (27.14) is obtained by using the continuity of the tangential component of $\mathbf{H}$.

§28. Magnetic symmetry of crystals

There is a profound difference between the electric properties of crystals and their magnetic properties, which results from a difference in the behaviour of charges and currents with respect to a change in the sign of the time.

The invariance of the equations of motion with respect to this change means that the formal substitution $t \to -t$, on being applied to any state of thermodynamic equilibrium of a body, must give some possible equilibrium state. There are then two possibilities: either the state obtained by changing the sign of t is the same as the original state, or it is not.

In this section we denote by $\rho(x, y, z)$ and $\mathbf{j}(x, y, z)$ the true (microscopic) charge and current densities at any given point in the crystal, averaged only over time, and not over "physically infinitesimal" volumes as in the macroscopic theory. These are the functions which determine the electric and magnetic structure of the crystal respectively.

When t is replaced by $-t$, $\mathbf{j}$ changes sign. If the state of the body remains unchanged, it follows that $\mathbf{j} = -\mathbf{j}$, i.e. $\mathbf{j} = 0$. Thus there is a reason why bodies can exist in which the function $\mathbf{j}(x, y, z)$ is identically zero. In such bodies, not only the current density but also the (time) average magnetic field and magnetic moment vanish at every point (we are speaking, of course, of states in the absence of an external magnetic field). Such bodies may be said to have no "magnetic structure", and indeed the great majority of bodies fall into this category.

The charge density ρ, on the other hand, is unchanged when $t \to -t$. There is therefore no reason why this function should be identically zero. In other words, there are no crystals without "electric structure", and herein lies the essential difference, mentioned at the beginning of this section, between the electric and the magnetic properties of crystals.

Let us now consider crystals for which the change from t to $-t$ results in a change of state, so that $\mathbf{j} \neq 0$. We shall say that such bodies have a magnetic structure. First of all, we note that, although $\mathbf{j}$ is not zero, there can be no total current in an equilibrium state of the body, i.e. the integral $\int \mathbf{j}\, dV$ taken over an elementary cell must always be zero.† Otherwise the

† It should be emphasised that the cell spoken of here is the true elementary cell, whose definition involves the magnetic structure of the crystal, and which may be different from the purely crystallographic cell, which relates only to the symmetry of the charge distribution in the lattice.

current would produce a macroscopic magnetic field, and the crystal would have a magnetic energy per unit volume increasing rapidly with its dimensions. Since such a state is energetically unfavourable, it could not correspond to thermodynamic equilibrium.

The currents **j** may, however, produce a non-zero macroscopic magnetic moment, i.e. the integral $\int \mathbf{r}\times\mathbf{j}\, dV$, again taken over an elementary cell, need not be zero. Accordingly, the bodies for which $\mathbf{j} \neq 0$ may be divided into two types: those in which the macroscopic magnetic moment is not zero, called *ferromagnetics*, and those in which it is zero, called *antiferromagnetics*.

The symmetry of the current distribution **j** can be conveniently regarded as the symmetry of the arrangement and orientation of the magnetic moments of the individual atoms in the crystal. If $\mathbf{j} = 0$, all these moments are changing their orientation in the course of time in an entirely random manner, so that the mean value of each moment is zero. In a ferromagnetic, the atomic moments are oriented mainly in one direction, causing a non-zero total moment in each elementary cell. In an antiferromagnetic, the mean atomic moments are not zero, i.e. they are not randomly oriented, but they are so arranged as to balance one another in each cell.

What are the possible symmetry groups of the current distribution $\mathbf{j}(x, y, z)$? This symmetry contains, first of all, the usual rotations, reflections and translations, and so the possible symmetry groups of **j** always include the usual 230 crystallographic space symmetry groups. These, however, are by no means all. As has already been mentioned, the substitution $t \to -t$ changes the sign of the vector **j**. For this reason a new symmetry element comes in, namely that resulting from the reversal of all currents; we shall denote this transformation by R. If the current distribution itself has the symmetry R, it follows that $\mathbf{j} = -\mathbf{j}$, i.e. $\mathbf{j} = 0$, and the body has no magnetic structure. A non-zero function $\mathbf{j}(x, y, z)$ may, however, be symmetrical with respect to various combinations of R with the other symmetry elements (rotations, reflections and translations). Thus the problem of determining the possible types of symmetry of the current distribution (the *magnetic space groups*) amounts to the enumeration of all possible groups containing both the transformations of the ordinary space groups and the combinations of these with R.

If the symmetry of the current distribution is given, the crystallographic symmetry of the particle distribution, which is also the symmetry of the function $\rho(x, y, z)$, is determined. It is the symmetry of the space group which is obtained from the symmetry group of **j** by formally regarding the transformation R as the identity (as it is with respect to the function ρ).

If only the macroscopic properties of the body are of interest, however, it is not necessary to know the complete symmetry group of the function $\mathbf{j}(x, y, z)$. These properties depend only on the direction in the crystal, and the translational symmetry of the lattice does not affect them. As regards crystallographic structure, the "symmetry of directions" is specified by the

32 crystal classes. These are the symmetry groups consisting of rotations and reflections only, and are obtained from the space groups by regarding every translation as the identity, and the screw axes and glide planes as simple axes and planes of symmetry. As regards the magnetic properties, the macroscopic symmetry can be classified by groups (consisting of rotations, reflections and combinations of these with R) which may be called the *magnetic crystal classes*. They are related to the magnetic space groups in the same way as the ordinary crystal classes to the ordinary space groups. They include, firstly, the usual 32 classes, and those classes augmented by the element R. These augmented classes are, in particular, the macroscopic symmetry groups for all bodies having no magnetic structure, but they occur also in bodies with magnetic structure. This happens if the magnetic space symmetry group of such bodies includes R only in combination with translations, and not alone.

There are also 58 classes in which R enters only in combination with rotations or reflections. Each of these becomes one of the ordinary crystal classes if R is replaced by the identity.†

It should be noted that the occurrence of magnetic structure (ferromagnetic or antiferromagnetic) always involves comparatively weak interactions.‡ Hence the crystal structure of a magnetic body is only a slight modification of that in the non-magnetic phase, which usually changes into the magnetic phase when the temperature is reduced. In this respect ferromagnetics, in particular, differ from ordinary pyroelectrics, but are analogous to ferroelectrics.

If the magnetic crystal class of a body is specified, its macroscopic magnetic properties are qualitatively determined. The most important of these is the presence or absence of a macroscopic magnetic moment, i.e. of spontaneous magnetisation in the absence of an external field. The magnetic moment $\mathbf{M}$ is a vector, behaving as an axial vector (the vector product of two polar vectors) under rotation and reflection, and changing sign under the operation R. The crystal will possess spontaneous magnetisation if it has one or more directions such that a vector $\mathbf{M}$ in that direction and having

† These classes are isomorphous with those discovered by A. V. Shubnikov for the symmetry groups of polyhedra with faces of two colours (called by him *groups of mixed polarity*). The element R corresponds to the operation of changing the colour of each face. See A. V. Shubnikov, *Symmetry and antisymmetry of finite figures* (*Simmetriya i antisimmetriya konechnykh figur*), Moscow, 1951. A direct derivation as symmetry groups for the magnetic properties of bodies is given by B. A. Tavger and V. M. Zaĭtsev, *Zhurnal éksperimental'noĭ i teoreticheskoĭ fiziki* **30,** 564, 1956; *Soviet Physics JETP* **3,** 430, 1956.

The total number of magnetic space groups is 1651; they are derived (as Shubnikov groups) by N. V. Belov, N. N. Neronova and T. S. Smirnova, *Trudy Instituta Kristallografii* **11,** 33, 1955; A. M. Zamorzaev, *Kristallografiya* **2,** 15, 1957; *Soviet Physics: Crystallography* **2,** 10, 1958.

‡ The exchange interaction between the magnetic moments of atoms usually results in the saturation of the valency bonds and the formation of non-magnetic structures. A magnetic structure results only from the relatively weak exchange interactions between deep-lying d and f electrons of atoms of elements in the intermediate groups of Mendeleev's system.

the above-mentioned properties is invariant under all transformations belonging to the magnetic crystal class concerned.

We must again emphasise the difference between these (macroscopic) properties and the corresponding ones in electrostatics. The latter are qualitatively determined by the ordinary crystal class. In particular, a body is pyroelectric if its crystal class admits the existence of a polar vector **P** (the polarisation). It would, however, be entirely wrong to base conclusions about the existence or otherwise of a macroscopic magnetic moment on the behaviour of the axial vector **M** with respect to the transformations of the non-magnetic crystal class of the body concerned.

As an illustration, let us consider a tetragonal lattice of identical atoms, with magnetic moments parallel to the tetragonal axis.† The magnetic crystal class comprises the fourth-order axis $C_4^{(z)}$, two second-order axes combined with R ($C_2^{(x)}R$ and $C_2^{(y)}R$), the plane of symmetry $\sigma_h^{(z)}$ perpendicular to the z-axis, and two vertical planes of symmetry combined with R ($\sigma_v^{(x)}R$ and $\sigma_v^{(y)}R$). This group admits the existence of a vector **M** along the tetragonal axis. The crystallographic symmetry class is obtained by replacing R by unity, i.e. it is the class D_{4h}. This class does not admit the existence of an axial vector **M**, since the components M_x, M_y, M_z would change sign on reflection in the planes $\sigma^{(z)}$, $\sigma^{(x)}$, $\sigma^{(y)}$ respectively.

The properties of bodies with a spontaneous non-zero macroscopic magnetic moment (ferromagnetics) will be discussed in detail in Chapter V. In all other crystals, in fairly weak fields, the relation between **B** and **H** is linear:

$$B_i = \mu_{ik}H_k, \tag{28.1}$$

with no inhomogeneous term. The *magnetic permeability tensor* μ_{ik} is symmetrical. This follows from thermodynamic relations which will be derived in §30, in exactly the same way as the symmetry of the tensor ϵ_{ik} (§13).

We may also mention two further phenomena possible in principle. One is *piezomagnetism*, resulting from the existence of a linear relation between the magnetic field and the deformation of a body (analogously to piezoelectricity; see §17). The other results from a linear relation between the magnetic and electric fields in a substance, which would cause, for example, a magnetisation proportional to the electric field.‡ Both these phenomena can occur for certain magnetic crystal symmetry classes.||

§29. The magnetic field of a constant current

If a conductor carries a non-zero total current, the mean current density in it can be written as $\rho\mathbf{v} = c\,\mathbf{curl}\,\mathbf{M}+\mathbf{j}$. The first term, resulting from the

† Such, for example, is the lattice of iron in its ferromagnetic phase. Crystallographically, it is a cubic lattice slightly distorted along one of the fourth-order axes.

‡ Effects of this type but quadratic in the field must in principle exist even in isotropic bodies, but are negligible.

|| Examples of these are given by I. E. Dzyaloshinskiĭ, *Zhurnal ėksperimental'noĭ i teoreticheskoĭ fiziki* **33**, 807, 1957; **37**, 881, 1959 (*Soviet Physics JETP* **6 (33)**, 621, 1958; **10 (37)**, 628, 1960).

magnetisation of the medium, makes no contribution to the total current, so that the net charge transfer through a cross-section of the body is given by the integral $\int \mathbf{j}\cdot d\mathbf{f}$ of the second term. The quantity $\mathbf{j}$ is called the *conduction current density*.† The statements made in §20 apply to this current; in particular, the energy dissipated per unit time and volume is $\mathbf{E}\cdot\mathbf{j}$.

The distribution of the current $\mathbf{j}$ over the volume of the conductor is given by the equations of §20, which do not involve the magnetic field due to $\mathbf{j}$ itself, if we neglect the effect of this field on the conductivity of the body. Hence the magnetic field of the currents must be determined for a given current distribution. The equations satisfied by this field differ from those in §27 by the presence of a term $4\pi\mathbf{j}/c$ on the right-hand side of (27.7):

$$\operatorname{div} \mathbf{B} = 0, \tag{29.1}$$

$$\mathbf{curl}\, \mathbf{H} = 4\pi\mathbf{j}/c. \tag{29.2}$$

The conduction current density $\mathbf{j}$, which is proportional to the electric field, does not become infinite, and in particular is finite on a surface separating two media. Hence the term on the right of (29.2) does not affect the boundary condition that the tangential component of $\mathbf{H}$ is continuous.

To solve equations (29.1), (29.2), it is convenient to use the *vector potential* $\mathbf{A}$, defined by

$$\mathbf{B} = \mathbf{curl}\, \mathbf{A}, \tag{29.3}$$

so that equation (29.1) is satisfied identically. Equation (29.3) does not uniquely define the vector potential, to which the gradient of any scalar may be added without affecting (29.3). For this reason we can impose on $\mathbf{A}$ a further condition, which we take to be

$$\operatorname{div} \mathbf{A} = 0. \tag{29.4}$$

The equation for $\mathbf{A}$ is obtained by substituting (29.3) in (29.2). If the linear relation $\mathbf{B} = \mu\mathbf{H}$ holds we have

$$\mathbf{curl}\left(\frac{1}{\mu}\mathbf{curl}\, \mathbf{A}\right) = 4\pi\mathbf{j}/c. \tag{29.5}$$

In this form the equation is valid for any medium, homogeneous or not.

In a homogeneous medium, μ = constant, and since

$$\mathbf{curl}\,\mathbf{curl}\, \mathbf{A} = \mathbf{grad}\operatorname{div} \mathbf{A} - \triangle\mathbf{A} = -\triangle\mathbf{A}$$

we find from (29.5)

$$\triangle\mathbf{A} = -4\pi\mu\mathbf{j}/c. \tag{29.6}$$

If we have two or more adjoining media of different magnetic permeability μ, the general equation (29.5) has the form (29.6) in each homogeneous

---

† The quantity $c\,\mathbf{curl}\,\mathbf{M}$ is sometimes called the *molecular current density*. This name, however, is not in complete accordance with the actual physical picture of motion of charges in a conductor. For example, in a metal the conduction electrons, as well as those moving in the atoms, contribute to the magnetization $\mathcal{M}$.

medium, while at the interfaces the tangential component of the vector $(1/\mu)$ **curl A** must be continuous. Moreover, the tangential component of **A** itself must be continuous, since a discontinuity would mean that the induction **B** was infinite at the boundary.

The field equations are simpler in the two-dimensional problem of finding the magnetic field in a medium infinite and homogeneous in one direction (which we take as the z-direction), the currents which produce the field being everywhere in that direction, with the current density $j_z = j$ depending only on x and y. We make the plausible assumption (to be confirmed by the result) that the vector potential of such a field is also in the z-direction: $A_z = A(x, y)$. The condition (29.4) is then satisfied identically; the magnetic field is everywhere parallel to the xy-plane. We denote by **k** a unit vector in the z-direction; then

$$\mathbf{curl\,A} = \mathbf{curl}\,A\mathbf{k} = \mathbf{grad}\,A \times \mathbf{k},$$

$$\mathbf{curl}\left(\frac{1}{\mu}\mathbf{curl\,A}\right) = \mathbf{curl}\left(\frac{\mathbf{grad}\,A}{\mu}\times\mathbf{k}\right) = -\mathbf{k}\,\mathrm{div}\frac{\mathbf{grad}\,A}{\mu}.$$

Hence equation (29.5) becomes

$$\mathrm{div}\frac{\mathbf{grad}\,A}{\mu} = -\frac{4\pi}{c}j(x,y), \tag{29.7}$$

i.e. we in fact obtain one equation for the one scalar quantity $A(x, y)$. For a piecewise homogeneous medium, (29.7) becomes

$$\triangle A = -4\pi\mu j(x,y)/c, \tag{29.8}$$

with the boundary condition that A and $(1/\mu)\,\partial A/\partial n$ are continuous at an interface.†

The magnetic field is easily found if the current distribution is symmetrical about the z-axis: $j_z = j(r)$ (where r is the distance from that axis). In this case the lines of magnetic force are evidently the circles r = constant. The magnitude of the field is found at once from the formula

$$\oint \mathbf{H}\cdot\mathrm{d}\mathbf{l} = \frac{4\pi}{c}\int \mathbf{j}\cdot\mathrm{d}\mathbf{f}, \tag{29.9}$$

which is the integral form of (29.2). Thus

$$H(r) = 2J(r)/cr, \tag{29.10}$$

where $J(r)$ is the total current within the radius r.

---

† It should be noticed that the two-dimensional problem with a constant magnetic field is equivalent to the two-dimensional electrostatic problem of determining the electric field due to extraneous charges of density $\rho_{ex}(x, y)$ in a dielectric medium. The equation to be solved in the latter problem is $\mathrm{div}\,(\epsilon\,\mathbf{grad}\,\phi) = -4\pi\rho_{ex}$, where ϕ is the field potential; this differs from (29.7) only in that A, j/c and μ are replaced by ϕ, ρ_{ex} and $1/\epsilon$ respectively. The boundary conditions on A and ϕ are the same. A difference occurs, however, on passing to **E** and **B** from ϕ and **A** respectively. The vectors $\mathbf{E} = -\,\mathbf{grad}\,\phi$ and $\mathbf{B} = \mathbf{curl\,A}$ are the same in magnitude but in perpendicular directions at any given point.

The reduction of the vector equation (29.5) to a single scalar equation is possible also if the current distribution is axially symmetrical and has in cylindrical co-ordinates r, ϕ, z the form $j_r = j_z = 0$, $j_\phi = j(r, z)$. We seek the vector potential in the form $A_r = A_z = 0$, $A_\phi = A(r, z)$. The components of the magnetic induction $\mathbf{B} = \mathbf{curl}\,\mathbf{A}$ are $B_r = -\partial A/\partial z$, $B_z = (1/r)\partial(rA)/\partial r$, $B_\phi = 0$, and the ϕ-component of equation (29.2) gives

$$\frac{\partial}{\partial z}\left(\frac{1}{\mu}\frac{\partial A}{\partial z}\right) + \frac{\partial}{\partial r}\left(\frac{1}{\mu r}\frac{\partial}{\partial r}[rA]\right) = -\frac{4\pi}{c}j(r, z). \tag{29.11}$$

The equations for the magnetic field of the currents can be solved in a general form in the important case where the magnetic properties of the medium may be neglected, i.e. where we can put $\mu \equiv 1$. The vector potential then satisfies in all space the equation $\triangle \mathbf{A} = -4\pi\mathbf{j}/c$ with no conditions at the interfaces between different media (including the surface of the conductor on which the current flows). The solution of this equation which vanishes at infinity is†

$$\mathbf{A} = \frac{1}{c}\int \frac{\mathbf{j}}{R}\,\mathrm{d}V, \tag{29.12}$$

where R is the distance from the volume element $\mathrm{d}V$ to the point at which $\mathbf{A}$ is to be calculated. In taking the curl of this equation, we must remember that the integrand $\mathbf{j}/R$ is to be differentiated with respect to the co-ordinates of this point, of which $\mathbf{j}$ is independent, so that

$$\mathbf{curl}\,(\mathbf{j}/R) = \mathbf{grad}\,(1/R)\times\mathbf{j} = -\mathbf{R}\times\mathbf{j}/R^3,$$

where the radius vector $\mathbf{R}$ is from $\mathrm{d}V$ to the point under consideration. Thus

$$\mathbf{B} = \mathbf{H} = \frac{1}{c}\int \frac{\mathbf{j}\times\mathbf{R}}{R^3}\,\mathrm{d}V. \tag{29.13}$$

If the conductor on which the current flows is sufficiently thin (a thin wire), and if we are interested only in the field in the surrounding space, the thickness of the wire may be neglected. In what follows we shall often discuss such *linear currents*. The integration over the volume of the conductor is then replaced by an integration along its length: the formulae for linear currents are obtained from those for volume currents by making the substitution $\mathbf{j}\,\mathrm{d}V \to J\,\mathrm{d}\mathbf{l}$, where J is the total current in the conductor. For example, from formulae (29.12) and (29.13) we have

$$\mathbf{A} = \frac{J}{c}\oint \frac{\mathrm{d}\mathbf{l}}{R}, \qquad \mathbf{H} = \frac{J}{c}\oint \frac{\mathrm{d}\mathbf{l}\times\mathbf{R}}{R^3}. \tag{29.14}$$

The latter formula is *Biot and Savart's law*.

† See *The Classical Theory of Fields*, §5–8.

This simple formula for the magnetic field of a linear current does not depend on the assumption that $\mu = 1$. Since we neglect the thickness of the conductor, no boundary conditions at its surface need be applied, and the magnetic properties of the conducting material are of no importance (it may even be ferromagnetic). The solution of equation (29.6) for the field in the medium surrounding the conductor is therefore

$$\mathbf{A} = \frac{\mu J}{c}\int\frac{\mathrm{d}\mathbf{l}}{R}, \qquad \mathbf{B} = \frac{\mu J}{c}\int\frac{\mathrm{d}\mathbf{l}\times\mathbf{R}}{R^3}, \tag{29.15}$$

whatever the magnetic susceptibility of that medium. Thus the presence of the medium simply changes the magnetic induction by a factor μ. The field $\mathbf{H} = \mathbf{B}/\mu$ is unchanged.

The problem of determining the magnetic field of linear currents can also be solved as a problem of potential theory. Since we neglect the volume of conductors, we are in fact determining the field in a region containing no currents except along certain line singularities. In the absence of currents, a constant magnetic field has a scalar potential, which in a homogeneous medium satisfies Laplace's equation. There is, however, an important difference between the magnetic field potential and the electrostatic potential: the latter is always a one-valued function, because $\mathbf{curl\,E} = 0$ in all space (including charged regions) and so the change in the potential in going round any closed contour (i.e. the circulation of $\mathbf{E}$ round that contour) is zero. The circulation of the magnetic field round a contour enclosing a linear current is not zero, but $4\pi J/c$. Hence the potential changes by this amount on each passage round a contour enclosing a linear current, i.e. it is a many-valued function.

If the currents lie in a finite region of space (and $\mu = 1$ everywhere), the vector potential of the magnetic field at a great distance from the conductors is

$$\mathbf{A} = \mathscr{M}\times\mathbf{R}/R^3, \tag{29.16}$$

where

$$\mathscr{M} = \int\mathbf{r}\times\mathbf{j}\,\mathrm{d}V/2c \tag{29.17}$$

is the total magnetic moment of the system.†

For a linear current, this becomes

$$\mathscr{M} = J\oint\mathbf{r}\times\mathrm{d}\mathbf{l}/2c,$$

and can be transformed into an integral over a surface bounded by the line of the current. The product $\mathrm{d}\mathbf{f} = \frac{1}{2}\mathbf{r}\times\mathrm{d}\mathbf{l}$ is equal in magnitude to the area

† See *The Classical Theory of Fields*, §5–9. In the derivation there given, we use explicitly the idea of a current as the result of the motion of individual charged particles. Such a derivation is, of course, quite general, but formula (29.16) can also be obtained by macroscopic arguments (see Problem 4).

of the triangular surface element formed by the vectors $\mathbf{r}$ and $\mathbf{dl}$. The vector $\int \mathbf{df}$ is independent of the particular surface (bounded by the current) over which it is taken. Thus the magnetic moment of a closed linear current is

$$\mathscr{M} = J\int \mathbf{df}/c. \tag{29.18}$$

In particular, for a plane closed linear current the magnetic moment is simply JS/c, where S is the area of the plane enclosed by the current.

To conclude this section, we may briefly discuss the energy flux in a conductor. The energy dissipated as Joule heat in the conductor is derived from the energy of the electromagnetic field. In a steady state, the "equation of continuity" which expresses the law of conservation of energy is

$$-\operatorname{div} \mathbf{S} = \mathbf{j}\cdot\mathbf{E}, \tag{29.19}$$

where $\mathbf{S}$ is the energy flux density, given in a conductor by

$$\mathbf{S} = c\mathbf{E}\times\mathbf{H}/4\pi, \tag{29.20}$$

which is formally the same as the expression for the Poynting vector for the field in a vacuum. This is easily verified directly by calculating div $\mathbf{S}$ from the equations $\mathbf{curl}\,\mathbf{E} = 0$ and (29.2), when we obtain (29.19).

Formula (29.20) also follows independently from the obvious condition that the normal component of $\mathbf{S}$ must be continuous at the surface of a conductor, if we use the continuity of $\mathbf{E}_t$ and $\mathbf{H}_t$ and the validity of (29.20) in the vacuum outside the body.

PROBLEMS†

PROBLEM 1. Determine the scalar potential of the magnetic field of a closed linear current.

SOLUTION. We transform the line integral into one over a surface bounded by the line, obtaining

$$\mathbf{A} = \frac{J}{c}\oint\frac{\mathbf{dl}}{R} = \frac{J}{c}\int \mathbf{df}\times\mathbf{grad}\frac{1}{R},$$

$$\mathbf{B} = \mathbf{curl}\,\mathbf{A} = -\frac{J}{c}\int(\mathbf{df}\cdot\mathbf{grad})\,\mathbf{grad}\frac{1}{R}$$

(where we have used the fact that $\triangle(1/R) = 0$). Since $\mathbf{B} = -\mathbf{grad}\,\phi$, we have for the scalar potential

$$\phi = \frac{J}{c}\int\mathbf{df}\cdot\mathbf{grad}\frac{1}{R} = -\frac{J}{c}\int\frac{\mathbf{df}\cdot\mathbf{R}}{R^3}.$$

The integral is, geometrically, the solid angle Ω subtended by the closed contour at the point considered. The above-mentioned many-valuedness of the potential is seen from the fact that, as this point describes a closed path round the wire, the angle Ω changes suddenly from 2π to -2π.

PROBLEM 2. Find the magnetic field of a linear current flowing in a circle of radius a.

SOLUTION. We take the origin of cylindrical co-ordinates r, ϕ, z at the centre of the circle, with the angle ϕ measured from the plane which passes through the z-axis and the point at

† In Problems 1–4, $\mu \equiv 1$.

which the field is calculated. The vector potential has only one component, $A_\phi = A(r, z)$, and by formula (29.14) we have

$$A_\phi = \frac{J}{c}\oint \frac{\cos\phi \, dl}{R} = \frac{2J}{c}\int_0^\pi \frac{a\cos\phi \, d\phi}{\sqrt{(a^2+r^2+z^2-2ar\cos\phi)}}.$$

Putting $\theta = \frac{1}{2}(\phi-\pi)$, we find

$$A_\phi = \frac{4J}{ck}\sqrt{\frac{a}{r}}\,[(1-\tfrac{1}{2}k^2)K-E],$$

where $k^2 = 4ar/[(a+r)^2+z^2]$, and K and E are complete elliptic integrals of the first and second kinds:

$$K = \int_0^{\frac{1}{2}\pi} \frac{d\theta}{\sqrt{(1-k^2\sin^2\theta)}}, \qquad E = \int_0^{\frac{1}{2}\pi} \sqrt{(1-k^2\sin^2\theta)}\, d\theta.$$

The components of the induction are

$$B_\phi = 0,$$

$$B_r = -\frac{\partial A_\phi}{\partial z} = \frac{J}{c}\frac{2z}{r\sqrt{[(a+r)^2+z^2]}}\left[-K+\frac{a^2+r^2+z^2}{(a-r)^2+z^2}E\right],$$

$$B_z = \frac{1}{r}\frac{\partial}{\partial r}(rA_\phi) = \frac{J}{c}\frac{2}{\sqrt{[(a+r)^2+z^2]}}\left[K+\frac{a^2-r^2-z^2}{(a-r)^2+z^2}E\right].$$

Here we have used the easily verified formulae

$$\frac{\partial K}{\partial k} = \frac{E}{k(1-k^2)}-\frac{K}{k}, \qquad \frac{\partial E}{\partial k} = \frac{E-K}{k}.$$

On the axis ($r = 0$) we have $B_r = 0$, $B_z = 2\pi a^2 J/c(a^2+z^2)^{3/2}$, as can also be found by a straightforward calculation.

PROBLEM 3. Determine the magnetic field in a cylindrical hole in a cylindrical conductor of infinite length carrying a current uniformly distributed over its cross-section (Fig. 17).

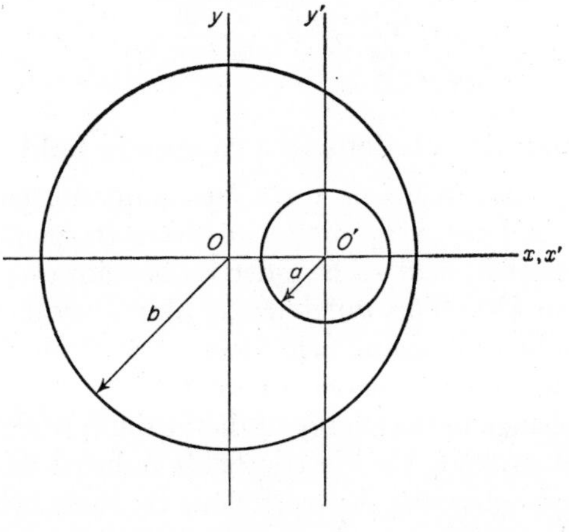

FIG. 17

SOLUTION. If there were no hole, the field in the cylinder would be given by $H'_x = -2\pi jy/c$, $H'_y = 2\pi jx/c$. The dimensions and axes are as shown in Fig. 17. If a current of density $-j$ were to flow in the inner cylinder, it would produce a field $H''_x = 2\pi jy'/c$, $H''_y = -2\pi jx'/c$. The required field in the hole is obtained by superposing these two fields. Since $x-x' = OO' = h$, and $y = y'$, we have $H_x = 0$, $H_y = 2\pi jh/c = 2hJ/(b^2-a^2)c$, i.e. a uniform field in the y-direction.

PROBLEM 4. Derive from (29.12) the formula (29.16) for the vector potential of the field far from the currents.

SOLUTION. We write $\mathbf{R} = \mathbf{R}_0 - \mathbf{r}$, where $\mathbf{R}_0$ and $\mathbf{r}$ are the radius vectors from the origin (situated somewhere among the currents) to the point considered and to the volume element dV respectively. Expanding the integrand in powers of $\mathbf{r}$ and using the fact that $\int \mathbf{j}\, dV \equiv 0$, we have $A_i \cong (R_k/cR^3)\int x_k j_i\, dV$. The suffix 0 to R is omitted. Integrating by parts the identity $\int x_i x_k \operatorname{div}\mathbf{j}\, dV = 0$ gives $\int (j_i x_k + j_k x_i)\, dV = 0$. Hence we can write

$$A_i = (R_k/2cR^3)\int (x_k j_i - x_i j_k)\, dV,$$

which is (29.16).

PROBLEM 5. Determine the magnetic field produced by a linear current in a magnetically anisotropic medium (A. S. VIGLIN).

SOLUTION. In the anisotropic medium surrounding the conductor we have

$$\operatorname{div}\mathbf{B} = \mu_{ik}\,\partial H_k/\partial x_i = 0, \tag{1}$$

where μ_{ik} is the magnetic permeability tensor of the medium. Instead of introducing the vector potential by $\mathbf{B} = \mathbf{curl}\,\mathbf{A}$, we use another vector $\mathbf{C}$ defined by

$$H_i = e_{ikl}\mu_{km}\,\partial C_l/\partial x_m, \tag{2}$$

where e_{ikl} is the antisymmetrical unit tensor. Then equation (1) is again satisfied identically. We can also impose on the vector $\mathbf{C}$ thus defined the condition

$$\operatorname{div}\mathbf{C} \equiv \partial C_l/\partial x_l = 0. \tag{3}$$

Substituting (2) in $\mathbf{curl}\,\mathbf{H} = 4\pi\mathbf{j}/c$, we obtain $e_{ikl}\,\partial H_l/\partial x_k = -\mu_{kp}\partial^2 C_i/\partial x_k\partial x_p = 4\pi j_i/c$ (using the condition (3) and the fact that $e_{ikl}e_{lmn} = \delta_{im}\delta_{kn} - \delta_{in}\delta_{km}$). The equation thus obtained for $\mathbf{C}$ is the same in form as that for the electric field potential resulting from charges in an anisotropic medium (§13, Problem 2). The solution is

$$\mathbf{C} = \frac{1}{c}\int \frac{\mathbf{j}\, dV}{\sqrt{(|\mu|\mu^{-1}{}_{ik}R_iR_k)}},$$

where $|\mu|$ is the determinant of the tensor μ_{ik}, and $\mathbf{R}$ the radius vector from the point considered to dV. For a linear current we have

$$\mathbf{C} = \frac{J}{c\sqrt{|\mu|}}\oint \frac{d\mathbf{l}}{\sqrt{(\mu^{-1}{}_{ik}R_iR_k)}}.$$

§30. Thermodynamic relations in a magnetic field

The thermodynamic relations for a magnetic substance in a magnetic field are, as we shall see, very similar to the corresponding relations for a dielectric in an electric field. Their derivation, however, is quite different from that given in §10. This difference is ultimately due to the fact that a magnetic field, unlike an electric field, does no work on charges moving in it (since the force acting on a charge is perpendicular to its velocity). Hence, to calculate the change in the energy of the medium when a magnetic field is applied, we must examine the electric fields induced by the change in the magnetic field and determine the work done by these fields on the currents which produce the magnetic field.

Thus the equation which relates electric and variable magnetic fields must be used. This equation is

$$\mathbf{curl}\,\mathbf{E} = -\frac{1}{c}\frac{\partial \mathbf{B}}{\partial t}; \tag{30.1}$$

it follows immediately on averaging the microscopic equation (1.3).

During a time δt, the field $\mathbf{E}$ does work $\delta t \int \mathbf{j}\cdot\mathbf{E}\,\mathrm{d}V$ on the currents $\mathbf{j}$. This quantity with the opposite sign is the work δR "done on the field" by the external e.m.f. which maintains the currents. Substituting

$$\mathbf{j} = c\,\mathbf{curl}\,\mathbf{H}/4\pi,$$

we have

$$\begin{aligned} \delta R &= -\delta t\frac{c}{4\pi}\int \mathbf{E}\cdot\mathbf{curl}\,\mathbf{H}\,\mathrm{d}V \\ &= \delta t\frac{c}{4\pi}\int \mathrm{div}\,(\mathbf{E}\times\mathbf{H})\,\mathrm{d}V - \delta t\frac{c}{4\pi}\int \mathbf{H}\cdot\mathbf{curl}\,\mathbf{E}\,\mathrm{d}V. \end{aligned}$$

The first integral, on being transformed to an integral over an infinitely distant surface, is seen to be zero. In the second integral we substitute $\mathbf{curl}\,\mathbf{E}$ from (30.1) and put $\delta\mathbf{B} = \delta t\,\partial\mathbf{B}/\partial t$ for the change in the magnetic induction, obtaining finally

$$\delta R = \int \mathbf{H}\cdot\delta\mathbf{B}\,\mathrm{d}V/4\pi. \tag{30.2}$$

This formula appears entirely analogous to the expression (10.2) for the work done in an infinitesimal change in the electric field. It must be pointed out, however, that the physical analogy between the two formulae is actually not complete, since $\mathbf{H}$, unlike $\mathbf{E}$, is not the mean value of the microscopic field.

Having derived formula (30.2), we can write down all the thermodynamic relations for a magnetic substance in a magnetic field by analogy with those given in §10 for a dielectric in an electric field, simply replacing $\mathbf{E}$ and $\mathbf{D}$ by $\mathbf{H}$ and $\mathbf{B}$ respectively. We shall give some of these formulae here for purposes of reference. The differentials of the total free energy and the total internal energy are

$$\begin{aligned} \delta\mathscr{F} &= -\mathscr{S}\delta T + \int \mathbf{H}\cdot\delta\mathbf{B}\,\mathrm{d}V/4\pi, \\ \delta\mathscr{U} &= T\delta\mathscr{S} + \int \mathbf{H}\cdot\delta\mathbf{B}\,\mathrm{d}V/4\pi, \end{aligned} \tag{30.3}$$

and those of the corresponding quantities per unit volume are

$$\begin{aligned} \mathrm{d}F &= -S\,\mathrm{d}T + \zeta\,\mathrm{d}\rho + \mathbf{H}\cdot\mathrm{d}\mathbf{B}/4\pi, \\ \mathrm{d}U &= T\,\mathrm{d}S + \zeta\,\mathrm{d}\rho + \mathbf{H}\cdot\mathrm{d}\mathbf{B}/4\pi. \end{aligned} \tag{30.4}$$

We need also the thermodynamic potentials

$$\tilde{U} = U - \mathbf{H}\cdot\mathbf{B}/4\pi, \qquad \tilde{F} = F - \mathbf{H}\cdot\mathbf{B}/4\pi, \tag{30.5}$$

for which

$$\begin{aligned} \mathrm{d}\tilde{F} &= -S\mathrm{d}T + \zeta\,\mathrm{d}\rho - \mathbf{B}\cdot\mathrm{d}\mathbf{H}/4\pi, \\ \mathrm{d}\tilde{U} &= T\mathrm{d}S + \zeta\,\mathrm{d}\rho - \mathbf{B}\cdot\mathrm{d}\mathbf{H}/4\pi. \end{aligned} \tag{30.6}$$

If the linear relation $\mathbf{B} = \mu\mathbf{H}$ holds, we can write the expressions for all these quantities in the form

$$\begin{aligned} U &= U_0(S,\rho) + B^2/8\pi\mu, \qquad & F &= F_0(T,\rho) + B^2/8\pi\mu, \\ \tilde{U} &= U_0(S,\rho) - \mu H^2/8\pi, \qquad & \tilde{F} &= F_0(T,\rho) - \mu H^2/8\pi. \end{aligned} \tag{30.7}$$

The work δR (or, what is the same thing, the change δF at constant temperature) can be written in a different form, in terms of the current density and the vector potential of the magnetic field. For this purpose we put $\delta\mathbf{B} = \mathbf{curl}\,\delta\mathbf{A}$ and

$$\begin{aligned} (\delta\mathscr{F})_T &= \frac{1}{4\pi}\int \mathbf{H}\cdot\mathbf{curl}\,\delta\mathbf{A}\,\mathrm{d}V \\ &= -\frac{1}{4\pi}\int \mathrm{div}\,(\mathbf{H}\times\delta\mathbf{A})\,\mathrm{d}V + \frac{1}{4\pi}\int \delta\mathbf{A}\cdot\mathbf{curl}\,\mathbf{H}\,\mathrm{d}V. \end{aligned}$$

The first integral is again zero, and the second gives

$$(\delta\mathscr{F})_T = \int \mathbf{j}\cdot\delta\mathbf{A}\,\mathrm{d}V/c. \tag{30.8}$$

A similar transformation gives

$$(\delta\tilde{\mathscr{F}})_T = -\int \mathbf{A}\cdot\delta\mathbf{j}\,\mathrm{d}V/c. \tag{30.9}$$

It is useful to note that in macroscopic electrodynamics the currents (sources of the magnetic field) are mathematically analogues of the potentials, not of the charges (the sources of the electric field). This is seen by comparing formulae (30.8) and (30.9) with the corresponding results for an electric field:

$$(\delta\mathscr{F})_T = \int \phi\delta\rho\,\mathrm{d}V, \qquad (\delta\tilde{\mathscr{F}})_T = -\int \rho\delta\phi\,\mathrm{d}V \tag{30.10}$$

(see (10.13), (10.14)). We observe that the charges and potentials appear in these formulae in the opposite order to the currents and potentials in formulae (30.8), (30.9).

On account of the complete formal correspondence between the thermodynamic relations (expressed in terms of field and induction) for electric and magnetic fields, the thermodynamic inequalities derived in §18 can also be applied to magnetic fields. In particular, we have seen that it follows from these inequalities that $\epsilon > 0$. In the electric case this result was of no interest, because it was weaker than the inequality $\epsilon > 1$ which follows on other grounds. In the magnetic case, however, the corresponding inequality $\mu > 0$ is very important, as it is the only restriction on the values which can be taken by the magnetic permeability.

§31. The total free energy of a magnetic substance

In §11 expressions have been derived for the total free energy $\mathscr{F}$ of a dielectric in an electric field. One of the thermodynamic properties of this quantity is that the change in it gives the work done by the electric field on the body when the charges producing the field remain constant. In a magnetic field a similar part is played by the free energy $\tilde{\mathscr{F}}$, since for given currents producing the field the change in $\tilde{\mathscr{F}}$ is the work done on the body.

The following derivation is entirely analogous to that given in §11. The "total" quantity $\tilde{\mathscr{F}}$ is defined as

$$\tilde{\mathscr{F}} = \int \left(\tilde{F} + \frac{\mathfrak{H}^2}{8\pi}\right) \mathrm{d}V, \tag{31.1}$$

where $\mathfrak{H}$ is the magnetic field which would be produced by the given currents in the absence of the magnetisable medium. The plus sign appears in the parenthesis (instead of the minus sign as in (11.1)) because the value of $\tilde{\mathscr{F}}$ for a magnetic field in a vacuum is $-\int(\mathfrak{H}^2/8\pi)\,\mathrm{d}V$ (see (30.7)). The integration in (31.1) is taken over all space, including the volume occupied by the conductors in which flow the currents producing the field.†

Let us calculate the change in $\tilde{\mathscr{F}}$ (for a given temperature and no departure from thermodynamic equilibrium in the medium) corresponding to an infinitesimal change in the field. Since $\delta\tilde{F} = -\mathbf{B}\cdot\delta\mathbf{H}/4\pi$, we have

$$\begin{aligned}\delta\tilde{\mathscr{F}} &= -\int(\mathbf{B}\cdot\delta\mathbf{H} - \boldsymbol{\mathfrak{H}}\cdot\delta\boldsymbol{\mathfrak{H}})\,\mathrm{d}V/4\pi \\ &= -\int(\mathbf{H}-\boldsymbol{\mathfrak{H}})\cdot\delta\boldsymbol{\mathfrak{H}}\,\mathrm{d}V/4\pi - \int\mathbf{B}\cdot(\delta\mathbf{H}-\delta\boldsymbol{\mathfrak{H}})\,\mathrm{d}V/4\pi - \int(\mathbf{B}-\mathbf{H})\cdot\delta\boldsymbol{\mathfrak{H}}\,\mathrm{d}V/4\pi.\end{aligned} \tag{31.2}$$

Introducing the vector potential $\boldsymbol{\mathfrak{A}}$ of the field $\boldsymbol{\mathfrak{H}}$, we can write in the first term

$$\begin{aligned}(\mathbf{H}-\boldsymbol{\mathfrak{H}})\cdot\delta\boldsymbol{\mathfrak{H}} &= (\mathbf{H}-\boldsymbol{\mathfrak{H}})\cdot\mathbf{curl}\,\delta\boldsymbol{\mathfrak{A}} \\ &= \mathrm{div}\,[\delta\boldsymbol{\mathfrak{A}}\cdot(\mathbf{H}-\boldsymbol{\mathfrak{H}})] + \delta\boldsymbol{\mathfrak{A}}\cdot\mathbf{curl}\,(\mathbf{H}-\boldsymbol{\mathfrak{H}}).\end{aligned}$$

† In §11 we took the integration in (11.1) over all space except the volume occupied by the charged conductors producing the field. This was possible because there is no electric field in a conductor, charged or not. There is a magnetic field, however, inside the conductors which carry the currents, and they cannot be excluded in calculating the total free energy.

By definition, the fields **H** and $\mathfrak{H}$ are produced by the same currents **j**, the distribution of which over the volume of the conductors is (see §29) independent of the field which they produce, i.e. is independent of the presence or absence of magnetic substances in the surrounding medium. Hence **curl H** and **curl** $\mathfrak{H}$ are both equal to $4\pi\mathbf{j}/c$, and so $\mathbf{curl}\,(\mathbf{H}-\mathfrak{H}) = 0$. The integral of $\mathrm{div}[\delta\mathfrak{A}\cdot(\mathbf{H}-\mathfrak{H})]$ is transformed into an integral over an infinitely distant surface, and so vanishes.

Similarly, we see that the second term on the right of (31.2) is zero; thus

$$\delta\mathscr{F} = -\int(\mathbf{B}-\mathbf{H})\cdot\delta\mathfrak{H}\,\mathrm{d}V/4\pi$$

$$= -\int\mathbf{M}\cdot\delta\mathfrak{H}\,\mathrm{d}V. \tag{31.3}$$

The expression which we have obtained for $\delta\mathscr{F}$ is exactly similar to (11.3) for the electrostatic problem. In particular, in a uniform magnetic field $\mathfrak{H}$ we have for $\mathrm{d}\mathscr{F}$ an expression analogous to (11.5):

$$\mathrm{d}\mathscr{F} = -\mathscr{S}\,\mathrm{d}T-\mathscr{M}\cdot\mathrm{d}\mathfrak{H}, \tag{31.4}$$

where $\mathscr{M}$ is the total magnetic moment of the body.

Without repeating the subsequent calculations, we shall write down the following formulae by analogy with those in §11. If the linear relation $\mathbf{B} = \mu\mathbf{H}$ holds, we have

$$\mathscr{F}-\mathscr{F}_0(V,T) = -\int\tfrac{1}{2}\mathfrak{H}\cdot\mathbf{M}\,\mathrm{d}V. \tag{31.5}$$

In particular, if the external field is homogeneous, then

$$\mathscr{F}-\mathscr{F}_0(V,T) = -\tfrac{1}{2}\mathfrak{H}\cdot\mathscr{M}. \tag{31.6}$$

In the general case of an arbitrary relation between **B** and **H**, $\mathscr{F}$ can be calculated from the formula

$$\mathscr{F} = \int\left(\tilde{F}+\frac{\mathbf{H}\cdot\mathbf{B}}{8\pi}-\tfrac{1}{2}\mathbf{M}\cdot\mathfrak{H}\right)\mathrm{d}V$$

$$= \int\left(F-\frac{\mathbf{H}\cdot\mathbf{B}}{8\pi}-\tfrac{1}{2}\mathbf{M}\cdot\mathfrak{H}\right)\mathrm{d}V. \tag{31.7}$$

In §11 we gave also the simpler formulae obtained when the dielectric susceptibility is small. The analogous case for the magnetic problem is especially important because, as mentioned above, the magnetic susceptibility of the majority of bodies is indeed small. In this case

$$\mathscr{F}-\mathscr{F}_0 = -\tfrac{1}{2}\chi\int\mathfrak{H}^2\,\mathrm{d}V. \tag{31.8}$$

We can also derive results for the magnetic field analogous to those obtained in §14. These concern the change in the thermodynamic quantities resulting from an infinitesimal change in the magnetic permeability μ, the field sources being assumed unchanged. It is clear from the foregoing that we must consider the change in $\tilde{\mathscr{F}}$, and not that in $\mathscr{F}$ as in §14. We shall not repeat the derivation, which is similar to that of (14.1), but merely give the result:

$$\delta\tilde{\mathscr{F}} = -\int \delta\mu\, H^2 \mathrm{d}V/8\pi. \tag{31.9}$$

In §14 we used this formula to deduce that the dielectric susceptibility of any substance is positive. In the magnetic case we cannot draw this conclusion, and the magnetic susceptibility may be of either sign. The reason for this marked difference is that the Hamiltonian of a system of charges moving in a magnetic field contains not only terms linear in the field (as in the electric case) but also quadratic terms. Hence, in determining the change in the free energy of the body in the magnetic field by means of perturbation theory as in (14.2), we have a contribution in the first approximation as well as the second. In such a case no general conclusion can be drawn concerning the sign of the variation. It is positive for paramagnetic bodies and negative for diamagnetic ones.

In §14 we also drew conclusions concerning the direction of motion of bodies in an electric field. Similar conclusions follow from (31.9), but, since μ may be either greater or less than 1, there is no universal result. For example, in an almost uniform field paramagnetic bodies ($\mu > 1$) move in the direction of H increasing, and diamagnetic bodies ($\mu < 1$) in the opposite direction.

§32. The energy of a system of currents

Let us consider a system of conductors with currents flowing in them and assume that neither the conductors nor the medium surrounding them are ferromagnetic, so that $\mathbf{B} = \mu\mathbf{H}$ everywhere. According to §30, the total free energy of the system is given in terms of the magnetic field of the currents by

$$\mathscr{F} = \int \mathbf{H}\cdot\mathbf{B}\, \mathrm{d}V/8\pi. \tag{32.1}$$

Here we omit the quantity $\mathscr{F}_0$, which is a constant (at a given temperature) and is not related to the currents. The integration in (32.1) is taken over all space, both inside and outside the conductors.

The same energy can also be expressed in terms of the currents by means of the integral

$$\mathscr{F} = \int \mathbf{A}\cdot\mathbf{j}\, \mathrm{d}V/2c; \tag{32.2}$$

cf. the derivation of (30.8) from (30.2). Here the integration extends only over the conductors, because $\mathbf{j} = 0$ outside them.

Since the field equations are linear, the magnetic field can be written as the sum of the fields resulting from each current alone with no current in the other conductors: $\mathbf{H} = \Sigma\mathbf{H}_a$. Then the total free energy (32.1) is

$$\mathscr{F} = \sum_a \mathscr{F}_{aa} + \sum_{a>b} \mathscr{F}_{ab}, \tag{32.3}$$

where

$$\mathscr{F}_{aa} = \int \mathbf{H}_a \cdot \mathbf{B}_a \, \mathrm{d}V/8\pi, \qquad \mathscr{F}_{ab} = \int \mathbf{H}_a \cdot \mathbf{B}_b \, \mathrm{d}V/4\pi. \tag{32.4}$$

We have put $\mathscr{F}_{ab} = \mathscr{F}_{ba}$, since $\mathbf{H}_a \cdot \mathbf{B}_b = \mu \mathbf{H}_a \cdot \mathbf{H}_b = \mathbf{H}_b \cdot \mathbf{B}_a$, where μ is the magnetic permeability at any point. The quantity $\mathscr{F}_{aa}$ may be called the *free self-energy* of the current in the ath conductor, and $\mathscr{F}_{ab}$ the *interaction energy* of the ath and bth conductors. It should be borne in mind, however, that these names are strictly correct only if the magnetic properties of both the conductors and the medium are neglected. Otherwise the field, and therefore the energy, of each current depend on the position and magnetic permeability of the other conductors.

The quantities (32.4) can also be expressed in terms of the currents $\mathbf{j}_a$ in each conductor, in accordance with formula (32.2):

$$\mathscr{F}_{aa} = \int \mathbf{j}_a \cdot \mathbf{A}_a \, \mathrm{d}V_a/2c, \qquad \mathscr{F}_{ab} = \int \mathbf{j}_a \cdot \mathbf{A}_b \, \mathrm{d}V_a/c = \int \mathbf{j}_b \cdot \mathbf{A}_a \, \mathrm{d}V_b/c. \tag{32.5}$$

The integral in $\mathscr{F}_{aa}$ is here taken only over the volume of the ath conductor; $\mathscr{F}_{ab}$ can be written as either of the two expressions, in which the integration is over the volume of the ath and bth conductor respectively.

When the distribution of the current density over the volume of the conductor is given, $\mathscr{F}_{aa}$ depends only on the total current J_a passing through a cross-section. Both the current density $\mathbf{j}$ and the field which it produces will be proportional to J_a. Hence the integral $\mathscr{F}_{aa}$ is proportional to J_a^2, and we write it

$$\mathscr{F}_{aa} = L_{aa} J_a^2/2c^2, \tag{32.6}$$

where L_{aa} is called the *self-inductance* of the conductor. Similarly, the interaction energy of two currents is proportional to the product $J_a J_b$:

$$\mathscr{F}_{ab} = L_{ab} J_a J_b/c^2. \tag{32.7}$$

The quantity L_{ab} is called the *mutual inductance* of the conductors. Thus the total free energy of a system of currents is

$$\mathscr{F} = \frac{1}{2c^2} \sum_a L_{aa} J_a^2 + \frac{1}{c^2} \sum_{a>b} L_{ab} J_a J_b = \frac{1}{2c^2} \sum_a \sum_b L_{ab} J_a J_b. \tag{32.8}$$

The condition that this quadratic form should be positive definite places certain restrictions on the values of the coefficients. In particular $L_{aa} > 0$ for all a, and $L_{aa}L_{bb} > L_{ab}^2$.

The calculation of the energy of currents in the general case of arbitrary three-dimensional conductors requires a complete solution of the field equations, and is a difficult problem. It becomes simpler if the magnetic permeability of both the conductors and the surrounding medium can be taken as unity. It should be noted that the energy of the currents is then no longer dependent on the thermodynamic state (in particular, on the temperature) of the bodies, and hence the free energy in the above formulae may be referred to simply as the energy.

For $\mu = 1$ the vector field potential due to the currents $\mathbf{j}$ is given by formula (29.12). Hence the self-energy of the ath conductor is

$$\mathscr{F}_{aa} = \frac{1}{2c^2}\int\int\frac{\mathbf{j}\cdot\mathbf{j}'}{R}\mathrm{d}V\,\mathrm{d}V', \tag{32.9}$$

where both integrations are taken over the volume of the conductor considered, and R is the distance between $\mathrm{d}V$ and $\mathrm{d}V'$. Similarly, the mutual energy of two conductors is

$$\mathscr{F}_{ab} = \frac{1}{c^2}\int\int\frac{\mathbf{j}_a\cdot\mathbf{j}_b}{R}\mathrm{d}V_a\,\mathrm{d}V_b, \tag{32.10}$$

where $\mathrm{d}V_a$ and $\mathrm{d}V_b$ are volume elements in the two conductors.

The mutual energy of two linear currents is particularly easy to calculate. In formula (32.10) we change from volume currents to linear ones by replacing $\mathbf{j}_a\mathrm{d}V_a$ and $\mathbf{j}_b\mathrm{d}V_b$ by $J_a\mathrm{d}\mathbf{l}_a$ and $J_b\mathrm{d}\mathbf{l}_b$ respectively, and we find that the mutual inductance is $L_{ab} = \oint\oint\mathrm{d}\mathbf{l}_a\cdot\mathrm{d}\mathbf{l}_b/R$. In this approximation, therefore, L_{ab} depends only on the shape, size and relative position of the two currents, and not on the distribution of current over the cross-section of each wire. It must be emphasised that this simple formula can be obtained for linear currents without imposing the condition that $\mu = 1$. In the approximation where the thickness of the wires is neglected, their magnetic properties have no effect on the field which they produce, and therefore no effect on their mutual energy. If the magnetic permeability μ of the medium surrounding the wires is different from unity, the vector potential is, by (29.15), simply multiplied by μ, and therefore so is the magnetic induction. The mutual inductance is therefore multiplied by the same factor, so that

$$L_{ab} = \mu\oint\oint\mathrm{d}\mathbf{l}_a\cdot\mathrm{d}\mathbf{l}_b/R. \tag{32.11}$$

The self-inductance of linear conductors is much more difficult to calculate; we shall discuss it in §33.

The total energy of a system of linear currents can be written in still another form. To do this, we return to the integral (32.2), which for linear currents becomes

$$\mathscr{F} = \frac{1}{2c}\sum_a J_a \oint \mathbf{A}\cdot d\mathbf{l}_a, \tag{32.12}$$

where **A** is the vector potential of the total field at the element $d\mathbf{l}_a$ of the ath conductor. The main error in going from (32.2) to (32.12) arises from neglecting the change in the field (including the field of the current considered) over the cross-section of the wire. Each of the contour integrals in (32.12) can be transformed into a surface integral:

$$\oint \mathbf{A}\cdot d\mathbf{l}_a = \int \mathbf{curl}\,\mathbf{A}\cdot d\mathbf{f}_a = \int \mathbf{B}\cdot d\mathbf{f}_a,$$

i.e. it is the flux of the magnetic induction or *magnetic flux* through the circuit of the ath current. We denote this flux by Φ_a. Then

$$\mathscr{F} = \frac{1}{2c}\sum_a J_a \Phi_a. \tag{32.13}$$

Similarly, the free energy $\tilde{\mathscr{F}}$ of a linear current J in an external magnetic field, i.e. the energy without the self-energy of the field sources, can be expressed in terms of the magnetic flux. Evidently

$$\tilde{\mathscr{F}} = J\Phi/c, \tag{32.14}$$

where Φ is the flux of the external field through the circuit of the current J. If the external field is uniform, and $\mu = 1$ in the external medium, then $\Phi = \mathfrak{H}\cdot\int d\mathbf{f}$. Introducing the magnetic moment of the current in accordance with (29.18), we have $\tilde{\mathscr{F}} = \mathscr{M}\cdot\mathfrak{H}$.

Knowing the energy of a system of currents as a function of their shape, size and relative position, we can determine the forces on the conductors by simply differentiating with respect to the appropriate co-ordinates. Here, however, the question arises which characteristics of the currents should be kept constant in the differentiation. It is most convenient to differentiate at constant current. In this case the free energy is represented by $\tilde{\mathscr{F}}$, and so the generalised force F_q in the direction of a generalised co-ordinate q is $F_q = -(\partial\tilde{\mathscr{F}}/\partial q)_{J,T}$. The suffixes show that the differentiation is effected at constant current and constant temperature. Since we omit the term independent of the currents in the free energy, $\mathscr{F}$ and $\tilde{\mathscr{F}}$ differ only in sign, and so

$$F_q = -\left(\frac{\partial\tilde{\mathscr{F}}}{\partial q}\right)_J = \left(\frac{\partial\mathscr{F}}{\partial q}\right)_J = \frac{1}{2c^2}\sum_{a,b} J_a J_b \frac{\partial L_{ab}}{\partial q}; \tag{32.15}$$

here and henceforward the suffix T to the derivatives is omitted, for brevity.

In particular, the forces exerted on a conductor by its own magnetic field are given by the formula

$$F_q = \frac{1}{2c^2} J^2 \frac{\partial L}{\partial q}, \tag{32.16}$$

where L is the self-inductance of the conductor. The nature of these forces can be seen as follows. For given current (and temperature), $\tilde{\mathscr{F}}$ tends to be a minimum. Since $\tilde{\mathscr{F}} = -LJ^2/2c^2$, this means that the forces on the conductor will tend to increase its self-inductance. The latter, having the dimensions of length, must be proportional to the dimension of the conductor. Thus the effect of the magnetic field is to increase the size of the conductor.

For a current in an external magnetic field we have†

$$\tilde{\mathscr{F}} = -\mathscr{F} = -\mathscr{M}\cdot\mathfrak{H}. \tag{32.17}$$

In all the above formulae for the energy it is assumed that there is a linear relation between the magnetic field and induction. In the general case where this relation is arbitrary, analogous differential relations can be set up. The change in the free energy resulting from an infinitesimal change in the field (at constant temperature) is, by (30.8), $\delta\mathscr{F} = \int \mathbf{j}\cdot\delta\mathbf{A}\,\mathrm{d}V/c$ or, for a system of linear currents,

$$\delta\mathscr{F} = \frac{1}{c}\sum_a J_a \oint \delta\mathbf{A}\cdot\mathrm{d}\mathbf{l}_a.$$

Proceeding as in the derivation of (32.13) from (32.12), we have

$$\delta\mathscr{F} = \frac{1}{c}\sum_a J_a \delta\Phi_a. \tag{32.18}$$

Similarly, we find from (30.9)

$$\delta\tilde{\mathscr{F}} = -\frac{1}{c}\sum_a \Phi_a \delta J_a. \tag{32.19}$$

Thus we can say that, for a system of linear currents, $\mathscr{F}$ is the thermodynamic potential with respect to the magnetic fluxes, and $\tilde{\mathscr{F}}$ with respect to the currents, the two potentials being related by

$$\tilde{\mathscr{F}} = \mathscr{F} - \frac{1}{c}\sum_a J_a \Phi_a. \tag{32.20}$$

† The factor $\frac{1}{2}$ which appears in (31.6) is absent in (32.17) because the magnetic moment of the current in the latter equation is independent of the field, whereas the magnetic moment in (31.6) is itself due to the field.

Whatever the magnetic properties of the substance, therefore, the thermodynamic relations

$$J_a/c = \partial\mathscr{F}/\partial\Phi_a, \qquad \Phi_a/c = -\partial\mathscr{F}/\partial J_a \tag{32.21}$$

hold. If these formulae are applied to the case where the field and induction are linearly related, so that $\mathscr{F}$ is given by (32.8), we obtain

$$\Phi_a = \frac{1}{c}\sum_b L_{ab}J_b. \tag{32.22}$$

Thus the inductances are the coefficients of proportionality between the magnetic fluxes and the currents which produce the magnetic field. The product $L_{ab}J_b/c$ is the magnetic flux through the circuit of the current J_a due to the current J_b ($b \neq a$), and $L_{aa}J_a/c$ is that due to the current J_a itself.

§33. The self-inductance of linear conductors

In calculating the self-inductance of a linear conductor its thickness cannot be entirely neglected as it was in calculating the mutual inductance of two conductors. If it were, we should obtain from (32.9) the self-inductance $L = \oint\oint \mathbf{dl}\cdot\mathbf{dl}'/R$, where both integrals are taken along the same circuit, and this integral is logarithmically divergent because of the contribution from small R.

The exact value of the self-inductance of a conductor depends on the distribution of current in it, which may vary with the manner of excitation of the current, i.e. with the manner of application of the electromotive force. For a linear conductor, however, the self-inductance does not, to a fairly high accuracy, depend on the distribution of current over the cross-section.†

Let us write the self-inductance as $L = L_e + L_i$, where L_e and L_i result from the magnetic field energy outside and inside the conductor respectively. For a linear conductor, the "external" part L_e makes the main contribution to the self-inductance. This is because most of the magnetic energy of a closed linear circuit resides in the field at distances from the wire large compared with its thickness. For the energy per unit length of an infinite straight wire is

$$(\mu_e/8\pi)\int H^2\cdot 2\pi r\,\mathrm{d}r = (\mu_e/8\pi)\int (2J/cr)^2\cdot 2\pi r\,\mathrm{d}r = (\mu_e J^2/c^2)\int \mathrm{d}r/r,$$

where r is the distance from the axis of the wire and μ_e the magnetic permeability of the external medium. This integral diverges logarithmically for large r. For a closed linear circuit, of course, this divergence disappears, because the integral is "cut off" at distances of the order of the dimension

† More precisely, it is independent of the distribution of current provided that the current density varies appreciably only over distances comparable with the thickness a of the wire. If, however, the distribution is such that the current density varies appreciably over distances small compared with a (as happens, for particular reasons, in the *skin effect* and in superconductors), then the self-inductance does depend on the distribution.

of the circuit. We obtain an approximate value for the energy on multiplying this integral by the total length l of the wire, and taking l as the upper limit and the radius a of the wire as the lower limit. The result is $(\mu_e J^2 l/c^2)\log(l/a)$, and hence the self-inductance is

$$L = 2\mu_e l \log(l/a). \tag{33.1}$$

This expression is said to be of *logarithmic accuracy*: its relative error is of the order of $1/\log(l/a)$, and the ratio l/a is assumed to be so large that its logarithm is large.†

A particular case of a linear conductor is a *solenoid*, which consists of a wire wound in a helix, with the turns very close together. Neglecting the thickness of the wire and the distance between the turns, we have simply a conducting cylindrical surface with a "surface" conduction current on it. The equation $\mathbf{curl\,H} = 4\pi\mathbf{j}/c$ within the conductor is here replaced by the boundary condition.

$$\mathbf{n}\times(\mathbf{H}_2-\mathbf{H}_1) = 4\pi\mathbf{g}/c, \tag{33.2}$$

where $\mathbf{g}$ is the surface current density, $\mathbf{H}_1$ and $\mathbf{H}_2$ the fields on each side of the surface, and $\mathbf{n}$ the unit normal vector into medium 2; cf. the derivation of (27.14).

If the solenoid is of infinite length, the magnetic field which it produces can be found very simply. The surface currents flow in circles, and their density $g = nJ$, where J is the current in the wire and n the number of turns per unit length of the solenoid. The field outside the cylinder is zero; the field inside is uniform and along the axis of the cylinder, and is $H = 4\pi nJ/c$. For this field evidently satisfies the equations $\operatorname{div}\mathbf{H} = 0$, $\mathbf{curl\,H} = 0$ in all space outside the conducting surface, and also the boundary condition (33.2) at that surface.

Accordingly, the field energy per unit length of the cylinder is

$$\mu_e H^2\pi b^2/8\pi = 2\pi^2 n^2 b^2 \mu_e J^2/c^2,$$

where b is the radius of the cylinder and μ_e pertains to the material within the solenoid. Neglecting the end effects, we can apply this formula also to a solenoid whose length h is finite, but large compared with b. Then the self-inductance is

$$L = 4\pi^2 n^2 b^2 h\mu_e = 2\pi\mu_e nbl, \tag{33.3}$$

where $l = 2\pi bnh$ is the total length of the wire. The greater self-inductance of a solenoid as compared with that of a straight wire of equal length (cf. (33.1)) is, of course, due to the mutual induction between adjoining turns.

† The assertion made above that the self-inductance is independent of the current distribution actually applies not only to the approximation (33.1) but also to the next approximation, in which terms not containing the large logarithm are included (or, what is the same thing, the argument of the logarithm includes a coefficient); see the Problems at the end of this section.

PROBLEMS†

PROBLEM 1. Determine the self-inductance of a closed circuit of thin wire of circular cross-section.

SOLUTION. The magnetic field in the wire can be taken to be the same as that inside an infinite straight cylinder: $H = 2Jr/ca^2$, where r is the distance from the axis of the wire and a its radius. Hence we find the internal part of the self-inductance:

$$L_i = \frac{2c^2}{J^2}\frac{\mu_i}{8\pi}\int H^2\,dV = \tfrac{1}{2}l\mu_i, \tag{1}$$

where l is the length of the wire.

To calculate L_e, we notice that the field outside a thin wire is independent of the distribution of current over its cross-section. In particular, the energy $\mathscr{F}_e$ of the external magnetic field is unchanged if we assume that the current flows only on the surface of the wire. The field inside the wire is then zero, and $\mathscr{F}_e$ may be calculated as the total energy from formula (32.2). On account of the assumed surface distribution of the current, the integral in this formula becomes a line integral along the axis of the wire, and so the external part of the self-inductance is

$$L_e = \frac{2c^2}{J^2}\frac{J}{2c}\oint [\mathbf{A}]_{r=a}\cdot d\mathbf{l},$$

where the value of $\mathbf{A}$ in the integrand is taken at the surface of the wire. In obtaining this formula we also use the fact that, in the approximation used here, the field is constant over the perimeter of a cross-section.

Having reduced the problem to that of calculating $\mathbf{A}$ for $r = a$, we now make a different assumption concerning the current distribution, namely that the whole current J flows along the axis of the wire. The field on the surface of the wire is, in the approximation considered, unchanged by this assumption (nor would it be changed for a straight wire of circular cross-section). Then, by formula (29.14), we have

$$[\mathbf{A}]_{r=a} = \frac{J}{c}\left[\oint \frac{d\mathbf{l}}{R}\right]_{r=a},$$

where R is the distance from the element $d\mathbf{l}$ of the axis to a given point on the surface of the wire. We divide the integral into two parts, one for which $R > \Delta$ and the other for which $R < \Delta$, where Δ is a distance small compared with the dimension of the circuit but large compared with the radius a of the wire.‡ In the integral where $R > \Delta$, a may be neglected and R taken simply as the distance between two points on the circuit. The vector integral where $R < \Delta$ may be assumed to be along the tangent at the point considered. Denoting by $\mathbf{t}$ the unit vector in that direction, we have

$$\left[\int_{R<\Delta} \frac{d\mathbf{l}}{R}\right]_{r=a} \cong \mathbf{t}\int_{-\Delta}^{\Delta} \frac{dl}{\sqrt{(a^2+l^2)}} = 2\mathbf{t}\sinh^{-1}(\Delta/a)$$

$$\cong 2\mathbf{t}\log(2\Delta/a).$$

This expression can be written as the integral

$$\int_{\Delta>R>\frac{1}{2}a} d\mathbf{l}/R,$$

where R is again the distance between points on the circuit. Adding the two integrals for $R > \Delta$ and $R < \Delta$, we obtain

$$[\mathbf{A}]_{r=a} = \frac{J}{c}\int_{R>\frac{1}{2}a} \frac{d\mathbf{l}}{R},$$

for which the arbitrary parameter Δ has disappeared, as it should.

---

† In Problems 1–6 we put $\mu_e = 1$.

‡ A similar procedure was used to calculate the capacity of a thin ring in §2, Problem 4.

The final result is therefore

$$L_e = \iint_{R>\frac{1}{2}a} \frac{\mathbf{dl}\cdot\mathbf{dl}'}{R}. \tag{2}$$

The integration here extends over all pairs of points on the circuit whose distance apart exceeds $\frac{1}{2}a$.

PROBLEM 2. Determine the self-inductance of a thin wire ring (of radius b) of circular cross-section (of radius a).

SOLUTION. The integrand in (2), Problem 1, depends only on the central angle ϕ subtended by the chord R, and $R = 2b \sin \frac{1}{2}\phi$, while $\mathbf{dl}\cdot\mathbf{dl}' = dl dl' \cos \phi$. Hence

$$L_e = 2\int_{\phi_0}^{\pi} \frac{\cos\phi\cdot 2\pi b\cdot b\, d\phi}{2b \sin\frac{1}{2}\phi} = 4\pi b[-\log\tan\tfrac{1}{4}\phi_0 - 2\cos\tfrac{1}{2}\phi_0].$$

The lower limit of integration is determined from $2b \sin \frac{1}{2}\phi_0 = \frac{1}{2}a$, whence $\phi_0 \cong a/2b$. Substituting this value and adding $L_i = \pi b\mu_i$, we have to the required accuracy

$$L = 4\pi b[\log(8b/a) - 2 + \tfrac{1}{4}\mu_i].$$

In particular, for $\mu_i = 1$ we obtain

$$L = 4\pi b[\log(8b/a) - (7/4)].$$

PROBLEM 3. Determine the extension of a ring of wire (with $\mu_i = 1$) under the action of the magnetic field of a current flowing in it.

SOLUTION. The internal stresses parallel and perpendicular to the axis are, by (32.16), given by

$$\pi a^2 \sigma_\parallel = \frac{J^2}{2c^2}\frac{\partial L}{\partial(2\pi b)}, \qquad 2\pi a b\sigma_\perp = \frac{J^2}{2c^2}\frac{\partial L}{\partial a}.$$

Substituting L from Problem 2, we have

$$\sigma_\parallel = \frac{J^2}{\pi a^2 c^2}\left[\log\frac{8b}{a} - \frac{3}{4}\right], \qquad \sigma_\perp = -\frac{J^2}{a^2 c^2}.$$

Hence the required relative extension of the ring is†

$$\frac{\Delta b}{b} = \frac{1}{E}(\sigma_\parallel - 2\sigma\sigma_\perp) = \frac{J^2}{\pi a^2 c^2 E}\left(\log\frac{8b}{a} - \frac{3}{4} + 2\pi\sigma\right),$$

where E is Young's modulus and σ Poisson's ratio for the wire.

PROBLEM 4. Determine the self-inductance per unit length of a system of two parallel straight wires (with $\mu_i = 1$) having circular cross-sections of radii a and b, with their axes a distance h apart, and carrying equal currents J in opposite directions (Fig. 18).

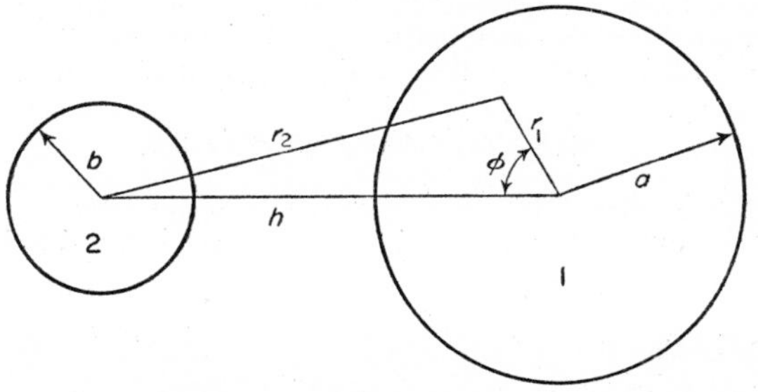

FIG. 18

† See *Theory of Elasticity*, §5, Pergamon Press, London, 1959.

SOLUTION. The vector potential of the magnetic field of each current is parallel to the axes of the wires, and so the two vector potentials can be added algebraically. For the magnetic field of wire 1, with a uniformly distributed current $+J$, we have in cylindrical co-ordinates

$$A_z = \frac{J}{c}\left(C - \frac{r^2}{a^2}\right) \text{ for } r < a,$$

$$A_z = \frac{J}{c}\left(C - 1 - 2\log\frac{r}{a}\right) \text{ for } r > a,$$

where C is an arbitrary constant; A_z is continuous at the surface of the wire. The formulae for wire 2 are obtained by substituting b for a and changing the sign of J. Integration over the cross-section of wire 1 in formula (32.2) gives

$$\frac{J^2}{2c^2\pi a^2}\int\left\{\left(C - \frac{r_1^2}{a^2}\right) - \left(C - 1 - 2\log\frac{r_2}{b}\right)\right\} df_1$$

$$= \frac{J^2}{2c^2\pi a^2}\int_0^a\int_0^{2\pi}\left\{1 - \frac{r_1^2}{a^2} + \log\frac{h^2 + r_1^2 - 2hr_1\cos\phi}{b^2}\right\} r_1\,d\phi\,dr_1 = \frac{J^2}{2c^2}\left(\frac{1}{2} + 2\log\frac{h}{b}\right).$$

The integration over the cross-section of wire 2 gives the same thing with a in place of b. The required self-inductance per unit length of the double wire is therefore

$$L = 1 + 2\log(h^2/ab).$$

PROBLEM 5. Determine the self-inductance of a toroidal solenoid.

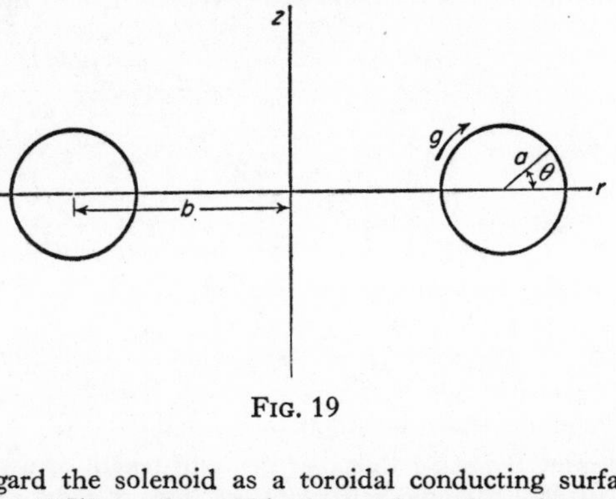

FIG. 19

SOLUTION. We regard the solenoid as a toroidal conducting surface carrying surface currents of density $g = NJ/2\pi r$, where N is the total number of turns and J the current; the co-ordinates and dimensions are as shown in Fig. 19. The magnetic field outside the solenoid is zero, and inside the solenoid $H_{ir} = H_{iz} = 0$, $H_{i\phi} = 2NJ/cr$, where r, z, ϕ are cylindrical co-ordinates; for this solution satisfies the equations $\operatorname{div}\mathbf{H} = 0$, $\mathbf{curl}\,\mathbf{H} = 0$ and the boundary condition (33.2).† The energy of the magnetic field in the solenoid is

$$\int (H_i^2/8\pi)\,dV = (N^2J^2/c^2)\oint z\,dr/r,$$

where the integration is taken along the perimeter of the cross-section, and is easily effected by putting $z = a\sin\theta$, $r = b + a\cos\theta$. The self-inductance is found to be

$$L = 4\pi N^2[b - \sqrt{(b^2 - a^2)}].$$

PROBLEM 6. Determine the end-effect correction of order l/h to the expression (33.3) (with $\mu_e = 1$) for the self-inductance of a cylindrical solenoid.

† It is valid also for an annular solenoid of any cross-section.

SOLUTION. The self-inductance is calculated as a double integral over the surface of the solenoid:

$$L = \frac{1}{J^2}\int\int \frac{\mathbf{g}_1\cdot\mathbf{g}_2}{R}\,\mathrm{d}f_1\,\mathrm{d}f_2,$$

where $\mathbf{g}$ is the surface current density ($g = nJ$). In cylindrical co-ordinates

$$L = 2\pi b^2 n^2 \int_0^h\int_0^h\int_0^{2\pi} \frac{\cos\phi\,\mathrm{d}\phi\,\mathrm{d}z_1\,\mathrm{d}z_2}{\sqrt{[(z_2-z_1)^2+4b^2\sin^2\frac{1}{2}\phi]}}$$

$$= 8\pi b^2 n^2 \int_0^h\int_0^\pi \frac{(h-\zeta)\cos\phi\,\mathrm{d}\phi\,\mathrm{d}\zeta}{\sqrt{(\zeta^2+4b^2\sin^2\frac{1}{2}\phi)}},$$

where ϕ is the angle between the diametral planes through $\mathrm{d}f_1$ and $\mathrm{d}f_2$, and $\zeta = z_2-z_1$. Effecting the integration with respect to ζ, we have for $h \gg b$

$$L \cong 8\pi b^2 n^2 \int_0^\pi \left[h\log\frac{h}{b\sin\frac{1}{2}\phi} - h + 2b\sin\tfrac{1}{2}\phi\right]\cos\phi\,\mathrm{d}\phi,$$

and finally

$$L = 4\pi^2 b^2 n^2 [h - 8b/3\pi].$$

PROBLEM 7. Determine the factor by which the self-inductance of a plane circuit changes when it is placed on the surface of a half-space of magnetic permeability μ_e. The internal part of the self-inductance is neglected.

SOLUTION. It is evident from symmetry that, in the absence of the half-space, the magnetic field of the current is symmetrical about the plane of the circuit, and the lines of magnetic force cross that plane normally. Let this field be $\mathbf{H}_0$. We can satisfy the field equations and the boundary conditions on the surface of the half-space by putting $\mathbf{H} = 2\mu_e\mathbf{H}_0/(\mu_e+1)$ in the vacuum and $\mathbf{B} = \mu_e\mathbf{H} = 2\mu_e\mathbf{H}_0/(\mu_e+1)$ in the medium: B_n and $\mathbf{H}_t$ are then continuous at the boundary, and the circulation of $\mathbf{H}$ along any line of force is equal to that of $\mathbf{H}_0$. Hence we easily see that, when the medium is present, the total energy of the field, and therefore the self-inductance of the circuit, are multiplied by $2\mu_e/(\mu_e+1)$.

§34. Forces in a magnetic field

To determine the forces on matter in a magnetic field hardly any further calculations are necessary, on account of the complete analogy with electrostatics. The analogy is due mainly to the fact that the expressions for the thermodynamic quantities in a magnetic field differ from those for an electric field only in that $\mathbf{E}$ and $\mathbf{D}$ are replaced by $\mathbf{H}$ and $\mathbf{B}$ respectively. In calculating the stress tensor in §15 we used the fact that the electric field satisfies the equation $\mathbf{curl}\,\mathbf{E} = 0$, and is therefore a potential field. The magnetic field satisfies the equation

$$\mathbf{curl}\,\mathbf{H} = 4\pi\mathbf{j}/c, \tag{34.1}$$

which reduces to $\mathbf{curl}\,\mathbf{H} = 0$ only in the absence of conduction currents. In calculating the stress tensor, however, we must always put $\mathbf{j} = 0$. Since $\mathbf{j}$ involves the derivatives of the magnetic field, anallowance for the currents. in calculating the stresses would amount to adding to the stress tensor σ_{ik}

the very small corrections due to the non-uniformity of the field; cf. the second footnote to §15.

Thus all the formulae obtained in §§15 and 16 for the stress tensor can be applied immediately for a magnetic field. For example, in a fluid medium with $\mathbf{B} = \mu\mathbf{H}$ we have

$$\sigma_{ik} = -p_0(\rho, T)\delta_{ik} - \frac{H^2}{8\pi}\left[\mu - \rho\left(\frac{\partial\mu}{\partial\rho}\right)_T\right]\delta_{ik} + \frac{\mu H_i H_k}{4\pi}. \tag{34.2}$$

From this the volume forces are calculated by the formula $f_i = \partial\sigma_{ik}/\partial x_k$. If the medium is a conductor carrying a current, the calculation differs from that in §15 in that the equation $\mathbf{curl\, H} = 0$ is replaced by (34.1).

Differentiating (34.2) and using also the equation $\mathrm{div}\,\mathbf{B} = \mathrm{div}\,(\mu\mathbf{H}) = 0$, we find

$$\mathbf{f} = -\mathbf{grad}\, p_0 + \frac{1}{8\pi}\mathbf{grad}\left[H^2\rho\left(\frac{\partial\mu}{\partial\rho}\right)_T\right] - \frac{H^2}{8\pi}\mathbf{grad}\,\mu - $$
$$-\frac{\mu}{8\pi}\mathbf{grad}\, H^2 + \frac{\mu}{4\pi}(\mathbf{H}\cdot\mathbf{grad})\mathbf{H}.$$

By a well-known formula of vector analysis,

$$\begin{aligned}(\mathbf{H}\cdot\mathbf{grad})\mathbf{H} &= \tfrac{1}{2}\mathbf{grad}\, H^2 - \mathbf{H}\times\mathbf{curl\, H} \\ &= \tfrac{1}{2}\mathbf{grad}\, H^2 + 4\pi\mathbf{j}\times\mathbf{H}/c.\end{aligned}$$

Thus

$$\mathbf{f} = -\mathbf{grad}\, p_0 + \frac{1}{8\pi}\mathbf{grad}\left[H^2\rho\left(\frac{\partial\mu}{\partial\rho}\right)_T\right] - \frac{H^2}{8\pi}\mathbf{grad}\,\mu + \frac{\mu}{c}\mathbf{j}\times\mathbf{H}. \tag{34.3}$$

The last term does not appear in the corresponding formula (15.12). It would, however, be incorrect to suppose that the presence of this term means that a force can be isolated in **f** which is due to the conduction current. The reason is that, by (34.1), the current **j** is inseparable from non-uniformity of the field, and another term in (34.3) also involves the space derivatives of the field. When the magnetic permeability of the medium is appreciably different from unity, all the terms in (34.3) are in general of the same order of magnitude.

If, however, as usually happens, μ is close to 1, the last term in (34.3) gives the main contribution to the force when a conduction current is present, and the remaining terms form only a small correction. In calculating the forces we can put $\mu = 1$, obtaining simply

$$\mathbf{f} = \mathbf{j}\times\mathbf{H}/c. \tag{34.4}$$

The term $-\mathbf{grad}\, p_0$ is of no interest henceforward, and we omit it. For $\mu = 1$ the properties of the substance have no effect on the magnetic phenomena, and the expression (34.4) for the force is equally valid for fluid and for solid conductors. The total force exerted by a magnetic field on a conductor carrying a current is given by the integral

$$\mathbf{F} = \int \mathbf{j} \times \mathbf{H} \, dV/c. \tag{34.5}$$

Formula (34.4) can, of course, be very easily obtained from the familiar expression for the Lorentz force. The macroscopic force on a body at rest in a magnetic field is just the averaged Lorentz force exerted on the charged particles in the body by the microscopic field $\mathbf{h}$: $\mathbf{f} = \overline{\rho \mathbf{v} \times \mathbf{h}}/c$. For $\mu = 1$ the field $\mathbf{h}$ is equal to the mean field $\mathbf{H}$, and the mean value of $\rho \mathbf{v}$ is the conduction current density.

When a conductor moves, the forces (34.4) do mechanical work on it. At first sight it might appear that this contradicts the result that the Lorentz forces do no work on moving charges. In reality, of course, there is no contradiction, since the work done by the Lorentz forces in a moving conductor includes not only the mechanical work but also the work done by the electromotive forces induced in the conductor during its motion. These two quantities of work are equal and opposite; see the second footnote to §49.

In the expression (34.4) $\mathbf{H}$ is the true value of the magnetic field due both to external sources and to the currents themselves on which the force (34.4) acts. In calculating the total force from (34.5), however, we can take $\mathbf{H}$ to be simply the external field $\mathfrak{H}$ in which the conductor carrying a current is placed. The field of the conductor itself cannot, by the law of conservation of momentum, contribute to the total force acting on the conductor.

The calculation of the forces is particularly simple for a linear conductor. Its magnetic properties are of no significance, and, if $\mu = 1$ in the surrounding medium, the total force on the conductor is given by the line integral

$$\mathbf{F} = J \oint d\mathbf{l} \times \mathfrak{H}/c. \tag{34.6}$$

This expression can be written as an integral over a surface bounded by the current circuit. Using Stokes' theorem, we replace $d\mathbf{l}$ by the operator $d\mathbf{f} \times \mathbf{grad}$, obtaining $\oint d\mathbf{l} \times \mathfrak{H} = \int (d\mathbf{f} \times \mathbf{grad}) \times \mathfrak{H}$. Now

$$\begin{aligned}(d\mathbf{f} \times \mathbf{grad}) \times \mathfrak{H} &= -d\mathbf{f}\,\mathrm{div}\,\mathfrak{H} + \mathbf{grad}\,(d\mathbf{f} \cdot \mathfrak{H}) \\ &= -d\mathbf{f}\,\mathrm{div}\,\mathfrak{H} + d\mathbf{f} \times \mathbf{curl}\,\mathfrak{H} + (d\mathbf{f} \cdot \mathbf{grad})\,\mathfrak{H}.\end{aligned}$$

But $\mathrm{div}\,\mathfrak{H} = 0$, and in the space outside the currents $\mathbf{curl}\,\mathfrak{H} = 0$ also. Thus

$$\mathbf{F} = J \int (d\mathbf{f} \cdot \mathbf{grad}) \mathfrak{H}/c. \tag{34.7}$$

In particular, in an almost uniform external field $\mathfrak{H}$ can be taken outside the integral, together with the operator **grad**. With the magnetic moment of the current given by (29.18), we then have the obvious result

$$\mathbf{F} = (\mathscr{M}\cdot\mathbf{grad})\mathfrak{H}. \tag{34.8}$$

Since $\mathscr{M}$ in this formula is constant, we can also write

$$\mathbf{F} = \mathbf{grad}(\mathscr{M}\cdot\mathfrak{H}), \tag{34.9}$$

in agreement with the expression (32.17) for the energy of the current. The torque acting on a current in an almost uniform field is easily seen to be given by the usual expression

$$\mathbf{K} = \mathscr{M}\times\mathfrak{H}. \tag{34.10}$$

PROBLEM

Determine the force on a straight wire carrying a current J and parallel to an infinite circular cylinder with magnetic permeability μ, radius a and axis at a distance b from the wire.

Solution. On account of the relation, mentioned in the second footnote to §29, between two-dimensional problems of electrostatics and magnetostatics, the field of the current is obtained from the result in §7, Problem 3, by changing the notation. The field in the space round the cylinder is the same as that produced in a vacuum by the current J and currents $+J'$ and $-J'$ through A and O' (Fig. 11, §7) respectively, where $J' = (\mu-1)J/(\mu+1)$. The field within the cylinder is the same as that due to a current $J'' = 2J/(\mu+1)$ through O. The force per unit length of the conductor is

$$F = JB/c = \frac{2JJ'}{c^2}\left(\frac{1}{OA} - \frac{1}{OO'}\right) = \frac{2J^2a^2(\mu-1)}{b(b^2-a^2)(\mu+1)c^2}.$$

Similarly we find (see §7, Problem 4) that a linear conductor passing through a cylindrical hole in a magnetic medium is attracted to the nearest surface of the hole by a force

$$F = 2J^2b(\mu-1)/(a^2-b^2)(\mu+1)c^2.$$

§35. Gyromagnetic phenomena

The possibilities of magnetising (non-ferromagnetic) bodies without applying an external magnetic field are severely limited by the requirement of invariance with respect to a change in the sign of the time. The electric polarisation of many bodies can be achieved without an external electric field by, for example, deforming them if they are piezoelectrics. Piezomagnetism, however, if it occurs at all, is a very rare phenomenon (see the end of §28), and certainly cannot occur in bodies having no magnetic structure.

Magnetisation without an external magnetic field generally involves setting the body in motion. A uniform translation, of course, is of no use, by Galileo's relativity principle. A uniform rotation, however, causes a magnetisation which is linearly dependent on the angular velocity $\mathbf{\Omega}$ (the *Barnett effect*); this relation between the vectors $\mathscr{M}$ and $\mathbf{\Omega}$ is possible because both change sign when the sign of the time is reversed. Since both are axial vectors, the relation can hold even in an isotropic body, where it reduces to a simple proportionality between $\mathscr{M}$ and $\mathbf{\Omega}$.

There must also be an inverse effect: a freely suspended body, on being magnetised, begins to rotate (the *Einstein–de Haas effect*). There is a simple thermodynamic relation between the two effects; it can be derived as follows.

As we know,† the thermodynamic potential with respect to the angular velocity (for given temperature and volume of the body) is the free energy $\mathscr{F}'$ of the body in a system of co-ordinates rotating with it. The angular momentum $\mathbf{L}$ of the body is

$$\mathbf{L} = -\partial\mathscr{F}'/\partial\mathbf{\Omega}. \tag{35.1}$$

The gyromagnetic phenomena are described by adding to the free energy a further term which is the first term, in an expansion in powers of $\mathbf{\Omega}$ and of the magnetisation $\mathbf{M}$ at each point in the body, which contains both $\mathbf{\Omega}$ and $\mathbf{M}$. This term is linear in both, i.e. it is

$$\mathscr{F}'_{\text{gyro}} = -\int \lambda_{ik}\Omega_i M_k \, \mathrm{d}V = -\lambda_{ik}\Omega_i\mathscr{M}_k, \tag{35.2}$$

where λ_{ik} is a constant tensor, in general unsymmetrical.

According to (35.1) and (35.2) the angular momentum acquired by the body as a result of magnetisation is related to its total magnetic moment by $L_{\text{gyro},i} = \lambda_{ik}\mathscr{M}_k$. It is usual to replace λ_{ik} by the inverse tensor, defined as $g_{ik} = (2mc/e)\lambda^{-1}{}_{ik}$, where e and m are the electron charge and mass. The dimensionless quantities g_{ik} are called *gyromagnetic coefficients*. Then

$$\mathscr{M}_i = (e/2mc)g_{ik}L_{\text{gyro},k}. \tag{35.3}$$

The expression (35.2) also shows that, as regards its magnetic effect, the rotation of the body is equivalent to an external field $\mathfrak{H}_i = \lambda_{ki}\Omega_k$ or

$$\mathfrak{H}_i = (2mc/e)g^{-1}{}_{ki}\Omega_k. \tag{35.4}$$

We thus have the possibility, in principle, of calculating the magnetisation caused by the rotation. For example, if the magnetic susceptibility χ_{ik} of the body is small, the magnetic moment which it acquires is independent of its shape and is

$$\mathscr{M}_i = \chi_{ik}\mathfrak{H}_k = (2mc/e)\chi_{ik}g^{-1}{}_{lk}\Omega_l.$$

Formulae (35.3) and (35.4) represent respectively the Einstein–de Haas and Barnett effects. We see that both effects are determined by the same tensor g_{ik}.

† See *Statistical Physics*, §26, Pergamon Press, London, 1958.

CHAPTER V

FERROMAGNETISM

§36. Ferromagnetics near the Curie point

THERE is a close analogy between the magnetic properties of ferromagnetics and the electric properties of ferroelectrics. Both exhibit spontaneous polarisation, magnetic or electric, in macroscopic volumes. In each case, this polarisation vanishes at a temperature corresponding to a second-order phase transition (the *Curie point*).

There are also, however, important differences between ferromagnetic and ferroelectric phenomena, arising from the difference in the microscopic interaction forces which bring about the spontaneous polarisation. In ferroelectrics, the interaction between the molecules in the crystal lattice is essentially anisotropic, and consequently the spontaneous polarisation vector is fairly closely related to certain directions in the crystal. In ferromagnetics, on the other hand, the spontaneous magnetisation is due mainly to the exchange interaction of the atoms, which is quite independent of the direction of the total magnetic moment relative to the lattice.† It is true that, together with the exchange interaction, there is also a direct magnetic interaction between the magnetic moments of the atoms. This interaction, however, is an effect of order v^2/c^2 (v being the electron velocities), since the magnetic moments themselves contain a factor v/c. The effects of this order include also the interaction of the magnetic moments of the atoms with the electric field of the crystal lattice. All these interactions, which may be called *relativistic* by virtue of the factor $1/c^2$ in them, are weak in comparison with the exchange interaction, so that they can result only in a comparatively slight dependence of the energy of the crystal on the direction of magnetisation.‡

Consequently, the magnetisation of a ferromagnetic is a quantity which, in the first approximation (i.e. on the basis of the exchange interaction), is conserved. This fact endows with greater physical significance the thermodynamic theory given below, in which the magnetisation **M** is regarded as

---

† The exchange interaction is a quantum effect resulting from the symmetry of the wave functions of the system with respect to interchanges of the particles. The interchange symmetry of the wave functions, and therefore the exchange interaction, depend only on the total spin of the system, and not on the direction of the spin; see *Quantum Mechanics*, §60, Pergamon Press, London, 1958. The importance of the exchange interaction in ferromagnetics was first pointed out by YA. I. FRENKEL', YA. G. DORFMAN and W. HEISENBERG (1928).

‡ The order of magnitude of the ratio of the relativistic and exchange interactions is given by the ratio $U_{\text{aniso}}/N\Theta$, where U_{aniso} is the *magnetic anisotropy energy* per unit volume (see §37), N the number of atoms per unit volume, and Θ the temperature of the Curie point. This ratio is usually between 10^{-4} and 10^{-5}.

an independent variable, the actual value of which (as a function of temperature, field, etc.) is afterwards determined by the appropriate conditions of thermal equilibrium.

We denote by Φ_0 the thermodynamic potential per unit volume of the substance when $\mathbf{H} = 0$, regarded as a function of the independent variable $\mathbf{M}$ (and of the other thermodynamic variables). We shall neglect the relativistic interactions, i.e. take into account only the exchange interaction. Then Φ_0 may be a function of the magnitude of $\mathbf{M}$, but not of its direction.

In order to find the thermodynamic quantities when $\mathbf{H}$ is not zero, we start from the relation $\partial\tilde{\Phi}/\partial\mathbf{H} = -\mathbf{B}/4\pi = -(\mathbf{H}+4\pi\mathbf{M})/4\pi$. Integrating this for a given value of the independent variable $\mathbf{M}$, and using the fact that $\tilde{\Phi} = \Phi = \Phi_0$ for $\mathbf{H} = 0$, we obtain

$$\tilde{\Phi} = \Phi_0(M) - \mathbf{M}\cdot\mathbf{H} - H^2/8\pi. \tag{36.1}$$

Hence the potential Φ is

$$\Phi = \tilde{\Phi} + \mathbf{H}\cdot\mathbf{B}/4\pi = \Phi_0 + H^2/8\pi$$
$$= \Phi_0 + (\mathbf{B}-4\pi\mathbf{M})^2/8\pi. \tag{36.2}$$

When the magnetic anisotropy of the ferromagnetic is neglected the directions of the vectors $\mathbf{M}$ and $\mathbf{H}$ are, of course, the same and so the vectors in formulae (36.1) and (36.2) may be replaced by their magnitudes.

Near the Curie point, the magnetisation M is small. Using the general theory of second-order phase transitions,† we expand $\Phi_0(M)$ as a series in powers of the small quantity M. The expansion of an isotropic function in powers of the vector quantity M can contain only even powers:

$$\tilde{\Phi} = \Phi_{00} + \tfrac{1}{2}aM^2 + \tfrac{1}{4}bM^4 - MH - H^2/8\pi, \tag{36.3}$$

where Φ_{00}, a, b are functions only of temperature (and pressure).

The Curie point $T = \Theta$ is given by the vanishing of the coefficient a: $a > 0$ for $T > \Theta$ and $a < 0$ for $T < \Theta$.‡ Near the Curie point, the function $a(T)$ can be expanded in powers of $T-\Theta$, i.e. we can write

$$a = \alpha(T-\Theta), \tag{36.4}$$

where α is a positive quantity independent of temperature. The coefficient b is positive near the Curie point and may be replaced by its value at that point.

For $H = 0$ the minimum thermodynamic potential above the Curie point, where $a > 0$, is given by $M = 0$, i.e. there is no spontaneous polarisation. Below the Curie point, the value of M is given by the condition

$$\partial\tilde{\Phi}/\partial M = [\alpha(T-\Theta) + bM^2]M = 0.$$

Φ is a minimum when the expression in brackets is zero, i.e. when

$$M = \sqrt{[\alpha(\Theta-T)/b]}. \tag{36.5}$$

† See *Statistical Physics*, Chapter XIV, Pergamon Press, London, 1958.

‡ This relation of the phases occurs in all known ferromagnetics, although it is not thermodynamically necessary.

Thus, as we approach the Curie point, the spontaneous magnetisation decreases as $\sqrt{(\Theta - T)}$.

Like any second-order phase transition, the transition at the Curie point (with $H = 0$) is accompanied by a discontinuity in the specific heat. Neglecting higher powers of M, we have for the entropy

$$S = -\partial\tilde{\Phi}/\partial T = S_{00} - \tfrac{1}{2}M^2 \partial a/\partial T = S_{00} - \tfrac{1}{2}\alpha M^2.$$

In the non-ferromagnetic phase $M = 0$ and $S = S_{00}$, while in the ferromagnetic phase M is given by (36.5), so that

$$S = S_{00} + \alpha^2(T - \Theta)/2b.$$

Hence the change in the specific heat $C_p = T\partial S/\partial T$ is

$$\Delta C_p = \alpha^2\Theta/2b. \tag{36.6}$$

Now let $H \neq 0$. The condition $\partial\tilde{\Phi}/\partial M = 0$ which determines the magnetisation becomes

$$\alpha(T - \Theta)M + bM^3 = H. \tag{36.7}$$

We define the magnetic susceptibility as

$$\chi = (\partial M/\partial H)_{H\to 0}.$$

From (36.7)

$$\frac{\partial M}{\partial H}[\alpha(T - \Theta) + 3bM^2] = 1.$$

Above the Curie point $M = 0$ when $H = 0$, so that

$$\chi = 1/\alpha(T - \Theta), \tag{36.8}$$

i.e. we have paramagnetism with susceptibility inversely proportional to $T - \Theta$ (the *Curie–Weiss law*). Below the Curie point M is given by formula (36.5) when $H = 0$, and we obtain

$$\chi = 1/2\alpha(\Theta - T). \tag{36.9}$$

It should be pointed out that this quantity is not the susceptibility in the ordinary sense of the word (i.e. the coefficient of proportionality between M and H), since $M \neq 0$ even when $H = 0$.†

The susceptibility (36.9) can actually attain values of the order of unity only in the immediate neighbourhood of the Curie point. Except in this region, which is of little interest, we may suppose that the magnetisation M changes only very slightly with the magnetic field and may be regarded as a constant for any given temperature. In the following sections we shall assume this to be true.

---

† Formulae (36.8) and (36.9) are quantitatively correct for $\chi \gtrsim 1$ only in crystals of the cubic system. For uniaxial crystals the *anisotropy energy* (see §37) should be taken into account, which in this case is proportional to M^2, and for very small M may even exceed the term $\tfrac{1}{2}aM^2$ in (36.3).

This constitutes a further difference between ferromagnetics and ferroelectrics: for the latter, $\partial P/\partial E$ is in general not small even near the Curie point. The reason again lies in the smallness of the magnetic moments of the atoms in comparison with the electric dipole moments of the molecules.

§37. The magnetic anisotropy energy

As already mentioned, the anisotropy of the magnetic properties of ferromagnetics is due to the relativistic interactions between their atoms, and these interactions are comparatively weak. In the macroscopic theory, the anisotropy is described by the addition to the thermodynamic potential of the *magnetic anisotropy energy*, which depends on the direction of magnetisation.

The calculation of the anisotropy energy from the microscopic theory would require the use of quantum perturbation theory, the energy of the perturbation being represented by the terms in the Hamiltonian of the crystal which pertain to the relativistic interactions. The general form of the desired expressions, however, can be deduced without such calculations, from simple arguments concerning symmetry.

The Hamiltonian of the relativistic interactions contains terms of the first and second powers in the electron spin vector operators; these are respectively the *spin–orbit* and *spin–spin* interactions. When perturbation theory is applied, therefore, the anisotropy energy is obtained as a power series in the direction cosines of the magnetisation vector. Now the anisotropy energy U_{aniso}, like the potential Φ itself, is invariant with respect to a change in the sign of the time, while the magnetisation **M** changes sign under this transformation. Hence it follows that the anisotropy energy must be an even function of the direction cosines of the vector **M**, and so, in the first non-zero approximation of perturbation theory, we shall obtain an expression of the form

$$U_{\text{aniso}} = \tfrac{1}{2}\beta_{ik}M_iM_k, \tag{37.1}$$

where β_{ik} is a dimensionless symmetrical tensor of rank two, whose components are functions of temperature. Near the Curie point, the expression (37.1) may also be regarded as the first term in an expansion of the anisotropy energy in powers of the vector **M**, which in this range of temperature is a small quantity (but we must emphasise that this interpretation of formula (37.1) is not valid for other ranges of temperature). Hence it follows that, as $T \to \Theta$, the quantities β_{ik} tend to finite non-zero values.

In uniaxial and biaxial crystals, a symmetrical tensor of rank two has respectively two and three independent components. Here, however, it must also be borne in mind that there is one quadratic combination, namely $M_x^2+M_y^2+M_z^2 = M^2$, which is independent of the direction of **M** and so cannot appear in the anisotropy energy. Hence the expression (37.1) for uniaxial and biaxial crystals contains only one and two independent coefficients respectively.

For example, in uniaxial crystals the anisotropy energy can be written

$$U_{\text{aniso}} = \tfrac{1}{2}\beta(M_x^2+M_y^2) = \tfrac{1}{2}\beta M^2 \sin^2\theta, \tag{37.2}$$

where θ is the angle between $\mathbf{M}$ and the z-axis, taken to be along the principal axis of symmetry of the crystal. If the constant β is positive, the anisotropy energy is least when the magnetisation is in the z-direction, and the z-axis is said to be the *direction of easy magnetisation.* If, however, $\beta < 0$, the direction of easy magnetisation lies in the xy-plane, in which case it is natural to write the anisotropy energy as

$$U_{\text{aniso}} = \tfrac{1}{2}|\beta| M_z^2, \tag{37.3}$$

which is equivalent to (37.2) but is such that $U_{\text{aniso}} = 0$ again corresponds to the direction of easy magnetisation.† The expression (37.3) is isotropic in the xy-plane. Hence the direction of easy magnetisation is here determined by terms of higher order (see Problem 1).

Let us examine the relation between the magnetisation of a uniaxial ferromagnetic and the magnetic field in it, assuming for definiteness that $\beta > 0$.‡ It should be recalled that we suppose the magnitude of $\mathbf{M}$ to be independent of $\mathbf{H}$, so that only rotations of $\mathbf{M}$ are considered. It is evident from symmetry that the vector $\mathbf{M}$ lies in a plane through the z-axis and the direction of $\mathbf{H}$ (if terms of higher order, anisotropic in the xy-plane, are neglected in the anisotropy energy). We take this as the xz-plane. The thermodynamic potential, including the anisotropy energy, is||

$$\begin{aligned}\tilde{\Phi} &= \Phi_0(M)+\tfrac{1}{2}\beta M_x^2-\mathbf{M}\cdot\mathbf{H}-H^2/8\pi \\ &= \Phi_0(M)+\tfrac{1}{2}\beta M^2\sin^2\theta - M(H_x\sin\theta+H_z\cos\theta)-H^2/8\pi. \end{aligned}\tag{37.4}$$

The dependence of $\mathbf{M}$ on $\mathbf{H}$ is given by the equilibrium condition $\partial\tilde{\Phi}/\partial\theta = 0$, whence

$$\beta M\sin\theta\cos\theta = H_x\cos\theta - H_z\sin\theta. \tag{37.5}$$

This is an algebraic equation of the fourth degree for $\xi = \sin\theta$:

$$(\beta M\xi - H_x)^2(1-\xi^2) = H_z^2\xi^2,$$

in which the coefficients of odd powers of ξ are not zero. This equation has either two or four real roots (all less than unity). Since all such roots correspond to extrema of $\tilde{\Phi}(\theta)$, it is clear that, in the first case, this function has one minimum and one maximum and, in the second case, two minima and two maxima. In other words, the number of possible directions of the

† An example of a uniaxial ferromagnetic is hexagonal cobalt, for which $\beta > 0$ below ~200 °C and $\beta < 0$ above that temperature. At room temperature, $\beta = 4{\cdot}2$.

‡ This case will always be taken when uniaxial crystals are discussed.

|| In the following discussion we shall use the expression (37.2) for the anisotropy energy. It should be pointed out, however, that the expansion of which (37.2) is the first term is usually not rapidly convergent in practice. For a satisfactory quantitative description of the phenomena, therefore, the next (fourth-order) term should be included; for a hexagonal crystal this term is proportional to $\sin^4\theta$.

magnetisation **M** for a given field **H** is one and two respectively. In the second case, one direction (corresponding to the lower minimum of $\tilde{\Phi}$) is thermodynamically completely stable, while the other (corresponding to the higher minimum) is thermodynamically metastable.

Either of the two cases can occur, depending on the values of H_x and H_z. When these two parameters vary continuously, one case passes into the other at the point where one maximum and one minimum coalesce. The curve of $\tilde{\Phi}(\theta)$ then has a point of inflection instead of an extremum, i.e. both $\partial\tilde{\Phi}/\partial\theta$ and $\partial^2\tilde{\Phi}/\partial\theta^2$ are zero. Writing equation (37.5) in the form

$$\frac{H_x}{\sin\theta} - \frac{H_z}{\cos\theta} = \beta M$$

and differentiating with respect to θ, we have $H_x/\sin^3\theta = -H_z/\cos^3\theta$. Eliminating θ from these two equations gives

$$H_x^{2/3} + H_z^{2/3} = (\beta M)^{2/3}. \tag{37.6}$$

In the H_xH_z-plane equation (37.6) represents a closed curve of the kind shown in Fig. 20. It divides the plane into two parts, in one of which metastable states can exist, while in the other they cannot. It is evident without further investigation that the region where metastable states do not exist is that outside the curve, because for $H \to \infty$ only one direction of **M** can be stable, namely that of the field **H**.

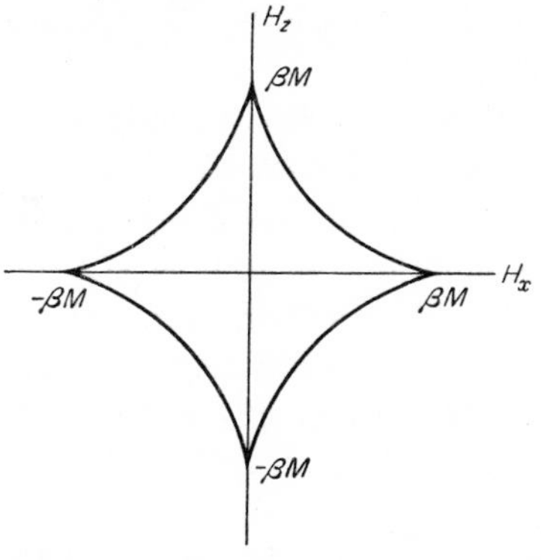

FIG. 20

The existence of metastable states means that what is called *hysteresis* can occur; this is an irreversible change of state in a ferromagnetic body when the external magnetic field is varied. The curve shown in Fig. 20 is therefore the "absolute limit" of hysteresis; this phenomenon cannot occur for fields outside the curve.†

† The whole of the discussion in this chapter concerns only thermodynamic equilibrium states in ferromagnetics and therefore reversible processes in them. In particular, we entirely ignore the mechanism of hysteresis phenomena; these may arise from defects in the crystal, internal stresses, a polycrystalline state, and so on.

States in which the field **H** is perpendicular to the direction of easy magnetisation ($H_x = H$, $H_z = 0$) require special consideration. The thermodynamic potential is

$$\tilde{\Phi} = \Phi_0 - \frac{H^2}{8\pi} + \tfrac{1}{2}\beta M^2 \sin^2\theta - HM\sin\theta. \tag{37.7}$$

If $H > \beta M$, $\tilde{\Phi}$ has only one minimum, at $\theta = \frac{1}{2}\pi$, i.e. the magnetisation is parallel to the field. If, however, $H < \beta M$, then $\tilde{\Phi}$ has a minimum when

$$M_x = M\sin\theta = H/\beta, \tag{37.8}$$

to which there correspond two possible positions of the vector **M** (at angles θ and $\pi - \theta$), symmetrical about the x-axis. Thus in this case there are two equilibrium states, which have the same value of $\tilde{\Phi}$ and are therefore equally stable.

This result is very important, since it means that two "phases" can exist in contact in which the field **H** is the same but the magnetisation **M** (and therefore the induction **B**) is different. Thus a new possibility appears for reducing the total thermodynamic potential of the body: its volume may be divided into separate regions, in each of which the magnetisation has one of its two possible directions. These regions are called ***regions of spontaneous magnetisation*** or ***domains***. The actual determination of the thermodynamic equilibrium structure of a ferromagnetic requires a consideration of the shape and size of the body as a whole. We shall return to this problem in §39.

Let us consider a portion of the body which is small compared with the total volume but large compared with the domains. The field H_x can be regarded as constant in this portion; we denote by $\bar{\mathbf{M}}$ and $\bar{\mathbf{B}}$ the values of **M** and **B** averaged over its volume. As well as H_x, the transverse component $M_x = H_x/\beta$ of the magnetisation is constant. The longitudinal component M_z, however, has opposite signs in different domains, so that its mean value certainly cannot exceed $|M_z|$. Since $H_z = 0$ everywhere, the mean induction is therefore

$$\bar{B}_x = H_x\left(1 + \frac{4\pi}{\beta}\right), \qquad \bar{B}_z < 4\pi\sqrt{\left(M^2 - \frac{H_x^2}{\beta^2}\right)}. \tag{37.9}$$

These formulae give the range of values of the mean induction corresponding to the domain structure of a uniaxial ferromagnetic.

Let us now consider ferromagnetic crystals of the cubic system. Their properties are markedly different from those of uniaxial and biaxial crystals. The reason is that the only quadratic combination which is invariant with respect to the cubic symmetry transformations and which can be formed from the components of the vector **M** is the sum $M_x^2 + M_y^2 + M_z^2$, which is independent of the direction of **M**. Hence the first non-vanishing term in the expansion of the anisotropy energy for a cubic crystal is the fourth-order term, not the second-order one. For this reason, the magnetic anisotropy effects in cubic crystals are in general less strong than in uniaxial and biaxial crystals.

Cubic symmetry admits the following two quartic invariants formed from the components of the vector **M**: $M_x^2M_y^2+M_x^2M_z^2+M_y^2M_z^2$ and $\frac{1}{2}(M_x^4+M_y^4+M_z^4)$. These invariants, however, are not independent, because their sum is the quantity $\frac{1}{2}(M_x^2+M_y^2+M_z^2)^2$, which is independent of the direction of **M**. Hence the anisotropy energy of a cubic ferromagnetic includes (in the approximation considered†) only one constant, and may be written

$$U_{\text{aniso}} = \beta(M_x^2M_y^2+M_x^2M_z^2+M_y^2M_z^2), \tag{37.10}$$

or, equivalently,

$$U_{\text{aniso}} = -\tfrac{1}{2}\beta(M_x^4+M_y^4+M_z^4). \tag{37.11}$$

If $\beta > 0$ (as, for example, in iron), the anisotropy energy has equal minimum values for three positions of the vector **M**, namely parallel to the edges of the cube (the x, y and z axes or, in crystallographic notation, [100], [010], [001]). Thus, in this case, the crystal has three equivalent axes of easy magnetisation.

If, on the other hand, $\beta < 0$ (as, for example, in nickel), then the anisotropy energy has minima when $M_x^2 = M_y^2 = M_z^2 = \frac{1}{3}M^2$, i.e. when the vector **M** is parallel to one of the four spatial diagonals of the cube [111], [$\bar{1}$11], etc. These are then the directions of easy magnetisation.

It should be noticed that, strictly speaking, a ferromagnetic cubic crystal, when spontaneously magnetised along one of the directions of easy magnetisation, ceases to possess cubic symmetry, and so there is a displacement of the atoms, i.e. a distortion of the crystal lattice. Such a crystal, when magnetised parallel to an edge of the cube, becomes slightly tetragonal, while one magnetised parallel to a spatial diagonal becomes rhombohedral. In this respect cubic crystals differ from uniaxial crystals with the direction of easy magnetisation along the principal axis of symmetry, where a magnetisation in this direction evidently does not change the symmetry of the crystal.

The relation between **M** and **H** for a cubic crystal can in principle be investigated in the same way as was done above for a uniaxial crystal. However, we shall not pause to discuss this, because the equations are more complex, and explicit analytical formulae cannot be obtained.

PROBLEMS

Problem 1. Find the terms of the next order (after the second) in the expansion of U_{aniso} for a uniaxial crystal, which give rise to anisotropy in the xy-plane.

---

† The next approximation involves terms of the sixth order. In calculating the number of independent sextic invariants, we must exclude both M^6, which is independent of the direction of **M**, and expressions which differ from the quartic invariants by a factor M^2. This leaves only one invariant, which may be taken as $M_x^2M_y^2M_z^2$.

SOLUTION. The problem reduces to finding the independent combinations of lowest (even) order, formed from the components of the vector **M**, which are invariant with respect to the symmetry transformations of the crystal concerned and which contain M_x and M_y otherwise than in the form $M_x^2+M_y^2$. For tetragonal symmetry there is one such combination, which may be taken as $M_x^2M_y^2$; the combination $\frac{1}{2}(M_x^4+M_y^4)$ gives together with $M_x^2M_y^2$ the sum $\frac{1}{2}(M_x^2+M_y^2)^2$, and is therefore not independent.

For hexagonal symmetry, the anisotropy in the xy-plane appears only in the sixth-order terms; the invariant combination of this order may be taken as

$$\frac{1}{6i}[(M_x+iM_y)^6-(M_x-iM_y)^6] = 2M_xM_y\left(M_x^4-\frac{10}{3}M_x^2M_y^2+M_y^4\right).$$

Rhombohedral symmetry admits this sixth-order term and also one independent quartic combination, for example

$$\tfrac{1}{2}M_z[(M_x+iM_y)^3+(M_x-iM_y)^3] = M_xM_z(M_x^2-3M_y^2).$$

The determination of the direction of easy magnetisation in the xy-plane requires a consideration of both these terms, since M_z is small.

PROBLEM 2. A uniaxial ferromagnetic crystal is in the shape of a spheroid, the axis of easy magnetisation being the axis of revolution, and is placed in an external magnetic field $\mathfrak{H}$. Determine the range of values of $\mathfrak{H}$ for which the body has a domain structure.

SOLUTION. According to the general properties of an ellipsoid in a uniform external field (§8), the induction $\bar{\mathbf{B}}$ and field $\bar{\mathbf{H}}$ (= **H**) averaged over the domain structure are related to $\mathfrak{H}$ by

$$n\bar{B}_z+(1-n)H_z = \mathfrak{H}_z, \qquad \tfrac{1}{2}(1-n)\bar{B}_x+\tfrac{1}{2}(1+n)H_x = \mathfrak{H}_x,$$

where n is the demagnetisation coefficient in the direction of the axis of revolution (taken as the z-axis). Putting $H_z = 0$ and using formulae (37.9), we obtain

$$H_x = \frac{\mathfrak{H}_x}{1+2\pi(1-n)/\beta}, \qquad \bar{B}_z = \frac{\mathfrak{H}_z}{n} < 4\pi\sqrt{\left(M^2-\frac{H_x^2}{\beta^2}\right)}.$$

Elimination of H_x gives the required inequality

$$\frac{\mathfrak{H}_z^2}{(4\pi n)^2}+\frac{\mathfrak{H}_x^2}{[\beta+2\pi(1-n)]^2} < M^2$$

for the range in which there is a domain structure.

PROBLEM 3. Determine the magnetisation averaged over the crystallites (which have uniaxial symmetry) for a polycrystalline body in a strong magnetic field ($H \gg 4\pi M$).

SOLUTION. In a particular crystallite, let θ and ψ be the angles between the direction of easy magnetisation and, respectively, **M** and **H**. It is evident that, in a strong field, **M** and **H** will be in almost the same direction, i.e. the angle $\vartheta \equiv \theta-\psi$ is small. Putting in (37.4) $\mathbf{M}\cdot\mathbf{H} = MH\cos(\theta-\psi)$ and equating to zero the derivative $\partial\tilde{\Phi}/\partial\theta$, we have $\vartheta \cong \sin\vartheta = -(\beta M/H)\sin\theta\cos\theta$. The average magnetisation is clearly parallel to **H**, and is

$$\bar{M} = M\,\overline{\cos\vartheta} = M(1-\tfrac{1}{2}\overline{\vartheta^2}) = M\left(1-\frac{\beta^2M^2}{2H^2}\,\overline{\sin^2\theta\cos^2\theta}\right).$$

The bar denotes averaging over the crystallites. Assuming that all directions of the axis of easy magnetisation of the crystallites are equally probable, we have

$$\bar{M} = M\left(1-\frac{\beta^2M^2}{15H^2}\right).$$

Thus the mean magnetisation approaches saturation in the manner $\bar{M}-M \sim 1/H^2$.

PROBLEM 4. The same as Problem 3, but for the case where the crystallites have cubic symmetry.

SOLUTION. The conditions for a minimum of the expression

$$-\tfrac{1}{2}\beta(M_x^4+M_y^4+M_z^4)-(H_xM_x+H_yM_y+H_zM_z),$$

with the subsidiary condition $M_x^2+M_y^2+M_z^2 =$ constant, are $2\beta M_x^3+H_x = \lambda M_x$, $2\beta M_y^3+$

$+H_y = \lambda M_y$, $2\beta M_z^3 + H_z = \lambda M_z$, where λ is an undetermined Lagrangian multiplier. For large H, we therefore have

$$M_x \cong \frac{1}{\lambda} H_x + \frac{1}{\lambda^4} 2\beta H_x^3 + \ldots, \text{ etc.};$$

adding the squares of the three equations, we obtain $M^2 \cong H^2/\lambda^2$, i.e. $\lambda \cong H/M$. The angle ϑ between **M** and **H** is found from

$$\vartheta^2 \cong \sin^2\vartheta = \frac{(\mathbf{M}\times\mathbf{H})^2}{M^2H^2}$$

$$= \frac{4\beta^2M^6}{H^{10}} \sum H_x^2 H_y^2 (H_x^2 - H_y^2)^2,$$

where the summation is over cyclic permutations of the suffixes x, y, z. Averaging this expression over the orientations of the crystallites is equivalent to averaging over directions of the vector **H**. The latter averaging is effected by integrating over the angles which specify the direction of **H**, and the result is†

$$\bar{M} = M(1 - \tfrac{1}{2}\overline{\vartheta^2}) = M\left(1 - \frac{8\beta^2M^6}{105H^2}\right).$$

§38. Magnetostriction of ferromagnetics

A change in the magnetisation of a ferromagnetic in a magnetic field causes a deformation in it; this phenomenon is called *magnetostriction*, and may be due to either exchange interactions or relativistic interactions in the body. Since the exchange energy depends only on the magnitude of the magnetisation, its value can change only when this magnitude changes in the magnetic field. Although the latter change is, in general, very small, the exchange energy is large compared with the anisotropy energy. Hence the magnetostriction effects from each type of interaction may be of comparable magnitude.

This happens, for instance, in uniaxial crystals. Marked deformations resulting from a change in the direction of **M** occur in fields $H \sim \beta M$; the change in the magnitude M is considerable when $H \sim 4\pi M$. These two values of H are almost the same, and so it is in general necessary to take account of both effects in discussing the magnetostriction of uniaxial ferromagnetics. We shall not pause here to derive the formulae, which are fairly complex.

In cubic crystals the situation is different, because the anisotropy energy is of the fourth order and therefore relatively small. A considerable magnetostriction, due to the change in the direction of **M**, occurs even in comparatively weak fields, where the change in the magnitude M may be entirely neglected. Let us consider these effects.

† For a cubic crystal there is also a range of fields in which MH is large compared with the anisotropy energy but small compared with $4\pi M^2$. The formula derived here is then invalid, because in deriving it we have neglected the fields in the body resulting from the differing directions of magnetisation in different crystallites. A more exact investigation for this case gives the same $1/H^2$ law but with a different coefficient. We shall not discuss this problem in more detail, because the results, for some reason not yet understood, disagree with those of experiment.

The change in the relativistic interaction energy in the deformed body is described by the inclusion in the thermodynamic potential $\tilde{\Phi}$ of *magnetoelastic terms* depending on the components of the elasticity stress tensor σ_{ik} and the direction of the vector **M** (N. S. Akulov, 1928). The first such terms which do not vanish are linear in σ_{ik}, and quadratic in the direction cosines of **M** because of the symmetry with respect to a change in the sign of the time. In general, therefore, the magnetoelastic energy is given by an expression of the form

$$U_{\text{m-el}} = -\lambda_{iklm}\sigma_{ik}M_l M_m, \tag{38.1}$$

where λ_{iklm} is a tensor of rank four, symmetrical with respect to the pairs of suffixes i,k and l,m (but not with respect to interchange of the two pairs). Near the Curie point, where the expansion in powers of the direction cosines of the vector **M** is equivalent to one in powers of its components, the quantities λ_{iklm} tend to constants.

In calculating the number of independent components of the tensor λ_{iklm} it must be borne in mind that the terms in (38.1) which involve the components of **M** in the form $M_x^2+M_y^2+M_z^2$ are independent of the direction of **M**, and so may be omitted from the magnetoelastic energy.† Thus we find that, in a cubic crystal, the magnetoelastic energy contains two independent coefficients; we shall write it as

$$\begin{aligned} U_{\text{m-el}} = &-\lambda_1(\sigma_{xx}M_x^2+\sigma_{yy}M_y^2+\sigma_{zz}M_z^2)- \\ &-2\lambda_2(\sigma_{xy}M_xM_y+\sigma_{xz}M_xM_z+\sigma_{yz}M_yM_z). \end{aligned} \tag{38.2}$$

The strain tensor is obtained by differentiating $\tilde{\Phi}$ with respect to the various components σ_{ik}: $u_{ik} = -\partial\tilde{\Phi}/\partial\sigma_{ik}$, where $\tilde{\Phi}$ includes also the ordinary elastic energy (with reversed sign; see the first footnote to §17). For a cubic crystal, the latter energy involves three independent elastic coefficients, and is of the form

$$\begin{aligned} U_{\text{el}} = &\tfrac{1}{2}k_1(\sigma_{xx}^2+\sigma_{yy}^2+\sigma_{zz}^2)+k_2(\sigma_{xx}\sigma_{yy}+\sigma_{xx}\sigma_{zz}+\sigma_{yy}\sigma_{zz})+ \\ &+k_3(\sigma_{xy}^2+\sigma_{xz}^2+\sigma_{yz}^2). \end{aligned} \tag{38.3}$$

The strain tensor is‡

$$\begin{aligned} u_{xx} &= k_1\sigma_{xx}+k_2(\sigma_{yy}+\sigma_{zz})+\lambda_1M_x^2, \\ u_{xy} &= k_3\sigma_{xy}+\lambda_2M_xM_y, \end{aligned} \tag{38.4}$$

and similarly for the other components.

These formulae give all the magnetostriction effects in the range of fields considered. In particular, if there are no internal stresses the change in the deformation resulting from a change in the direction of magnetisation is

† There is consequently some arbitrariness in the choice of the λ_{iklm}, which simply reflects the arbitrariness involved in choosing the direction of **M** for which (applied mechanical forces being absent) we regard the crystal as undeformed.

‡ In differentiating $\tilde{\Phi}$ the second footnote to §17 should be recalled.

given by $u_{xx} = \lambda_1 M_x^2$, $u_{xy} = \lambda_2 M_x M_y$, etc. It should be recalled that the magnitude of the deformation itself is to some extent arbitrary, because the direction of **M** for which the deformation is supposed zero is arbitrarily chosen.

Let us now consider magnetostriction in fields so strong ($H \gg 4\pi M$) that the anisotropy energy is unimportant and there is no domain structure, so that the directions of **M** and **H** may be assumed to coincide.

Since the anisotropy energy is neglected, the particular symmetry of the crystal is of no importance, and the formulae given below are valid for any ferromagnetic.

Let the body be placed in a uniform external magnetic field $\mathfrak{H}$. Its total thermodynamic potential $\tilde{\Phi}$ is†

$$\tilde{\Phi} = -\mathcal{M}\cdot\mathfrak{H} = -MV\mathfrak{H}, \tag{38.5}$$

where $\mathcal{M} = MV$ is the total magnetic moment of a body uniformly magnetised in the direction of the field; we omit the term $\tilde{\Phi}_0$ which is unrelated to the magnetic field. The strain tensor averaged over the volume of the body is $\bar{u}_{ik} = -(1/V)\partial\tilde{\Phi}/\partial\sigma_{ik}$, whence

$$\bar{u}_{ik} = \frac{\mathfrak{H}}{V}\frac{\partial(MV)}{\partial\sigma_{ik}}. \tag{38.6}$$

Thus the deformation is determined by the dependence of the magnetisation on the internal stresses.

For cubic symmetry, any symmetrical tensor of rank two characterising the properties of the crystal reduces to a scalar multiple of δ_{ik}. This is true, in particular, of the tensor $\partial(MV)/\partial\sigma_{ik}$, so that the magnetostriction deformation amounts in this case to a uniform compression or extension.

If we are interested only in the change δV in the total volume of the body, we can obtain it by simply differentiating $\tilde{\Phi}$ with respect to the pressure:

$$\delta V = \partial\tilde{\Phi}/\partial p = -\mathfrak{H}\partial(MV)/\partial p, \tag{38.7}$$

where p is to be regarded as a uniform pressure applied to the surface of the body.

PROBLEM

Determine the change in volume in magnetostriction of a ferromagnetic ellipsoid in an external field $\mathfrak{H} \sim 4\pi M$ parallel to one of its axes. The ferromagnetic is assumed to be a cubic crystal.‡

SOLUTION. When the anisotropy energy is neglected, the range for which the domain structure exists is given by $\bar{B} < 4\pi M$ when $H = 0$. The bar denotes averaging over the

† Here the definition of $\tilde{\Phi}$ is that given in §12, which is applicable except when the deformation of the body is appreciably inhomogeneous.

‡ In a uniaxial ferromagnetic with $\mathfrak{H} \sim 4\pi M$ the anisotropy energy would have to be taken into account, but this is not necessary in a cubic crystal.

volume of the body; cf. §37. In an ellipsoid $n\bar{B}+(1-n)\bar{H} = \mathfrak{H}$; putting $H = 0$, we find that the domain structure exists when $\mathfrak{H} < 4\pi nM$. Since $n\bar{B} = 4\pi n\bar{M} = \mathfrak{H}$, the mean magnetisation is $\bar{M} = \mathfrak{H}/4\pi n$. Hence the thermodynamic potential is

$$\tilde{\Phi} = -V \int_0^{\mathfrak{H}} \bar{M}\, d\mathfrak{H} = -\mathfrak{H}^2 V/8\pi n. \quad (1)$$

If $\mathfrak{H} > 4\pi nM$, the ellipsoid is magnetised entirely in the direction of the field, and $\bar{M} = M$. Then

$$\tilde{\Phi} = -M\mathfrak{H}V + 2\pi M^2 Vn. \quad (2)$$

The expressions (1) and (2) are the same for $\mathfrak{H} = 4\pi Mn$.

The required change in volume is obtained by differentiating $\tilde{\Phi}$ with respect to pressure:

$$\delta V = -\frac{\mathfrak{H}^2}{8\pi n}\frac{\partial V}{\partial p} \quad \text{for } \mathfrak{H} < 4\pi nM,$$

$$\delta V = -\mathfrak{H}\frac{\partial(MV)}{\partial p} + 2\pi n\frac{\partial(M^2 V)}{\partial p} \quad \text{for } \mathfrak{H} > 4\pi nM.$$

For $\mathfrak{H} \gg 4\pi nM$ we obtain (38.7).

§39. The domain structure of ferromagnetics

As already mentioned in §37, there is a wide range of states in which a ferromagnetic must have what is called a *domain structure*, i.e. it must consist of various regions in which the directions of magnetisation are different.† This is true, in particular, of a ferromagnetic body which is not in an external magnetic field.

Some conclusions concerning the shape of the surfaces separating the domains may be obtained directly from the boundary conditions on the magnetic field. Since the field **H** is the same in adjoining domains, the condition of continuity of the normal induction B_n reduces to the continuity of M_n. In uniaxial crystals, the sign of M_z is different in different domains, but M_x and M_y are the same. Under these conditions the continuity of M_n means that the surface of separation must be parallel to the z-axis, i.e. to the direction of easy magnetisation.

Let us first examine the properties of the bounding surfaces as such, leaving aside the actual shape of the domains. These "surfaces" are in reality fairly narrow transition layers in which the direction of the magnetisation varies continuously between its directions in the two adjoining domains. The "width" of such a layer and the manner in which **M** varies within it are given by the conditions of thermodynamic equilibrium. The additional energy due to the non-uniformity of the magnetisation must be taken into account. The largest contribution to this "non-uniformity energy" is given by the exchange interaction. Macroscopically, this energy can be expressed

† The concept of domains was first put forward by P. Weiss (1907). The thermodynamic theory of domains was given by L. D. Landau and E. M. Lifshitz (1935).

in terms of the space derivatives of **M**, which can be done in a general form if the gradient of the direction of **M** is supposed relatively small, i.e. if the change in the direction of the magnetic moments occurs over distances large compared with the distances between the atoms. In the present case, this condition is evidently fulfilled, because a considerable difference in the directions of the magnetic moments of adjoining atoms would lead to a very large increase in the exchange energy, and is therefore thermodynamically unfavourable.

We denote the "non-uniformity energy" by $U_{\text{non-u}}$. The greatest terms in its expansion in powers of the various derivatives of the components of **M** are those quadratic in the first derivatives; there can be no linear terms, on account of the symmetry with respect to a change in the sign of the time. Next, because it originates from exchange forces, $U_{\text{non-u}}$ cannot depend on the absolute direction of **M** at a given point in the crystal. The most general expression satisfying these conditions is

$$U_{\text{non-u}} = \tfrac{1}{2}\alpha_{ik}\frac{\partial M_l}{\partial x_i}\frac{\partial M_l}{\partial x_k}, \tag{39.1}$$

where α_{ik} is a symmetrical tensor. This quadratic form (in the derivatives) must, furthermore, be positive definite. In a uniaxial crystal, the tensor α_{ik} has two independent components, and the non-uniformity energy is of the form

$$U_{\text{non-u}} = \tfrac{1}{2}\alpha_1\left[\left(\frac{\partial \mathbf{M}}{\partial x}\right)^2 + \left(\frac{\partial \mathbf{M}}{\partial y}\right)^2\right] + \tfrac{1}{2}\alpha_2\left(\frac{\partial \mathbf{M}}{\partial z}\right)^2, \tag{39.2}$$

α_1 and α_2 being positive. In a cubic crystal we have $\alpha_1 = \alpha_2$.

The following remark should be made concerning (39.1). A thermodynamic meaning attaches not to $U_{\text{non-u}}$ itself, but only to its integral over the volume of the body. It is therefore not necessary to include in $U_{\text{non-u}}$ the terms containing products of the components of **M** and their second derivatives with respect to the co-ordinates, even though such terms are formally of the same order of magnitude as those in (39.1). The reason is that, on being integrated over the volume, they become products of first derivatives, i.e. they are included in (39.1).†

As an example, let us consider the boundary between domains in a uniaxial crystal, assuming that the vector **M** is parallel or antiparallel to the direction of easy magnetisation (the z-axis). This is true, for example, in the absence of an external magnetic field.

The structure of the transition layer is determined by the condition that its total free energy should be a minimum.‡ Here the exchange energy

† The symmetry of the crystal may admit terms containing products of the first derivatives $\partial M_l/\partial x_i$ and the components M_l. Such terms, on integration over the volume, would give expressions depending only on the properties of the surface of the body.

‡ Here it is more correct to speak of the total free energy, and not of the total thermodynamic potential, because the deformation in the layer may be by no means homogeneous.

tends to increase the thickness of the layer (i.e. to make the direction of **M** vary less rapidly). The anisotropy energy has the opposite effect, because any deviation of **M** from the direction of easy magnetisation increases this energy.

We take the x-axis perpendicular to the plane of the layer; the direction of **M** depends only on x. The rotation of the vector **M** across the layer must take place in the yz-plane, i.e. $M_x = 0$ everywhere. This is seen as follows. The non-uniformity and anisotropy energies are independent of the plane in which the rotation of the magnetisation takes place. The presence of a non-zero component M_x would necessarily result in a magnetic field which was thermodynamically unfavourable, because of the additional magnetic energy. For $M_x = 0$ in the domains; if $M_x \neq 0$ in the transition layer, then $\operatorname{div} \mathbf{M} = \partial M_x/\partial x \neq 0$; since $\operatorname{div} \mathbf{B} = \operatorname{div} \mathbf{H} + 4\pi \operatorname{div} \mathbf{M} = 0$, this implies that $\operatorname{div} \mathbf{H} \neq 0$ and therefore that $\mathbf{H} \neq 0$.

Let θ be the angle between **M** and the z-axis. Then the components of **M** are $M_x = 0$, $M_y = M \sin\theta$, $M_z = M\cos\theta$. The sum of the non-uniformity and anisotropy energies is given by the integral

$$\int_{-\infty}^{\infty} [\tfrac{1}{2}\alpha_1(M_y'^2 + M_z'^2) + \tfrac{1}{2}\beta M_y^2]\,dx = \tfrac{1}{2}M^2 \int_{-\infty}^{\infty} (\alpha_1\theta'^2 + \beta\sin^2\theta)\,dx, \tag{39.3}$$

where the prime denotes differentiation with respect to x. The remaining terms in the free energy are independent of the structure of the layer, and so can be omitted here. To determine the function $\theta(x)$ which makes this integral a minimum, we write down the corresponding Euler's equation $\alpha_1\theta'' - \beta\sin\theta\cos\theta = 0$, of which the first integral is $\theta'^2 - (\beta/\alpha_1)\sin^2\theta = \text{constant}$. Assuming the thickness of the transition layer small compared with that of the domains themselves, we can write the boundary conditions on this equation as

$$\begin{aligned} &\theta = 0 \text{ for } x = -\infty, \qquad \theta = \pi \text{ for } x = +\infty, \\ &\theta' = 0 \text{ for } x = \pm\infty \quad (\text{i.e. for } \theta = 0 \text{ or } \pi). \end{aligned} \tag{39.4}$$

These state that adjoining domains are magnetised in opposite directions. Then the constant is zero and, integrating the equation $\theta'^2 = (\beta/\alpha_1)\sin^2\theta$, we obtain

$$\cos\theta = -\tanh[x\sqrt{(\beta/\alpha_1)}], \tag{39.5}$$

which gives the manner of variation of the direction of magnetisation in the transition layer. The "thickness" of this layer is $\delta \sim \sqrt{(\alpha_1/\beta)}$.

Substituting (39.5) in (39.3), we have

$$\beta M^2 \int_{-\infty}^{\infty} \frac{dx}{\cosh^2[x\sqrt{(\beta/\alpha_1)}]},$$

or, effecting the integration,

$$2M^2\sqrt{(\alpha_1\beta)}. \tag{39.6}$$

If we regard the boundary between domains as a geometrical surface, then (39.6) is the "surface tension" which must be ascribed to this surface in order to take account of the energy needed to create the boundary.

The shape and size of the domains in thermodynamic equilibrium are given by the condition that the total thermodynamic potential should be a minimum. They depend considerably on the actual shape and size of the body. In the simplest case, that of a ferromagnetic in the form of a flat plate, the domains may in principle form either parallel layers, or "filaments" across the body. In what follows we shall, for definiteness, speak of layers.†

The formation of an entire new boundary between domains results in an increase in the total "surface tension" energy. This energy consequently tends to reduce the number of domains, i.e. to increase their thickness. The excess energy near the outer surface of the body has the opposite effect. In the body the magnetic field $\mathbf{H} = 0$, and the anisotropy energy is also zero, because the vector $\mathbf{M}$ is in a direction of easy magnetisation. Near the surface, however, this is not so.

In the limiting case where the coefficient β in the anisotropy energy is large, the layers must emerge at the surface with no change in the direction of $\mathbf{M}$ (Fig. 21a, where for definiteness we suppose that the surface is perpendicular to the direction of easy magnetisation). Near the surface there is a magnetic field which penetrates into the surrounding space, and into the body, to distances of the order of the layer thickness *a*.

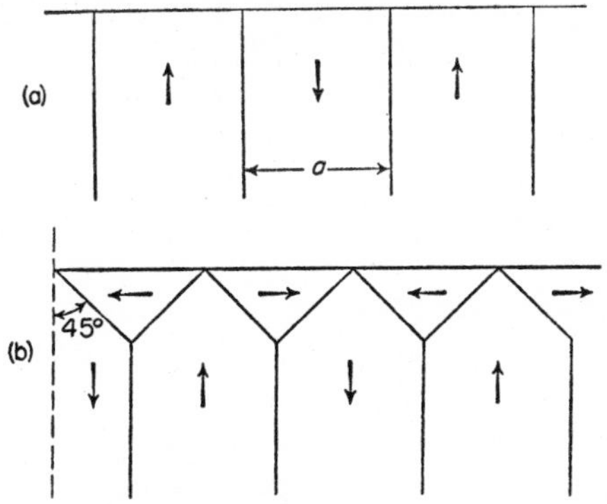

FIG. 21

In the opposite case of small β, a more favourable disposition is that where there is no magnetic field, and $\mathbf{M}$ deviates from the direction of easy magnetisation. For $\mathbf{H} = 0$ we must have everywhere $\operatorname{div}\mathbf{B} = 4\pi \operatorname{div}\mathbf{M} = 0$, and M_n must be continuous at all domain boundaries and at the free surface.

† The layered structure of domains seems to be the more usual.

This is achieved by the setting up of "domains of closure" of triangular cross-section (Fig. 21b), in which the magnetisation is parallel to the surface of the body. The total volume of these regions, and therefore the anisotropy energy in them, are proportional to the layer thickness a.

Thus in all cases the emergence of the domains at the surface of the body results in an excess energy which is the greater, the greater the thickness of the domains. This effect therefore tends to reduce the domain thickness.

The actual thickness of the domains is determined by the equilibrium of the two oppositely acting effects. Let us suppose, for example, that the domains (in a plate) have the form of plane layers of constant thickness. The number of domains is proportional to $1/a$, while the surface-tension energy at the surfaces separating them is proportional to their total area, i.e. to L/a, where L is the total dimension of the body in the direction of the domains, i.e. the thickness of the plate. The energy of the emergence of the domains at the surface of the plate is proportional to a. The sum of these two energies has, as a function of a, a minimum when a has a value proportional to $\sqrt{L}$.

Thus the thickness of the domains increases with the dimension of the body, but the quantitative law $a \sim \sqrt{L}$ of this increase is based on the assumption that the domains are of constant thickness, and clearly cannot be valid for all values of L. The reason is that the thickness of the domains at the surface of the body cannot exceed some limiting value a_k which depends on the properties of the ferromagnetic substance but not on the shape and size of the body. The value of a_k is determined by the point at which, as a increases, the "splitting" of the domain near the surface to a depth $\sim a$ becomes thermodynamically favourable. Such a point must necessarily be reached, since the energy of the emergence of one domain increases as a^2, whereas the excess surface-tension energy resulting from the splitting of the domain increases only as a.

Thus we conclude that, as the size of the body, and therefore the domain thickness, increase, a progressive "branching" of the domains occurs as they approach the surface of the body (E. M. Lifshitz, 1948). We shall not pause to investigate further the various possibilities, which have not yet been clearly ascertained.†

As the dimensions of the body decrease, the formation of any domains at all ultimately becomes thermodynamically unfavourable, so that sufficiently small ferromagnetic particles are uniformly magnetised single domains. The criterion giving their dimension L is obtained by comparing the magnetic energy of a uniformly magnetised particle with the non-uniformity energy which would result if there were considerable non-uniformity in the distribution of the magnetisation over its volume. The former energy is of the

---

† See S. V. Vonsovskiĭ and Ya. S. Shur, *Ferromagnetism* (*Ferromagnetizm*), Moscow, 1948; C. Kittel, *Reviews of Modern Physics* **21**, 541, 1949; E. M. Lifshitz, *Zhurnal éksperimental'noĭ i teoreticheskoĭ fiziki* **15**, 97, 1945.

order M^2V, and the latter of the order of $\alpha M^2V/L^2$. The condition for a single domain to be formed is therefore

$$L^2 \ll \alpha. \tag{39.7}$$

The thermodynamic potential of a uniformly magnetised particle in the absence of an external field is found by putting $\mathfrak{H} = 0$ in the formula

$$\tilde{\mathscr{G}} = \int \left[\tilde{\Phi} + \frac{\mathbf{H}\cdot\mathbf{B}}{8\pi} - \tfrac{1}{2}\mathfrak{H}\cdot\mathbf{M}\right] dV$$

(cf. 31.7)) and substituting for $\tilde{\Phi}$ the sum of the expression (36.1) and the anisotropy energy U_{aniso}:

$$\tilde{\mathscr{G}} = VU_{\text{aniso}} - \tfrac{1}{2}\mathbf{M}\cdot\int \mathbf{H}\, dV. \tag{39.8}$$

The unimportant constant $\tilde{\mathscr{G}}_0$ is omitted. Since **M** and **H** are linearly related, the second term is quadratic in the components of **M**:

$$\tilde{\mathscr{G}} = VU_{\text{aniso}} + \tfrac{1}{2}Va_{ik}M_iM_k, \tag{39.9}$$

where the symmetrical tensor a_{ik} depends only on the shape of the particle. If the particle is ellipsoidal, for example, **H** is constant in it, and (when $\mathfrak{H} = 0$) is related to **M** by

$$H_i + n_{ik}(B_k - H_k) = H_i + 4\pi n_{ik}M_k = 0$$

(cf. (8.10)). In this case, therefore, the components a_{ik} are given in terms of those of the demagnetisation coefficient tensor by $a_{ik} = 4\pi n_{ik}$.

The direction of magnetisation of the particle in an external magnetic field $\mathfrak{H}$ is given by the condition that $\tilde{\mathscr{G}}$, which now includes a term $-V\mathfrak{H}\cdot\mathbf{M}$, should be a minimum. For a cubic crystal we can put simply

$$\tilde{\mathscr{G}} = \tfrac{1}{2}Va_{ik}M_iM_k - V\mathfrak{H}\cdot\mathbf{M}, \tag{39.10}$$

neglecting the anisotropy energy. In uniaxial (and in biaxial) ferromagnetics, however, the anisotropy energy is a quantity of the same order as the remaining terms. Writing this energy in the form (37.1), we have

$$\tilde{\mathscr{G}} = \tfrac{1}{2}V(a_{ik} + \beta_{ik})M_iM_k - V\mathfrak{H}\cdot\mathbf{M}. \tag{39.11}$$

In this form the problem is mathematically identical with the one in §37 concerning the dependence of the local magnetisation **M** on the local field **H**, the only difference being that **H** is replaced by $\mathfrak{H}$, and β_{ik} by a_{ik} or $a_{ik} + \beta_{ik}$.

PROBLEMS

PROBLEM 1. Determine the "surface-tension" coefficient at a boundary between domains in a cubic crystal, if the surface of separation makes an angle χ with the plane (100) (the yz-plane) and the domains are magnetised in the direction [001] of easy magnetisation (the z-axis).

SOLUTION. As well as the crystallographic co-ordinates x, y, z we use co-ordinates x', y', z'; the z and z' axes coincide, and the yz and $y'z'$ planes are at an angle χ. The necessity of having no considerable magnetic field tends (as in a uniaxial crystal) to keep the vector **M** in the $y'z'$-plane in the transition layer. The presence of magnetic anisotropy in the $x'y'$-plane, however, causes **M** to depart slightly from the $y'z'$-plane. Since the anisotropy energy in a cubic crystal is small, the component $M_{x'}$ is also small and can be neglected with sufficient accuracy. Then $M_{x'} = 0$, $M_{y'} = M \sin\theta$, $M_{z'} = M\cos\theta$, where θ is the angle between **M** and the z-axis, or $M_x = M\sin\theta\sin\chi$, $M_y = M\sin\theta\cos\chi$, $M_z = M\cos\theta$.

For the sum of the non-uniformity and anisotropy energies in the transition layer we find

$$\int_{-\infty}^{\infty}\left\{\tfrac{1}{2}\alpha M^2\left(\frac{d\theta}{dx'}\right)^2 + \beta M^4(\sin^2\theta\ \cos^2\theta + \tfrac{1}{4}\ \sin^4\theta\ \sin^2 2\chi)\right\} dx'. \tag{1}$$

Minimising this integral with the same boundary conditions (39.4) gives

$$\sinh x'\sqrt{(2\beta M^2/\alpha)} = -\frac{2\cot\theta}{\sin 2\chi}. \tag{2}$$

Substituting in (1) and effecting the integration, we obtain the required surface tension:

$$M^3\sqrt{(2\alpha\beta)}\left\{1 + \frac{\sin^2 2\chi}{2\sqrt{(4-\sin^2 2\chi)}}\cosh^{-1}\frac{2}{|\sin 2\chi|}\right\}. \tag{3}$$

Formula (3) is valid for any angle χ. Equation (2) for the structure of the transition layer becomes invalid, however, when $\chi \cong 0$ or $\frac{1}{2}\pi$. In this case a finite width of the transition layer is obtained only when the magnetostriction in it is taken into account.

PROBLEM 2. Determine the energy of the magnetic field near the surface of a ferromagnetic at which plane-parallel domains perpendicular to the surface emerge without change in the direction of magnetisation (Fig. 21a).

SOLUTION. The problem of determining the magnetic field near such a surface is equivalent to the electrostatic problem of the field due to a plane divided into strips charged alternately positively and negatively with surface charge density $\sigma = \pm M$.

Let the surface of the body be the plane $z = 0$, and let the x-axis be perpendicular to the plane of the domains. The "surface charge density" $\sigma(x)$ is a periodic function with period $2a$ (a being the width of the domains), and its value in a typical period is $\sigma = -M$ for $-a < x < 0$, $\sigma = +M$ for $0 < x < a$. Its expansion in Fourier series is

$$\sigma(x) = \sum_{n=0}^{\infty} c_n \sin\frac{(2n+1)\pi x}{a}, \qquad c_n = 4M/(2n+1)\pi.$$

The field potential satisfies Laplace's equation

$$\frac{\partial^2\phi}{\partial x^2} + \frac{\partial^2\phi}{\partial z^2} = 0;$$

we seek ϕ as a series

$$\phi(x, z) = \sum_{n=0}^{\infty} b_n \sin\frac{(2n+1)\pi x}{a}\, e^{\mp(2n+1)\pi z/a},$$

where the two signs in the exponent relate to the half-spaces $z > 0$ and $z < 0$. The coefficients b_n are given by the boundary condition

$$-[\partial\phi/\partial z]_{z=0+} + [\partial\phi/\partial z]_{z=0-} = 4\pi\sigma,$$

whence $b_n = 2ac_n/(2n+1)$.

The required field energy can be calculated as the integral $\frac{1}{2}\int \sigma\phi \, df$ over the "charged surface". The energy per unit area is

$$\frac{1}{2}\frac{1}{2a}\int_{-a}^{a} [\sigma\phi]_{z=0}\, dx = \frac{1}{4}\sum_{n=0}^{\infty} c_n b_n$$

$$= \frac{8aM^2}{\pi^2}\sum_{n=0}^{\infty}\frac{1}{(2n+1)^3}.$$

The value of the sum is 1·052, and so the energy is 0·852 aM^2.

§40. The antiferromagnetic Curie point

The passage of a body from an antiferromagnetic to a paramagnetic state usually takes place by a second-order phase transition, as in ferromagnetics. Since there is no spontaneous magnetisation in either the antiferromagnetic or the paramagnetic state, the change in the macroscopic magnetic properties of the substance as it passes through the antiferromagnetic Curie point affects only its magnetic susceptibility. In accordance with the general properties of second-order transitions, the components of the tensor μ_{ik} are continuous at the transition point, but their first derivatives with respect to the temperature are discontinuous.

The general theory of second-order phase transitions must be used for a quantitative investigation of antiferromagnetic transitions. The parameters in terms of which the thermodynamic potential must be expanded near the transition point are here some linear combinations (depending on the particular magnetic symmetry of the lattice) of the mean magnetic moments $\mathbf{m}_1$, $\mathbf{m}_2$, ... at the various points of the elementary cell. As the transition point is approached, all these parameters tend, as usual, to zero as $\sqrt{(\Theta - T)}$.

The thermodynamic potential of an antiferromagnetic may involve terms of various types, resulting both from the exchange interaction of the magnetic moments and from their relativistic interaction; cf. the beginning of §36. The former type contain combinations of the moments $\mathbf{m}_1$, $\mathbf{m}_2$, ... depending only on their relative orientation, and not on their orientation with respect to the crystal lattice. The relativistic terms, however, depend on the directions of the moments in the crystal, i.e. they lead to magnetic anisotropy of the crystal.

As in ferromagnetics, the strong exchange interaction is the principal effect which causes an ordered arrangement of magnetic moments in an antiferromagnetic. The relativistic interactions cause the crystallographic anisotropy of its magnetic properties.

There are certain types of magnetic symmetry which admit ferromagnetism, yet have exchange interactions which do not alone result in ferromagnetism. In such cases the spontaneous magnetisation is due only to the relativistic interactions, and is therefore very small. Such a body is antiferromagnetic, but the disposition of the magnetic moments deviates somewhat from that of a pure antiferromagnetic, in such a way that the magnetic moments in a certain direction do not completely balance (I. E. DZYALOSHINSKIĬ, 1957†). The ratio of the "ferromagnetic moment" to the value which it would have for a pure ferromagnetic is of the same order as the ratio of the relativistic and exchange energy densities ($\sim 10^{-3}$ to 10^{-5}).

In sufficiently strong magnetic fields, the antiferromagnetic structure of the crystal must be thermodynamically unstable, and the orientation of all moments in the direction of the field becomes energetically favourable. This change in orientation usually involves a change (reduction) in the elementary cell of the magnetic structure of the lattice, and, like any change in the symmetry properties, can occur only at a definite phase-transition point, which in most cases is a second-order-transition point. The "critical field" H_{cr} which destroys the antiferromagnetism is a function of temperature which vanishes for $T = \Theta$, Θ being the transition point in the absence of the field. Thus the region of existence of the antiferromagnetic phase in the TH-plane is bounded by a certain curve.

† *Zhurnal éksperimental'noĭ i teoreticheskoĭ fiziki* **32**, 1547, 1957; *Soviet Physics JETP* **5**, 1259, 1957.

CHAPTER VI

SUPERCONDUCTIVITY

§41. The magnetic properties of superconductors

AT TEMPERATURES close to absolute zero many metals enter a peculiar state whose most striking property, discovered by KAMERLINGH ONNES in 1911, is what is called *superconductivity*, i.e. the complete absence of electric resistance to a constant current. Superconductivity first occurs at a definite temperature for each metal, called the *superconductivity transition point.*

This absence of electric resistance, however, is not the most fundamental property of a superconductor. The transition involves profound changes in the magnetic properties of the metal and, as we shall see, the change in its electric properties is a necessary consequence.

The magnetic properties of a superconducting metal can be described as follows. The magnetic field does not penetrate into the superconductor; since the mean magnetic field in the medium is, by definition, the magnetic induction **B**, we can say that throughout a superconductor

$$\mathbf{B} = 0 \tag{41.1}$$

(W. MEISSNER and R. OCHSENFELD, 1933). This property holds whatever the conditions under which the transition to the superconducting state occurs. For example, if the metal is cooled in a magnetic field, then at the transition point the lines of magnetic force cease to enter the body.†

However, it should be mentioned that the equation $\mathbf{B} = 0$ is not valid in a thin surface layer. It is found by experiment that the magnetic field penetrates into a superconductor to a depth large compared with the distances between the atoms, and usually of the order of 10^{-5} cm, but depending on the metal concerned and on the temperature. For the same reason, the equation $\mathbf{B} = 0$ does not hold at all in thin films of metal or colloidal particles whose thickness or dimension is of the order of the "penetration depth".

In what follows, we shall consider only thick superconductors, and neglect the penetration of the magnetic field into a thin surface layer.

† It should be mentioned that only "pure" superconductors, i.e. metallic elements and chemical compounds containing them in certain proportions, exhibit the above properties. We shall discuss only substances of these kinds. In superconducting alloys, the Meissner effect is not complete, and the magnetic field may penetrate into the superconductor, although there is still no electric resistance.

The proof below that the vanishing of **B** implies zero resistance must therefore be taken as showing that this equation is a sufficient, but not necessary, condition for the resistance to be zero.

As we know, the normal component of the induction must be continuous at any boundary between two media; this condition follows from the equation div $\mathbf{B} = 0$, which is universally valid. Since $\mathbf{B} = 0$ in a superconductor, the normal component of the external field must be zero on the surface, i.e. the field outside a superconductor must be everywhere tangential to its surface, the lines of magnetic force having the surface as their envelope.

Using this result, we can easily find the forces acting on a superconductor in a magnetic field. As in §5 for an ordinary conductor in an electric field, we calculate the force per unit surface area as $\sigma_{ik}n_k$, where $\sigma_{ik} = (H_iH_k - \frac{1}{2}H^2\delta_{ik})/4\pi$ is the Maxwell stress tensor for a magnetic field in a vacuum. Since in the present case $\mathbf{n}\cdot\mathbf{H}_e = 0$, where $\mathbf{H}_e$ is the field just outside the body, we find

$$\mathbf{F}_s = -H_e^2\mathbf{n}/8\pi, \tag{41.2}$$

i.e. the surface is subject to a compression, of magnitude equal to the field energy density.

According to equation (27.4)

$$\mathbf{curl\,B} = 4\pi\overline{\rho\mathbf{v}}/c, \tag{41.3}$$

and from the equation $\mathbf{B} = 0$ it follows that the mean current density is also zero everywhere inside the superconductor. That is, no macroscopic volume currents can flow in a superconductor. It should be emphasised that in a superconductor the conduction current cannot meaningfully be isolated from $\overline{\rho\mathbf{v}}$ as it can in an ordinary conductor. For the same reason the magnetisation $\mathbf{M}$, and therefore $\mathbf{H}$, have no physical significance here.

Thus any electric current which flows in a superconductor must be a surface current. The surface current density $\mathbf{g}$ is given, according to (27.14), by the discontinuity in the tangential component of the induction at the boundary of the body. Since $\mathbf{B} = 0$ inside the superconductor, and $\mathbf{B} = \mathbf{H}$ outside it, we have

$$\mathbf{g} = c\mathbf{n}\times\mathbf{H}_e/4\pi. \tag{41.4}$$

The presence of surface currents is not peculiar to superconductors. Similar currents can occur in any magnetised body, and their density is $\mathbf{g} = c\mathbf{n}\times(\mathbf{H}_e - \mathbf{B})/4\pi$. Since the tangential component of $\mathbf{H} = \mathbf{B}/\mu$ is continuous on the surface of a normal (not superconducting) body, we have $\mathbf{n}\times\mathbf{H}_e = \mathbf{n}\times\mathbf{B}/\mu$, and so the expression for $\mathbf{g}$ can be written

$$\mathbf{g} = \frac{c}{4\pi}\mathbf{n}\times\mathbf{B}\frac{1-\mu}{\mu}. \tag{41.5}$$

A fundamental difference between superconductors and other bodies, however, appears when we consider the total current through a cross-section of the body. In a non-superconductor the surface currents always balance, and the total current is zero. This is seen from the condition (41.5) which relates the current density $\mathbf{g}$ to the magnetic induction inside the body, and so to the current **g** at every point on the surface. In superconductors, however, the condition (41.5) has no meaning. For the transition from the ordinary state (with magnetic permeability μ) to the superconducting state corresponds formally to the limit $B \to 0$ and $\mu \to 0$. The right-hand side of (41.5) then becomes indeterminate, and there is no condition which restricts the possible values of the current.

Thus we have the important result that the currents flowing on the surface of a superconductor may amount to a non-zero total current. Of course, this can occur only in a multiply-connected body (a ring, for example), or in a simply-connected superconductor forming part of a closed circuit which includes also a source of the electromotive force needed to maintain the currents in the parts of the circuit which are not superconducting.

It is very important to note that a steady flow of current on a superconductor is possible even if no electric field is present. This means that no dissipation of energy occurs, whose replacement would involve the doing of work by an external field. This property of a superconductor may also be described by saying that it has no electric resistance, a result which is thus a necessary consequence of its magnetic properties.

§42. The superconductivity current

Let us consider in more detail some properties of superconductors which depend on their shape.

If a superconductor is a simply-connected body, then no steady distribution of surface currents on it can exist in the absence of an external magnetic field. This can be seen as follows. The surface currents would produce in the surrounding space a constant magnetic field vanishing at infinity. Like any constant magnetic field in a vacuum, this field would have a potential ϕ, and by the boundary conditions on the superconductor the normal derivative $\partial\phi/\partial n$ would vanish at the surface. We know from potential theory, however, that if $\partial\phi/\partial n = 0$ on the surface of a simply-connected body and at infinity, then ϕ is a constant in all space outside the body. Thus a magnetic field of this kind cannot exist, and therefore neither can the assumed surface currents.

An external magnetic field, on the other hand, causes currents to flow on the surface of a simply-connected superconductor, and these currents can be observed through the appearance of a magnetic moment of the whole body. This "magnetisation" is easily calculated for an ellipsoidal superconductor.†

Let $\mathfrak{H}$ be the external field, parallel to one of the principal axes of the ellipsoid. The relation $(1-n)\mathbf{H}+n\mathbf{B} = \mathfrak{H}$ holds for the magnetic field $\mathbf{H}$ inside a non-superconducting ellipsoid, n being the demagnetisation coefficient for the axis in question (see (8.7)). In a superconductor there is no

† In the present section we always assume that the magnetic field does not exceed the value at which superconductivity ceases (see §43).

"field" **H**, as we have already shown, and so the magnetisation $\mathbf{M} = (\mathbf{B}-\mathbf{H})/4\pi$ also lacks its usual significance. Nevertheless, it is here convenient to introduce **H** and **M** as formal auxiliary quantities in the calculation of the total magnetic moment $\mathcal{M} = \mathbf{M}V$ (V being the volume of the ellipsoid), which retains its usual meaning. Putting $\mathbf{B} = 0$ in the superconducting ellipsoid, we find

$$\mathbf{H} = \mathfrak{H}/(1-n), \tag{42.1}$$

and

$$\mathcal{M} = -V\mathbf{H}/4\pi = -V\mathfrak{H}/4\pi(1-n). \tag{42.2}$$

In particular, for a long cylinder in a longitudinal field $n = 0$, so that $\mathbf{H} = \mathfrak{H}$ and $\mathcal{M} = -V\mathfrak{H}/4\pi$.† These values of $\mathcal{M}$ are the same as would be found if the body had a diamagnetic volume susceptibility of $-1/4\pi$.

The magnetic field $\mathbf{H}_e$ just outside the ellipsoid is everywhere tangential to it, and so its magnitude can be determined at once from the condition that the tangential component of **H** is continuous. Within the ellipsoid $\mathbf{H} = \mathfrak{H}/(1-n)$; taking the tangential component, we have

$$(1-n)H_e = \mathfrak{H}\sin\theta, \tag{42.3}$$

where θ is the angle between the direction of the external field $\mathfrak{H}$ and the normal to the surface at the point considered. The greatest value of H_e occurs on the equator of the ellipsoid, and is $\mathfrak{H}/(1-n)$.

It may be pointed out once more that there is no fundamental difference between the currents which cause the "magnetisation" of a superconductor and those which produce the total current in it: their physical nature is the same. This important fact makes possible, in particular, an immediate determination of the gyromagnetic coefficients for any superconductor. The momentum density of the electrons which form the "magnetising" currents differs from the current density only by a factor m/e, e and m being the charge and mass of the electron. From the definition of the gyromagnetic coefficients (see (35.3)) it follows at once that for a superconductor $g_{ik} = \delta_{ik}$.

Let us now consider multiply-connected superconductors. Their properties are very different from those of simply-connected ones, mainly because it is no longer true that a steady distribution of surface currents is impossible in the absence of an external magnetic field. Moreover, the surface currents need not balance out, and may result in a non-zero total superconductivity current on the body, even if no external e.m.f. is applied.

Let us consider a doubly-connected body (i.e. a ring), with no external magnetic field. We shall show that the state of such a body is entirely determined if the total current J on it is given. The problem of determining the field of the ring can again be solved as a problem of potential theory, but the

† These relations for a cylinder follow immediately from the continuity condition on **H**, and are therefore valid for a cylinder of any cross-section, circular or otherwise.

potential ϕ is now a many-valued function, which changes by $4\pi J/c$ when we go round any closed path interlinked with the ring (cf. §29). In order to state the problem in mathematically precise terms, we must draw some open surface which spans the ring. Then the problem is to solve Laplace's equation with the boundary conditions $\partial\phi/\partial n = 0$ on the surface of the ring, $\phi = 0$ at infinity, and $\phi_2 - \phi_1 = 4\pi J/c$ on the chosen surface, where ϕ_1 and ϕ_2 are the values of the potential on the two sides of that surface. Such a problem is known from potential theory to have a unique solution, which does not depend on the form of the chosen surface. From the field near the surface of the ring, we can in turn uniquely determine the surface current distribution.

The self-inductance of a superconducting ring is entirely determinate together with the current distribution. Here there is a marked difference from ordinary conductors, where the current distribution, and therefore the precise value of the self-inductance, depend on the manner of excitation of the current (§33).†

In §32 we introduced the concept of the magnetic flux Φ through a linear conductor circuit, and showed that $\Phi = LJ/c$, where L is the self-inductance of the conducting circuit. For a superconducting ring, the magnetic flux is meaningful for any thickness, not necessarily small, of the ring. For, since the magnetic field is tangential, the magnetic flux through any part of the surface of the ring is zero; the magnetic flux through every surface spanning the ring is therefore the same. Moreover, the formula

$$\Phi = LJ/c \tag{42.4}$$

remains valid, the self-inductance L being again defined in terms of the total energy of the magnetic field of the current. The total energy of the magnetic field of the superconductor is given by the integral $\int (H^2/8\pi)\mathrm{d}V$, taken over all space outside the body. Again spanning the ring by a surface C, we can use the field potential and write

$$\begin{aligned}\int H^2 \,\mathrm{d}V/8\pi &= -\int \mathbf{H}\cdot\mathbf{grad}\,\phi \,\mathrm{d}V/8\pi \\ &= \int \phi \,\mathrm{div}\,\mathbf{H}\,\mathrm{d}V/8\pi - \oint H_n \phi \,\mathrm{d}f/8\pi.\end{aligned}$$

The first term is zero, because $\mathrm{div}\,\mathbf{H} = 0$. The surface integral is taken over an infinitely remote surface, the surface of the ring, and the two sides

† The self-inductance of a superconducting ring of radius b, made of wire whose cross-section is a circle of small radius a, is the same as the external part of the inductance of a non-superconducting ring, namely $L = 4\pi b[\log(8b/a) - 2]$; see §33, Problem 2. The exact solution of the problem of a current in a superconducting circular ring was first given by V. A. Fok, *Physikalische Zeitschrift der Sowjetunion* **1**, 215, 1932.

of the surface C. The first two of these give zero, so that

$$\int H^2 \,\mathrm{d}V/8\pi = \oint_C H_n(\phi_2-\phi_1)\,\mathrm{d}f/8\pi$$

$$= (J/2c)\oint_C H_n \,\mathrm{d}f = J\Phi/2c,$$

where Φ is the magnetic flux through the surface C. Comparing this with the definition of the self-inductance, we have $J\Phi/2c = LJ^2/2c^2$, which gives (42.4).

If the ring is in an external magnetic field, the total magnetic flux Φ is composed of the flux LJ/c and the flux Φ_e of the external field. A very important property of a superconducting ring is that, even if the external field and the current vary, the magnetic flux through the ring remains constant:

$$LJ/c+\Phi_e = \Phi_0, \text{ a constant.} \tag{42.5}$$

This follows immediately from the integral form of Maxwell's equation in the space outside the body:

$$\frac{1}{c}\frac{\partial}{\partial t}\oint_C \mathbf{H}\cdot\mathrm{d}\mathbf{f} = -\oint \mathbf{E}\cdot\mathrm{d}\mathbf{l}.$$

If the integration on the left-hand side is taken over a surface C which spans the ring, the contour of integration on the right-hand side is a line on the surface of the ring. On the surface of a superconductor, the tangential component of $\mathbf{E}$ is zero (since $\mathbf{E} = 0$ inside a superconductor and $\mathbf{E}_t$ is continuous on the surface). Hence the left-hand side is zero, and therefore $\mathrm{d}\Phi/\mathrm{d}t = 0$.

The relation (42.5) gives the variation of the current in the ring when the external field changes. For example, if the ring is made superconducting in an external field of flux Φ_0, which is then removed, a steady current $J = c\Phi_0/L$ flows in the ring.

The constancy of the magnetic flux through a superconducting ring holds not only when the external field changes but also when the shape of the ring or its position in space is altered.† An intuitive statement of this result is that the lines of force can never intersect the surface of the superconductor, and so cannot escape from the aperture of the ring.

The above results can be immediately generalised to the case of multiply-connected superconducting bodies, including sets of rings. The state of an n-ply connected system in the absence of an external field is completely

† This statement follows at once from the relation between the induced e.m.f. and the change in the magnetic flux through the circuit when it is moved (§49).

determined by the $n-1$ total currents J_a. The relation (42.5) becomes the system of equations

$$\sum_b L_{ab} J_b + \Phi_{e,a} = \Phi_{0,a}. \tag{42.6}$$

These equations hold, not only for any external field, but also for any change in shape or relative position.

PROBLEM

Determine the magnetic moment of a superconducting disc in an external magnetic field perpendicular to its plane.†

SOLUTION. The problem of a superconductor in a constant magnetic field is identical with the electrostatic problem of a dielectric of permeability $\epsilon = 0$. Regarding the disc as the limit of a spheroid as $c \to 0$ (cf. §4, Problem 4), and using (8.9), we find with appropriate change of notation (the field $\mathfrak{H}$ being along the z-axis) $\mathscr{M} = -2a^3\mathfrak{H}/3\pi$.

§43. The critical field

A cylindrical superconductor in a longitudinal magnetic field has an additional magnetic energy $-\frac{1}{2}\mathfrak{H}\cdot\mathscr{M} = \mathfrak{H}^2 V/8\pi$. For a non-superconducting cylinder, on the other hand, the total energy would be almost unchanged when the external field was applied (we shall neglect the slight diamagnetism or paramagnetism of a non-superconducting metal, i.e. take $\mu = 1$). Thus it is clear that, in sufficiently strong magnetic fields, the superconducting state must be thermodynamically less favourable than the normal state, and so the superconductivity must be destroyed.

The value of the longitudinal magnetic field at which the superconductivity of a cylindrical body is destroyed depends on the metal concerned and on the temperature (and pressure). This value is called the *critical field* H_{cr}, and is one of the most important characteristics of a superconductor.‡

When the critical field is reached, the superconductivity is destroyed throughout the cylinder, because of the uniformity of the field over the surface. In bodies of other shapes, however, the destruction of superconductivity is a more complex process, in which the volume occupied by matter in the normal state gradually extends as $\mathfrak{H}$ increases over some range (§44).

Thus, at any temperature below the transition point, the metal can exist in either the superconducting or the normal state, denoted by the suffixes *s* and *n* respectively. We denote by $\mathscr{F}_{s0}(V,T)$ and $\mathscr{F}_n(V,T)$ the total free energies of the superconducting and normal body in the absence of an external

---

† We consider this problem principally with a view to using the result elsewhere (see §75, Problem 2). For a superconducting disc the magnetic fields must in reality be very weak, since its superconductivity is very easily destroyed (see §43).

‡ There is a sharp transition between the superconducting and normal states only in "pure" superconductors (see the footnote to §41), which are the only ones considered here. In alloys, the destruction of superconductivity and the penetration of the magnetic field occur gradually over a fairly wide range of fields, so that there is no critical field in the sense here defined.

magnetic field; these quantities depend on the substance concerned and on the volume, but not on the shape, of the body. The free energy in the normal state does not change when the external field is applied, and so we omit the suffix 0 in $\mathscr{F}_{n0}$. In the superconducting state, however, the magnetic field considerably affects the free energy.

For a superconducting cylinder, with given V and T, the free energy in a longitudinal external field $\mathfrak{H}$ is

$$\mathscr{F}_s = \mathscr{F}_{s0}(V, T) + \mathfrak{H}^2 V/8\pi. \tag{43.1}$$

From this we can derive all the other thermodynamic quantities. Differentiating (43.1) with respect to the volume, we find the pressure on the body:

$$p = p_0(V, T) - \mathfrak{H}^2/8\pi, \tag{43.2}$$

where $p_0(V, T)$ is the pressure (for given V and T) in the absence of the field. The equation (43.2) gives the relation between p, V and T, i.e. it is the equation of state for a superconducting cylinder in an external magnetic field. We see that the volume $V(p, T)$ in the presence of the magnetic field is the same as the volume with no magnetic field but a pressure $p + \mathfrak{H}^2/8\pi$. This result accords, of course, with formula (41.2) for the force on the surface of a superconductor in a magnetic field.

The thermodynamic potential† of the superconducting cylinder is $\Phi_s = \mathscr{F}_s + pV = \mathscr{F}_{s0}(V, T) + p_0 V$, the volume V being expressed in terms of p and T by (43.2). Hence we can write

$$\Phi_s(p, T) = \Phi_{s0}\left(p + \frac{\mathfrak{H}^2}{8\pi}, T\right), \tag{43.3}$$

where $\Phi_{s0}(p, T)$ is the thermodynamic potential in the absence of the field. Differentiating this equation with respect to T and to p, we obtain analogous relations for the entropy and the volume:

$$\mathscr{S}_s(p, T) = \mathscr{S}_{s0}\left(p + \frac{\mathfrak{H}^2}{8\pi}, T\right), \tag{43.4}$$

$$V_s(p, T) = V_{s0}\left(p + \frac{\mathfrak{H}^2}{8\pi}, T\right). \tag{43.5}$$

We can now write down the condition which determines the critical field. The transition of the cylinder from the superconducting to the normal state occurs when Φ_n becomes less than Φ_s (for given p and T). At the transition point we have $\Phi_s = \Phi_n$, i.e.

$$\Phi_{s0}\left(p + \frac{H_{cr}^2}{8\pi}, T\right) = \Phi_n(p, T). \tag{43.6}$$

This is an exact thermodynamic relation.‡ The change in the thermodynamic

† Here defined as in §12.

‡ We give here calculations more accurate than is usually necessary, so as to exhibit more clearly the interrelation between the various thermodynamic quantities.

potential in the magnetic field is usually a small correction to $\mathscr{G}_{s0}(p, T)$. We can then expand the left-hand side of equation (43.6) in series, taking the first two terms:

$$\mathscr{G}_{s0}(p, T)+\frac{H_{cr}^2}{8\pi}V_{s0}(p, T) = \mathscr{G}_n(p, T), \tag{43.7}$$

where $V_{s0}(p, T) = \partial \mathscr{G}_{s0}(p, T)/\partial p$ is the volume of the superconducting cylinder in the absence of the field. Thus, in this approximation, we can say that the thermodynamic potential per unit volume is greater by $H_{cr}^2/8\pi$ in the normal state than its value in the superconducting state.

We denote by $T_{cr} = T_{cr}(p)$ the transition temperature in the absence of the magnetic field. Experiment shows that the transition concerned is a second-order phase transition. Hence, in particular, $H_{cr}(T)$ must tend continuously to zero at $T = T_{cr}$. We know from the general theory of second-order phase transitions† that the change in the thermodynamic potential near the transition point is proportional to the square of $T-T_{cr}$. We can therefore deduce from (43.7) that the critical field in this temperature range varies as the temperature difference $T-T_{cr}$:

$$H_{cr} = \text{constant}\times(T_{cr}-T). \tag{43.8}$$

Differentiating both sides of equation (43.6) with respect to temperature (for given pressure), remembering that H_{cr} is a function of T, and using (43.4), (43.5), we have

$$\mathscr{S}_n-\mathscr{S}_s = -V_s\frac{\partial}{\partial T}\left(\frac{H_{cr}^2}{8\pi}\right), \tag{43.9}$$

where all the quantities $\mathscr{S}_n$, $\mathscr{S}_s$, V_s are for the point of transition between the two states of the body (i.e. for $H = H_{cr}$). Multiplying by T, we obtain the heat of the transition:

$$Q = T(\mathscr{S}_n-\mathscr{S}_s) = -\frac{V_s H_{cr} T}{4\pi}\left(\frac{\partial H_{cr}}{\partial T}\right)_p. \tag{43.10}$$

When the transition occurs at $T = T_{cr}$ (i.e. in the absence of the magnetic field), the quantity Q vanishes with H_{cr}, in accordance with the fact that we have a second-order phase transition. A transition at $T < T_{cr}$ (in a magnetic field) involves absorption or evolution of heat, i.e. it is a first-order phase transition. Experiment shows that H_{cr} increases monotonically with decreasing temperature throughout the range from T_{cr} to zero. Hence the derivative $\partial H_{cr}/\partial T$ is always negative, and we see from (43.10) that $Q > 0$, i.e. heat is absorbed in the (isothermal) transition from the superconducting to the normal state.

---

† See *Statistical Physics*, §135, Pergamon Press, London, 1958.

As $T \to 0$, the entropy of the whole body must vanish, by Nernst's theorem. Hence it follows from (43.9) that $\partial H_{cr}/\partial T = 0$ for $T = 0$, i.e. the curve of $H_{cr}(T)$ intersects the H_{cr}-axis at right angles.

We may differentiate the difference $\mathcal{S}_n - \mathcal{S}_s$ (43.9) again with respect to temperature, and again use equations (43.4), (43.5). Since also $(\partial \mathcal{S}/\partial p)_T = -(\partial V/\partial T)_p$, the result is

$$\frac{\partial \mathcal{S}_n}{\partial T} - \frac{\partial \mathcal{S}_s}{\partial T} = -V_s \frac{\partial^2}{\partial T^2}\left(\frac{H_{cr}^2}{8\pi}\right) - 2\frac{\partial V_s}{\partial T}\frac{\partial}{\partial T}\left(\frac{H_{cr}^2}{8\pi}\right) - \frac{\partial V_s}{\partial p}\left[\frac{\partial}{\partial T}\left(\frac{H_{cr}^2}{8\pi}\right)\right]^2. \tag{43.11}$$

Multiplying both sides of this equation by T, we obtain the difference of the specific heats (at constant pressure) of the two phases. The terms involving the thermal-expansion coefficient and the compressibility are usually very small in comparison with the remaining terms; neglecting them, we have

$$\mathcal{C}_s - \mathcal{C}_n = \frac{V_s T}{4\pi} H_{cr} \frac{\partial^2 H_{cr}}{\partial T^2} + \frac{V_s T}{4\pi}\left(\frac{\partial H_{cr}}{\partial T}\right)^2. \tag{43.12}$$

This formula could also be obtained by direct differentiation of the approximate relation (43.7). In this approximation the difference between V_s and V_{s0}, and between $\mathcal{C}_s$ and $\mathcal{C}_{s0}$, may be neglected.

For $T = T_{cr}$, the first term in (43.12) is zero, and we obtain the following formula, which relates the change in specific heat in the second-order phase transition (in the absence of an external magnetic field) to the temperature dependence of H_{cr}:

$$\mathcal{C}_s - \mathcal{C}_n = \frac{V_s T}{4\pi}\left(\frac{\partial H_{cr}}{\partial T}\right)^2 \tag{43.13}$$

(A. J. Rutgers, 1933). Hence we see, in particular, that in this case $\mathcal{C}_s > \mathcal{C}_n$. As the temperature falls, i.e. when the superconductivity is destroyed by the magnetic field, the difference $\mathcal{C}_s - \mathcal{C}_n$ changes sign, because the difference $\mathcal{S}_n - \mathcal{S}_s$ is zero for $T = 0$ and for $T = T_{cr}$, and must have a maximum in between.

We can similarly discuss effects related to the change in volume in the transition. To do so, we differentiate equation (43.6) with respect to pressure (for given temperature), H_{cr} being a function of p. This gives

$$V_n = V_s \frac{\partial}{\partial p}\left(p + \frac{H_{cr}^2}{8\pi}\right)$$

or

$$V_n - V_s = \frac{V_s H_{cr}}{4\pi}\frac{\partial H_{cr}}{\partial p}, \tag{43.14}$$

which determines the change in volume at the transition point.† For $T = T_{cr}$ this difference is zero, like the entropy difference. The transition at temperatures $T < T_{cr}$, however, is accompanied by a change in volume, which may be of either sign, depending on the sign of the derivative $(\partial H_{cr}/\partial p)_T$. For $T = T_{cr}$ there is no change in volume, but the compressibility is discontinuous; the discontinuity is easily found by differentiating equation (43.14). It may be noted that, if we substitute in (43.14)

$$\left(\frac{\partial H_{cr}}{\partial p}\right)_T = -\left(\frac{\partial H_{cr}}{\partial T}\right)_p \left(\frac{\partial T}{\partial p}\right)_{H_{cr}}$$

(obtained by differentiating the equation $H_{cr}(p, T) = \text{constant}$), we obtain the Clapeyron–Clausius equation

$$\left(\frac{\partial p}{\partial T}\right)_{H_{cr}} = \frac{Q}{T(V_n - V_s)}, \tag{43.15}$$

where the derivative $(\partial p/\partial T)_{H_{cr}}$ defines the change in pressure needed to keep the applied external field critical when the temperature changes.

The physical significance of the critical field H_{cr} is much wider than would appear from its definition in terms of the behaviour of a superconducting cylinder. The equation $H = H_{cr}$ is a condition of equilibrium which must be fulfilled at every point of a surface separating normal and superconducting phases in the same body. This is evident from the following simple arguments. If a cylinder is in a longitudinal magnetic field H_{cr}, then both the boundary conditions on the magnetic field and the conditions of thermodynamic stability are satisfied for all states in which an interior cylindrical part is in the superconducting state and the rest of the body is in the normal state, and the field at the boundary between these parts is H_{cr}. Thus the surface of separation, on which $H = H_{cr}$, is in "neutral equilibrium" with respect to its location. This is a characteristic property of phase equilibrium.

In a variable magnetic field, the boundary between the superconducting and normal phases changes its position. The kinetics of this process is very complex, and its discussion requires a simultaneous solution of the equations of electrodynamics and of thermal conduction, taking into account the heat evolved in the phase transition. We shall not pause to carry out this investigation,‡ but merely give the boundary condition which must be satisfied at the moving boundary between the normal and superconducting phases.

To derive this condition we take a co-ordinate system K' moving with the velocity $\mathbf{v}$ of the boundary between the phases. By the formulae for transformation of fields, the electric field $\mathbf{E}'$ in the system K' is related to the fields $\mathbf{E}$ and $\mathbf{B}$ in a fixed system K by $\mathbf{E}' = \mathbf{E} + \mathbf{v} \times \mathbf{B}/c$; see (49.1). Since the

---

† This difference must of course be distinguished from the change in volume (magnetostriction) of the superconductor when the field changes from zero to H_{cr}. This can be found from (43.5): $V_s(p, T) - V_{s0}(p, T) \cong (H_{cr}^2/8\pi)(\partial V_s/\partial p)_T$.

‡ It has been completed by I. M. Lifshitz, *Zhurnal éksperimental'noĭ i teoreticheskoĭ fiziki* **20**, 834, 1950; *Doklady Akademii Nauk SSSR* **90**, 363, 1953.

boundary is at rest in the system K', the usual condition of continuity of the tangential component of $\mathbf{E}'$ holds, i.e. $\mathbf{n}\times\mathbf{E}' = \mathbf{n}\times\mathbf{E}-v\mathbf{B}/c$ must be continuous, where $\mathbf{n}$ is a unit vector normal to the surface, in the direction of the velocity $\mathbf{v}$. In the superconducting phase $\mathbf{E} = \mathbf{B} = 0$, and in the normal phase $B = H_{cr}$ at the boundary. We therefore find that a tangential electric field appears on the moving boundary, its direction being perpendicular to that of the magnetic field and its magnitude being

$$E = vH_{cr}/c. \qquad (43.16)$$

§44. The intermediate state

If a superconducting body of any shape is in an external magnetic field $\mathfrak{H}$ which is gradually increased, a stage is finally reached where the field at some point on the surface of the body becomes equal to the critical field H_{cr}, but $\mathfrak{H}$ itself is still less than H_{cr}. For example, on the surface of an ellipsoid placed in a field $\mathfrak{H}$ parallel to one of its axes, the greatest value of the field occurs on the equator (see (42.3)), and is equal to H_{cr} when $\mathfrak{H} = H_{cr}(1-n)$.

When $\mathfrak{H}$ increases further, the body cannot remain entirely in the superconducting state. Nor can it pass entirely into the normal state, because then the field would become $\mathfrak{H}$ everywhere. Hence the superconductivity must be lost only in part.

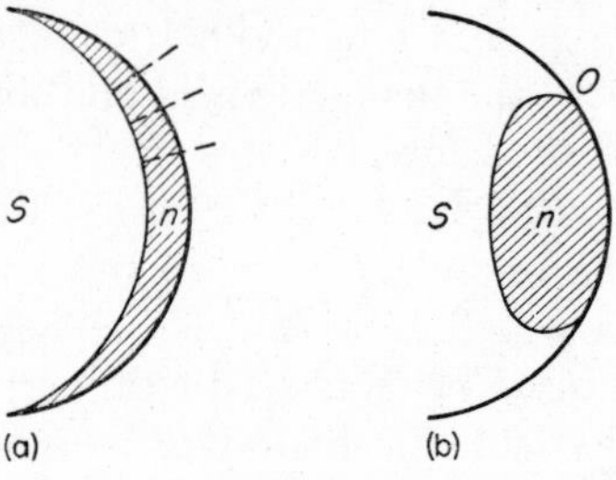

FIG. 22

At first sight one might imagine that this process occurs as follows. As $\mathfrak{H}$ increases, the superconductivity is lost in a gradually increasing part of the body, while a gradually decreasing part remains superconducting, and the whole body becomes normal when $\mathfrak{H} = H_{cr}$. It is easy to see, however, that such states of the body are thermodynamically unstable. On the surface separating the superconducting and normal phases the magnetic field is, as we know, tangential to the surface, and its magnitude is H_{cr}. That is, the lines of force are on the surface. If the boundary is convex to the normal phase, the equipotential surfaces of the field, being at right angles to the lines of force, will diverge into the normal region, as shown by dashed lines in Fig. 22a. The field decreases, however, in the direction in which the equipotential surfaces diverge, so that we should have $H < H_{cr}$ in the shaded region, contrary to the supposition that this region is in the normal state.

If, on the other hand, the boundary of the superconducting phase is concave, then the lines of force on that boundary must have a bend on the free surface of the superconducting region, to which the field is tangential (at the point *O*, in Fig. 22b). At a bend in a line of force, however, the field becomes infinite, which again contradicts the boundary conditions at the surface of the superconductor.

The above arguments represent essentially another form of the situation which leads to the domain structure of ferroelectrics and ferromagnetics. Here also the conditions of thermodynamic stability have the result that, if the magnetic field reaches the value H_{cr} at even one point on the surface, the body is divided into numerous parallel alternating thin layers of normal and superconducting matter (L. LANDAU, 1937). This state of the superconductor is called the *intermediate* state. As $\mathfrak{H}$ increases, the total volume of the normal layers increases, and when $\mathfrak{H} = H_{cr}$ the body becomes entirely normal.

It should be emphasised that a body of arbitrary shape need not be entirely in the intermediate state. There may also be regions in the purely superconducting and purely normal states; these must be separated by the region which is in the intermediate state. A simpler case is the ellipsoid already considered. In a field parallel to the axis the intermediate state occurs in the range

$$H_{cr}(1-n) < \mathfrak{H} < H_{cr}, \tag{44.1}$$

and the whole volume of the ellipsoid is in this state.†

The shape and size of the normal and superconducting layers in the intermediate state are determined by the conditions of thermodynamic equilibrium of the body as a whole, in the same manner as the shape of the domains in a ferromagnetic (§39). As there, the thickness of the layers is determined by two oppositely acting factors. The "surface tension" at the boundaries of the normal and superconducting phases tends to reduce the number of layers, i.e. to increase their thickness. The "energy of emergence" of the layers at the free surface of the body has the opposite tendency. The layer thickness increases with the size of the body, and consequently (for the same reasons as in ferromagnetic domains) they must eventually branch near the surface.‡

The intermediate state can also be described in an averaged manner if the thickness of the regions under consideration is large compared with the layer thickness (R. E. PEIERLS, and F. LONDON, 1936). In this description it is

† For a sphere (for example), $n = \frac{1}{3}$, and the intermediate state exists in the range $\frac{2}{3}H_{cr} < \mathfrak{H} < H_{cr}$. For a cylinder in a transverse field, $n = \frac{1}{2}$, and the corresponding range is $\frac{1}{2}H_{cr} < \mathfrak{H} < H_{cr}$. For a cylinder in a longitudinal field, $n = 0$; there is no intermediate state, and the superconductivity is totally destroyed at $\mathfrak{H} = H_{cr}$. Finally, for a flat plate in a transverse field $n = 1$, and it is in the intermediate state for any field $\mathfrak{H} < H_{cr}$.

‡ The thickness of unbranched layers is calculated in Problem 2. A discussion of a model with multiple branching has been given by L. LANDAU, *Zhurnal éksperimental'noĭ i teoreticheskoĭ fiziki* **13**, 377, 1943; *Journal of Physics* **7**, 99, 1943.

The interrelation between the two models is considered by E. M. LIFSHITZ and YU. V. SHARVIN, *Doklady Akademii Nauk SSSR* **79**, 783, 1951.

In certain conditions, when the external field is near zero or H_{cr}, a "filamentary" structure may be thermodynamically more favourable than the layered structure; see E. R. ANDREW, *Proceedings of the Royal Society* A**194**, 98, 1948.

assumed that there is inside the body a magnetic induction $\bar{\mathbf{B}}$ which varies from zero in the purely superconducting state to H_{cr} in the purely normal state. If we ascribe a non-zero induction to the matter in the intermediate state, we must also ascribe to it a definite magnetic "field" $\bar{\mathbf{H}}$. To determine the relation between these quantities, we must consider the true structure of the intermediate state.

The magnetic field in a normal layer at its boundary with a superconducting layer is H_{cr}, and by virtue of the assumed smallness of the layer thickness we can suppose that the field has this value everywhere in the normal layers. In the superconducting layers $\mathbf{B} = 0$. Hence, averaging the magnetic field over a volume large compared with the layer thickness, we find that the mean induction $\bar{B} = x_n H_{cr}$, where x_n is the fraction of the volume that is in the normal state. Next, we determine the thermodynamic potential per unit volume of the body, taking as zero the value for the purely superconducting state. In the absence of a magnetic field, unit volume of the normal phase has an excess thermodynamic potential $H_{cr}^2/8\pi$.† When a magnetic field is present, a further $H_{cr}^2/8\pi$ is added as magnetic energy, giving altogether $H_{cr}^2/4\pi$. The mean thermodynamic potential per unit volume in the intermediate state is therefore

$$\Phi = x_n H_{cr}^2/4\pi = H_{cr}\bar{B}/4\pi. \tag{44.2}$$

The relation between $\bar{\mathbf{B}}$ and $\bar{\mathbf{H}}$ is obtained from the general thermodynamic relation $\mathbf{H} = 4\pi\partial\Phi/\partial\mathbf{B}$. In the present case we find that $\bar{\mathbf{H}}$ is parallel to $\mathbf{B}$ and its magnitude is

$$H = H_{cr}. \tag{44.3}$$

i.e. it is independent of the induction.

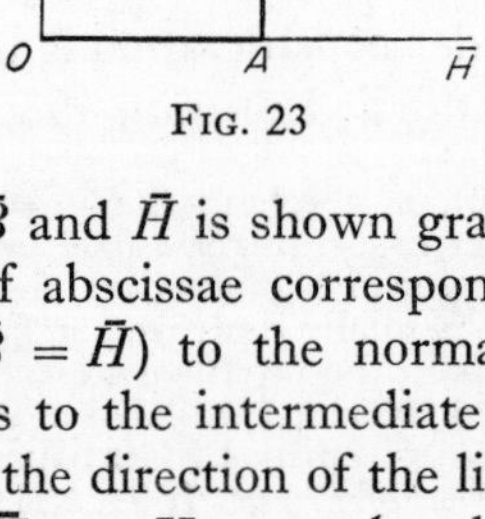

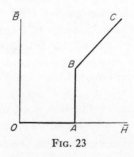

FIG. 23

If the relation between $\bar{B}$ and $\bar{H}$ is shown graphically (Fig. 23), then the segment OA of the axis of abscissae corresponds to the superconducting state, and the line BC ($\bar{B} = \bar{H}$) to the normal state. The vertical line AB ($\bar{H} = H_{cr}$) corresponds to the intermediate state.

Let $\mathbf{n}$ be a unit vector in the direction of the lines of force of the averaged magnetic field. Putting $\bar{\mathbf{H}} = H_{cr}\mathbf{n}$ and substituting in the equation

† Here we neglect all magnetostriction effects. Instead of the change in the thermodynamic potential we could therefore speak of the (equal) change in the free energy.

$\mathbf{curl}\,\bar{\mathbf{H}} = 0$ (which holds in the absence of a volume current), we find that $\mathbf{curl}\,\mathbf{n} = 0$. Since $\mathbf{n}^2 = 1$, we have

$$\mathbf{grad}\,\mathbf{n}^2 = 2(\mathbf{n}\cdot\mathbf{grad})\mathbf{n}+2\mathbf{n}\times\mathbf{curl}\,\mathbf{n} = 0,$$

and therefore $(\mathbf{n}\cdot\mathbf{grad})\mathbf{n} = 0$. This means that the direction of the vector $\mathbf{n}$ is constant. Thus the lines of force of the mean field are straight lines.

Let us apply these results to an ellipsoid in the intermediate state. For a uniform field inside the ellipsoid, the relation $(1-n)\bar{H}+n\bar{B} = \mathfrak{H}$ holds, whatever the relation between **B** and **H**. Putting $\bar{H} = H_{cr}$, we have

$$\bar{B} = \frac{\mathfrak{H}}{n} - \frac{1-n}{n}H_{cr}. \tag{44.4}$$

Thus the mean induction in the ellipsoid varies linearly with the external field, from zero when $\mathfrak{H} = (1-n)H_{cr}$ to H_{cr} when $\mathfrak{H} = H_{cr}$.

We may also write down an expression for the total thermodynamic potential $\mathcal{G}$ of an ellipsoid in the intermediate state. To do so, we start from the general formula

$$\mathcal{G} = \int\left[\Phi - \frac{\mathbf{H}\cdot\mathbf{B}}{8\pi} - \frac{(\mathbf{B}-\mathbf{H})\cdot\mathfrak{H}}{8\pi}\right]\mathrm{d}V$$

(cf. (31.7)), which is also valid whatever the relation between **B** and **H**. Substituting Φ, H and B from (44.2)–(44.4), we obtain

$$\mathcal{G}_i = \frac{V}{8\pi}\left[H_{cr}^2 - \frac{1}{n}(H_{cr}-\mathfrak{H})^2\right], \tag{44.5}$$

V being the volume of the ellipsoid; $\mathcal{G}_i$ is taken to be zero in the purely superconducting state of the ellipsoid, in the absence of a magnetic field. For a superconducting ellipsoid in an external field $\mathfrak{H}$ we have $\mathcal{G}_s = -\frac{1}{2}\mathcal{M}\cdot\mathfrak{H} = V\mathfrak{H}^2/8\pi(1-n)$, in accordance with (31.6) and (42.2). These two equations give the same result for $\mathfrak{H} = H_{cr}(1-n)$, as they should.

Finally, it should be emphasised that the "averaged" description of the intermediate state given here is in reality not very accurate, because of the comparatively large thickness of the layers. For the same reason, this description fails to reproduce certain phenomena related to the properties of the layer structure. These include the fact that the transition from the superconducting to the intermediate state actually occurs only when $\mathfrak{H}$ slightly exceeds $(1-n)H_{cr}$. The reason for this "delay" is as follows. The passage into the intermediate state occurs when that state becomes thermodynamically stable, i.e. when $\mathcal{G}_i < \mathcal{G}_s$. The layered structure, however, has not only the "volume" energy (44.5) allotted to it in the "averaged" description but also additional energy resulting from the existence of the boundaries between the layers and their change in shape near the surface of the body. This results in some displacement of the transition point towards stronger fields.†

† See the references in the second footnote to this section.

PROBLEMS

PROBLEM 1. Determine the specific heat of an ellipsoid in the intermediate state.

SOLUTION. The entropy and thence the specific heat, are found by differentiating the thermodynamic potential (44.5) with respect to temperature. Neglecting the terms containing the thermal-expansion coefficient, we obtain

$$\mathscr{C}_i-\mathscr{C}_s = \frac{VT}{4\pi n}[(1-n)(H_{cr}'^2+H_{cr}H_{cr}'')-\mathfrak{H}H_{cr}''],$$

the prime denoting differentiation with respect to T; $\mathscr{C}_s$ is the specific heat of the body in the superconducting state, whose slight dependence on $\mathfrak{H}$ we here neglect. Hence it follows that, as $\mathfrak{H}$ varies (at constant temperature), the specific heat changes discontinuously at the point $\mathfrak{H} = (1-n)H_{cr}$ from $\mathscr{C}_s$ to

$$\mathscr{C}_s+\frac{VT(1-n)}{4\pi n}H_{cr}'^2,$$

and thereafter varies linearly with $\mathfrak{H}$, reaching the value

$$\mathscr{C}_s-\frac{VT}{4\pi}(H_{cr}'^2+H_{cr}H_{cr}'')+\frac{VT}{4\pi n}H_{cr}'^2 = \mathscr{C}_n+\frac{VT}{4\pi n}H_{cr}'^2$$

for $\mathfrak{H} = H_{cr}$, whence it falls discontinuously to $\mathscr{C}_n$.

PROBLEM 2. Determine the shape and size of the normal and superconducting layers in a flat plate in the intermediate state in an external magnetic field $\mathfrak{H}$ perpendicular to the plate; the layers are assumed unbranched (L. LANDAU, 1937).

SOLUTION. The normal and superconducting regions are layers parallel to the field, except near the surface of the plate. The lines of magnetic force (shown dashed in Fig. 24) pass only through the normal layers, and the boundaries of the superconducting layers are also lines of force, since $B_n = 0$ there. Since also $H = H_{cr}$ on the boundary between the normal and superconducting phases, the conditions at the boundaries of a superconducting layer are

$$\begin{aligned} &\text{on } BC && H_x = 0,\\ &\text{on } BA \text{ and } CD && H_x^2+H_y^2 = H_{cr}^2, \end{aligned} \qquad (1)$$

the co-ordinate axes being taken as shown in Fig. 24. Far from the plate, the field $\mathbf{H}$ must be the same as the external field $\mathfrak{H}$, i.e.

$$\text{for } x \to -\infty \qquad H_x = \mathfrak{H}, \qquad H_y = 0. \qquad (2)$$

We use the scalar and vector potentials: $H_x = -\partial\phi/\partial x = \partial A/\partial y$, $H_y = -\partial\phi/\partial y = -\partial A/x\partial$, and the complex potential $w = \phi-iA$ (cf. §3, (3)).

On a line of force A = constant. We put $A = 0$ on the line of force which reaches O and then branches into OCD and OBA, forming the boundary of one superconducting layer. The difference between the values of A at the boundaries of two successive superconducting layers is equal to the magnetic flux across the segment $a = a_s+a_n$, namely $\mathfrak{H}a$. Hence the value of A at the boundary of any superconducting layer is an integral multiple of $\mathfrak{H}a$. Using also the "complex field" $\eta = H_x-iH_y = -dw/dz$, $z = x+iy$, we can write the conditions (1) as

$$\begin{aligned} &\text{on } BC && \text{re}\,\eta = 0,\\ &\text{on } BA \text{ and } CD && |\eta| = H_{cr}. \end{aligned} \qquad (3)$$

We introduce a new variable

$$\zeta = \exp(-2\pi w/\mathfrak{H}a)-1 \qquad (4)$$

and regard η as a function of ζ. ζ is real on all boundary lines of force and on their continuations beyond the plate: $\zeta = \exp(-2\pi\phi/\mathfrak{H}a)-1$.

Since ϕ is determined apart from a constant, its value at any one point can be chosen arbitrarily. Let $\phi = 0$ at O. Then $\zeta = 0$ there also. On the limiting line of force considered, far from the plate, $\zeta = -1$ (since for $x \to -\infty$ we have $\phi \to -\mathfrak{H}x \to +\infty$). The value of ζ at B or C, where the line of force enters the plate, is ζ_0, say. On CD and BA, ζ varies from ζ_0 to ∞. Then the conditions (1) and (3) can be written

$$\text{for } \zeta = -1 \qquad \eta = \mathfrak{H}, \tag{5}$$

$$\text{for } 0 < \zeta < \zeta_0 \qquad \operatorname{re} \eta = 0, \tag{6}$$

$$\text{for } \zeta_0 < \zeta \qquad |\eta| = H_{cr}.$$

The function $\eta(\zeta)$ must, furthermore, be everywhere finite.

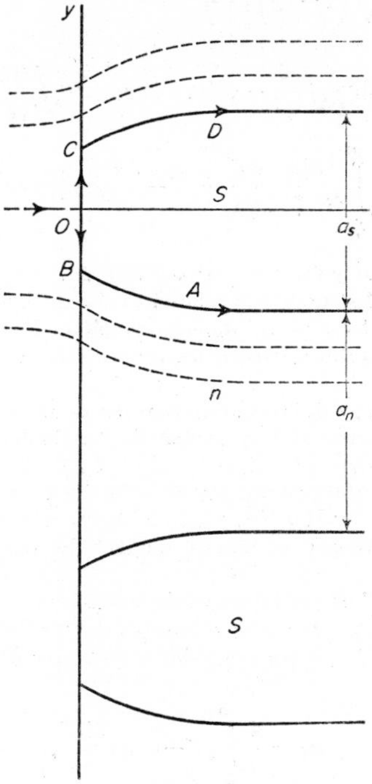

FIG. 24

The conditions (6) are satisfied by the function

$$\eta = H_{cr}\left[\sqrt{\left(1-\frac{\zeta_0}{\zeta}\right)} - \sqrt{\left(-\frac{\zeta_0}{\zeta}\right)}\right]. \tag{7}$$

For real negative ζ the two roots are real, and are taken with the signs shown. For $0 < \zeta < \zeta_0$ both are imaginary, and we take

$$\eta = \mp i H_{cr}\left[\sqrt{\frac{\zeta_0}{\zeta}} - \sqrt{\left(\frac{\zeta_0}{\zeta}-1\right)}\right],$$

with the minus and plus signs on OC and OB respectively. For $\zeta > \zeta_0$

$$\eta = H_{cr}\left[\sqrt{\left(1-\frac{\zeta_0}{\zeta}\right)} \mp i\sqrt{\frac{\zeta_0}{\zeta}}\right],$$

with the minus and plus signs on CD and BA respectively. The value of ζ_0 is found from the condition (5), and is

$$\zeta_0 = \frac{1}{4}\left(\frac{1}{h} - h\right)^2, \tag{8}$$

where $h = \mathfrak{H}/H_{cr}$.

The shape of the layer, i.e. the shape of the limiting line of force, is obtained by integrating the relation $dz = -dw/\eta$ over real ζ:

$$z = -\int \frac{dw}{\eta} = \frac{ah}{2\pi}\int \frac{d\zeta}{\eta(\zeta+1)}.$$

Substituting $\eta(\zeta)$, taking real and imaginary parts, and choosing appropriately the constants of integration, we obtain the following parametric equations of the line CD:

$$x = \frac{ah}{2\pi}\int_{\zeta_0}^{\zeta} \sqrt{\left(1-\frac{\zeta_0}{\zeta}\right)}\frac{d\zeta}{\zeta+1}$$

$$= \frac{ah}{\pi}\left[\cosh^{-1}\sqrt{\frac{\zeta}{\zeta_0}} - \sqrt{(\zeta_0+1)}\cosh^{-1}\sqrt{\frac{\zeta(\zeta_0+1)}{\zeta_0(\zeta+1)}}\right], \qquad (9)$$

$$y = Y - \frac{ah}{2\pi}\int_{\zeta}^{\infty}\sqrt{\frac{\zeta_0}{\zeta}}\frac{d\zeta}{\zeta+1} = Y - \frac{ah}{\pi}\sqrt{\zeta_0}(\tfrac{1}{2}\pi - \tan^{-1}\sqrt{\zeta}),$$

where $Y = \frac{1}{2}a_s$ is the value of y for $x \to \infty$; see Fig. 24.

The period a of the layered structure is related to the thicknesses a_s and a_n of the superconducting and normal layers by $a = a_s + a_n$, $a\mathfrak{H} = a_n H_{cr}$. The latter equation follows from the continuity of the magnetic flux, which passes entirely through normal layers. Hence $a_s = a(1-h)$, $a_n = ah$.

The period a is determined by the condition that the total thermodynamic potential of the plate is a minimum. The existence of "surface tension" at the boundaries between the normal and superconducting phases gives a term $\mathscr{G}_1 = 2l\Delta \cdot H_{cr}^2/8\pi a$ in the thermodynamic potential per unit area of the surface of the plate. Here l is the thickness of the plate, and the surface-tension coefficient is written as $\Delta \cdot H_{cr}^2/8\pi$, where Δ has the dimensions of length. In calculating this part of the energy we can, of course, neglect the curvature of the layers near the surface of the plate.

The "energy of emergence" of the layers at the surface of the plate can be written as the sum of two parts. First, the increase in the volume of the normal layers as compared with the volume they would occupy if they were everywhere plane-parallel gives an additional energy

$$\mathscr{G}_2 = \frac{4}{a}\int_0^{\infty}(Y-y)\,dx\frac{H_{cr}^2}{8\pi},$$

where the factor 4 takes into account the presence of four angles (such as B and C in Fig. 24) on the two sides of each of the $1/a$ superconducting layers.

Second, the emergence of the layers at the surface of the plate changes the energy of the system in the external field, i.e. the energy $-\frac{1}{2}\mathscr{M}\cdot\mathfrak{H}$. The magnetic moment of the plate is due to currents on the surfaces of the superconducting layers. When the tangential component of the induction changes discontinuously from H to zero, the surface current density is $g = \pm cH/4\pi$. Hence the magnetic moment per unit length in the z-direction and per boundary surface of the superconducting layer is

$$-\int_{OCD}\frac{H}{4\pi}y\,ds, \qquad ds = \sqrt{(dx^2+dy^2)}.$$

If the layer did not emerge at the surface, there would be no segment OC, and on CD we should have $y = Y$. Hence the excess magnetic moment for each of the four angles is

$$-\int_{OCD}\frac{H}{4\pi}y\,ds + \int_0^{\infty}\frac{H_{cr}}{4\pi}Y\,dx.$$

Accordingly, the excess energy is

$$\mathscr{G}_3 = -\tfrac{1}{2}\mathfrak{H}\cdot\frac{4}{a}\left[\int\limits_0^\infty \frac{H_{\mathrm{cr}}}{4\pi} Y\,\mathrm{d}x - \int\limits_{OCD} \frac{H}{4\pi} y\,\mathrm{d}s\right]$$

$$= \frac{\mathfrak{H}}{2\pi a}\left[H_{\mathrm{cr}}\int\limits_{CD}(-Y\,\mathrm{d}x + y\,\mathrm{d}s) + \int\limits_{OC} H_y\,\mathrm{d}y\right].$$

The coordinates x and y, expressed in terms of ζ, are proportional to a. Hence all the integrals in $\mathscr{G}_2+\mathscr{G}_3$ are proportional to a^2, and this part of the thermodynamic potential is therefore proportional to a. The sum $\mathscr{G}_1+\mathscr{G}_2+\mathscr{G}_3$ is therefore of the form†

$$\mathscr{G} = \frac{H_{\mathrm{cr}}^2}{4\pi}\left[\frac{l\Delta}{a} + af(h)\right].$$

The condition that this is a minimum gives $a = \sqrt{[l\Delta/f(h)]}$.

It should be noted that, in normal layers near the surface of the plate, the magnetic field may be considerably less than H_{cr}, i.e. there is a situation corresponding to that shown in Fig. 22a. In this case the unfavourable thermodynamic state is made possible by the surface-tension energy, which prevents further reduction in the layer thickness.

† The integrals in $\mathscr{G}_2$ and $\mathscr{G}_3$ cannot be expressed in terms of elementary functions. The function $f(h)$ has been tabulated by E. M. Lifshitz and Yu. V. Sharvin, *loc. cit.*

CHAPTER VII

QUASI-STATIC ELECTROMAGNETIC FIELD

§45. Eddy currents

So FAR we have discussed only constant electric and magnetic fields, and have used Maxwell's equation

$$\mathbf{curl}\,\mathbf{E} = -\frac{1}{c}\frac{\partial \mathbf{B}}{\partial t} \tag{45.1}$$

only as a step in deriving the expression for the energy of a magnetic field (§30).

The nature of the variable electromagnetic fields in matter depends greatly on the kind of matter concerned and on the order of magnitude of the frequency of the field. In the present section we shall consider the phenomena which occur in extended conductors placed in a variable external magnetic field. We shall assume that the rate of change of the field is not too large, and therefore satisfies various conditions which will be derived below. Electromagnetic fields and currents which satisfy these conditions are said to be *quasi-static*.

We shall first of all suppose that the wavelength $\lambda \sim c/\omega$ which corresponds (in the vacuum or dielectric surrounding the conductor) to the field frequency ω is large compared with the dimension l of the body: $\omega \ll c/l$. Then the magnetic field distribution outside the conductor at any instant can be described by the equations of a static field:

$$\operatorname{div} \mathbf{B} = 0, \qquad \mathbf{curl}\,\mathbf{H} = 0, \tag{45.2}$$

all effects due to the finite velocity of propagation of electromagnetic disturbances being neglected. Of course, this neglect is permissible only at distances from the body which are small compared with λ; these are the only distances which need be considered in determining the field inside the body.

The complete system of field equations inside the conductor consists of (45.1) together with†

$$\operatorname{div} \mathbf{B} = 0, \tag{45.3}$$

$$\mathbf{curl}\,\mathbf{H} = 4\pi\sigma\mathbf{E}/c. \tag{45.4}$$

† In an anisotropic body, $\sigma\mathbf{E}$ on the right-hand side of (45.4) must be replaced by the vector $\sigma_{ik}E_k$.

The second of these equations has been derived, strictly speaking, only for constant currents and magnetic fields. It is therefore necessary to specify conditions under which this equation can reliably be used for variable fields. In equation (45.4) the current has been written in terms of the electric field in accordance with the relation $\mathbf{j} = \sigma\mathbf{E}$ with constant σ, which holds for a steady state. This relation remains valid if the period of the field is large compared with the characteristic times of microscopic conduction. That is, the field frequency must be small compared with the reciprocal mean free time of the electrons in the conductor. For typical metals at room temperature, the limiting frequencies given by this condition lie in the infra-red region of the spectrum.†

There is another condition which restricts the applicability of the equations in this case. Being macroscopic equations, they presuppose that the electron mean free path is small compared with the distances over which the field changes appreciably. We shall return to this condition later.

In equations (45.1) and (45.4), **E** is the induced electric field resulting from the variation of the magnetic field. When **H** is known, the field **E** can be immediately determined by equation (45.4). The equation for **H** is obtained by eliminating **E** from (45.1) and (45.4):

$$\frac{4\pi}{c^2}\frac{\partial \mathbf{B}}{\partial t} = -\mathbf{curl}\frac{\mathbf{curl}\,\mathbf{H}}{\sigma}. \tag{45.5}$$

In a homogeneous medium of constant conductivity σ and constant magnetic permeability μ, the factor $1/\sigma$ can be taken in front of the curl operator, and by (45.3) we have $\operatorname{div}\mathbf{B} = \mu \operatorname{div}\mathbf{H} = 0$. Hence $\mathbf{curl}\,\mathbf{curl}\,\mathbf{H} = -\triangle\mathbf{H}$, and we obtain the equation

$$\triangle\mathbf{H} = \frac{4\pi\mu\sigma}{c^2}\frac{\partial \mathbf{H}}{\partial t}. \tag{45.6}$$

With the equation $\operatorname{div}\mathbf{H} = 0$ this suffices to determine the magnetic field. It may be noted that equation (45.6) is a heat-conduction equation, the thermometric conductivity χ being represented by $c^2/4\pi\mu\sigma$.

The boundary conditions on the magnetic field at the surface of a conductor are evident from the form of the equations, and are as before

$$B_{n1} = B_{n2}, \qquad \mathbf{H}_{t1} = \mathbf{H}_{t2}. \tag{45.7}$$

† For poor conductors (e.g. semiconductors), equation (45.4) is valid only if a further condition, which may be more stringent, is satisfied. For such bodies it may be possible to define both a conductivity and a dielectric constant. Then a term $-(\epsilon/c)\,\partial\mathbf{E}/\partial t$ is added to the right-hand side of (45.4), and the condition for this term to be small in comparison with $4\pi\sigma\mathbf{E}/c$ is $\sigma/\omega \gg \epsilon$. In good conductors (e.g. metals), on the other hand, $\sigma/\omega \gg 1$ throughout the frequency range in which the conductivity can be regarded as constant (see also the sixth footnote to this section).

The expression on the right-hand side of equation (45.4), being bounded, does not affect the second of (45.7). For $\mu = 1$ we can put simply†

$$\mathbf{H}_1 = \mathbf{H}_2. \tag{45.8}$$

The continuity of $\mathbf{H}_t$ implies that of $(\mathbf{curl\,H})_n$ and therefore, by (45.4), that of $(\sigma\mathbf{E})_n$. Outside the conductor, $\sigma = 0$, and we therefore conclude that on the surface $E_{n,i} = 0$, where the suffix i denotes the field inside the conductor. Since E_n is zero, so is $j_n = \sigma E_n$. Thus the system of equations under consideration necessarily implies the vanishing of the normal component of the current density on the surface of the conductor. In other words, in this approximation a variable magnetic field cannot cause the appearance of free charges on the surface of the conductor.

The boundary condition (45.8) is insufficient for a complete formulation of the problem if the conductor is composite and its parts have different conductivities. At the interfaces between the parts we must use both the continuity of $\mathbf{H}$ and that of $\mathbf{E}_t$; the latter implies the condition

$$(\mathbf{curl\,H})_{t1}/\sigma_1 = (\mathbf{curl\,H})_{t2}/\sigma_2 \tag{45.9}$$

on the magnetic field.

Having established the basic equations, let us now examine the nature of the variable fields which they describe. Suppose that a conductor is placed in an external magnetic field which is suddenly removed. The field in and around the conductor does not vanish immediately; the manner of its decay with time is given by equation (45.6). To solve a problem of this kind, we use the following procedure. We seek solutions of equation (45.6) which have the form $\mathbf{H} = \mathbf{H}_m(x, y, z)e^{-\gamma_m t}$, where γ_m is a constant. The equation for the function $\mathbf{H}_m(x, y, z)$ is then

$$(c^2/4\pi\sigma)\triangle\mathbf{H}_m = -\gamma_m\mathbf{H}_m. \tag{45.10}$$

For a conductor of given shape, this equation has non-zero solutions (satisfying the necessary boundary conditions) only for certain γ_m, the *eigenvalues* of (45.10), all of which are real and positive.‡ The corresponding functions

---

† For ordinary diamagnetic and paramagnetic bodies, μ is very nearly 1, and the inclusion of μ in the following formulae would be a pointless refinement. Values of μ differing considerably from 1 occur in ferromagnetic metals, whose magnetic properties (in sufficiently weak fields) can be described in terms of a large constant permeability. For quite moderate frequencies, however, such substances exhibit a dispersion of μ (i.e. a dependence of μ on the frequency ω), together with a decrease of μ almost to 1. We shall therefore put $\mu = 1$ in the present chapter.

‡ This is easily seen as follows. So as to avoid having to take account of the boundary conditions at the surface of the body, we start from equation (45.5) and suppose σ to vanish continuously outside the body. Multiplying both sides of the equation

$$-4\pi\gamma_m\mathbf{H}_m/c^2 = -\mathbf{curl}\,[(1/\sigma)\,\mathbf{curl\,H}_m]$$

by $\mathbf{H}_m{}^*$ and integrating over all space, we have

$$\frac{4\pi}{c^2}\gamma_m\int|\mathbf{H}_m|^2\,dV = \int\mathbf{H}_m{}^*\cdot\mathbf{curl}\frac{\mathbf{curl\,H}_m}{\sigma}\,dV = \int\frac{1}{\sigma}|\mathbf{curl\,H}_m|^2\,dV,$$

whence it is evident that the γ_m are real and positive.

$\mathbf{H}_m(x, y, z)$ form a complete set of orthogonal vector functions. Let the field distribution at the initial instant be $\mathbf{H}_0(x, y, z)$. On expanding this in terms of the functions $\mathbf{H}_m$:

$$\mathbf{H}_0(x, y, z) = \sum_m c_m \mathbf{H}_m(x, y, z),$$

we obtain the solution of the problem:

$$\mathbf{H}(x, y, z, t) = \sum_m c_m e^{-\gamma_m t} \mathbf{H}_m(x, y, z) \tag{45.11}$$

gives the manner of decay of the field with time.

The rate of decay is determined principally by the term in the sum for which γ_m is least; let this be γ_1. The "decay time" of the field may be defined as $\tau = 1/\gamma_1$. The order of magnitude of τ is evident from equation (45.10). Since $\triangle \mathbf{H} \sim \mathbf{H}/l^2$, where l is the dimension of the conductor, we have

$$\tau \sim 4\pi\sigma l^2/c^2. \tag{45.12}$$

Another type of problem concerns the behaviour of a conductor in an external magnetic field which varies with frequency ω. The magnetic field penetrates into the conductor and induces in it a variable electric field, which in turn causes currents to appear; these are called *eddy currents*.† A general idea of the way in which the field penetrates into the conductor can be obtained from the analogy already mentioned between equation (45.6) and the equation of thermal conduction. It is known from the theory of thermal conduction that a quantity which satisfies such an equation is "propagated" through a distance $\sim \sqrt{(\chi t)}$ in time t. We can therefore immediately conclude that the magnetic field penetrates into the conductor to a distance δ, given in order of magnitude by $\delta \sim \sqrt{(c^2/\sigma\omega)}$. The same is true, of course, of the induced electric field and currents.

In a variable field of frequency ω, all quantities depend on the time through a factor $e^{-i\omega t}$. Equation (45.6) then becomes

$$\triangle \mathbf{H} = -4\pi i\sigma\omega \mathbf{H}/c^2. \tag{45.13}$$

Let us consider two limiting cases. If the *penetration depth* δ is large compared with the dimension of the body (low frequencies), we can put the right-hand side of (45.13) equal to zero as a first approximation. Then the magnetic field distribution at any instant will be the same as it would be in a steady state with the same external field. Let this solution be $\mathbf{H}_{st}$; it is independent of the frequency (or rather involves the frequency only in the time factor $e^{-i\omega t}$). The induced electric field appears only in the next approximation, being absent in the steady state. This corresponds to the fact that **curl** $\mathbf{H}_{st} = 0$, and so the value of $\mathbf{E}_{st}$ obtained from (45.4) is zero. To calculate $\mathbf{E}$,

† In Russian "Foucault currents".

therefore, we must use equation (45.1), according to which

$$\mathbf{curl}\,\mathbf{E} = i\omega\mathbf{H}_{st}/c. \tag{45.14}$$

This equation, together with div $\mathbf{E} = 0$ (which follows from (45.4) when σ is constant in the body), entirely determines the electric field distribution. It is seen to be proportional to the frequency ω.

The opposite limiting case is that where $\delta \ll l$ (high frequencies). The condition for the macroscopic field equations to be applicable, mentioned at the beginning of this section, requires that δ should still be large compared with the mean free path of the conduction electrons.†

When $\delta \ll l$ the magnetic field penetrates only into a thin surface layer of the conductor. In calculating the field outside the conductor we can neglect the thickness of this layer, i.e. assume that the magnetic field does not penetrate into the conductor at all. In this sense a conductor in a high-frequency magnetic field behaves like a superconductor in a constant field, and the field outside it must be calculated by solving the corresponding steady-state problem for a superconductor of the same shape.

The true field distribution in the surface layer of the conductor can be investigated in a general manner by regarding small regions of the surface as plane. It is necessary to solve equation (45.13) for a conducting medium bounded by a plane surface, outside which the field has a given value $\mathbf{H}_0 e^{-i\omega t}$, say. This vector is obtained as shown above, by solving the problem for a semi-infinite medium, and is parallel to the surface of the conductor. The boundary condition (45.8) shows that the magnetic field in the conductor is also $\mathbf{H}_0 e^{-i\omega t}$ at the surface.

We take the surface of the conductor as the xy-plane, the conducting medium being in $z > 0$. Since the conditions of the problem are independent of x and y, the required field $\mathbf{H}$ depends only on the z co-ordinate (and on the time). We therefore have div $\mathbf{H} = \partial H_z/\partial z = 0$, and since $H_z = 0$ at the boundary it must be zero everywhere. By (45.13), the equation for $\mathbf{H}$ is $\partial^2\mathbf{H}/\partial z^2 + k^2\mathbf{H} = 0$, where $k = \sqrt{(4\pi i\sigma\omega/c^2)} = (1+i)\sqrt{(2\pi\sigma\omega)}/c$. The solution of this equation which vanishes far from the surface is e^{ikz}. Using the boundary condition at $z = 0$, we obtain

$$\mathbf{H} = \mathbf{H}_0 e^{-z/\delta} e^{iz/\delta - i\omega t} \tag{45.15}$$

where the penetration depth δ is

$$\delta = c/\sqrt{(2\pi\sigma\omega)} \text{ and } k = (1+i)/\delta. \tag{45.16}$$

The electric field is now determined by means of equation (45.4). If $\mathbf{n}$ is a unit vector in the z-direction, we have

$$\mathbf{E} = \sqrt{(\omega/8\pi\sigma)}(1-i)\mathbf{H}\times\mathbf{n}. \tag{45.17}$$

Thus $E \sim H\delta/\lambda$.

† This condition is, in fact, the first to be violated in metals as the frequency increases. The condition $\omega \ll 1/\tau$, where τ is the mean free time, may, however, be the more stringent for semiconductors of low conductivity.

If the field $\mathbf{H}_0 e^{-i\omega t}$ is "linearly polarised", then $\mathbf{H}_0$ can be made real by a suitable choice of the origin of time. We then take the direction of $\mathbf{H}_0$ as the y-axis. Taking the real part in (45.16) and (45.17), we have

$$H = H_y = H_0 e^{-z/\delta} \cos\left(\frac{z}{\delta} - \omega t\right),$$
$$E = E_x = H_0 \sqrt{(\omega/4\pi\sigma)} e^{-z/\delta} \cos\left(\frac{z}{\delta} - \omega t - \frac{1}{4}\pi\right). \tag{45.18}$$

The eddy current density $\mathbf{j} = \sigma\mathbf{E}$ has the same distribution as $\mathbf{E}$.

The presence of eddy currents implies a dissipation of the field energy, which appears as Joule heat. The time average energy Q dissipated in the conductor per unit time is $Q = \int \overline{\mathbf{j}\cdot\mathbf{E}} dV = \int \sigma\overline{\mathbf{E}^2} dV$. It can also be calculated as the mean field energy entering the conductor per unit time:

$$Q = \oint \overline{\mathbf{S}} \cdot d\mathbf{f} = (c/4\pi) \oint \overline{\mathbf{E}\times\mathbf{H}} \cdot d\mathbf{f}, \tag{45.19}$$

the integral being taken over the surface of the conductor.†

We have already seen that, in the limiting case $\delta \gg l$, the amplitude of the magnetic field inside the conductor is independent of the frequency, while that of the electric field is proportional to ω. The energy dissipation Q at low frequencies is therefore proportional to ω^2. When $\delta \ll l$, on the other hand, the magnetic and electric fields on the surface of the conductor are given by formulae (45.15) and (45.17) with $z = 0$. The Poynting vector is normal to the surface, and its mean value is $\bar{S} = (c/16\pi)\sqrt{(\omega/2\pi\sigma)}|\mathbf{H}_0|^2$, the variation of $\mathbf{H}_0$ over the surface being given by the solution of the problem of the static field outside a superconductor of the same shape (cf. above). The energy dissipation is

$$Q = \frac{c}{16\pi}\sqrt{\frac{\omega}{2\pi\sigma}} \oint |\mathbf{H}_0|^2 \, df. \tag{45.20}$$

Thus at high frequencies it is proportional to $\sqrt{\omega}$.

The energy dissipation can also be expressed in terms of the total magnetic moment $\mathscr{M}$ acquired by the conductor in the magnetic field. In a periodic field, the magnetic moment is likewise a periodic function of time, with the same frequency. According to formula (31.4), the rate of variation of the free energy is given by $-\mathscr{M} \cdot d\mathfrak{H}/dt$, where $\mathfrak{H}$ is a uniform external

---

† If any two quantities $a(t)$ and $b(t)$ are written in complex form (proportional to $e^{-i\omega t}$), the real parts must of course be taken before calculating their product. If, however, we are interested only in the time average value of the product, it may be calculated as $\frac{1}{2}$ re ab^*. The terms containing $e^{\pm 2i\omega t}$ give zero on averaging, and so $\frac{1}{4}\overline{(a+a^*)(b+b^*)} = \frac{1}{4}(ab^* + a^*b)$. In particular, $\bar{\mathbf{S}}$ can be calculated as the real part of the "complex Poynting vector":

$$\bar{\mathbf{S}} = \mathrm{re}\left[\frac{c}{4\pi} \cdot \tfrac{1}{2}\mathbf{E} \times \mathbf{H}^*\right]. \tag{45.19a}$$

field in which the conductor is placed. This expression does not immediately give the required energy dissipation, because the energy of the body changes not only on account of dissipation but also by the periodic movement of energy between the body and the surrounding field. If we average over time, however, the latter contribution vanishes, and the mean dissipation of energy per unit time is

$$Q = -\overline{\mathcal{M}\cdot \mathrm{d}\mathfrak{H}/\mathrm{d}t}. \tag{45.21}$$

If $\mathcal{M}$ and $\mathfrak{H}$ are written in complex form, then $\mathrm{d}\mathfrak{H}/\mathrm{d}t = -i\omega\mathfrak{H}$, and Q can be calculated as

$$Q = -\tfrac{1}{2}\,\mathrm{re}(i\omega\mathcal{M}\cdot\mathfrak{H}^*) = \tfrac{1}{2}\omega\,\mathrm{im}(\mathcal{M}\cdot\mathfrak{H}^*). \tag{45.22}$$

The origin of the factor $\frac{1}{2}$ is explained in the last footnote.

The components of the magnetic moment $\mathcal{M}$ are linear functions of the external field:

$$\mathcal{M}_i = V\alpha_{ik}\mathfrak{H}_k, \tag{45.23}$$

where the dimensionless coefficients $\alpha_{ik}(\omega)$ depend on the shape of the body and on its orientation in the external field, but not on its volume V. In this formula we assume that $\mathcal{M}$ and $\mathfrak{H}$ are written in complex form, so that the α_{ik} are also in general complex. The tensor $V\alpha_{ik}$ may be called the *magnetic polarisability tensor* for the body as a whole. This tensor is symmetrical:†

$$\alpha_{ik} = \alpha_{ki}. \tag{45.24}$$

We can therefore write

$$\begin{aligned}\mathcal{M}\cdot\mathfrak{H}^* = V\alpha_{ik}\mathfrak{H}_i^*\mathfrak{H}_k &= \tfrac{1}{2}V\alpha_{ik}(\mathfrak{H}_i^*\mathfrak{H}_k+\mathfrak{H}_i\mathfrak{H}_k^*)\\ &= V\alpha_{ik}\,\mathrm{re}(\mathfrak{H}_i\mathfrak{H}_k^*).\end{aligned}$$

If also we write the complex quantities α_{ik} as $\alpha_{ik}'+i\alpha_{ik}''$, the energy dissipation (45.22) becomes

$$Q = \tfrac{1}{2}V\omega\alpha_{ik}''\mathrm{re}(\mathfrak{H}_i\mathfrak{H}_k^*). \tag{45.25}$$

Thus the energy dissipation is determined by the imaginary part of the magnetic polarisability. We have already seen that Q is proportional to ω^2 for low frequencies, and to $\sqrt{\omega}$ for high frequencies. We can therefore conclude that the quantities α_{ik}'' in these two limiting cases are proportional to ω and to $1/\sqrt{\omega}$ respectively. Since they decrease both as $\omega \to 0$ and $\omega \to \infty$, they must have a maximum in between.

The magnetic moment of a conductor in a variable magnetic field is due mainly to the conduction currents set up in the body; it is not zero even if $\mu = 1$, when the moment in a constant field vanishes. The latter can be obtained from $\mathcal{M}(\omega)$ by taking the limit as $\omega \to 0$. Hence it follows that the real part α_{ik}' of the polarisability tends to a constant limit as $\omega \to 0$

† See *Statistical Physics*, §124, Pergamon Press, London, 1958.

(the limit being zero for $\mu = 1$), corresponding to magnetisation in a constant field. In the limit $\omega \to \infty$, when the magnetic field does not penetrate into the body, α_{ik}' tends to a different constant limit, corresponding to the steady magnetisation of a superconductor of the same shape.

PROBLEMS

PROBLEM 1. Determine the magnetic polarisability of an isotropic conducting sphere of radius a in a uniform periodic external field.

SOLUTION. The field $\mathbf{H}_i$ inside the sphere satisfies the equations $\triangle\mathbf{H}_i+k^2\mathbf{H}_i = 0$, $\operatorname{div}\mathbf{H}_i = 0$, where $k = (1+i)/\delta$. We write this field in the form $\mathbf{H}_i = \mathbf{curl}\,\mathbf{A}$, where $\mathbf{A}$ satisfies the equation $\triangle\mathbf{A}+k^2\mathbf{A} = 0$; since $\mathbf{H}$ is an axial vector, $\mathbf{A}$ is a polar vector. By symmetry, the only constant vector on which the required solution can depend is the external field $\mathfrak{H}$. We denote by f the spherically symmetrical solution, finite for $r = 0$, of the scalar equation $\triangle f+k^2f = 0$, namely $f = (1/r)\sin kr$. Then the polar vector $\mathbf{A}$, which satisfies the vector equation $\triangle\mathbf{A}+k^2\mathbf{A} = 0$ and depends linearly on the constant axial vector $\mathfrak{H}$, can be written as $\mathbf{A} = \beta\,\mathbf{curl}\,(f\mathfrak{H})$, where β is a constant. Thus we have

$$\mathbf{H}_i = \beta\,\mathbf{curl}\,\mathbf{curl}\,(f\mathfrak{H})$$
$$= \beta\left(\frac{f'}{r}+k^2f\right)\mathfrak{H}-\beta\left(\frac{3f'}{r}+k^2f\right)(\mathbf{n}\cdot\mathfrak{H})\mathbf{n},$$

where $\mathbf{n}$ is a unit vector in the direction of $\mathbf{r}$; the second derivative f'' has been eliminated by means of the equation $\triangle f+k^2f = 0$.

The field $\mathbf{H}_e$ outside the sphere satisfies the equations $\mathbf{curl}\,\mathbf{H}_e = 0$, $\operatorname{div}\mathbf{H}_e = 0$. We put $\mathbf{H}_e = -\mathbf{grad}\,\phi+\mathfrak{H}$; ϕ satisfies the equation $\triangle\phi = 0$ and vanishes at infinity. Since ϕ depends linearly on the constant vector $\mathfrak{H}$, we have $\phi = -V\alpha\,\mathfrak{H}\cdot\mathbf{grad}\,(1/r)$, where $V = 4\pi a^3/3$. Thus

$$\mathbf{H}_e = V\alpha\,\mathbf{grad}\,[(\mathfrak{H}\cdot\mathbf{grad})(1/r)]+\mathfrak{H}$$
$$= \frac{V\alpha}{r^3}[3(\mathbf{n}\cdot\mathfrak{H})\mathbf{n}-\mathfrak{H}]+\mathfrak{H}.$$

It is evident that $V\alpha\mathfrak{H}$ is the magnetic moment of the sphere, so that $V\alpha$ is its magnetic polarisability (by symmetry, the tensor α_{ik} reduces to a scalar $\alpha\delta_{ik}$).

On the surface of the sphere ($r = a$), all the components of $\mathbf{H}$ must be continuous. Equating separately the components parallel and perpendicular to $\mathbf{n}$, we obtain two equations to determine α and β. The polarisability per unit volume is found to be

$$\alpha = \alpha'+i\alpha'' = -\frac{3}{8\pi}\left[1-\frac{3}{a^2k^2}+\frac{3}{ak}\cot ak\right],$$
$$\alpha' = -\frac{3}{8\pi}\left[1-\frac{3}{2}\frac{\delta}{a}\frac{\sinh(2a/\delta)-\sin(2a/\delta)}{\cosh(2a/\delta)-\cos(2a/\delta)}\right],$$
$$\alpha'' = -\frac{9\delta^2}{16\pi a^2}\left[1-\frac{a}{\delta}\frac{\sinh(2a/\delta)+\sin(2a/\delta)}{\cosh(2a/\delta)-\cos(2a/\delta)}\right].$$

In the limit of low frequencies ($\delta \gg a$),

$$\alpha' = -\frac{1}{105\pi}\left(\frac{a}{\delta}\right)^4 = -\frac{4\pi}{105}\frac{a^4\sigma^2\omega^2}{c^4},$$
$$\alpha'' = \frac{1}{20\pi}\left(\frac{a}{\delta}\right)^2 = \frac{a^2\sigma\omega}{10c^2}.$$

For high frequencies ($\delta \ll a$),

$$\alpha' = -\frac{3}{8\pi}\left[1-\frac{3\delta}{2a}\right] = -\frac{3}{8\pi}\left[1-\frac{3c}{2a\sqrt{(2\pi\sigma\omega)}}\right],$$
$$\alpha'' = \frac{9}{16\pi}\frac{\delta}{a} = \frac{9c}{16\pi a\sqrt{(2\pi\sigma\omega)}}.$$

The limiting value $V\alpha' = -\frac{1}{2}a^3$ corresponds to the magnetic moment of a superconducting sphere; the corresponding value of α'' could be found from formula (45.20), using the expression (42.3) for the field at the surface of a superconducting sphere.

PROBLEM 2. The same as Problem 1, but for a conducting cylinder (of radius a) in a uniform periodic magnetic field perpendicular to its axis.

SOLUTION. This problem is the "two-dimensional analogue" of Problem 1. In what follows all vector operations are two-dimensional operations in a plane perpendicular to the axis of the cylinder, and $\mathbf{r}$ is the radius vector in that plane. The field inside the cylinder is of the form

$$\mathbf{H}_i = \beta\,\mathbf{curl}\,\mathbf{curl}\,(f\mathfrak{H})$$
$$= \beta\left(\frac{f'}{r}+k^2f\right)\mathfrak{H}-\beta\left(\frac{2f'}{r}+k^2f\right)(\mathbf{n}\cdot\mathfrak{H})\mathbf{n},$$

where $f = J_0(kr)$ is the symmetrical solution of the two-dimensional equation $\triangle f+k^2f = 0$ which is finite for $r = 0$. The field outside the cylinder is

$$\mathbf{H}_e = -2V\alpha\,\mathbf{grad}\,[(\mathfrak{H}\cdot\mathbf{grad})\log r]+\mathfrak{H}$$
$$= \frac{2V\alpha}{r^2}[2(\mathbf{n}\cdot\mathfrak{H})\mathbf{n}-\mathfrak{H})+\mathfrak{H},$$

where $V = \pi a^2$. The magnetic moment per unit length of the cylinder is $V\alpha\mathfrak{H}$ (see §3, Problem 2). From the condition $\mathbf{H}_i = \mathbf{H}_e$ for $r = a$, as in Problem 1, we obtain

$$\alpha = -\frac{1}{2\pi}\left[1-\frac{2}{ka}\frac{J_1(ka)}{J_0(ka)}\right],$$

using the relation $J_0'(kr) = -kJ_1(kr)$.

For $\delta \gg a$, expanding the Bessel functions in powers of ka, we have

$$\alpha' = -\frac{1}{24\pi}\left(\frac{a}{\delta}\right)^4 = -\frac{\pi a^4\sigma^2\omega^2}{6c^4},$$
$$\alpha'' = \frac{1}{8\pi}\left(\frac{a}{\delta}\right)^2 = \frac{a^2\sigma\omega}{4c^2}.$$

For $\delta \ll a$, we use the asymptotic expressions for the Bessel functions, obtaining

$$\alpha' = -\frac{1}{2\pi}\left(1-\frac{\delta}{a}\right) = -\frac{1}{2\pi}\left(1-\frac{c}{a\sqrt{(2\pi\sigma\omega)}}\right),$$
$$\alpha'' = \frac{1}{2\pi}\frac{\delta}{a} = \frac{c}{2\pi a\sqrt{(2\pi\sigma\omega)}}.$$

PROBLEM 3. The same as Problem 2, but for a magnetic field parallel to the axis of the cylinder.

SOLUTION. The magnetic field is everywhere parallel to the axis of the cylinder. Outside the cylinder we have $\mathbf{H}_e = \mathfrak{H}$, and inside it $\mathbf{H}_i = f\mathfrak{H}$, where f is the symmetrical solution of the two-dimensional equation $\triangle f+k^2f = 0$ which is 1 for $r = a$ and finite for $r = 0$: $\mathbf{H}_i = \mathfrak{H}J_0(kr)/J_0(ka)$. The eddy currents in the cylinder are azimuthal (i.e. the only non-zero component is j_ϕ), and are given in terms of the field $H_z = H$ by $4\pi j/c = -\partial H/\partial r$. The magnetic moment generated per unit length of the cylinder by the conduction currents is $\mathscr{M} = \pi a^2\alpha\mathfrak{H} = (1/2c)\int jr\,dV = -\frac{1}{4}\int(\partial H/\partial r)r^2\,dr$; it is parallel to the axis. Evaluating the ntegral, we have

$$\alpha = -\frac{1}{4\pi}\left[1-\frac{2}{ka}\frac{J_1(ka)}{J_0(ka)}\right].$$

Thus the longitudinal polarisability of the cylinder is half the transverse polarisability derived in Problem 2.

PROBLEM 4. Determine the least decay coefficient for the magnetic field in a conducting sphere.

SOLUTION. The solutions of equations (45.10) for a sphere include functions of various symmetries. The most symmetrical solution is that which is defined by an arbitrary constant scalar. This solution is inapplicable, however, for the following reason: it would be spherically symmetrical ($H = H_r(r)$) and would have to be $H = \text{constant}/r$ in order to satisfy the equation $\operatorname{div} \mathbf{H} = (1/r)\partial(rH)/\partial r = 0$, which is valid both outside and inside the sphere; but this function is not finite at the centre of the sphere.

The least value of γ corresponds to one of the solutions defined by an arbitrary constant vector. The form of these solutions is evidently the same as has been found in Problem 1, the only difference being that the constant term in the field $\mathbf{H}_e$ must be omitted so as to have $\mathbf{H} = 0$ at infinity. The quantity k is now real ($=\sqrt{(4\pi\sigma\gamma/c^2)}$), and the vector $\mathfrak{H}$ is the arbitrary constant vector. From the boundary condition $\mathbf{H}_i = \mathbf{H}_e$ at $r = a$ we obtain two equations, and on eliminating α and β we find $\sin ka = 0$. The smallest non-zero root of this equation is $ka = \pi$, and so the smallest value of γ is $\pi c^2/4\sigma a^2$.

§46. The skin effect

Let us consider the distribution of current density over the cross-section of a conductor in which a non-zero and variable total current is flowing. From the results of §45 we should expect that, as the frequency increases, the current will tend to be concentrated near the surface of the conductor. This phenomenon is called the *skin effect*.

The exact solution of the problem of the skin effect depends, in general, not only on the shape of the conductor but also on the manner of excitation of the current in it, i.e. the nature of the variable external magnetic field which induces the current. An important particular case, however, is that where the current flows in a wire of thickness small compared with its length; here the current distribution is independent of the manner of excitation.

In calculating the current distribution over the cross-section of a thin wire, the latter may be regarded as straight. The electric field is parallel to the axis of the wire, and the magnetic field vector $\mathbf{H}$ is in a plane perpendicular to the axis.

Let us consider a wire of circular cross-section. This is a particularly simple case, because the form of the field outside the wire is immediately obvious. By symmetry, $\mathbf{E} = \text{constant}$ over the surface of the wire (though the value of the constant varies with time). With this boundary condition, the only solution of the equations $\operatorname{div} \mathbf{E} = 0$, $\mathbf{curl}\, \mathbf{E} = 0$ outside the wire is $\mathbf{E} = \text{constant}$. Similarly, the magnetic field outside the wire must be the same as it would be outside a wire carrying a constant current equal to the instantaneous value of the variable current.

Inside the wire, the electric field satisfies the equation $\triangle \mathbf{E} = (4\pi\sigma/c^2)\partial \mathbf{E}/\partial t$, which is the same as equation (45.6) for $\mathbf{H}$; it is obtained by eliminating $\mathbf{H}$ from (45.1) and (45.4), just as (45.6) was obtained by eliminating $\mathbf{E}$. In cylindrical co-ordinates, with the z-axis along the axis of the wire, the only non-zero component of $\mathbf{E}$ is E_z, which depends only on r. For a periodic field of frequency ω we have

$$\frac{1}{r}\frac{\partial}{\partial r}\left(r\frac{\partial E}{\partial r}\right) + k^2 E = 0, \qquad k = \frac{\sqrt{(2i)}}{\delta} = \frac{1+i}{\delta}, \tag{46.1}$$

where δ is the penetration depth (45.16). The solution of this equation which remains finite at $r = 0$ is

$$E = E_z = \text{constant} \times J_0(kr)e^{-i\omega t}, \tag{46.2}$$

where J_0 is the Bessel function. The current density $j = \sigma E$ is similarly distributed.

The magnetic field $H_\phi = H$ is found from the electric field by equation (45.1):

$$i\omega H_\phi/c = (\mathbf{curl\, E})_\phi = -\partial E_z/\partial r. \tag{46.3}$$

Since $J_0'(u) = -J_1(u)$, we obtain

$$H = H_\phi = -\text{ constant} \times i\sqrt{(4\pi\sigma i/\omega)}J_1(kr)e^{-i\omega t}, \tag{46.4}$$

the constant being the same as in (46.2); it is easily determined from the condition that $H = 2I/ca$ on the surface of the wire, a being the radius of the wire and I the total current in it.

In the limiting case of low frequencies ($a/\delta \ll 1$) we can take the first few terms of the expansions of the Bessel functions at every point in the cross-section:

$$\begin{aligned} E_z &= \text{constant} \times \left[1 - \frac{1}{2}i(r/\delta)^2 - \frac{1}{16}(r/\delta)^4\right]e^{-i\omega t}, \\ H_\phi &= \text{constant} \times \frac{2\pi\sigma}{c}r\left[1 - \frac{1}{4}i(r/\delta)^2 - \frac{1}{48}(r/\delta)^4\right]e^{-i\omega t}. \end{aligned} \tag{46.5}$$

The amplitude of E, and therefore that of the current density, increase as $1+(r/2\delta)^4$ with increasing distance r from the axis.

In the opposite limiting case of high frequencies ($a/\delta \gg 1$) we can use the asymptotic formula

$$J_0[u\sqrt{(2i)}] \sim u^{-\frac{1}{2}}e^{(1-i)u}, \tag{46.6}$$

which is valid for large values of the argument, over most of the cross-section. Retaining only the rapidly varying exponential factor, we have

$$\begin{aligned} E_z &= \text{constant} \times e^{-(a-r)/\delta}e^{i(a-r)/\delta - i\omega}, \\ H_\phi &= \text{constant} \times (1+i)\sqrt{\frac{2\pi\sigma}{\omega}}e^{-(a-r)/\delta}e^{i(a-r)/\delta - i\omega t}. \end{aligned} \tag{46.7}$$

These formulae are, of course, the same as (45.15)–(45.17), which are valid near the surface of a conductor of any shape when the skin effect is strong.

In the general case of a wire whose cross-section is not circular, the exact calculation of the skin effect is considerably more involved, since the fields inside and outside the wire must be determined simultaneously. Only in the limiting case of strong skin effect is the problem again simplified, because the field outside the wire may then be determined as the static field outside a superconductor of the same shape (§45).

§47. The complex resistance

If the frequency of the variable current is low, the instantaneous current $J(t)$ in a linear circuit is determined by the instantaneous e.m.f. $\mathscr{E}$:

$$\mathscr{E}(t) = RJ(t), \tag{47.1}$$

where R is the resistance of the wire to a constant current.

There is no reason, however, to expect a direct relation between the values of $\mathscr{E}$ and J at the same instant for all frequencies. We can say only that the value of $J(t)$ must be a linear function of the values of $\mathscr{E}(t)$ at all previous instants. This relation may be symbolically written as $J = \hat{Z}^{-1}\mathscr{E}$ or, conversely,

$$\mathscr{E} = \hat{Z}J, \tag{47.2}$$

where $\hat{Z}$ is some linear operator.† If the functions $\mathscr{E}(t)$ and $J(t)$ are expanded as Fourier integrals, then for each "monochromatic" component (depending on time through a factor $e^{-i\omega t}$), the effect of the linear operator $\hat{Z}$ is simply multiplication by a quantity Z which depends on the frequency:

$$\mathscr{E} = Z(\omega)J. \tag{47.3}$$

The function $Z(\omega)$ is in general complex. It is called the *complex resistance* or *impedance* of the conductor.

It is evident from a comparison of (47.3) and (47.1) that the ordinary resistance R is the zero-order term in an expansion of the function $Z(\omega)$ in powers of ω. To find the next term, we must take account both of R and of the self-inductance L of the conductor.‡

Let us consider a linear circuit containing a variable e.m.f. $\mathscr{E}(t)$. By the definition of $\mathscr{E}$, the work done per unit time by the electric field on the charges moving in the wire is $\mathscr{E}J$. This work goes partly into Joule heat and partly to change the energy of the magnetic field of the current. By the definition of R and L, the Joule heat evolved in the wire per unit time is RJ^2, and the magnetic energy of the current is $LJ^2/2c^2$. The law of conservation of energy therefore gives the equation

$$\mathscr{E}J = RJ^2 + \frac{\mathrm{d}}{\mathrm{d}t}\frac{LJ^2}{2c^2} = RJ^2 + \frac{1}{c^2}LJ\frac{\mathrm{d}J}{\mathrm{d}t},$$

or

$$\mathscr{E} = RJ + \frac{1}{c^2}L\frac{\mathrm{d}J}{\mathrm{d}t}. \tag{47.4}$$

---

† We shall not pause here to discuss the general properties of this operator, since they are entirely analogous to those of the operator $\hat{\epsilon}$, which will be examined in detail in §§58 and 62.

‡ Here, and in what follows, R and L denote the values for constant current.

In order to use the quadratic expressions $\mathscr{E}J$ and J^2 we must write $\mathscr{E}$ and J as real functions. Having derived the linear equation (47.4), however, we can take complex monochromatic components: $\mathscr{E} = \mathscr{E}_0 e^{-i\omega t}$, $J = J_0 e^{-i\omega t}$. Then equation (47.4) gives the algebraic relation

$$\mathscr{E} = \left(R - \frac{i}{c^2}\omega L\right) J,$$

whence

$$Z = R - \frac{i}{c^2}\omega L. \tag{47.5}$$

Taking the real part in $J = \mathscr{E}/Z$, we have

$$J(t) = \frac{\mathscr{E}_0}{\sqrt{(R^2 + \omega^2 L^2/c^4)}} \cos(\omega t - \phi), \qquad \tan\phi = \omega L/c^2 R, \tag{47.6}$$

which determines the amplitude of the current and the phase difference between the current and the e.m.f.

The real part of the expression (47.5) is the resistance R, which determines the energy dissipation in the circuit. It is easy to see that, whatever the function $Z(\omega)$, a similar relation holds between re Z and the energy dissipation for a given current. On averaging with respect to time the power $\mathscr{E}J$ required to maintain the periodic current in the circuit, we obtain the part of this power which continually makes good the dissipative losses. The energy dissipation in the circuit per unit time is therefore $Q = \frac{1}{2}\,\text{re}\,(\mathscr{E}J^*)$, where $\mathscr{E}$ and J are expressed in complex form; see the penultimate footnote to §45. Substituting $\mathscr{E} = ZJ$ and denoting the real and imaginary parts of Z by Z' and Z'' respectively:†

$$Z = Z' + iZ'', \tag{47.7}$$

we obtain $Q = \frac{1}{2}Z'|J|^2$ or, in terms of the real function $J(t)$,

$$Q = Z'(\omega)\overline{J^2}, \tag{47.8}$$

which gives the required relation.

It may be noted that, since Q is necessarily positive, Z' is also positive:

$$Z' > 0. \tag{47.9}$$

We may calculate $Z(\omega)$ for a wire of circular cross-section for any frequency,‡ i.e. without neglecting the skin effect. To do so, we again use the law of conservation of energy, but in a different form. We divide the power $\mathscr{E}J$ (where $\mathscr{E}$ and J are real) into two parts, one being the change in the magnetic field energy outside the wire, and the other the total energy consumed inside the wire (both in changing the field and in evolution of

† Sometimes called the *resistance* and *reactance* (in Russian: *active* and *reactive* resistances).
‡ That is, any which satisfies the quasi-steady condition.

heat). The second part can be calculated as the total energy flux entering the conductor through its surface per unit time. Thus we have

$$\mathscr{E}J = \frac{\mathrm{d}}{\mathrm{d}t}\left(\frac{L_e J^2}{2c^2}\right) + \frac{cEH}{4\pi}\cdot 2\pi a l = \frac{L_e}{c^2}J\frac{\mathrm{d}J}{\mathrm{d}t} + \tfrac{1}{2}cEHal,$$

where L_e is the external part of the self-inductance of the wire, E and H the electric and magnetic fields at its surface, a its radius, and l its length. The field H is related to the current J by $H = 2J/ca$. Hence, dividing the above equation by J, we have

$$\mathscr{E} = \frac{1}{c^2}L_e\frac{\mathrm{d}J}{\mathrm{d}t} + El.$$

This is a linear equation, and hence we can use complex quantities. Then

$$\mathscr{E} = ZJ = -\frac{i\omega L_e}{c^2}J + El,$$

whence

$$Z = -\frac{i\omega}{c^2}L_e + \frac{El}{J} = -\frac{i\omega}{c^2}L_e + \frac{2El}{caH}. \tag{47.10}$$

For general frequencies, E and H are given by (46.2) and (46.4), and we have

$$Z = -\frac{i\omega}{c^2}L_e + \tfrac{1}{2}Rka\frac{J_0(ka)}{J_1(ka)}, \tag{47.11}$$

where $R = l/\pi a^2\sigma$. When the skin effect is weak, we use the expansions (46.5); taking terms as far as $(a/\delta)^4$ and separating the real part, we find

$$Z' = R\left[1 + \frac{1}{48}\left(\frac{a}{\delta}\right)^4\right] = R\left[1 + \frac{1}{12}\left(\frac{\pi\sigma\omega a^2}{c^2}\right)^2\right]. \tag{47.11a}$$

In the opposite case of a strong skin effect we use the expressions (46.7), obtaining

$$\left.\begin{aligned} Z' &= Ra/2\delta = (l/ca)\sqrt{(\omega/2\pi\sigma)}, \\ Z'' &= -\frac{\omega}{c^2}\left[L_e + \frac{2\delta}{a}L_i\right] = -\frac{\omega}{c^2}\left[L_e + \frac{lc}{a\sqrt{(2\pi\sigma\omega)}}\right]. \end{aligned}\right\} \tag{47.12}$$

It is seen from (47.11a) that we can put $Z' = R$ if $(\pi\sigma\omega a^2/c^2)^2 \ll 12$. We also have $Z''/Z' = \omega L/c^2R = (\pi\sigma\omega a^2/c^2)\,2\log(l/a)$, where L is given by (33.1). Comparing this with the inequality just given, we see that the range of frequencies in which the expression (47.5) can be used to take the self-inductance into account depends on the ratio l/a and is fairly narrow.

In practice, however, the most important case is that in which the self-inductance of the circuit is due mainly to coils in it, whose self-inductance is large compared with that of an uncoiled wire (see §33). In such circuits formula (47.5) (i.e. equation (47.4) with constant R and L) can be used over a fairly wide range of frequencies.

Let us consider a circuit in a variable external magnetic field $\mathbf{H}_e$, which may be generated in any manner. We denote by $\mathbf{E}_e$ the electric field which would be induced by the variable field $\mathbf{H}_e$ in the absence of conductors. Both $\mathbf{H}_e$ and $\mathbf{E}_e$ vary only very slightly over the thickness of a thin wire (unlike the field of the currents in the wire). We can therefore discuss the circulation of $\mathbf{E}_e$ round the current circuit without specifying the exact position of the contour of integration in the wire. This circulation is just the e.m.f. $\mathscr{E}$ induced in the circuit by the variable external magnetic field. By the integral form of Maxwell's equation we have

$$\mathscr{E} = \oint \mathbf{E}_e \cdot \mathrm{d}\mathbf{l} = -\frac{1}{c}\frac{\partial}{\partial t}\int \mathbf{H}_e \cdot \mathrm{d}\mathbf{f} = -\frac{1}{c}\frac{\mathrm{d}\Phi_e}{\mathrm{d}t}, \tag{47.13}$$

where Φ_e is the flux of the external field through the circuit. Substituting this expression in equation (47.4), we obtain

$$RJ + \frac{1}{c^2}L\frac{\mathrm{d}J}{\mathrm{d}t} = -\frac{1}{c}\frac{\mathrm{d}\Phi_e}{\mathrm{d}t}. \tag{47.14}$$

Taking the self-inductance term to the right-hand side, we have

$$RJ = -\frac{1}{c}\frac{\mathrm{d}\Phi_e}{\mathrm{d}t} - \frac{L}{c^2}\frac{\mathrm{d}J}{\mathrm{d}t} = -\frac{1}{c}\frac{\mathrm{d}\Phi}{\mathrm{d}t},$$

where $\Phi = \Phi_e + LJ/c$ is the total magnetic flux from the external magnetic field and the field of the current. In this form the equation gives Ohm's law for the whole circuit, i.e. the equality of RJ to the total e.m.f. in the circuit.

The formulation of equation (47.14) as expressing Ohm's law makes possible a generalisation of it to the case where the shape of the circuit also varies with time. The self-inductance L is then a function of time, and (47.14) becomes

$$RJ = -\frac{1}{c^2}\frac{\mathrm{d}}{\mathrm{d}t}(LJ) - \frac{1}{c}\frac{\mathrm{d}\Phi_e}{\mathrm{d}t}. \tag{47.15}$$

In deriving this from the law of conservation of energy we should have to take into account also the work done in deforming the conductor.

If there are several circuits in proximity, carrying currents J_a, then for each of them Φ_e in equation (47.14) is the sum of the magnetic fluxes due to all the other circuits (and to the external field, if any). The magnetic flux through the ath circuit due to the current J_b is $L_{ab}J_b/c$, where L_{ab} is the mutual inductance of the two circuits. We therefore have the following set of equations for the variable currents in the circuits:

$$R_a J_a + \frac{1}{c^2}\sum_b L_{ab}\frac{\mathrm{d}J_b}{\mathrm{d}t} = \mathscr{E}_a. \tag{47.16}$$

The sum over b includes the self-inductance term ($b = a$), and $\mathscr{E}_a$ is the e.m.f. produced in the ath circuit by sources external to the system of currents considered.

For periodic currents of a single frequency, the system of differential equations (47.16) becomes a set of algebraic equations:

$$\sum_b Z_{ab}J_b = \mathscr{E}_a, \tag{47.17}$$

where the quantities

$$Z_{ab} = \delta_{ab}R_a - \frac{i\omega}{c^2}L_{ab} \tag{47.18}$$

form the *impedance matrix*. Like (47.5), the expressions (47.18) represent the first terms in an expansion of the functions $Z_{ab}(\omega)$ in powers of the frequency.

It should be noted that, in this approximation, the circuits have no mutual effect on the real parts of their impedances. Such an effect arises because the magnetic field of the variable current in one conductor generates eddy currents, and therefore an additional dissipation of energy, in the other conductor. For linear conductors this effect is negligible, but it may become important if extended conductors are located near them.

Finally, let us consider how the equations of variable currents in linear circuits obtained in this section are related to the general equations of a variable magnetic field in arbitrary conductors. We shall take the simple example of the current set up in a circuit when a constant e.m.f. $\mathscr{E}_0$ is removed at time $t = 0$. From equation (47.4) we have†

$$\begin{aligned} J &= \mathscr{E}_0/R \text{ for } t < 0, \\ J &= (\mathscr{E}_0/R)e^{-c^2Rt/L} \text{ for } t > 0. \end{aligned} \tag{47.19}$$

We see that, after the removal of the e.m.f., the current decays exponentially with time, the decrement being

$$\gamma = c^2R/L. \tag{47.20}$$

If the problem is exactly formulated, this γ is the smallest of the γ_m obtained by solving the exact equation (45.10) for the conductor in question. Among the γ_m for a linear conductor there is one, the smallest, which is less than the others by a factor of the order of log (l/a), and this is (47.20).

† Strictly speaking, these formulae are invalid for very small t, when the high-frequency terms in the Fourier expansions of the functions are important and so equation (47.4) cannot be used. During this short interval of time, however, the current J cannot change significantly, and so formula (47.19) gives the current at subsequent times with sufficient accuracy.

§48. Capacity in a quasi-steady current circuit

A variable current, unlike a constant one, can flow in an open circuit as well as in a closed one. Let us consider a linear circuit whose ends are connected to the plates of a condenser, which are at a small distance apart. When a variable current flows in the circuit, the condenser plates will be periodically charged and discharged, thereby acting as sources and sinks of current in the open circuit.

Since the distance between the condenser plates is small, the magnetic energy of the current can again be taken as $LJ^2/2c^2$, where L is the self-inductance of the closed circuit which would be obtained by joining the condenser plates by a short piece of wire. In applying the law of conservation of energy, however, we must take into account not only the magnetic energy but also that of the electric field in the condenser. The latter energy is $e^2/2C$, where C is the capacity of the condenser and $\pm e(t)$ the charges on its plates. Proceeding as in the derivation of equation (47.4), we obtain†

$$\mathscr{E}J = RJ^2+\frac{\mathrm{d}}{\mathrm{d}t}\frac{LJ^2}{2c^2}+\frac{\mathrm{d}}{\mathrm{d}t}\frac{e^2}{2C} = RJ^2+\frac{1}{c^2}LJ\frac{\mathrm{d}J}{\mathrm{d}t}+\frac{e}{C}\frac{\mathrm{d}e}{\mathrm{d}t}.$$

The current J is equal to the rate of decrease and increase of the charges on the two plates: $J = \mathrm{d}e/\mathrm{d}t$. Dividing both sides of the equation by J and expressing J in terms of e, we have

$$\frac{1}{c^2}L\frac{\mathrm{d}^2e}{\mathrm{d}t^2}+R\frac{\mathrm{d}e}{\mathrm{d}t}+\frac{e}{C} = \mathscr{E}. \tag{48.1}$$

This is the required equation for a variable current in a circuit with a capacity.

If $\mathscr{E}$ is a periodic function of time having frequency ω, then equation (48.1) reduces to an algebraic relation between $\mathscr{E}$ and the charge e, or between $\mathscr{E}$ and the current $J = -i\omega e$. We have, in fact, $JZ = \mathscr{E}$, where the impedance Z is defined by

$$Z = R-i\left(\frac{\omega L}{c^2}-\frac{1}{\omega C}\right). \tag{48.2}$$

Taking real parts in the relation $J = \mathscr{E}/Z$, we obtain

$$J(t) = \frac{\mathscr{E}_0\cos(\omega t-\phi)}{\sqrt{\left[R^2+\left(\frac{\omega L}{c^2}-\frac{1}{\omega C}\right)^2\right]}},\qquad \tan\phi = \left(\frac{\omega L}{c^2}-\frac{1}{\omega C}\right)\frac{1}{R}, \tag{48.3}$$

which give the current in a circuit to which an external e.m.f. $\mathscr{E} = \mathscr{E}_0 \cos \omega t$ is applied.

† In the present section we neglect the skin effect.

If $\mathscr{E} = 0$, the current in the circuit consists of "free" electric oscillations. The (complex) frequency of these oscillations is given by $Z = 0$, whence

$$\omega = -i\frac{Rc^2}{2L} \pm \sqrt{\left[\frac{c^2}{LC} - \left(\frac{Rc^2}{2L}\right)^2\right]}. \tag{48.4}$$

We may have either periodic oscillations damped with decrement $Rc^2/2L$ or an aperiodically damped discharge, depending on the sign of the radicand. In the limit as $R \to 0$ we have undamped oscillations whose frequency is given by *Thomson's formula*: $\omega = c/\sqrt{(LC)}$.

Equation (48.1) can be immediately generalised to a system of several inductively coupled circuits containing condensers. The current J_a in the ath circuit is related to the charges $\pm e_a$ on the corresponding condenser by $J_a = \mathrm{d}e_a/\mathrm{d}t$, and equation (48.1) is replaced by the set of equations

$$\sum_b \frac{1}{c^2} L_{ab} \frac{\mathrm{d}^2 e_b}{\mathrm{d}t^2} + R_a \frac{\mathrm{d}e_a}{\mathrm{d}t} + \frac{e_a}{C_a} = \mathscr{E}_a. \tag{48.5}$$

For periodic (monochromatic) currents, these equations give the algebraic equations

$$\sum_b Z_{ab} J_b = \mathscr{E}_a, \tag{48.6}$$

the matrix elements Z_{ab} being given by the formulae

$$Z_{ab} = \delta_{ab}\left(R_a + \frac{i}{\omega C_a}\right) - \frac{i\omega}{c^2} L_{ab}. \tag{48.7}$$

The eigenfrequencies of the current system are given by the condition of compatibility of equations (48.6) when $\mathscr{E}_a = 0$, i.e. by the condition for the determinant $|Z_{ab}|$ to vanish:

$$|Z_{ab}| = 0. \tag{48.8}$$

If the resistances R are not zero, all the "frequencies" have a non-zero imaginary part, and the electric oscillations are therefore damped.

It should be noticed that equations (48.5) are formally identical with the mechanical equations of motion of a system with several degrees of freedom which executes small damped oscillations. The generalised co-ordinates are represented by the charges e_a, and the generalised velocities by the currents $J_a = \mathrm{d}e_a/\mathrm{d}t$. The "Lagrangian" of the system is

$$\mathscr{L} = \sum_{a,b} \frac{1}{2c^2} L_{ab} \dot{e}_a \dot{e}_b - \sum_a \frac{e_a^2}{2C_a} + \sum_a e_a \mathscr{E}_a. \tag{48.9}$$

The kinetic and potential energies of the mechanical system are represented by the magnetic and electric energies of the current system, and the quantities $\mathscr{E}_a$ correspond to the externally applied forces which cause the forced oscillations of the system. The quantities R_a appear in the *dissipative function*

$$R = \sum_a \tfrac{1}{2} R_a \ddot{e}_a^2. \qquad 48.10)$$

Equations (48.5) are the analogues of Lagrange's equations

$$\frac{\mathrm{d}}{\mathrm{d}t}\frac{\partial \mathscr{L}}{\partial \dot{e}_a} - \frac{\partial \mathscr{L}}{\partial e_a} = -\frac{\partial R}{\partial \dot{e}_a}. \qquad (48.11)$$

PROBLEMS

PROBLEM 1. Determine the eigenfrequencies of electric oscillations in two inductively coupled circuits containing self-inductances L_1 and L_2 and capacities C_1 and C_2, neglecting the resistances R_1 and R_2.

SOLUTION. The required frequencies are determined from the condition

$$|Z_{ab}| = Z_{11}Z_{22} - Z_{12}^2 = 0,$$

where

$$Z_{11} = -i\left(\frac{\omega}{c^2}L_1 - \frac{1}{\omega C_1}\right), \quad Z_{22} = -i\left(\frac{\omega}{c^2}L_2 - \frac{1}{\omega C_2}\right), \quad Z_{12} = -\frac{i\omega}{c^2}L_{12}.$$

Calculation gives

$$\omega_{1,2}^2 = c^2 \frac{L_1C_1 + L_2C_2 \mp \sqrt{[(L_1C_1 - L_2C_2)^2 + 4C_1C_2L_{12}^2]}}{2C_1C_2(L_1L\ -L_{12}^2)}.$$

Both frequencies are purely real, owing to the fact that R_1 and R_2 have been neglected. As $L_{12} \to 0$, ω_1 and ω_2 tend to $c/\sqrt{(L_1C_1)}$ and $c/\sqrt{(L_2C_2)}$. These are the frequencies for the two circuits separately.

PROBLEM 2. The same as Problem 1, but for a circuit consisting of a resistance R, a capacity C and an inductance L connected in parallel.

SOLUTION. The impedances of the three branches are $Z_1 = R$, $Z_2 = i/\omega C$, $Z_3 = -i\omega L/c^2$, and the currents in them are such that $J_1 + J_2 + J_3 = 0$, $Z_1J_1 = Z_2J_2 = Z_3J_3$. Hence we have $1/Z_1 + 1/Z_2 + 1/Z_3 = 0$, whence

$$\omega = -\frac{i}{2RC} \pm \sqrt{\left[\frac{c^2}{LC} - \frac{1}{4R^2C^2}\right]}.$$

PROBLEM 3. Discuss the propagation of electric oscillations in a circuit consisting of an infinite succession of identical meshes containing impedances

$$Z_1 = -i\left(\frac{\omega}{c^2}L_1 - \frac{1}{\omega C_1}\right), \quad Z_2 = -i\left(\frac{\omega}{c^2}L_2 - \frac{1}{\omega C_2}\right),$$

as shown in Fig. 25. Find the range of frequencies which can be propagated in the circuit without damping.†

† The condition for the quasi-steady theory to be applicable to such a periodic circuit is that the dimension of one mesh should be small compared with the "wavelength" c/ω.

SOLUTION. The current in mesh α is denoted by i_α, as shown in Fig. 25. Kirchhoff's second law gives for this mesh $Z_1 i_\alpha + Z_2(2i_\alpha - i_{\alpha-1} - i_{\alpha+1}) = 0$. This is a linear difference equation in the integral variable α, with constant coefficients. We seek the solution in the form $i_\alpha = \text{constant} \times q^\alpha$, obtaining for the parameter q the equation

$$q^2 - \left(2 + \frac{Z_1}{Z_2}\right)q + 1 = 0. \tag{1}$$

Let $-4 \leqq Z_1/Z_2 \leqslant 0$, corresponding to values of ω^2 lying between c^2/L_1C_1 and $c^2(4/C_2+1/C_1)/(4L_2+L_1)$. Then equation (1) has two complex conjugate roots with moduli $|q| = 1$. This means that the current does not decrease from one mesh to the next, i.e. the electric oscillations are propagated in the circuit without being damped. Putting $q = e^{ikl}$, where l is the length of one mesh and k is the "wave number" of the oscillations propagated in the circuit, we can calculate the velocity of propagation u from the general result $u = d\omega/dk$.

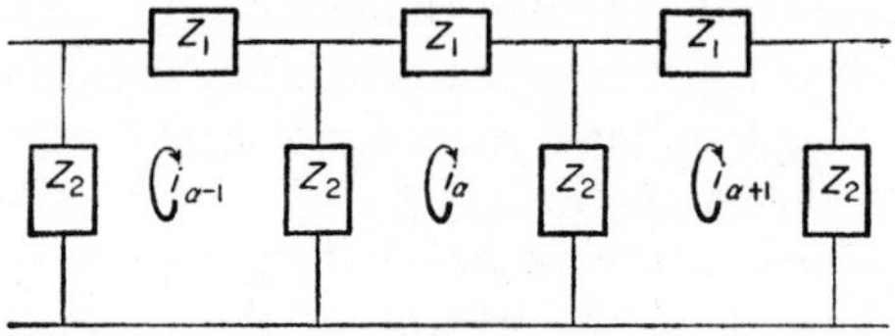

FIG. 25

If, however, ω is outside the range mentioned, equation (1) has two real roots q_1 and q_2, say; since $q_1q_2 = 1$, one root (q_1, say) is less than 1 in absolute magnitude, while q_2 is greater. It is easy to see that the propagation of undamped oscillations in the circuit is then impossible. To elucidate the reason for this, let us consider a circuit of large but finite length. An initial oscillatory impulse is given to one end of the circuit, the other end being closed in some manner. This closure corresponds mathematically to a certain boundary condition, by means of which we can determine the ratio of the coefficients c_1 and c_2 in the general solution $c_1q_1^{-(\alpha_k-\alpha)} + c_2q_2^{-(\alpha_k-\alpha)}$, where α_k is the "co-ordinate" of the end of the circuit. This ratio is of the order of unity. As $\alpha_k - \alpha$ increases, the second term in the solution rapidly becomes very small compared with the first term, because $|q_2| > 1$. Thus the solution is $i_\alpha = c_1q_1^{-(\alpha_k-\alpha)}$ everywhere except for a small part near the end of the circuit, and $|i_\alpha|$ decreases towards the end of the circuit.

It should be emphasised that this damping does not involve dissipative absorption, because there is no resistance in the circuit; it can be imagined as being the result of reflection of the oscillatory impulse from each successive mesh of the circuit.

§49. Motion of a conductor in a magnetic field

Hitherto we have tacitly assumed that a conductor in an electromagnetic field is at rest in the frame of reference K in which **E**, **H**, etc. are defined. In particular, the relation $\mathbf{j} = \sigma\mathbf{E}$ between the current and the field is generally valid only for conductors at rest.

To determine the corresponding relation in a moving conductor, we change from the frame K to another frame K' in which the conductor, or some part of it, is at rest at the instant considered. In this frame we have $\mathbf{j} = \sigma\mathbf{E}'$, where $\mathbf{E}'$ is the electric field in K'. The well-known formula for the transformation of fields† gives $\mathbf{E}'$ in terms of the fields in K:

$$\mathbf{E}' = \mathbf{E} + \mathbf{v} \times \mathbf{B}/c, \tag{49.1}$$

† See *The Classical Theory of Fields*, §3–10, Addison-Wesley Press, Cambridge (Mass.) 1951; Pergamon Press, London, 1959. The microscopic values of the electric and magnetic fields are replaced by their averaged values $\bar{\mathbf{e}} = \mathbf{E}$, $\bar{\mathbf{h}} = \mathbf{B}$.

where $\mathbf{v}$ is the velocity of K' relative to K, i.e. in this case the velocity of the conductor, which we of course suppose small compared with the velocity of light. Thus we find

$$\mathbf{j} = \sigma(\mathbf{E} + \mathbf{v} \times \mathbf{B}/c). \tag{49.2}$$

This gives the relation between the current and the field in moving conductors. The following remark should be made concerning its derivation. In going from one frame of reference to the other we have transformed the field but left the current $\mathbf{j}$ unaltered. The correct transformation of the current density gives only terms of a higher order of smallness if $v \ll c$. In formula (49.2) the second term, which appears as a result of the field transformation, is in general not small compared with the first term, despite the factor v/c. For example, if the electric field is due to electromagnetic induction from a variable magnetic field, its order of magnitude contains a factor $1/c$ as compared with the magnetic field.

The energy dissipation in a conductor when a given current flows in it cannot, of course, depend on the motion of the conductor. The rate of evolution of Joule heat per unit volume in a moving conductor is therefore given in terms of the current density by the same expression j^2/σ as for a conductor at rest. The expression $\mathbf{j}\cdot\mathbf{E}$, however, is replaced by† $j^2/\sigma = \mathbf{j}\cdot(\mathbf{E}+\mathbf{v}\times\mathbf{B}/c)$.

Thus, in a moving conductor, the sum $\mathbf{E}+\mathbf{v}\times\mathbf{B}/c$ acts as an "effective" electric field producing the conduction current. Hence the e.m.f. acting in a closed linear circuit C is given by the integral

$$\mathscr{E} = \oint_C (\mathbf{E} + \mathbf{v} \times \mathbf{B}/c)\cdot d\mathbf{l}. \tag{49.3}$$

This expression can be transformed as follows. According to Maxwell's equation, $\mathbf{curl}\,\mathbf{E} = -(1/c)\partial\mathbf{B}/\partial t$, and so

$$\oint_C \mathbf{E}\cdot d\mathbf{l} = \int_S \mathbf{curl}\,\mathbf{E}\cdot d\mathbf{f} = -\frac{1}{c}\frac{\partial}{\partial t}\int_S \mathbf{B}\cdot d\mathbf{f}$$

or, denoting by Φ the magnetic flux through the surface S, which spans the circuit C,

$$\oint \mathbf{E}\cdot d\mathbf{l} = -\frac{1}{c}\left(\frac{\partial \Phi}{\partial t}\right)_{\mathbf{v}=0}.$$

† It is seen from this formula that the additional heat evolved in time δt in a conductor moving in a magnetic field is

$$\delta t \int \mathbf{j}\cdot\mathbf{v}\times\mathbf{B}\,dV/c = -\int \mathbf{u}\cdot\mathbf{j}\times\mathbf{B}\,dV/c,$$

where $\mathbf{u} = \mathbf{v}\delta t$ is the displacement in time δt. This expression is equal and opposite to the work done on the conductor in time δt by the volume forces $\mathbf{f} = \mathbf{j}\times\mathbf{B}/c$. This explains the apparent contradiction mentioned in §34.

The time derivative with the suffix $\mathbf{v} = 0$ denotes the rate of change of the magnetic flux due to the time variation of the magnetic field, the position of the contour C remaining unchanged.

In the second term in (49.3), we put $\mathbf{v} = d\mathbf{u}/dt$, where $d\mathbf{u}$ is an infinitesimal displacement of the circuit element dl. Then

$$\oint_C \mathbf{v} \times \mathbf{B} \cdot d\mathbf{l} = \oint d\mathbf{u} \times \mathbf{B} \cdot d\mathbf{l}/dt = -\oint_s \mathbf{B} \cdot d\mathbf{f}/dt,$$

where $d\mathbf{f} = d\mathbf{u} \times d\mathbf{l}$ is an element of area on the "side" surface s between two infinitely close positions C and C' of the current circuit, which it occupies at times t and $t+dt$ (Fig. 26). Since the total magnetic flux through any closed surface is zero, the flux through s must evidently equal the difference of the fluxes through surfaces spanning C and C'. Thus

$$\oint_C \mathbf{v} \times \mathbf{B} \cdot d\mathbf{l} = -(\partial\Phi/\partial t)_{\mathbf{B}=\mathrm{constant}},$$

where the time derivative denotes the rate of change of the magnetic flux due to the motion of the conductor in a constant field.

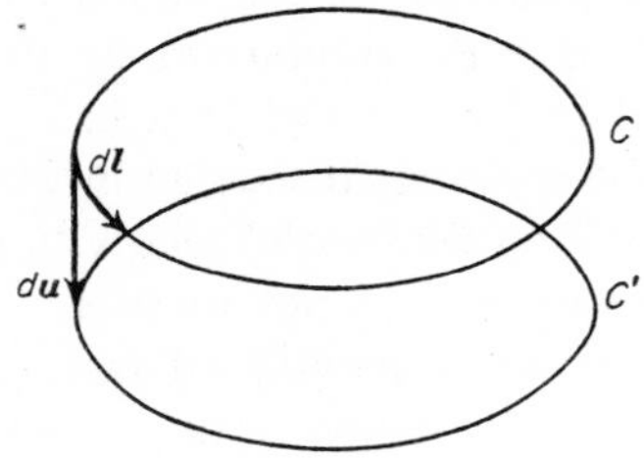

FIG. 26

Adding the two terms, we have finally

$$\mathscr{E} = -(1/c)\, d\Phi/dt, \tag{49.4}$$

where the time derivative now denotes the total rate of change of the magnetic flux through the moving circuit. Thus the expression (49.4), which is *Faraday's law*, is valid whatever the reason for the change in the magnetic flux, whether variation of the field itself (already discussed in §47, formula (47.13)) or motion of the conductor.

In a constant magnetic field, the change in the flux is due entirely to the motion of the circuit. If the circuit moves in such a way that every point of it moves along a line of force, then the flux through the circuit does not vary. This is an obvious result of the fact that the magnetic flux through any closed surface is zero, and the flux through the "side" surface described by the moving circuit is in this case identically zero (since $B_n = 0$ on this surface). Thus we can say that, to induce an e.m.f., the conductor must certainly move so as to cross lines of magnetic force.

The electromagnetic field in a moving conductor is given by the equations

$$\mathbf{curl}\,\mathbf{E} = -(1/c)\partial\mathbf{B}/\partial t,$$
$$\mathbf{curl}\,\mathbf{H} = 4\pi\mathbf{j}/c = (4\pi\sigma/c)(\mathbf{E}+\mathbf{v}\times\mathbf{B}/c),$$
$$\mathrm{div}\,\mathbf{B} = 0.$$

Expressing **E** in terms of **H** by means of the second equation and substituting in the first, we obtain

$$\frac{\partial\mathbf{B}}{\partial t}-\mathbf{curl}\,(\mathbf{v}\times\mathbf{B}) = -\frac{c^2}{4\pi}\mathbf{curl}\left(\frac{\mathbf{curl}\,\mathbf{H}}{\sigma}\right). \tag{49.5}$$

In a homogeneous conductor with constant conductivity σ and constant magnetic permeability μ, we have

$$\frac{\partial\mathbf{H}}{\partial t}-\mathbf{curl}\,(\mathbf{v}\times\mathbf{H}) = \frac{c^2}{4\pi\sigma\mu}\triangle\mathbf{H}, \qquad \mathrm{div}\,\mathbf{H} = 0. \tag{49.6}$$

These equations generalise those obtained in §45.

It should be pointed out, however, that, if there is only one conductor moving as a whole (without change of shape) in an external magnetic field, then the solution of the problem is considerably simplified if we use a system of co-ordinates fixed in the conductor. In this system the conductor is at rest, and the external field varies with time in a given manner, so that we return to the eddy-current problems discussed in §45. This possibility does not depend on Galileo's (or on Einstein's) relativity principle, since the new system of co-ordinates is in general not inertial. The equivalence of the problems results from the above-mentioned fact that the electromagnetic induction is independent of the cause of the change in the magnetic flux. This equivalence can also be demonstrated mathematically. To do so, we expand the expression **curl** ($\mathbf{v}\times\mathbf{B}$), using the facts that div $\mathbf{B} = 0$ and (for motion of the body as a whole) div $\mathbf{v} = 0$ (i.e. the body is "incompressible"). Then the left-hand side of equation (49.5) becomes

$$\partial\mathbf{B}/\partial t+(\mathbf{v}\cdot\mathbf{grad})\mathbf{B}-(\mathbf{B}\cdot\mathbf{grad})\mathbf{v}. \tag{49.7}$$

This sum is just the time derivative of **B** with respect to axes fixed in a rotating body. For the sum of the first two terms is the "substantial" time derivative $\mathrm{d}\mathbf{B}/\mathrm{d}t$, which gives the rate of change of **B** at a point moving with velocity **v**. The third term takes into account the change in the direction of **B** relative to the body; it is zero for pure translation ($\mathbf{v}$ = constant) and equals $-\mathbf{\Omega}\times\mathbf{B}$ for rotation ($\mathbf{v} = \mathbf{\Omega}\times\mathbf{r}$, where $\mathbf{\Omega}$ is the angular velocity).

To conclude this section, let us consider the phenomenon of *unipolar induction*, which occurs when a magnetised conductor rotates. If a stationary wire is connected to the rotating magnet by means of two sliding contacts A and B (Fig. 27) then a current flows in the wire. It is not difficult to calculate the e.m.f. which produces the current; the simplest procedure is to use a system of co-ordinates rotating with the magnet. If $\mathbf{\Omega}$ is the angular velocity of rotation of the magnet, then in the new system the wire rotates with angular velocity $-\mathbf{\Omega}$, while the magnet is at rest. Thus we have a conductor moving in a given constant magnetic field $\mathbf{B}$ due to a fixed magnet. We neglect the distortion of the field by the wire itself. According to formula (49.3), the e.m.f. between the ends of the wire is

$$\mathscr{E} = \frac{1}{c}\int\limits_{ACB} \mathbf{v}\times\mathbf{B}\cdot d\mathbf{l} = -\frac{1}{c}\int\limits_{ACB} \mathbf{B}\times(\mathbf{r}\times\mathbf{\Omega})\cdot d\mathbf{l}, \qquad (49.8)$$

taken along the wire. This is the required solution.

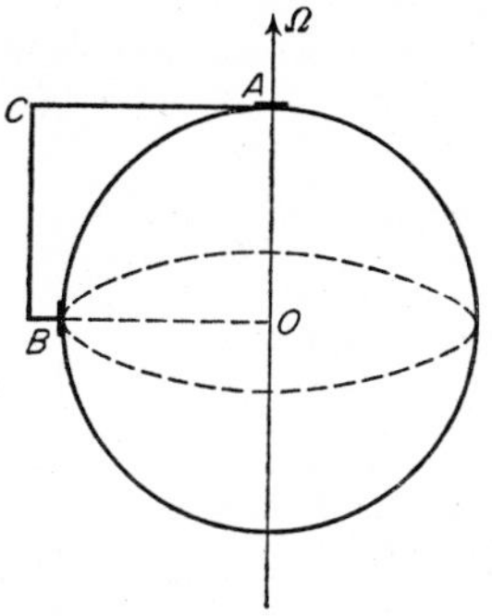

FIG. 27

PROBLEMS

PROBLEM 1. Determine the magnetic moment of a conducting sphere (with $\mu = 1$) rotating uniformly in a uniform constant magnetic field, and the torque on the sphere.

SOLUTION. Let the external field have components $\mathfrak{H}_x$, 0, $\mathfrak{H}_z$ in a fixed system of co-ordinates with the z-axis in the direction of the angular velocity vector $\mathbf{\Omega}$. In a co-ordinate system ξ, η, z which rotates with the sphere, the field components are $\mathfrak{H}_\xi = \mathfrak{H}_x \cos \Omega t$, $\mathfrak{H}_\eta = -\mathfrak{H}_x \sin \Omega t$, $\mathfrak{H}_z$, or, in complex form, $\mathfrak{H}_\xi = \mathfrak{H}_x e^{-i\Omega t}$, $\mathfrak{H}_\eta = -i\mathfrak{H}_x e^{-i\Omega t}$, $\mathfrak{H}_z$.

Thus variable fields of frequency Ω act along the ξ and η axes, and the magnetic moment which they induce is

$$\mathscr{M}_\xi = V \operatorname{re} (\alpha\mathfrak{H}_\xi) = V\mathfrak{H}_x(\alpha' \cos \Omega t + \alpha'' \sin \Omega t),$$
$$\mathscr{M}_\eta = V \operatorname{re} (\alpha\mathfrak{H}_\eta) = V\mathfrak{H}_x(-\alpha' \sin \Omega t + \alpha'' \cos \Omega t),$$

where $V\alpha$ is the complex magnetic polarisability of the sphere, which has been determined in §45, Problem 1. Along the z-axis, on the other hand, the magnetic field is constant, and therefore causes no magnetic moment (if $\mu = 1$). The components of the magnetic moment in the fixed system of co-ordinates are $\mathscr{M}_x = V\alpha'\mathfrak{H}_x$, $\mathscr{M}_y = V\alpha''\mathfrak{H}_x$, $\mathscr{M}_z = 0$. Thus in this problem α' and α'' give the components of the magnetic moment of the sphere respectively parallel and perpendicular to the plane of the vectors $\mathbf{\Omega}$ and $\mathfrak{H}$.

The torque on the sphere is $\mathbf{K} = \mathscr{M} \times \mathfrak{H}$. Its components relative to the fixed axes are

$$K_x = V\alpha''\mathfrak{H}_x\mathfrak{H}_z, \qquad K_y = -V\alpha'\mathfrak{H}_x\mathfrak{H}_z, \qquad K_z = -V\alpha''\mathfrak{H}_x^2.$$

PROBLEM 2. Determine the e.m.f. due to unipolar induction between the pole and the equator (Fig. 27) of a uniformly magnetised sphere rotating uniformly about the direction of magnetisation.

SOLUTION. When the sphere rotates about its direction of magnetisation, it generates a constant field, and, since no currents flow within the sphere, we find from (49.5) that **curl** $(\mathbf{v}\times\mathbf{B}) = 0$. Hence the integral of $\mathbf{v}\times\mathbf{B}$ along the closed contour $OACBO$ (Fig. 27) is zero, and so the integration along ACB in formula (49.8) may be replaced by one along the path AOB, which lies inside the sphere. The integral along the segment AO of the axis of rotation is zero, since $\mathbf{\Omega}$ and $\mathbf{r}$ are parallel; the integral along the radius OB gives, since $\mathbf{B}$ and $\mathbf{\Omega}$ are parallel within the sphere,

$$\mathscr{E} = \frac{1}{c}\int_0^a B_0\Omega r dr = B_0\Omega a^2/2c,$$

where a is the radius of the sphere and B_0 the magnetic induction in it. In a uniformly magnetised sphere (in the absence of an external field) the induction is related to the magnetisation by $B_0+2H = 0$ (cf. (8.1)) and $B_0-H = 4\pi M$, whence $B_0 = 8\pi M/3$. In terms of the total magnetic moment of the sphere we have finally $\mathscr{E} = \Omega\mathscr{M}/ca$.

PROBLEM 3. Determine the total charge which flows along a closed linear circuit when the magnetic flux through the circuit changes for any reason from one constant value (Φ_1) to another (Φ_2).

SOLUTION. The required total charge is the integral

$$\int_{-\infty}^{\infty} J\,\mathrm{d}t,$$

where $J(t)$ is the induction current in the circuit. Mathematically, this integral is the Fourier component of the function $J(t)$ that has the frequency $\omega = 0$. It is therefore related to the corresponding component of the e.m.f. by

$$\int_{-\infty}^{\infty} \mathscr{E}\,\mathrm{d}t = Z(0)\int_{-\infty}^{\infty} J\,\mathrm{d}t;$$

see (47.3). Putting $Z(0) = R$, where R is the resistance of the circuit to a constant current and $\mathscr{E} = -(1/c)\,\mathrm{d}\Phi/\mathrm{d}t$, we have

$$\int_{-\infty}^{\infty} J\,\mathrm{d}t = \frac{1}{cR}(\Phi_1-\Phi_2).$$

§50. Excitation of currents by acceleration

In discussing the motion of a conductor in §49 we have neglected possible effects of the acceleration, if any. The accelerated motion of a metal, however, is equivalent to the action of additional inertia forces on the conduction electrons. If $\dot{\mathbf{v}}$ is the acceleration of the conductor and m the mass of the electron, then the force on an electron is $-m\dot{\mathbf{v}}$. It affects the electron in the same way as an electric field $m\dot{\mathbf{v}}/e$, where $-e$ is the charge on the electron. Thus the "effective" electric field on the conduction electrons in an accelerated metal is

$$\mathbf{E}' = \mathbf{E}+m\dot{\mathbf{v}}/e. \tag{50.1}$$

The current density is accordingly

$$\mathbf{j} = \sigma\mathbf{E}' = \sigma(\mathbf{E}+m\dot{\mathbf{v}}/e). \tag{50.2}$$

Expressing **E** in terms of **E**′ from (50.1), we substitute in the equation **curl E** $= -(1/c)\partial\mathbf{H}/\partial t$ (as usual, we put $\mu = 1$). Then

$$\mathbf{curl\,E}' = -\frac{1}{c}\frac{\partial\mathbf{H}}{\partial t}+\frac{m}{e}\mathbf{curl}\,\dot{\mathbf{v}}. \tag{50.3}$$

We write **v** as a sum $\mathbf{v} = \mathbf{u}+\mathbf{\Omega}\times\mathbf{r}$, where **u** is the translational velocity and **Ω** the angular velocity of rotation of the body. Differentiating with respect to time, we find the acceleration to be $\dot{\mathbf{v}} = \dot{\mathbf{u}}+\mathbf{\Omega}\times\mathbf{v}+\dot{\mathbf{\Omega}}\times\mathbf{r} = \dot{\mathbf{u}}+\mathbf{\Omega}\times\mathbf{u}+ +\mathbf{\Omega}\times(\mathbf{\Omega}\times\mathbf{r})+\dot{\mathbf{\Omega}}\times\mathbf{r}$. The first two terms are independent of **r**, and therefore give zero on differentiation with respect to the co-ordinates. The third term can be written as $\mathbf{\Omega}\times(\mathbf{\Omega}\times\mathbf{r}) = -\frac{1}{2}\,\mathbf{grad}\,(\mathbf{\Omega}\times\mathbf{r})^2$, and its curl is therefore zero. Finally, $\mathbf{curl}\,(\dot{\mathbf{\Omega}}\times\mathbf{r}) = 2\dot{\mathbf{\Omega}}$. Thus, substituting for $\dot{\mathbf{v}}$ in equation (50.3), we have $\mathbf{curl\,E}' = -(1/c)\partial\mathbf{H}/\partial t+2m\dot{\mathbf{\Omega}}/e$ or

$$\mathbf{curl\,E}' = -\frac{1}{c}\frac{\partial\mathbf{H}'}{\partial t}, \tag{50.4}$$

where

$$\mathbf{H}' = \mathbf{H}-2mc\mathbf{\Omega}/e. \tag{50.5}$$

Since **Ω** is independent of the co-ordinates, the equation $\mathbf{curl\,H} = 4\pi\mathbf{j}/c$ is still valid if **H** is replaced by **H**′:

$$\mathbf{curl\,H}' = 4\pi\sigma\mathbf{E}'/c. \tag{50.6}$$

Eliminating **E**′ from equations (50.4) and (50.6), we obtain for **H**′ the equation

$$\triangle\mathbf{H}' = (4\pi\sigma/c^2)\partial\mathbf{H}'/\partial t, \tag{50.7}$$

which is the same as the equation for **H** in a conductor at rest.

Outside the body, the field satisfies the equation $\triangle\mathbf{H} = 0$ (the wavelength being supposed large compared with the dimension of the body), and **H**′ satisfies the same equation.

Finally, on the surface of the conductor **H**′, like **H**, is continuous. The only difference is in the condition at infinity, where **H** tends to zero but **H**′ tends to the limit $-2mc\mathbf{\Omega}/e$.

Thus the problem of determining the variable magnetic field **H** near a non-uniformly rotating body is equivalent to that of determining the field **H**′ near a body at rest in a uniform external magnetic field

$$\mathfrak{H} = -2mc\mathbf{\Omega}/e. \tag{50.8}$$

The required field $\mathbf{H}_e$ outside the conductor is obtained by subtracting $\mathfrak{H}$ from the solution **H**′ of this latter problem.†

† Misunderstanding may arise from the appearance of the angular velocity **Ω** itself, and not its time derivative, in formula (50.8). We may therefore emphasise that the above discussion, and therefore the significance here attached to the quantity (50.8), pertain only to non-uniform rotation. In particular, the field (50.8) is unrelated to the gyromagnetic effect (which appears even when the rotation is uniform, and is a small quantity here neglected).

The magnetic field thus produced, like any variable field, induces electric currents in the conductor itself. In a simply-connected body, these currents appear in the form of a magnetic moment. In a non-uniformly rotating ring, the effect appears as an e.m.f.—the *Stewart–Tolman effect.*

PROBLEMS

PROBLEM 1. Determine the magnetic moment of a non-uniformly rotating sphere of radius a. The rate of rotation is assumed so small that the penetration depth $\delta \gg a$.

SOLUTION. The magnetic moment of the sphere in the field $\mathfrak{H}(t)$ (50.8) is $\mathcal{M} = V\hat{\alpha}\mathfrak{H}$, where $\hat{\alpha}$ is an operator whose action on the Fourier components of the function $\mathfrak{H}(t)$ is given by the formulae of §45, Problem 1. For the components with frequencies ω such that $\delta \gg a$ we have $\mathcal{M} = V\alpha(\omega)\mathfrak{H} \cong -4\pi ma^5\sigma i\omega\mathbf{\Omega}/15ce$. This formula, when written $\mathcal{M} = (4\pi ma^5\sigma/15ce)\, \mathrm{d}\mathbf{\Omega}/\mathrm{d}t$, does not contain ω explicitly, and is therefore valid also for the functions $\mathcal{M}$ and $\mathbf{\Omega}$ themselves, as well as their individual Fourier components (on the assumption that the Fourier expansion contains chiefly terms whose frequencies satisfy the above condition).

PROBLEM 2. Determine the total charge which flows along a thin circular ring when it ceases a uniform rotation about an axis perpendicular to its plane.

SOLUTION. In the formula obtained in §49, Problem 3, Φ must be taken as the flux of the field $\mathfrak{H}$ (50.8). The total charge transferred when the angular velocity changes from $\mathbf{\Omega}$ to zero is

$$\int_{-\infty}^{\infty} J\, \mathrm{d}t = \frac{2mc}{eRc}\Omega\pi b^2 = \frac{m\sigma V}{2\pi e}\Omega,$$

where b is the radius of the ring and V its volume.

PROBLEM 3. Determine the current in a superconducting circular ring which ceases to rotate uniformly.

SOLUTION. From the condition that the total magnetic flux through the ring is constant (see (42.5)), we have

$$J = \frac{2mc^2}{eL}\Omega\pi b^2 = \frac{mc^2 b\Omega}{2e[\log(8b/a)-2]}.$$

See the third footnote to §42 concerning the value of L.

CHAPTER VIII

MAGNETIC FLUID DYNAMICS

§51. The equations of motion for a fluid in a magnetic field

IF A conducting fluid moves in a magnetic field, electric fields are induced in it and electric currents flow. The magnetic field exerts forces on these currents which may considerably modify the flow. Conversely, the currents themselves modify the magnetic field. Thus we have a complex interaction between the magnetic and the fluid-dynamic phenomena, and the flow must be examined by combining the field equations with those of fluid dynamics.

We shall use equations (49.6) as the field equations in a moving conducting medium. The magnetic permeability of the media considered in magnetic fluid dynamics differs only slightly from unity, and the difference is unimportant as regards the phenomena under discussion. We shall therefore take $\mu = 1$ throughout the present chapter. The equations are then

$$\operatorname{div} \mathbf{H} = 0, \tag{51.1}$$

$$\partial \mathbf{H}/\partial t = \mathbf{curl}\,(\mathbf{v} \times \mathbf{H}) + (c^2/4\pi\sigma)\,\triangle\mathbf{H}. \tag{51.2}$$

By using these equations we assume that certain conditions are fulfilled. The period of variation of the field must be large compared with the mean free time of the conduction electrons. Then the relation between the current and the electric field involves the same conductivity σ as for a constant current (see §45).† Here we assume that σ is constant in the medium, and therefore, in particular, that the conductivity is independent of the magnetic field. For this to be so, the mean free path of the electrons must be small in comparison with the radius of curvature of their orbits in the magnetic field. That is, the mean free time must be small compared with the reciprocal of the electron Larmor frequency eH/mc. This condition may not hold if the medium is rarefied and the magnetic field is strong.

The equations of fluid dynamics are the equation of continuity

$$\partial\rho/\partial t + \operatorname{div}(\rho\mathbf{v}) = 0, \tag{51.3}$$

† In the second footnote to §45 the further condition $\sigma/\omega \gg 1$ was mentioned as being necessary for poor conductors. In good conductors this condition is always satisfied if the other conditions are. In the present case the frequency is represented by V/L, where L and V are characteristic parameters of length and velocity which determine the properties of the flow. Thus we assume the condition $\sigma L/V \gg 1$ to hold.

where ρ is the fluid density, and the Navier–Stokes equation

$$\frac{\partial \mathbf{v}}{\partial t} + (\mathbf{v}\cdot\mathbf{grad})\mathbf{v} = -\frac{1}{\rho}\,\mathbf{grad}\,p + \frac{\eta}{\rho}\triangle\mathbf{v} + \frac{1}{\rho}(\zeta + \tfrac{1}{3}\eta)\,\mathbf{grad}\,\mathrm{div}\,\mathbf{v} + \frac{\mathbf{f}}{\rho},$$

where η and ζ are the two coefficients of viscosity for the fluid, and $\mathbf{f}$ is the volume density of external (in this case, electromagnetic) forces. By formula (34.4) we have $\mathbf{f} = \mathbf{j}\times\mathbf{H}/c = (\mathbf{curl\,H})\times\mathbf{H}/4\pi$. Thus the equation of motion of the fluid is

$$\frac{\partial \mathbf{v}}{\partial t} + (\mathbf{v}\cdot\mathbf{grad})\mathbf{v} = -\frac{1}{\rho}\,\mathbf{grad}\,p - \frac{1}{4\pi\rho}\mathbf{H}\times\mathbf{curl\,H} + \frac{\eta}{\rho}\triangle\mathbf{v} + \frac{1}{\rho}(\zeta + \tfrac{1}{3}\eta)\,\mathbf{grad}\,\mathrm{div}\,\mathbf{v}. \quad (51.4)$$

To these equations we must add the equation of state

$$p = p(\rho, T), \quad (51.5)$$

which relates the pressure, density and temperature of the fluid, and the equation of heat transfer. In ordinary fluid dynamics the latter is†

$$\rho T\left(\frac{\partial s}{\partial t} + \mathbf{v}\cdot\mathbf{grad}\,s\right) = \sigma'_{ik}\frac{\partial v_i}{\partial x_k} + \mathrm{div}\,(\kappa\,\mathbf{grad}\,T).$$

Here s is the entropy per unit mass of the fluid, and the left-hand side of the equation is the quantity of heat generated per unit time and volume in a moving fluid particle. The right-hand side is the energy dissipated per unit time and volume. The first term is due to viscosity; σ'_{ik} is the viscous stress tensor:

$$\sigma'_{ik} = \eta\left(\frac{\partial v_i}{\partial x_k} + \frac{\partial v_k}{\partial x_i} - \frac{2}{3}\delta_{ik}\frac{\partial v_l}{\partial x_l}\right) + \zeta\delta_{ik}\frac{\partial v_l}{\partial x_l}.$$

The second term gives the dissipation due to thermal conduction, κ being the thermal conductivity. In a conducting fluid, a term giving the Joule heat must be added. The rate of evolution of this heat per unit volume is $j^2/\sigma = (c^2/16\pi^2\sigma)(\mathbf{curl\,H})^2$. The equation of heat transfer in magnetic fluid dynamics is therefore

$$\rho T\left(\frac{\partial s}{\partial t} + \mathbf{v}\cdot\mathbf{grad}\,s\right) = \sigma'_{ik}\frac{\partial v_i}{\partial x_k} + \mathrm{div}(\kappa\,\mathbf{grad}\,T) + \frac{c^2}{16\pi^2\sigma}(\mathbf{curl\,H})^2. \quad (51.6)$$

Equations (51.1)–(51.6) form a complete system of equations of magnetic fluid dynamics, on the assumptions stated at the beginning of this section.

† See *Fluid Mechanics*, §49, Pergamon Press, London, 1959.

Equations (51.4) and (51.6) can also be written in forms which express the laws of conservation of momentum and energy respectively. The Navier–Stokes equation of ordinary fluid dynamics can be written (using the equation of continuity) in the form†

$$\partial(\rho v_i)/\partial t = -\partial \Pi_{ik}/\partial x_k, \tag{51.7}$$

where Π_{ik} is the momentum flux density tensor: $\Pi_{ik} = \rho v_i v_k + p\delta_{ik} - \sigma'_{ik}$. Equation (51.4) can be brought to the same form, but Π_{ik} now contains an additional term. We have $\mathbf{H}\times\mathbf{curl}\,\mathbf{H} = \frac{1}{2}\,\mathbf{grad}\,H^2 - (\mathbf{H}\cdot\mathbf{grad})\mathbf{H}$. Thus

$$\Pi_{ik} = \rho v_i v_k + p\delta_{ik} - \sigma'_{ik} - (H_i H_k - \tfrac{1}{2}H^2\delta_{ik})/4\pi. \tag{51.8}$$

The added term is the Maxwell stress tensor of the magnetic field, as it should be.

The equation of heat transfer can be transformed (using the other equations of fluid dynamics) into an equation of conservation of energy. In ordinary fluid dynamics we have $\partial(\frac{1}{2}\rho v^2 + \rho\epsilon)/\partial t = -\mathrm{div}\,\mathbf{q}$, where $\mathbf{q}$ is the energy flux density:

$$\mathbf{q} = \rho\mathbf{v}(\tfrac{1}{2}v^2 + w) - \mathbf{v}\cdot\boldsymbol{\sigma}' - \kappa\,\mathbf{grad}\,T;$$

ϵ and $w = \epsilon + p/\rho$ are respectively the internal energy and heat function per unit mass of fluid. When a magnetic field is present in the conducting medium, the energy density includes also the magnetic energy $H^2/8\pi$, and the energy flux density includes also the Poynting vector $c\mathbf{E}\times\mathbf{H}/4\pi$. Expressing $\mathbf{E}$ in the latter in terms of $\mathbf{H}$ we obtain

$$\mathbf{q} = \rho\mathbf{v}(\tfrac{1}{2}v^2 + w) + \frac{1}{4\pi}\mathbf{H}\times(\mathbf{v}\times\mathbf{H}) - \\ - \frac{c^2}{16\pi^2\sigma}\mathbf{H}\times\mathbf{curl}\,\mathbf{H} - \mathbf{v}\cdot\boldsymbol{\sigma}' - \kappa\,\mathbf{grad}\,T, \tag{51.9}$$

and the equation of conservation of energy is

$$\frac{\partial}{\partial t}\left(\tfrac{1}{2}\rho v^2 + \rho\epsilon + \frac{H^2}{8\pi}\right) = -\,\mathrm{div}\,\mathbf{q}. \tag{51.10}$$

It is not difficult to verify by direct calculation that equations (51.6) and (51.10) are equivalent.

The equations are somewhat simplified if the moving fluid can be supposed incompressible. The equation of continuity (51.3) then reduces to $\mathrm{div}\,\mathbf{v} = 0$, while in equation (51.4) the last term is zero. For reference, we shall write out here the complete system of equations for an incompressible fluid (in equations (51.2) and (51.4) we have transformed the terms

† See *Fluid Mechanics*, §15.

curl(v×H) and **H×curl H** respectively by the appropriate formulae of vector analysis):

$$\operatorname{div}\mathbf{H} = 0, \qquad \operatorname{div}\mathbf{v} = 0, \tag{51.11}$$

$$\partial\mathbf{H}/\partial t + (\mathbf{v}\cdot\mathbf{grad})\mathbf{H} = (\mathbf{H}\cdot\mathbf{grad})\mathbf{v} + (c^2/4\pi\sigma)\,\triangle\mathbf{H}, \tag{51.12}$$

$$\frac{\partial\mathbf{v}}{\partial t} + (\mathbf{v}\cdot\mathbf{grad})\mathbf{v} = -\frac{1}{\rho}\mathbf{grad}\left(p + \frac{H^2}{8\pi}\right) + \frac{1}{4\pi\rho}(\mathbf{H}\cdot\mathbf{grad})\mathbf{H} + \nu\triangle\mathbf{v}, \tag{51.13}$$

where $\nu = \eta/\rho$ is the kinematic viscosity. Equation (51.6) is not needed in solving the problem of incompressible flow unless we are interested in the temperature distribution and its effect on the flow.

Let us return to the general equation (51.2). In the limiting case of very high conductivity it becomes

$$\partial\mathbf{H}/\partial t = \mathbf{curl}(\mathbf{v}\times\mathbf{H}), \tag{51.14}$$

an equation which has a very important physical interpretation. We expand the right-hand side, using the fact that $\operatorname{div}\mathbf{H} = 0$:

$$\partial\mathbf{H}/\partial t = (\mathbf{H}\cdot\mathbf{grad})\mathbf{v} - (\mathbf{v}\cdot\mathbf{grad})\mathbf{H} - \mathbf{H}\operatorname{div}\mathbf{v}.$$

Substituting from the equation of continuity (51.3)

$$\operatorname{div}\mathbf{v} = -\frac{1}{\rho}\frac{\partial\rho}{\partial t} - \frac{\mathbf{v}\cdot\mathbf{grad}\,\rho}{\rho},$$

we obtain after a simple rearrangement of terms

$$\left(\frac{\partial}{\partial t} + \mathbf{v}\cdot\mathbf{grad}\right)\frac{\mathbf{H}}{\rho} = \left(\frac{\mathbf{H}}{\rho}\cdot\mathbf{grad}\right)\mathbf{v}.$$

The left-hand side is the "substantial" derivative, which gives the rate of change of $\mathbf{H}/\rho$ for a given fluid particle as it moves about. Denoting this derivative by $\mathrm{d}/\mathrm{d}t$, we have

$$\frac{\mathrm{d}}{\mathrm{d}t}(\mathbf{H}/\rho) = \left(\frac{\mathbf{H}}{\rho}\cdot\mathbf{grad}\right)v. \tag{51.15}$$

Let us now consider some "fluid line", i.e. a line which moves with the fluid particles composing it. Let $\delta\mathbf{l}$ be an element of length of this line; we shall determine how $\delta\mathbf{l}$ varies with time. If $\mathbf{v}$ is the fluid velocity at one end of the element $\delta\mathbf{l}$, then the fluid velocity at the other end is $\mathbf{v}+(\delta\mathbf{l}\cdot\mathbf{grad})\mathbf{v}$. During a time interval $\mathrm{d}t$, the length of $\delta\mathbf{l}$ therefore changes by $\mathrm{d}t(\delta\mathbf{l}\cdot\mathbf{grad})\mathbf{v}$, i.e. $\mathrm{d}(\delta\mathbf{l})/\mathrm{d}t = (\delta\mathbf{l}\cdot\mathbf{grad})\mathbf{v}$. We see that the rates of change of the vectors $\delta\mathbf{l}$ and $\mathbf{H}/\rho$ are given by identical formulae. Hence it follows that, if these vectors are initially in the same direction, they will remain parallel, and their lengths will remain in the same ratio. In other words, if two infinitely close fluid particles are on the same line of force at any time, then they will always be on that line of force, and the value of H/ρ will be proportional to the distance between the particles.

Passing now from particles at an infinitesimal distance apart to those at any distance apart, we conclude that every line of force moves with the fluid particles which lie on it. We can picture this by saying that (in the limit $\sigma \to \infty$ which we are considering) the lines of magnetic force are "frozen" in the fluid and move with it. The quantity H/ρ varies at every point proportionally to the extension of the corresponding "fluid line". If the fluid may be supposed incompressible ρ = constant, and the field H varies as the extension of the lines of force.

These results can be viewed in another way: as any closed fluid contour moves about in the course of time, it cuts no line of force, i.e. the "number" of lines of force passing through the contour remains unchanged. This means (cf. §49) that the flux of the magnetic field through any surface spanning the fluid contour does not vary with time.

To the question of when in fact dissipative processes in the fluid may be neglected there is no general answer, since the necessary conditions depend greatly on the nature of the motion and are, for instance, completely different for steady and for non-steady flows. We shall not investigate the general problem here.

PROBLEM

Determine the velocity distribution in an incompressible viscous conducting fluid in steady flow between two parallel solid planes, when a uniform external magnetic field $\mathbf{H}_0$ is applied perpendicular to the planes (J. Hartmann, 1937).

Solution. It is natural to assume that the fluid velocity is everywhere in the same direction, which we take as that of the x-axis, and depends only on the co-ordinate z (whose direction is perpendicular to the planes). The same is true of the longitudinal field H_x resulting from the motion. The pressure p, however, depends on x also, because there must be a constant pressure gradient in the direction of motion in order to maintain a steady flow. The equation $\operatorname{div} \mathbf{v} = 0$ is satisfied identically, while from $\operatorname{div} \mathbf{H} = 0$ it follows that $H_z = \text{constant} = H_0$. The z-component of equation (51.13) gives

$$p + \frac{H_x^2}{8\pi} = P(x), \tag{1}$$

where $P(x)$ is a function of x only. The pressure gradient in the x-direction is

$$-\partial p/\partial x = -\mathrm{d}P/\mathrm{d}x = \text{constant}.$$

The x-components of equations (51.12) and (51.13) give

$$H_0 \frac{\mathrm{d}v}{\mathrm{d}z} + \frac{c^2}{4\pi\sigma} \frac{\mathrm{d}^2 H_x}{\mathrm{d}z^2} = 0, \tag{2}$$

$$\eta \frac{\mathrm{d}^2 v}{\mathrm{d}z^2} + \frac{H_0}{4\pi} \frac{\mathrm{d}H_x}{\mathrm{d}z} = \text{constant} \equiv \frac{\mathrm{d}P}{\mathrm{d}x}. \tag{3}$$

The boundary conditions for viscous flow are $v = 0$ for $z = \pm a$, where $2a$ is the distance between the solid planes, and the plane $z = 0$ lies half-way between them The magnetic field must satisfy the conditions $H_x = 0$ for $z = \pm a$, since the magnetic field outside the fluid is just $\mathbf{H}_0$, and the tangential magnetic field component is continuous at the boundary.

The solution of equations (2) and (3) which satisfies these conditions is

$$v = v_0 \frac{\cosh(a/\Delta) - \cosh(z/\Delta)}{\cosh(a/\Delta) - 1},$$

$$H_x = -v_0 \frac{4\pi}{c} \sqrt{(\sigma\eta)} \frac{(z/a)\sinh(a/\Delta) - \sinh(z/\Delta)}{\cosh(a/\Delta) - 1}, \tag{4}$$

where $\Delta = (c/H_0)\sqrt{(\eta/\sigma)}$. The constant v_0 is the fluid velocity on the median plane $z = 0$. Its relation to the pressure gradient is given by substituting (4) in (3). The fluid velocity averaged over the cross-section is

$$\bar{v} = \frac{1}{2a} \int_{-a}^{a} v \, dz = -\frac{dP}{dx} \frac{a\Delta}{\eta} \left(\coth\frac{a}{\Delta} - \frac{\Delta}{a} \right).$$

The effect of the magnetic field on the flow is characterised by the ratio

$$a/\Delta = (aH_0/c)\sqrt{(\sigma/\eta)}.$$

For $a/\Delta \ll 1$ we have

$$v = v_0\left(1 - \frac{z^2}{a^2}\right), \qquad \bar{v} = -\frac{dP}{dx}\frac{a^2}{3\eta},$$

in accordance with the results of ordinary fluid dynamics. If $a/\Delta \gg 1$, then

$$v = v_0(1 - e^{-(a-|z|)/\Delta}), \qquad \bar{v} = -\frac{dP}{dx}\frac{ac}{H_0\sqrt{(\sigma\eta)}},$$

When the magnetic field increases, the velocity profile is flattened over the major part of the cross-section, and the mean velocity is reduced (for a given pressure gradient).

§52. Hydromagnetic waves

Let us consider the propagation of small disturbances in a homogeneous conducting medium in a uniform constant magnetic field $\mathbf{H}_0$. We shall assume that the viscosity, thermal conductivity and electric resistance $(1/\sigma)$ of the medium are so small that their effects, due to the dissipation of energy, on the propagation of perturbations may be neglected in a first approximation.† Then the perturbations will be propagated as undamped waves.‡

Omitting all dissipative terms, we can rewrite the fundamental equations (51.1)–(51.4) as

$$\operatorname{div} \mathbf{H} = 0, \tag{52.1}$$

$$\partial \mathbf{H}/\partial t = \mathbf{curl}\,(\mathbf{v} \times \mathbf{H}), \tag{52.2}$$

$$\partial \rho/\partial t + \operatorname{div}(\rho \mathbf{v}) = 0, \tag{52.3}$$

$$\frac{\partial \mathbf{v}}{\partial t} + (\mathbf{v}\cdot\mathbf{grad})\,\mathbf{v} = -\frac{\mathbf{grad}\,p}{\rho} + \frac{1}{4\pi\rho}(\mathbf{curl}\,\mathbf{H}) \times \mathbf{H}. \tag{52.4}$$

† It should be noted that, by putting $1/\sigma = 0$, we extend the range of frequencies in which the equations are applicable: the conditions that σ should exhibit no dispersion and should be independent of the magnetic field are now irrelevant.

‡ The condition for this approximation to be valid is that the wave damping coefficient (calculated in the Problem at the end of this section) should be small.

Equation (51.6) reduces to the equation of conservation of entropy (the condition for adiabatic flow). If the unperturbed medium is homogeneous, then this condition means that s = constant in the perturbed medium also, i.e. the flow is isentropic.

We write

$$\mathbf{H} = \mathbf{H}_0 + \mathbf{h}, \qquad \rho = \rho_0 + \rho', \qquad p = p_0 + p', \tag{52.5}$$

where the suffix 0 denotes the constant equilibrium value, and $\mathbf{h}$, ρ' and p' are the small variations in the wave. The velocity $\mathbf{v}$, which is zero in equilibrium, is a small quantity of the same order. Since the flow is isentropic, the changes in pressure and density are related by $p' = (\partial p/\partial \rho)_s \rho'$. But $(\partial p/\partial \rho)_s$ is the square of the velocity of sound, which we denote by u_0: $p' = u_0{}^2\rho'$. Neglecting terms of higher order than the first in equations (52.1)–(52.4), we obtain the linear equations

$$\left.\begin{aligned} \operatorname{div}\mathbf{h} = 0, \qquad \partial\mathbf{h}/\partial t &= \mathbf{curl}\,(\mathbf{v}\times\mathbf{H}),\\ \partial\rho'/\partial t + \rho\operatorname{div}\mathbf{v} &= 0,\\ \partial\mathbf{v}/\partial t &= -(u_0{}^2/\rho)\,\mathbf{grad}\,\rho' - (\mathbf{H}\times\mathbf{curl}\,\mathbf{h})/4\pi\rho. \end{aligned}\right\} \tag{52.6}$$

Here and in what follows we omit, for brevity, the suffix zero to the equilibrium values. For a perturbation periodic in time, the first of these equations follows from the second and can be omitted.

We shall seek solutions of these equations which are proportional to $\exp[i(\mathbf{k}\cdot\mathbf{r}-\omega t)]$, i.e. which describe the propagation of plane waves with wave vector $\mathbf{k}$ and frequency ω. The system of equations (52.6) then gives the algebraic equations

$$-\omega\mathbf{h} = \mathbf{k}\times(\mathbf{v}\times\mathbf{H}), \qquad \omega\rho' = \rho\mathbf{k}\cdot\mathbf{v},$$

$$-\omega\mathbf{v} + (u_0{}^2/\rho)\rho'\mathbf{k} = -\mathbf{H}\times(\mathbf{k}\times\mathbf{h})/4\pi\rho.$$

The first of these shows that the vector $\mathbf{h}$ is perpendicular to the wave vector $\mathbf{k}$, which we shall take to be along the x-axis, with the plane of $\mathbf{k}$ and $\mathbf{H}$ as the xy-plane. We also introduce the *phase velocity* of the wave, $u = \omega/k$. Eliminating ρ' from the third equation by means of the second equation, and rewriting the result in components, we have

$$uh_z = -v_zH_x, \qquad uv_z = -H_xh_z/4\pi\rho, \tag{52.7}$$

$$\begin{aligned} uh_y = v_xH_y - v_yH_x, \qquad uv_y &= -H_xh_y/4\pi\rho,\\ v_x\left(u - \frac{u_0{}^2}{u}\right) &= H_yh_y/4\pi\rho. \end{aligned} \tag{52.8}$$

We have here separated the equations into two groups, the first involving only h_z and v_z and the second only h_y, v_x and v_y. It therefore follows that perturbations of the two groups of variables are propagated independently. The density, and therefore the pressure, belong to the second group, since

$$\rho' = \rho v_x/u. \tag{52.9}$$

The compatibility condition for the two equations (52.7) is

$$u \equiv u_1 = H_x/\sqrt{(4\pi\rho)}. \tag{52.10}$$

In these waves the component h_z of the magnetic field which is perpendicular to the directions of propagation and of the constant field **H** oscillates, and with it the velocity v_z, which is related to h_z by

$$v_z = -h_z/\sqrt{(4\pi\rho)}. \tag{52.11}$$

The relation between ω and k (the *dispersion relation*, as it is called) given by (52.10) involves the direction of the wave vector:

$$\omega = \mathbf{H}\cdot\mathbf{k}/\sqrt{(4\pi\rho)}.$$

The physical velocity of propagation of the waves is called the *group velocity* and is given by the derivative $\partial\omega/\partial\mathbf{k}$. In the present case we have $\partial\omega/\partial\mathbf{k} = \mathbf{H}/\sqrt{(4\pi\rho)}$, which does not involve the direction of **k**. The direction of propagation of the wave, in the sense of the direction of its group velocity, is the direction of **H**.

Let us now consider waves described by equations (52.8). Equating to zero the determinant of these equations, we obtain

$$(u^2 - u_0{}^2)\left(u^2 - \frac{H_x{}^2}{4\pi\rho}\right) = \frac{u^2 H_y{}^2}{4\pi\rho}.$$

The roots of this quartic equation for u are†

$$u_{2,3} = \frac{1}{2}\left\{\sqrt{\left(u_0{}^2 + \frac{H^2}{4\pi\rho} + \frac{H_x u_0}{\sqrt{(\pi\rho)}}\right)} \pm \right.$$
$$\left. \pm \sqrt{\left(u_0{}^2 + \frac{H^2}{4\pi\rho} - \frac{H_x u_0}{\sqrt{(\pi\rho)}}\right)}\right\}. \tag{52.12}$$

Thus we obtain two more types of wave. In these waves the quantities h_y, v_x and v_y (and the density ρ') oscillate. The vectors **h** and **v** are in the plane of **H** and **k**.

In the limiting case where $H^2 \ll 4\pi\rho u_0{}^2$ we have $u_2 \cong u_0$, and it follows from equations (52.8) that $v_y \ll v_x$. In other words, in the limit waves of this type become ordinary sound waves propagated with velocity u_0. The weak transverse field in the wave is related to v_x by $h_y \cong v_x H_y/u_0$.

In the same limiting case, u_3 is the same as u_1 to a first approximation, and $v_x \cong 0$, $v_y \cong -h_y/\sqrt{(4\pi\rho)}$ as in a wave of the first type, but with the vectors **v** and **h** parallel to the plane of **k** and **H** instead of perpendicular to it.

We see also that in an incompressible fluid (corresponding formally to the limit $u_0 \to \infty$) only one type of wave occurs, with two independent directions of polarisation. The dispersion relation for these waves is given by

---

† The roots of the quartic equation $x^4 + px^2 + q = 0$ can be written

$$x = \pm\tfrac{1}{2}\{\sqrt{(-p+2\sqrt{q})} \pm \sqrt{(-p-2\sqrt{q})}\}.$$

formula (52.10); the vectors **v** and **h** are perpendicular to **k** and are related by

$$\mathbf{v} = -\mathbf{h}/\sqrt{(4\pi\rho)}. \tag{52.13}$$

Such waves were first discussed by H. ALFVÉN (1942).†

There is a simple interpretation of the result that, in a longitudinal magnetic field, transverse displacements of the fluid are propagated in the form of waves. We have seen at the end of §51 that the lines of magnetic force behave like fluid lines when $\sigma \to \infty$. The transverse displacement of the fluid particles results in a curvature of these lines, and therefore in their stretching and, at some points, in their compression. The forces in a magnetic field (expressed by the Maxwell stress tensor) are such as would occur if the lines of magnetic force tended to contract and also to repel one another.‡ Hence a curvature of the lines results in "quasi-elastic" forces which tend to straighten them, leading to further oscillations.

It is interesting that, in an incompressible fluid, the plane hydromagnetic wave given by formulae (52.10) and (52.13) is in fact an exact solution of the equations, valid for any transverse field **h** (not necessarily small). (This statement does not apply, however, to a superposition of several plane waves propagated in different directions.) For, let us return to the exact equations (52.1)–(52.4). In an incompressible fluid, equation (52.3) becomes div $\mathbf{v} = 0$. If we seek a solution in which all quantities depend on only one co-ordinate x and the time t, we find from this equation that v_x = constant, and by taking another system of co-ordinates moving uniformly in the x-direction we can put $v_x = 0$. From the equation div $\mathbf{H} = 0$ it follows that H_x = constant. Denoting the transverse components of **H** by **h**, we obtain from equations (52.2) and (52.4) (with $v_x = 0$) $\partial\mathbf{h}/\partial t = H_x\partial\mathbf{v}/\partial x$, $\partial\mathbf{v}/\partial t = (H_x/4\pi\rho)\partial\mathbf{h}/\partial x$, i.e. the exact equations necessarily reduce to the linear equations for a plane wave with the phase velocity (52.10), **v** and **h** being related by (52.13). The x-component of equation (52.4) is

$$\frac{1}{\rho}\frac{\partial p}{\partial x} + \frac{1}{4\pi\rho}\mathbf{h}\cdot\frac{\partial\mathbf{h}}{\partial x} = 0,$$

whence

$$p + h^2/8\pi = \text{constant}, \tag{52.14}$$

which gives the manner of variation of pressure in the wave.

Let us return to formulae (52.8) and (52.12), and consider the opposite limiting case, where $H^2 \gg 4\pi\rho u_0^2$. We then have, in the first approximation, $u_2 = H/\sqrt{(4\pi\rho)}$. Since this expression is independent of **k**, the group velocity is of magnitude u_2 and its direction is that of **k**. In this wave the

---

† They are sometimes called *hydromagnetic waves*. In the general case, where the magnetic fields are not small, the waves cannot be divided into hydromagnetic waves and ordinary sound waves.

‡ For, let a line of force be along the z-axis. Then the longitudinal stress Π_{zz} (51.8) contains a negative term $-H^2/8\pi$, and the transverse stresses Π_{xx} and Π_{yy} contain a positive term $H^2/8\pi$.

vector $\mathbf{v}$ is perpendicular to $\mathbf{H}$ (Fig. 28), and its magnitude is given in terms of $h = h_y$ by $v = h/\sqrt{(4\pi\rho)}$. For u_3 we have in this limiting case $u_3 = u_0 H_x/H$. The group velocity is $\partial\omega/\partial\mathbf{k} = u_0\mathbf{H}/H$. The vector $\mathbf{v}$ in this case is antiparallel to $\mathbf{H}$, and its magnitude is given by $v = hH^2/4\pi\rho u_0 H_y$.

When the relation between H^2 and ρu_0^2 is arbitrary, both u_2 and u_3 depend on the direction of the wave vector. When the angle between $\mathbf{k}$ and $\mathbf{H}$ increases, u_2 increases monotonically and u_3 decreases monotonically. It is easy to see that the inequalities

$$u_3 \leqslant u_1 \leqslant u_2, \qquad u_2 \geqslant u_0, \qquad u_3 \leqslant u_0 \tag{52.15}$$

always hold. If $\mathbf{k}$ is parallel to $\mathbf{H}$ ($H_y = 0$, $H_x = H$), u_2 and u_3 are respectively equal to the greater and the smaller of u_0 and $u_1 = H/\sqrt{(4\pi\rho)}$. If $\mathbf{k}$ is perpendicular to $\mathbf{H}$ ($H_x = 0$, $H_y = H$), then

$$u_2 = \sqrt{\left(u_0^2 + \frac{H^2}{4\pi\rho}\right)}, \tag{52.16}$$

while u_1 and u_3 are zero, i.e. only one type of wave exists.

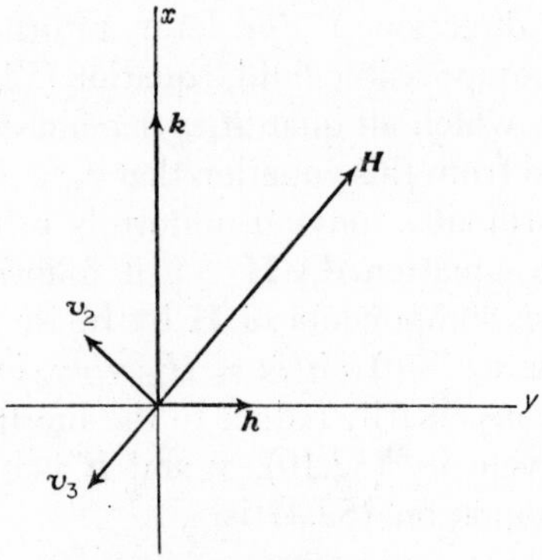

FIG. 28

In this last case it is possible to find exact solutions of the equations of magnetic fluid dynamics for a plane wave, without assuming its amplitude to be small (S. A. KAPLAN and K. P. STANYUKOVICH, 1954). When $H_x = 0$, $H_y = H$, equation (52.1) is satisfied identically, and equations (52.2)–(52.4) give

$$\partial H/\partial t + \partial(v_x H)/\partial x = 0, \tag{52.17}$$

$$\partial\rho/\partial t + \partial(v_x\rho)/\partial x = 0, \tag{52.18}$$

$$\frac{\partial v_x}{\partial t} + v_x\frac{\partial v_x}{\partial x} + \frac{1}{8\pi\rho}\frac{\partial H^2}{\partial x} = -\frac{1}{\rho}\frac{\partial p}{\partial x}. \tag{52.19}$$

From the first two of these equations it is easily seen that the ratio $H/\rho = b$ satisfies the equation $\partial b/\partial t + v_x \partial b/\partial x = 0$ or $\mathrm{d}b/\mathrm{d}t = 0$, where the total derivative signifies the rate of change in a given fluid particle as it moves about. Hence, if the fluid is homogeneous at some initial instant, so that b is constant, then at all subsequent instants we have†

$$H/\rho = b = \text{constant.} \tag{52.20}$$

Substituting in the third equation $H = \rho b$, we obtain

$$\frac{\partial v_x}{\partial t} + v_x \frac{\partial v_x}{\partial x} = -\frac{1}{\rho}\frac{\partial}{\partial x}\left(p + \frac{b^2}{8\pi}\rho^2\right). \tag{52.21}$$

Thus the magnetic field has been eliminated from the equations, and the problem reduces to the solution of equations (52.18) and (52.21). These equations differ from those for one-dimensional motion in ordinary fluid dynamics only by a change in the equation of state of the gas: the true pressure $p = p(\rho)$ (for given entropy s) must be replaced by $p^*(\rho) = p(\rho) + b^2\rho^2/8\pi$. This fact enables us to apply the results of ordinary fluid dynamics to this case of magnetic fluid flow. In particular, the formulae giving the exact solution for one-dimensional travelling waves (Riemann's solution)‡ can be applied, the velocity of sound being represented by

$$u^* = \sqrt{\left(\frac{\partial p^*}{\partial \rho}\right)_s} = \sqrt{\left(u_0^2 + \frac{b^2}{4\pi}\rho\right)}$$
$$= \sqrt{\left(u_0^2 + \frac{H^2}{4\pi\rho}\right)},$$

in accordance with formula (52.16).

PROBLEM

Determine the absorption coefficient (assumed small) for a hydromagnetic wave in an incompressible fluid.

SOLUTION. The absorption coefficient for a wave is defined as $\gamma = \bar{Q}/2\bar{q}$, where $\bar{Q}$ is the (time) average energy dissipated per unit time and volume, and $\bar{q}$ is the mean energy flux density in the wave. The amplitude of the wave decreases as $e^{-\gamma x}$ during its propagation. Q is given by the right-hand side of equation (51.6); in an incompressible fluid we have for a wave propagated in the x-direction (and so $v_x = 0$)

$$Q = \eta(\partial \mathbf{v}/\partial x)^2 + (c^2/16\pi^2\sigma)(\partial \mathbf{h}/\partial x)^2.$$

In the energy flux density (51.9), we can omit the small dissipative terms, leaving $q_x = -H_x\mathbf{h}\cdot\mathbf{v}/4\pi$. Using formulae (52.10) and (52.13), we have the result

$$\gamma = \frac{\omega^2}{2u_1^3}\left(\frac{\eta}{\rho} + \frac{c^2}{4\pi\sigma}\right).$$

---

† In accordance with the general results (§51) concerning the relation between H/ρ and "fluid" lines of force, if we take into account the invariability of the length of these lines with time in the present case.

‡ See *Fluid Mechanics*, §94.

§53. Tangential and rotational discontinuities

The equations of motion for an "ideal" magnetic fluid (having zero viscosity, thermal conductivity and electric resistance) admit discontinuous flows as in ordinary fluid dynamics. To elucidate the conditions which must be satisfied on a surface of discontinuity, let us consider an element of the surface and use a system of co-ordinates in which it is at rest.†

First of all, the mass flux must be continuous at a surface of discontinuity: the mass of fluid entering from one side must be equal to the mass leaving on the other side. Thus $\rho_1 v_{1n} = \rho_2 v_{2n}$, where the suffixes 1 and 2 refer to the two sides of the discontinuity, and the suffix n denotes the component of a vector normal to the surface. In what follows we shall denote the difference between the values of any quantity on the two sides of the surface of discontinuity by enclosing it in square brackets. Thus $[\rho v_n] = 0$.

Next, the energy flux must be continuous. Using the expression (51.9) and omitting the dissipative terms, we obtain

$$[q_n] = [\rho v_n(\tfrac{1}{2}v^2 + w) + v_n H^2/4\pi - H_n \mathbf{v}\cdot\mathbf{H}/4\pi] = 0.$$

The momentum flux must also be continuous. This condition means that $[\Pi_{ik}n_k] = 0$, where Π_{ik} is the momentum flux density tensor, and $\mathbf{n}$ is a unit vector normal to the surface. Using (51.8), we therefore have

$$[p + \rho v_n^2 + (\mathbf{H}_t^2 - H_n^2)/8\pi] = 0,$$
$$[\rho v_n \mathbf{v}_t - H_n \mathbf{H}_t/4\pi] = 0,$$

where the suffix t denotes the component tangential to the surface.

Finally, the normal component of the magnetic field and the tangential component of the electric field must be continuous. If the conductivity of the medium is infinite, the induced electric field is given by $\mathbf{E} = -\mathbf{v}\times\mathbf{H}/c$, and the condition $[\mathbf{E}_t] = 0$ leads to $[H_n \mathbf{v}_t - \mathbf{H}_t v_n] = 0$.

In what follows it is more convenient to use the specific volume of the fluid ($V = 1/\rho$) in place of its density. The mass flux density through the discontinuity is denoted by $j = \rho v_n = v_n/V$.

Since j and H_n are continuous, we can write the remaining boundary conditions in the following form:

$$j[w + \tfrac{1}{2}j^2V^2 + \tfrac{1}{2}\mathbf{v}_t^2 + V\mathbf{H}_t^2/4\pi] = H_n[\mathbf{H}_t\cdot\mathbf{v}_t]/4\pi, \tag{53.1}$$

$$[p] + j^2[V] + [\mathbf{H}_t^2]/8\pi = 0, \tag{53.2}$$

$$j[\mathbf{v}_t] = H_n[\mathbf{H}_t]/4\pi, \tag{53.3}$$

$$H_n[\mathbf{v}_t] = j[V\mathbf{H}_t]. \tag{53.4}$$

This is the fundamental system of equations of discontinuities in magnetic fluid dynamics.

† This condition fixes only the velocity of the co-ordinate system in the direction norma to the surface. Any constant vector may be added to its tangential velocity.

In ordinary fluid dynamics, discontinuities of two entirely different kinds are possible: shock waves and tangential discontinuities.† Mathematically, the two types occur because some of the boundary conditions can be written as the vanishing of a product of two factors, and the two different solutions are obtained by equating the factors to zero in turn. This feature is not present in magnetic fluid dynamics, and it might therefore be supposed that only one type of discontinuity occurs. In reality, however, it is found that essentially different types of discontinuity again occur (F. DE HOFFMANN and E. TELLER, 1950).

Let us consider, first of all, discontinuities for which $j = 0$. This means that $v_{1n} = v_{2n} = 0$, i.e. the fluid moves parallel to the surface of discontinuity. If $H_n \neq 0$, we see from equations (53.1)–(53.4) that the velocity, pressure and magnetic field must be continuous. The density (and therefore the entropy, temperature, etc.) may have any discontinuity. Such a surface may be called a *contact discontinuity*, and is simply the boundary between two media at rest which have different densities and temperatures.

If both j and H_n are zero, then three of the four equations (53.1)–(53.4) are satisfied identically, and therefore this is clearly a special case. We thus find a type of discontinuity which may be called a *tangential discontinuity*, as in ordinary fluid dynamics. At such a discontinuity the velocity and the magnetic field are tangential and can have any discontinuity in both magnitude and direction:

$$j = 0, \qquad H_n = 0, \qquad [\mathbf{v}_t] \neq 0, \qquad [\mathbf{H}_t] \neq 0. \tag{53.5}$$

The density discontinuity also can take any value, but the pressure discontinuity is related to that of $\mathbf{H}_t$ by equation (53.2):

$$[V] \neq 0, \qquad \left[p + \frac{\mathbf{H}_t^2}{8\pi}\right] = 0. \tag{53.6}$$

The discontinuities of the other thermodynamic quantities (entropy, temperature, etc.) are related to those of V and p by the equation of state.

Another type of discontinuity is one in which the fluid density is continuous. Since the flux $j = v_n/V$ is continuous, the normal velocity component is therefore continuous also:

$$j \neq 0, \qquad [V] = 0, \qquad [v_n] = 0. \tag{53.7}$$

On the right-hand side of equation (53.4) we can take V outside the brackets and divide this equation by equation (53.3), obtaining

$$j = H_n/\sqrt{(4\pi V)} \tag{53.8}$$

and

$$[\mathbf{v}_t] = \sqrt{(V/4\pi)}[\mathbf{H}_t]. \tag{53.9}$$

† See *Fluid Mechanics*, §81.

In equation (53.1) we put $w = \epsilon + pV$; since V is continuous, this equation can be rewritten as

$$j[\epsilon] + jV\left[p + \frac{\mathbf{H}_t^2}{8\pi}\right] + \tfrac{1}{2}j\left[\left(\mathbf{v}_t - \sqrt{\frac{V}{4\pi}}\mathbf{H}_t\right)^2\right] = 0,$$

H_n being replaced in accordance with (53.8). The second term is zero by (53.2) and the third term is zero by (53.9), so that we find $[\epsilon] = 0$, i.e. the internal energy also is continuous. Every other thermodynamic quantity is determined if ϵ and V are given. Hence all the other thermodynamic quantities, including the pressure, are continuous. It then follows from (53.2) that $\mathbf{H}_t^2$ is continuous, i.e.

$$[p] = 0, \qquad [H_t] = 0. \tag{53.10}$$

The fact that H_t and H_n are both continuous means that the magnitude of $\mathbf{H}$ itself and its angle to the surface are likewise continuous.

Formulae (53.7)–(53.10) give all the properties of the discontinuities under consideration. The thermodynamic quantities are continuous, but the magnetic field is turned through an angle about the normal, its magnitude remaining unchanged. The vector $\mathbf{H}_t$, and therefore (by (53.9)) the tangential velocity component, are discontinuous, but the normal velocity component $v_n = jV$ is continuous, and its value is

$$v_n = H_n\sqrt{(V/4\pi)} = H_n/\sqrt{(4\pi\rho)}. \tag{53.11}$$

We shall call these *rotational discontinuities*.

It is useful to note that, by a suitable choice of the co-ordinate system, we can always ensure that the fluid velocity is parallel to the field on each side of a rotational discontinuity. To achieve this, we use a co-ordinate system moving with velocity $\mathbf{v}_{1t} - \mathbf{H}_{1t}\sqrt{(V/4\pi)} = \mathbf{v}_{2t} - \mathbf{H}_{2t}\sqrt{(V/4\pi)}$. (Compare the first footnote to this section.) In the new system the ratio of each component of $\mathbf{v}$ to the corresponding component of $\mathbf{H}$ on either side of the discontinuity is $\sqrt{(V/4\pi)}$, i.e.

$$\mathbf{v}_1 = \mathbf{H}_1\sqrt{(V/4\pi)}, \qquad \mathbf{v}_2 = \mathbf{H}_2\sqrt{(V/4\pi)}. \tag{53.12}$$

Thus in this system of co-ordinates the velocity is rotated with the magnetic field, its magnitude and angle to the normal remaining unchanged.

The velocity v_n is also minus the velocity of propagation of the discontinuity relative to the fluid. This is equal to the phase velocity u_1 of one of the three types of hydromagnetic wave (§52). The occurrence of this equality for all rotational discontinuities is to some extent accidental, but when the discontinuities of the various quantities are small the equality must hold. For such a discontinuity is a weak perturbation, in which the velocity $\mathbf{v}$ and the magnetic field $\mathbf{H}$ receive small increments perpendicular to the plane through $\mathbf{H}$ and the normal $\mathbf{n}$. This perturbation is of the type whose phase velocity is u_1. The physical velocity of propagation of the front of a small perturbation is the normal component of the group velocity, i.e. its component in the direction of the vector **k**. Since the relation between ω and **k** is linear, we have $\mathbf{k}\cdot\partial\omega/\partial\mathbf{k} = \omega$, and so this component is the same as the phase velocity $\omega/k = u_1$.

Although tangential and rotational discontinuities form two different types, there are also discontinuities having the properties of both. These discontinuities are such that **v** and **H** are tangential in direction and continuous in magnitude.

In ordinary fluid dynamics, tangential discontinuities are always unstable with respect to infinitesimal perturbations, and so are rapidly broadened into turbulent regions. A magnetic field, however, has a stabilising effect on the motion of a conducting fluid, and in this case tangential discontinuities may be stable. This result is a natural consequence of the fact that a perturbation involving fluid displacements transverse to the field leads to a stretching of the lines of magnetic force "frozen" in it, and therefore to the appearance of forces which tend to restore the unperturbed flow. An investigation of such discontinuities in an incompressible fluid by S. I. Syrovatskiĭ (1953) has given the following two inequalities, which must both be satisfied if the discontinuity is stable:

$$\begin{aligned} H_1^2 + H_2^2 &> 2\pi\rho v^2, \\ (\mathbf{H}_1 \times \mathbf{H}_2)^2 &\geqslant 2\pi\rho\{(\mathbf{H}_1 \times \mathbf{v})^2 + (\mathbf{H}_2 \times \mathbf{v})^2\}, \end{aligned} \tag{53.13}$$

where $\mathbf{v} = \mathbf{v}_2 - \mathbf{v}_1$ is the discontinuity of the velocity; see Problem 1.†

In reality, however, the existence of a small but finite viscosity and electric resistance in the fluid means that such tangential discontinuities cannot exist indefinitely, even if the conditions (53.13) are fulfilled. Although no turbulence occurs, the sharp discontinuity is replaced by a gradually widening transitional region, in which the velocity and the magnetic field change smoothly from one value to another. This is easily seen from the equations of motion (51.12) and (51.13) if the dissipative terms are retained. We take the x-axis in the direction of the normal to the discontinuity. Assuming all quantities to depend on x (and possibly on the time), we can write the transverse components of these equations as

$$\begin{aligned} \partial\mathbf{H}_t/\partial t &= (c^2/4\pi\sigma)\, \partial^2\mathbf{H}_t/\partial x^2, \\ \partial\mathbf{v}_t/\partial t &= \nu\partial^2\mathbf{v}_t/\partial x^2, \end{aligned} \tag{53.14}$$

the fluid being supposed incompressible. If we assume steady flow, the left-hand sides of equations (53.14) are zero, and the only solution which remains finite as $x \to \pm\infty$ is $\mathbf{H}_t$ = constant, $\mathbf{v}_t$ = constant, which contradicts the assumption that these quantities undergo a change at the discontinuity. Thus a tangential discontinuity cannot have a constant width such as is found for (e.g.) a weak shock wave. Equations (53.14) are heat-conduction

† If the densities of the incompressible fluids on the two sides of the discontinuity are different, then ρ in these inequalities must be replaced by $2\rho_1\rho_2/(\rho_1+\rho_2)$.

equations. As we know from the theory of thermal conduction, a discontinuity in a quantity satisfying such an equation is gradually smoothed out into a transitional region, whose width increases as the square root of the time. Since the coefficients in the two equations (53.14) are different, the widths δ_v and δ_H of the transitional regions for the velocity and the magnetic field are also different:

$$\delta_v \sim \sqrt{(\nu t)}, \qquad \delta_H = \sqrt{(c^2 t/\sigma)}. \tag{53.15}$$

Rotational discontinuities in an incompressible fluid are stable with respect to infinitesimal perturbations, whatever the strength of the magnetic field (S. I. Syrovatskiĭ, 1953). Like tangential discontinuities, however, they cannot have constant widths, but are gradually smoothed out by the viscosity and electric resistance of the fluid (see Problem 2).

PROBLEMS

Problem 1. Derive the condition for the stability of a tangential discontinuity in an incompressible perfectly conducting non-viscous fluid in a magnetic field (S. I. Syrovatskiĭ).

Solution.† We write $\mathbf{v} = \mathbf{v}_0 + \mathbf{v}'$, $p = p_0 + p'$, $\mathbf{H} = \mathbf{H}_0 + \mathbf{H}'$, where $\mathbf{v}_0$, p_0 and $\mathbf{H}_0$ are the constant (on each side of the discontinuity) unperturbed values, and $\mathbf{v}'$, p' and $\mathbf{H}'$ are small perturbations. Substituting in equations (51.11)–(51.13), we have for an ideal fluid

$$\operatorname{div} \mathbf{u}' = 0, \qquad \operatorname{div} \mathbf{v}' = 0, \tag{1}$$

$$\partial \mathbf{u}'/\partial t = (\mathbf{u}\cdot\mathbf{grad})\mathbf{v}' - (\mathbf{v}\cdot\mathbf{grad})\mathbf{u}' \tag{2}$$

$$\begin{aligned}\frac{\partial \mathbf{v}'}{\partial t} + (\mathbf{v}\cdot\mathbf{grad})\mathbf{v}' &= -\frac{1}{\rho}\,\mathbf{grad}\, p' - \mathbf{u}\times\mathbf{curl}\,\mathbf{u}' \\ &= -\frac{1}{\rho}\,\mathbf{grad}\,(p' + \rho\mathbf{u}\cdot\mathbf{u}') + (\mathbf{u}\cdot\mathbf{grad})\mathbf{u}',\end{aligned} \tag{3}$$

where for brevity we have omitted the suffix 0 and put $\mathbf{u} \equiv \mathbf{H}/\sqrt{(4\pi\rho)}$. We take the divergence of equation (3) and use (1), obtaining

$$\triangle(p' + \rho\mathbf{u}\cdot\mathbf{u}') = 0. \tag{4}$$

Let $x = 0$ be the plane of the discontinuity, to which the vectors $\mathbf{v}$ and $\mathbf{u}$ are parallel. In each of the half-spaces $x > 0$ and $x < 0$ we seek all quantities $\mathbf{v}'$, $\mathbf{u}'$, p' in a form proportional to $\exp\{i(\mathbf{k}\cdot\mathbf{r} - \omega t) + \kappa x\}$, where $\mathbf{k}$ is a vector in the yz-plane. From equation (4) we find that $k^2 - \kappa^2 = 0$, so that we must put $\kappa = k$ for $x < 0$ and $\kappa = -k$ for $x > 0$. We eliminate v'_x from the x-components of equations (2) and (3), obtaining‡

$$p' + \rho\mathbf{u}\cdot\mathbf{u}' = -u'_x \frac{i\rho}{\mathbf{k}\cdot\mathbf{u}\kappa}\{(\omega - \mathbf{k}\cdot\mathbf{v})^2 - (\mathbf{k}\cdot\mathbf{u})^2\}. \tag{5}$$

Let $\zeta = \zeta(y, z, t)$ be the displacement of the surface of discontinuity in the x-direction due to the perturbation. The conditions (53.5) and (53.6) must hold on the displaced surface:

$$\left.\begin{aligned} [p + \rho(\mathbf{u}+\mathbf{u}')^2] &\cong [p' + \rho\mathbf{u}\cdot\mathbf{u}'] = 0, \\ u_{n1} + u'_{n1} &\cong u'_{x1} - \mathbf{u}_1\cdot\mathbf{grad}\,\zeta = 0, \\ u_{n2} + u'_{n2} &\cong u'_{x2} - \mathbf{u}_2\cdot\mathbf{grad}\,\zeta = 0; \end{aligned}\right\} \tag{6}$$

† Cf. *Fluid Mechanics*, §30.

‡ The case where the expression in braces vanishes is of no interest, since ω is then real, whereas instability can occur only for complex ω.

the condition of zero mass flux through the surface is satisfied automatically. Putting $\zeta = \text{constant} \times \exp\{i(\mathbf{k}\cdot\mathbf{r}-\omega t)\}$ and eliminating ζ, u_{x1} and u_{x2} from the three equations (6), we obtain an equation giving the possible values of ω:

$$(\omega-\mathbf{k}\cdot\mathbf{v}_1)^2+(\omega-\mathbf{k}\cdot\mathbf{v}_2)^2 = (\mathbf{k}\cdot\mathbf{u}_1)^2+(\mathbf{k}\cdot\mathbf{u}_2)^2.$$

This quadratic equation has no complex root if

$$2(\mathbf{k}\cdot\mathbf{u}_1)^2+2(\mathbf{k}\cdot\mathbf{u}_2)^2-\{\mathbf{k}\cdot(\mathbf{v}_2-\mathbf{v}_1)\}^2 > 0,$$

or

$$\{2u_{1i}u_{1k}+2u_{2i}u_{2k}-(v_{2i}-v_{1i})(v_{2k}-v_{1k})\}k_ik_k > 0.$$

This quadratic form is positive-definite if the trace and determinant of the tensor of rank two in the braces are both positive, and hence we obtain the conditions (53.13).

PROBLEM 2. Find the manner of widening of a rotational discontinuity with time.

SOLUTION. Assuming all quantities to depend only on the co-ordinate x (and on the time), we find from the equations div $\mathbf{v} = 0$ and div $\mathbf{H} = 0$ that v_x = constant and H_x = constant. Let the co-ordinate system be such that the values of $\mathbf{v}$ and $\mathbf{H}$ on each side of the discontinuity (outside the transitional layer) are related by (53.12). Then $v_x = u_x$, where $\mathbf{u}$ has the same meaning as in Problem 1. For the transverse components $\mathbf{u}_t$ and $\mathbf{v}_t$ we have from equations (51.12) and (51.13)

$$\begin{aligned} \frac{\partial \mathbf{u}_t}{\partial t}+u_x\frac{\partial \mathbf{u}_t}{\partial x} &= u_x\frac{\partial \mathbf{v}_t}{\partial x}+\frac{c^2}{4\pi\sigma}\frac{\partial^2 \mathbf{u}_t}{\partial x^2}, \\ \frac{\partial \mathbf{v}_t}{\partial t}+u_x\frac{\partial \mathbf{v}_t}{\partial x} &= u_x\frac{\partial \mathbf{u}_t}{\partial x}+\nu\frac{\partial^2 \mathbf{v}_t}{\partial x^2}. \end{aligned} \qquad (1)$$

Since the difference $\mathbf{v}_t-\mathbf{u}_t$ tends to zero for $x \to \pm\infty$, because of the relations (53.12), this difference must be small in the transitional layer in comparison with the sum $\mathbf{v}_t+\mathbf{u}_t$. Adding the equations (1), we can therefore neglect a term in $\mathbf{v}_t-\mathbf{u}_t$, obtaining

$$\frac{\partial}{\partial t}(\mathbf{v}_t+\mathbf{u}_t) = \frac{1}{2}\left(\frac{c^2}{4\pi\sigma}+\nu\right)\frac{\partial^2}{\partial x^2}(\mathbf{v}_t+\mathbf{u}_t).$$

From this we see that the width of the discontinuity varies in a manner given by

$$\delta \sim \sqrt{\left\{\left(\frac{c^2}{4\pi\sigma}+\nu\right)t\right\}}.$$

§54. Shock waves

Let us now consider the type of discontinuity in which

$$j \neq 0, \qquad [V] \neq 0. \qquad (54.1)$$

Such discontinuities are called *shock waves*, as in ordinary fluid dynamics. They are characterised by a discontinuity of density and by the fact that the gas moves through them (v_{n1} and v_{n2} being non-zero). The normal component of the magnetic field may or may not be zero.

On comparing equations (53.3) and (53.4) we see that, when $H_n \neq 0$, the vectors $\mathbf{H}_{t2}-\mathbf{H}_{t1}$ and $V_2\mathbf{H}_{t2}-V_1\mathbf{H}_{t1}$ are parallel to the same vector $\mathbf{v}_{2t}-\mathbf{v}_{1t}$, and therefore to each other. Hence it follows that $\mathbf{H}_{t1}$ and $\mathbf{H}_{t2}$ are parallel, i.e. the vectors $\mathbf{H}_1$, $\mathbf{H}_2$ and the normal to the surface are coplanar, unlike what happens (in general) in tangential and rotational discontinuities. This result holds also when $H_n = 0$; in this case, which we shall discuss later, it follows from (53.4) that $V_1\mathbf{H}_{t1} = V_2\mathbf{H}_{t2}$.

The velocity discontinuity $\mathbf{v}_{t1}-\mathbf{v}_{t2}$ lies in the same plane as $\mathbf{H}_1$ and $\mathbf{H}_2$. We can evidently, without loss of generality, assume that the vectors $\mathbf{v}_1$ and $\mathbf{v}_2$ themselves lie in this plane, so that the motion in the shock wave is two-dimensional. Furthermore, it is easy to see that, if $H_n \neq 0$, a suitable transformation of the co-ordinates will always ensure that the vectors $\mathbf{v}$ and $\mathbf{H}$ are parallel on each side of the discontinuity. To achieve this, we use a co-ordinate system which moves with velocity $\mathbf{v}_t-(v_n/H_n)\mathbf{H}_t = \mathbf{v}_t-(jV/H_n)\mathbf{H}_t$ (the value of this expression is the same on each side of the discontinuity, by (53.4)). In the following formulae, however, the choice of this particular co-ordinate system is not implied.

Let us derive the relation for shock waves in magnetic gas dynamics which corresponds to the shock adiabatic (Hugoniot adiabatic) in ordinary gas dynamics. Eliminating $[\mathbf{v}_t]$ from (53.3) and (53.4) we have

$$j^2[VH_t] = H_n^2[H_t]/4\pi; \tag{54.2}$$

here we have replaced $\mathbf{H}_t$ by H_t, since $\mathbf{H}_{t1}$ and $\mathbf{H}_{t2}$ are parallel. In order to eliminate $[\mathbf{v}_t]$ from equation (53.1), we rewrite that equation as

$$[w] + \tfrac{1}{2}j^2[V^2] + \tfrac{1}{2}\left[\left(\mathbf{v}_t - \frac{H_n}{4\pi j}\mathbf{H}_t\right)^2\right] + $$
$$+ [VH_t^2]/4\pi - H_n^2[H_t^2]/32\pi^2 j^2 = 0.$$

The third term is zero by equation (53.3) and so $\mathbf{v}_t$ does not appear. In the last term we substitute j^2 from (54.2) and in the second term from (53.2), i.e.

$$j^2 = \{p_2 - p_1 + (H_{t2}^2 - H_{t1}^2)/8\pi\}/(V_1 - V_2). \tag{54.3}$$

A simple calculation then gives

$$\epsilon_2 - \epsilon_1 + \tfrac{1}{2}(p_2 + p_1)(V_2 - V_1) +$$
$$+ (V_2 - V_1)(H_{t2} - H_{t1})^2/16\pi = 0. \tag{54.4}$$

This is the equation of the shock adiabatic in magnetic gas dynamics. It differs from the ordinary equation by the presence of the third term.

We may also write out again equation (53.3), which gives the discontinuity of v_t in terms of that of H_t:

$$v_{t2} - v_{t1} = H_n(H_{t2} - H_{t1})/4\pi j. \tag{54.5}$$

Equations (54.2)–(54.5) form a complete system of equations of shock waves. As the discontinuities of all quantities tend to zero, the velocity of propagation of the shock wave must tend to its value for small perturbations. In ordinary gas dynamics this means that the velocity of a weak shock wave tends to the velocity of sound. In magnetic gas dynamics, however, there are two different velocities u_2 and u_3 with which weak shock waves can be propagated.†

† The velocity u_1 is, as mentioned in §53, the velocity of propagation of perturbations corresponding to rotational discontinuities.

Let us consider weak shock waves in more detail, and ascertain in which direction the various quantities change in them. Expanding equation (54.4) in powers of the discontinuities of pressure and entropy, we obtain†

$$T(s_2 - s_1) = \frac{1}{12}\left(\frac{\partial^2 V}{\partial p^2}\right)_s (p_2 - p_1)^3 - \\ - \frac{1}{16\pi}\left(\frac{\partial V}{\partial p}\right)_s (p_2 - p_1)(H_{t2} - H_{t1})^2. \qquad (54.6)$$

When the gas passes through the shock wave, its entropy can only increase: $s_2 > s_1$. By an inequality of thermodynamics, we have $(\partial V/\partial p)_s < 0$, and the derivative $(\partial^2 V/\partial p^2)_s$ is in fact positive for all the substances in question here. Hence we see from (54.6) that the inequality $s_2 > s_1$ implies that $p_2 > p_1$, and therefore $V_2 < V_1$. Thus we have a compression wave, as in ordinary gas dynamics. This result, which we have proved for weak shock waves, seems to hold for shock waves of any intensity.

For weak shock waves we can also derive certain results concerning the direction of variation of the magnetic field. The changes in the various quantities when the state of the gas undergoes a slight perturbation are related by formulae (52.8) and (52.9). The changes $\delta\rho = \rho_2 - \rho_1$ and $\delta(H_t^2) = H_{t2}^2 - H_{t1}^2$ are such that $\delta(H_t^2) = 8\pi(u^2 - u_0^2)\delta\rho$. Since $u_2 > u_0$ and $u_3 < u_0$ (see (52.15)), and from the above we necessarily have $\delta\rho > 0$, we see that the quantities H_t^2, and therefore $H^2 = H_t^2 + H_n^2$, vary in opposite directions in the two kinds of weak shock wave. The magnetic field is increased in a shock moving with velocity $\sim u_2$, but it is reduced in one moving with velocity $\sim u_3$.

Let us now consider shock waves in weak magnetic fields, i.e. assume that $H^2 \ll \rho u^2$ on either side of the discontinuity. No restriction is placed on the discontinuity of any quantity; in particular, the discontinuity in the magnetic field may be comparable with the magnitude of that field.

There are again two possibilities. If the discontinuities of density and pressure are not small, we can neglect, in a first approximation, the last term in equation (54.4) and the magnetic field in formula (54.3). We thereby return to the formulae of ordinary fluid dynamics. Thus the relation between the discontinuities of the various thermodynamic quantities, and the rate of propagation of the shock, will be the same as for ordinary shock waves. The change in the magnetic field can be found from the relation (54.2). Since the right-hand side of this equation is of the third order of smallness with respect to the field, the same must be true of the left-hand side. As a first approximation we can put $[VH_t] = V_2 H_{t2} - V_1 H_{t1} \simeq 0$, whence $H_{t2}/H_{t1} = V_1/V_2 = \rho_2/\rho_1$. Since in an ordinary shock wave we always have $V_1 > V_2$ we see that the magnetic field is strengthened in a shock of this type.

† See *Fluid Mechanics*, §83.

Equations (54.2)–(54.4) admit also another type of solution. The assumption that the field is small is also compatible with equation (54.2) for a wave in which $V_1 \cong V_2$ and j^2 is the second-order quantity

$$j^2 = H_n^2/4\pi V, \tag{54.7}$$

where V is the common value of V_1 and V_2. It is seen from equation (54.3) that if we put $V_1 = V_2$, we must to the same approximation put

$$p_2 - p_1 = -(H_{t2}^2 - H_{t1}^2)/8\pi. \tag{54.8}$$

The continuity of the density means that a shock wave of this type can be regarded as a discontinuity in an incompressible fluid. The vector $\mathbf{H}_t$ (and therefore $\mathbf{v}_t$) has a discontinuity in magnitude but not in direction, and the discontinuity of pressure is given in terms of that of the magnetic field by formula (54.8) when the density is continuous. The rate of propagation of the discontinuity is $v_{n2} = v_{n1} = jV = H_n\sqrt{(V/4\pi)}$. This is a natural result, and the necessity for the existence of such discontinuities could have been foreseen. We saw in §52 that, in an incompressible fluid, there is only one velocity of propagation of small perturbations of the magnetic field, namely $\mathbf{H}/\sqrt{(4\pi\rho)}$. Hence the fronts of small perturbations move with velocity $u_1 = H_n/\sqrt{(4\pi\rho)}$, whether the change $\delta\mathbf{H}$ in the field is parallel or perpendicular to the plane of $\mathbf{H}$ and $\mathbf{n}$. The latter case corresponds to weak rotational discontinuities (already discussed in §53) and the former, when the discontinuities are small, is the type just considered.

To ascertain the direction of variation of the magnetic field strength in such discontinuities, we return to equation (54.4), which has not yet been used, and rewrite it in the form (54.6), in whose derivation the discontinuity in the magnetic field was not assumed small compared with that field itself. Substituting $p_2 - p_1$ from (54.8), we find that the second term on the right of (54.6) is of the fourth order in the field, whereas the first term is of the sixth order and may be omitted. It follows at once from the condition $s_2 > s_1$ that $H_{t2} < H_{t1}$, i.e. that the magnetic field is weakened in such a discontinuity.

Returning now to shock waves of any intensity in magnetic fields of any strength, we may consider two particular cases. Let the magnetic field in medium 1 be perpendicular to the shock wave front, i.e. $\mathbf{H}_{t1} = 0$. Then equation (54.2) becomes $j^2 V_2 H_{t2} = H_n^2 H_{t2}/4\pi$. Hence it follows that either $H_{t2} = 0$, or $j^2 = H_n^2/4\pi V_2$ with no restriction on H_{t2}. In the former case the magnetic field remains perpendicular to the surface of the discontinuity, and does not affect the properties of the shock wave, since it does not appear in the equations. In the second alternative we have a shock wave in which the field changes direction, propagated with velocity $v_{n2} = jV_2 = H_n/\sqrt{(4\pi\rho_2)}$ relative to the gas behind it.

Another particular case is a shock wave parallel to the field on either side of it ($H_n = 0$).† From (54.5) we then have $\mathbf{v}_{t2} = \mathbf{v}_{t1}$, i.e. the tangential

† For $H_n = 0$ there is only one type of shock wave, in accordance with the fact that u_3 is zero. The shock waves corresponding to u_3 become weak tangential discontinuities at rest relative to the fluid.

velocity component is continuous. By a suitable choice of co-ordinates therefore, we can always ensure that $v_t = 0$ on either side of the discontinuity, i.e. the gas moves perpendicularly to the discontinuity, and we shall henceforth assume this. From equation (54.2) we have $V_2H_2 = V_1H_1$. This relation shows that equations (54.3) and (54.4) can be written

$$j^2 = (p_2^* - p_1^*)/(V_1 - V_2), \quad \epsilon_2^* - \epsilon_1^* + \tfrac{1}{2}(p_2^* + p_1^*)(V_2 - V_1) = 0,$$

which differ from the ordinary equations for shock waves in the absence of a magnetic field only by a change in the equation of state: the true equation of state $p = p(V, s)$ must be replaced by $p^* = p^*(V, s)$, where $p^* = p + b^2/8\pi V^2$, and b denotes the constant product HV. Accordingly ϵ^* must be defined so as to satisfy the thermodynamic relation $(\partial\epsilon^*/\partial V)_s = -p^*$, whence $\epsilon^* = \epsilon + b^2/8\pi V$.

It has been shown in §53 that there are discontinuities which exhibit the properties of both tangential and rotational discontinuities. The discontinuities discussed here are related in this way to shock waves also. The transition between shock waves and rotational discontinuities is formed by a discontinuity in which there is no change in density and the only change in the magnetic field is that $\mathbf{H}_t$ is reversed. The transition between shock waves and tangential discontinuities is formed by discontinuities in which $v_n = 0$, $H_n = 0$, and $\mathbf{H}_t$ has any discontinuity in magnitude but none in direction.

We may summarise as follows the discontinuities discussed in §§53–4:

(1) *Contact discontinuities*:

$$j = 0, \quad [\mathbf{v}_t] = 0, \quad [V] \neq 0, \quad [p] = 0, \quad H_n \neq 0, \quad [\mathbf{H}_t] = 0.$$

(2) *Tangential discontinuities*:

$$j = 0, \quad [\mathbf{v}_t] \neq 0, \quad [V] \neq 0, \quad \left[p + \frac{H_t^2}{8\pi}\right] = 0, \quad H_n = 0, \quad [\mathbf{H}_t] \neq 0.$$

(3) *Rotational discontinuities*:

$$j \neq 0, \quad [\mathbf{v}_t] \neq 0, \quad [V] = 0, \quad [p] = 0, \quad H_n \neq 0,$$

$\mathbf{H}_t$ changes direction but not magnitude.

(4) *Shock waves*:

$j \neq 0$, $[V] \neq 0$, $\mathbf{H}_1$, $\mathbf{H}_2$ and $\mathbf{n}$ coplanar.

The following diagram shows the possible transitional cases:

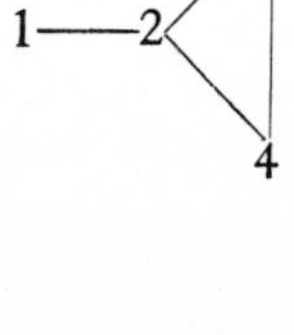

§55. The spontaneous magnetic field in turbulent motion of a conducting fluid

Turbulent motion of a conducting fluid has the remarkable property that it may lead to spontaneous magnetic fields which are quite strong. There are always small perturbations in a conducting fluid, resulting from causes extraneous to the fluid motion itself,† and accompanied by very weak electric and magnetic fields. The question is whether these perturbations are, on the average, amplified or damped by the turbulent motion in the course of time. The following arguments show that either may occur, depending on the properties of the fluid itself.‡

The manner of variation with time of magnetic field perturbations, once they have arisen, is determined by two physical agencies. The dissipation of magnetic energy, which is converted into the Joule heat of the induced currents, tends to diminish the field. The magnetic field tends to increase, on the other hand, by the purely magnetic effect of the "stretching" of the lines of force. We have shown at the end of §51 that, when a fluid of sufficiently high conductivity is in motion, the lines of magnetic force move as fluid lines, and the magnetic field varies proportionally to the stretching at each point on each line of force. In turbulent motion any two neighbouring particles move apart, on the average, in the course of time. As a result, the lines of force are stretched and the magnetic field is strengthened.

We shall show that in certain conditions these two opposite tendencies may balance, and this will provide a criterion distinguishing the cases where the magnetic field perturbations increase from those where they are damped.

While the magnetic field resulting from the motion remains weak its reciprocal effect on the motion can be neglected. That is, we may consider ordinary fluid turbulence as providing a given "background" on which the magnetic perturbations develop. We assume a steady turbulent velocity distribution, the word "steady" being used in the sense usual in turbulence theory, i.e. referring to the average values of the motion.||

Mathematically, we neglect the terms quadratic in the field in the equation of motion (51.13), returning to the ordinary Navier–Stokes equation:

$$\partial \mathbf{v}/\partial t + (\mathbf{v}\cdot\mathbf{grad})\,\mathbf{v} = -\,\mathbf{grad}\,(p/\rho) + \nu\triangle\mathbf{v}$$

(the fluid being supposed incompressible). If we use the formula $(\mathbf{v}\cdot\mathbf{grad})\mathbf{v} = \frac{1}{2}\,\mathbf{grad}\,v^2 - \mathbf{v}\times\mathbf{curl}\,\mathbf{v}$ and take the curl of the above equation, we obtain

$$\partial\boldsymbol{\Omega}/\partial t = \mathbf{curl}\,(\mathbf{v}\times\boldsymbol{\Omega}) + \nu\triangle\boldsymbol{\Omega}, \tag{55.1}$$

where we have put for brevity $\boldsymbol{\Omega} \equiv \frac{1}{2}\,\mathbf{curl}\,\mathbf{v}$.

---

† For example, the magnetomechanical effect in rotating parts of a fluid, or even thermal fluctuations.

‡ The results in §55 are due to G. K. Batchelor (1950).

|| The averaging is over times which are of the order of the periods of the corresponding turbulent fluctuations, but are, of course, small compared with the total time during which the system is observed.

Let us compare this equation with (51.2):

$$\partial \mathbf{H}/\partial t = \mathbf{curl}\,(\mathbf{v} \times \mathbf{H}) + (c^2/4\pi\sigma)\,\triangle \mathbf{H}, \tag{55.2}$$

which (for a given velocity distribution) determines the time variation of the magnetic field. We see that $\mathbf{\Omega}$ and $\mathbf{H}$ satisfy equations of the same form, which become identical if $\nu = c^2/4\pi\sigma$. In this case, therefore, there is a solution of equation (55.2) for which

$$\mathbf{H} = \text{constant} \times \mathbf{\Omega}. \tag{55.3}$$

Thus, if

$$\nu = c^2/4\pi\sigma, \tag{55.4}$$

a steady magnetic field (in the same sense of the word "steady") can exist. This field, on the average, neither increases nor decreases, whatever the value of the constant coefficient in (55.3). We may say that there is neutral equilibrium, in which the two factors, mentioned above as determining the magnetic field, are exactly balanced.

Hence, in turn, it is evident that, if the conductivity of the fluid exceeds $c^2/4\pi\nu$, the dissipative loss of electromagnetic energy will be insufficient to compensate the increase of the magnetic field by the stretching of the lines of force. Thus we obtain the inequality

$$4\pi\nu\sigma/c^2 > 1 \tag{55.5}$$

as the condition for the spontaneous appearance of magnetic fields by the growth of small magnetic perturbations.†

We can say that this is the condition for turbulent motion to be unstable with respect to infinitesimal magnetic perturbations. It is noteworthy that the criterion can be established quantitatively, and not merely in orders of magnitude.‡

The condition (55.5) as a criterion of the behaviour of the field is valid so long as the neglect of the reciprocal effect of the magnetic field on the flow, on which the derivation of (55.5) is based, holds good. The field will increase until some steady state, in which the reciprocal effect of the field cannot be neglected, is set up. Although, strictly speaking, the fluid-mechanical properties of the turbulence in this state are not those given *a priori*, the qualitative distribution and the order of magnitude of the resulting magnetic field can be determined as if they were.

---

† The condition (55.5) is very stringent. For example, in mercury ($\sigma \cong 10^{16}$ sec^{-1}, $\nu = 1{\cdot}2 \times 10^{-3}$ cm^2/sec), the quantity on the left of (55.5) is only $1{\cdot}5 \times 10^{-7}$. Since σ and ν increase with the mean free paths of the corresponding carriers of charge and mass, the condition (55.5) may be fulfilled, for example, in the Sun's chromosphere and corona, and in the ionised interstellar gas.

‡ It should be mentioned that the foregoing arguments, however convincing, are not entirely conclusive. For example, YA. B. ZEL'DOVICH has shown (*Zhurnal êksperimental'noĭ i teoreticheskoĭ fiziki* **31**, 154, 1956; *Soviet Physics JETP* **4**, 460, 1957) that they are invalid in a hypothetical case of "two-dimensional" turbulence.

It is easy to see that the magnetic field distribution must be similar to the turbulent distribution of $\mathbf{\Omega}$. For $\mathbf{\Omega}$ may be regarded as the angular velocity of the fluid at any given point. Since the lines of magnetic force move with the fluid, the vector $\mathbf{H}$ rotates with the same angular velocity. Hence, if at any two points of a turbulent flow the instantaneous values of $\mathbf{\Omega}$ are uncorrelated, the vectors $\mathbf{H}$ at those points will rotate in an uncorrelated manner, and their relative direction will vary randomly with time.

In this connection we may refer to some purely fluid-mechanical properties of turbulence.† Turbulent flow may be regarded as a superposition of turbulent eddies of various sizes, from the largest l (the "external scale" of the turbulence) to the smallest λ_0 (the "internal scale"). The former is equal to a characteristic length which gives the size of the region in which the turbulent flow occurs. The quantity λ_0 gives, in order of magnitude, the distances at which viscosity, and the energy dissipation which it entails, become important; it can be expressed in terms of l and the Reynolds number $R \sim ul/\nu$ of the turbulent flow as a whole (u being of the order of the change in the mean velocity over a distance l), or in terms of the energy ϵ dissipated in unit mass of the fluid in unit time:

$$\lambda_0 \sim (\nu^3/\epsilon)^{\frac{1}{4}} \sim l/R^{\frac{3}{4}}. \tag{55.6}$$

The correlation between the velocities $\mathbf{v}_1$ and $\mathbf{v}_2$ at two points 1 and 2 at a distance λ apart is determined mainly by the eddies of size λ. According to Kolmogorov and Obukhov's law, we have, for distances $\lambda \gg \lambda_0$, $\overline{\Delta v_i \Delta v_k} \sim \lambda^{2/3}$, where $\Delta\mathbf{v} = \mathbf{v}_2 - \mathbf{v}_1$. At distances $\lambda \ll \lambda_0$, on the other hand, $\overline{\Delta v_i \Delta v_k} \sim \lambda^2$. From this we can easily find the correlation of angular velocities. Since the components of $\mathbf{\Omega}_1$ and $\mathbf{\Omega}_2$ are expressed in terms of the derivatives of $\mathbf{v}_1$ and $\mathbf{v}_2$, we find, by differentiating $\overline{\Delta v_i \Delta v_k}$ once with respect to the co-ordinates of point 1 and once with respect to those of point 2,

$$\begin{aligned} \overline{\Omega_{1i}\Omega_{2k}} &\sim \lambda^{-4/3} \qquad \text{for } \lambda \gg \lambda_0, \\ \overline{\Omega_{1i}\Omega_{2k}} &\sim \text{constant} \quad \text{for } \lambda \ll \lambda_0. \end{aligned} \tag{55.7}$$

These formulae show that an appreciable correlation between the angular velocities exists only at distances up to those of the order of λ_0, falling off rapidly at greater distances.

From the above discussion, the distribution of the steady spontaneous magnetic field must be similar. The distribution is correlated only over regions of dimension $\sim \lambda_0$. At greater distances the relative direction of the vectors $\mathbf{H}$ is practically random.

The order of magnitude of the magnetic field can now be easily determined by estimating the terms in the complete equation of motion

$$\partial \mathbf{v}/\partial t + (\mathbf{v}\cdot\mathbf{grad})\,\mathbf{v} = -\,\mathbf{grad}\,(p/\rho) + \nu\triangle v - (1/4\pi\rho)\mathbf{H} \times \mathbf{curl}\,\mathbf{H}.$$

---

† See *Fluid Mechanics*, §§31–33.

Since the vector **H** changes its direction completely over distances $\sim \lambda_0$, the order of magnitude of the last term on the right-hand side is $H^2/4\pi\rho\lambda_0$. Let us now estimate the term $(\mathbf{v}\cdot\mathbf{grad})\mathbf{v}$. For eddies of size λ it is of the order of v_λ^2/λ, where v_λ is the change in the velocity over a distance λ. According to the formulae of turbulence theory we have

$$\begin{aligned} v_\lambda &\sim u(\lambda/l)^{\frac{1}{3}} \quad \text{for } \lambda \gg \lambda_0, \\ v_\lambda &\sim u(\lambda/l)\sqrt{\mathrm{R}} \text{ for } \lambda \ll \lambda_0. \end{aligned} \tag{55.8}$$

Hence the ratio $v_\lambda^2/\lambda \sim \lambda^{-1/3}$ for $\lambda \gg \lambda_0$ and $\sim \lambda$ for $\lambda \ll \lambda_0$. Its greatest value is therefore reached when $\lambda \sim \lambda_0$. Thus $(\mathbf{v}\cdot\mathbf{grad})\mathbf{v} \sim v_{\lambda_0}^2/\lambda_0$. Finally, if the two terms are comparable in magnitude, we have

$$H^2 \sim 4\pi\rho v_{\lambda_0}^2. \tag{55.9}$$

According to (55.6) and (55.8), $v_{\lambda_0} \sim u\mathrm{R}^{-1/4} \sim (\epsilon\nu)^{1/4}$. Hence we can also write

$$H^2 \sim 4\pi\rho u^2/\sqrt{\mathrm{R}} \sim 4\pi\rho\sqrt{(\epsilon\nu)}. \tag{55.10}$$

These formulae give the order of magnitude of the spontaneous magnetic field. It is of interest to compare the energy of this field with the kinetic energy of the turbulent flow. The latter energy resides mainly in the largest eddies (of size $\sim l$), and its order of magnitude is ρu^2. The magnetic energy resides mainly in the "magnetic eddies", which are of small size ($\sim \lambda_0$). By (55.9), it is comparable with the kinetic energy of the turbulent eddies of this same size, but, by (55.10), it is small in comparison with the total kinetic energy. A more exact mathematical formulation of these statements can be attained by expanding the spatial distribution of velocity and magnetic field as Fourier integrals. The kinetic energy then resides mainly in the components with small wave numbers ($k \sim 1/l$), while the magnetic energy is mainly in those with large wave numbers ($k \sim 1/\lambda_0$).

Turbulent flow results in a continuous transfer of energy from large eddies to small ones, with almost no viscous dissipation. This "energy flux" is dissipated only in the eddies of size λ_0. In the absence of a magnetic field, the dissipation is due entirely to the viscosity of the fluid, but in the turbulence here considered the energy in the eddies of size λ_0 is partly dissipated by viscosity, partly converted into the energy of the magnetic field and only then dissipated as Joule heat.

Let us estimate the time required to establish the steady state. For this purpose we return to equation (55.2). The two terms on the right-hand side are in order of magnitude respectively $Hv_{\lambda_0}/\lambda_0 = Hv_{\lambda_0}\lambda_0/\lambda_0^2 \sim H\nu/\lambda_0^2$ and $c^2H/4\pi\sigma\lambda_0^2$. Since we know precisely the condition (55.4) for the occurrence of neutral equilibrium, we also know the exact relation between the coefficients in these two terms, and can write

$$\frac{\partial H}{\partial t} \sim \left(\nu - \frac{c^2}{4\pi\sigma}\right)\frac{H}{\lambda_0^2}.$$

Hence we see that small perturbations increase with time according to the exponential function

$$\exp\left\{\left(\nu - \frac{c^2}{4\pi\sigma}\right)\frac{t}{\lambda_0^2}\right\}. \tag{55.11}$$

If $4\pi\sigma\nu/c^2 \gg 1$ we have simply $\exp(\nu t/\lambda_0^2)$. The time τ during which an initial small perturbation $\sim H_0$ develops into the steady field H (55.10) is then, in order of magnitude,

$$\tau \sim \frac{\lambda_0^2}{\nu}\log\frac{H^2}{H_0^2} \sim \left(\frac{\nu}{\epsilon}\right)^{\frac{1}{2}}\log\frac{\rho(\epsilon\nu)^{\frac{1}{2}}}{H_0^2}. \tag{55.12}$$

The random variation of the magnetic field with time in turbulent flow means that the (time) average value of $\mathbf{H}$ is zero. In other words, we can say that, in the case considered here (i.e. when a spontaneous field is possible), a non-zero mean field is incompatible with turbulence. The result must be that, when a moderate external magnetic field is applied to a fluid in turbulent motion (in a finite volume), the latter will behave like a superconductor. A strong field ($H^2 \gtrsim \rho u^2$) must necessarily penetrate into the fluid and will suppress the turbulence.

CHAPTER IX

THE ELECTROMAGNETIC WAVE EQUATIONS

§56. The field equations in a dielectric in the absence of dispersion

IN §45 we gave the equations for a variable electromagnetic field in a metal:

$$\mathbf{curl}\,\mathbf{H} = 4\pi\sigma\mathbf{E}/c, \qquad \mathbf{curl}\,\mathbf{E} = -(1/c)\,\partial\mathbf{B}/\partial t, \tag{56.1}$$

which hold when the field changes sufficiently slowly: the frequencies of the field must be such that the dependence of $\mathbf{j}$ on $\mathbf{E}$ (and of $\mathbf{B}$ on $\mathbf{H}$, if needed) is that corresponding to the static case.†

We shall now examine the corresponding problem for a variable electromagnetic field in a dielectric, and shall formulate equations valid for frequencies such that the relations between $\mathbf{D}$ and $\mathbf{E}$, and $\mathbf{B}$ and $\mathbf{H}$, are the same as when the fields are constant. If, as usually happens, these relations are simple proportionalities, this means that we can put

$$\mathbf{D} = \epsilon\mathbf{E}, \qquad \mathbf{B} = \mu\mathbf{H}, \tag{56.2}$$

with the static values of ϵ and μ.

These relations are not valid (or, as we say, ϵ and μ exhibit *dispersion*) at frequencies comparable with the eigenfrequencies of the molecular or electronic vibrations which lead to the electric or magnetic polarisation of the matter. The order of magnitude of such frequencies depends on the substance concerned, and varies widely. It may also be entirely different for electric and for magnetic phenomena.‡

The equations

$$\operatorname{div}\mathbf{B} = 0, \tag{56.3}$$

$$\mathbf{curl}\,\mathbf{E} = -(1/c)\,\partial\mathbf{B}/\partial t \tag{56.4}$$

are obtained immediately by replacing $\mathbf{e}$ and $\mathbf{h}$ in the exact microscopic Maxwell's equations by their averaged values $\mathbf{E}$ and $\mathbf{B}$, and therefore are always valid. The equation

$$\operatorname{div}\mathbf{D} = 0 \tag{56.5}$$

is obtained (§6) by averaging the exact microscopic equation $\operatorname{div}\mathbf{e} = 4\pi\rho$,

† The condition $l \ll \lambda$ does not relate to the validity of equations (56.1) as they stand. In the problems discussed in Chapter VII this condition was necessary in order to justify the neglect of retardation effects in the field outside the conductor.

‡ In diamond, for example, the electric polarisation is due to the electrons, and the dispersion of ϵ begins only in the ultra-violet. In a polar liquid such as water, the polarisation is due to the orientation of molecules with permanent dipole moments, and the dispersion of ϵ appears at frequencies $\omega \sim 10^{11}$, i.e. in the centimetre wavelength range. The dispersion of μ in ferromagnetics may begin at even lower frequencies.

using only the fact that the total charge on the body is zero. This result is evidently independent of the assumption made in §6 that the field is static, and equation (56.5) is therefore valid in variable fields also.

A further equation is to be obtained by averaging the exact equation

$$\mathbf{curl\,h} = \frac{1}{c}\frac{\partial \mathbf{e}}{\partial t} + \frac{4\pi}{c}\rho\mathbf{v}. \tag{56.6}$$

A direct averaging gives

$$\mathbf{curl\,B} = \frac{1}{c}\frac{\partial \mathbf{E}}{\partial t} + \frac{4\pi}{c}\overline{\rho\mathbf{v}}. \tag{56.7}$$

When the macroscopic field depends on time, the establishment of the relation between the mean value $\overline{\rho\mathbf{v}}$ and the other quantities is fairly difficult. It is simpler to effect the averaging in the following more formal way.

Let us assume for the moment that extraneous charges of volume density ρ_{ex} are placed in the dielectric. The motion of these charges causes an "extraneous current" $\mathbf{j}_{ex}$, and the conservation of charge is expressed by an equation of continuity:

$$\partial\rho_{ex}/\partial t + \operatorname{div}\mathbf{j}_{ex} = 0.$$

Instead of equation (56.5) we have $\operatorname{div}\mathbf{D} = 4\pi\rho_{ex}$; see (6.8). Differentiating this equation with respect to time and using the equation of continuity, we obtain $\partial(\operatorname{div}\mathbf{D})/\partial t = 4\pi\,\partial\rho_{ex}/\partial t = -4\pi\operatorname{div}\mathbf{j}_{ex}$, or

$$\operatorname{div}\left(\frac{\partial \mathbf{D}}{\partial t} + 4\pi\mathbf{j}_{ex}\right) = 0.$$

Hence it follows that the vector in parentheses can be written as the curl of another vector, which we denote by $c\mathbf{H}$. Thus

$$\mathbf{curl\,H} = \frac{4\pi}{c}\mathbf{j}_{ex} + \frac{1}{c}\frac{\partial \mathbf{D}}{\partial t}. \tag{56.8}$$

Outside the body this must be the same as the exact Maxwell's equation for the field in a vacuum, and therefore $\mathbf{H}$ is the magnetic field. Inside the body, in the static case, the current $\mathbf{j}_{ex}$ is related to the magnetic field by the equation $\mathbf{curl\,H} = 4\pi\mathbf{j}_{ex}/c$, where $\mathbf{H}$ is the quantity introduced in §27 and related in a definite manner to the mean field $\mathbf{B}$. Hence it follows that, in the limit of zero frequency, the vector $\mathbf{H}$ in equation (56.8) is the static quantity $\mathbf{H}(\mathbf{B})$, and our present assumption that the field varies "slowly" means that the same relation $\mathbf{H}(\mathbf{B})$ holds between these variable fields. Thus $\mathbf{H}$ is a definite quantity, so that we can drop the auxiliary quantity $\mathbf{j}_{ex}$ and obtain the final equation

$$\mathbf{curl\,H} = (1/c)\,\partial\mathbf{D}/\partial t. \tag{56.9}$$

This equation replaces in dielectrics the first equation (56.1) for the field in metals. It might be supposed that the term in $\partial \mathbf{E}/\partial t$ ought to be included when this equation is used for variable fields in metals also, giving

$$\mathbf{curl}\,\mathbf{H} = \frac{4\pi}{c}\sigma\mathbf{E} + \frac{\epsilon}{c}\frac{\partial \mathbf{E}}{\partial t}. \tag{56.10}$$

In good conductors such as the true metals, however, the introduction of this term is pointless. The two terms on the right-hand side of (56.10) are essentially the first two terms in an expansion in powers of the field frequency. Since this frequency is assumed small, the second term must represent at most a small correction. In actual fact, in metals the corrections for the effect of the spatial non-uniformity of the field become important sooner than the frequency correction (see the sixth footnote to §45).

There are, however, substances, namely poor conductors, for which equation (56.10) may be meaningful. For such reasons as the small number of conduction electrons in semiconductors, or the small mobility of the ions in electrolyte solutions, these substances exhibit anomalously low conductivity, and hence the second term on the right of equation (56.10) may be comparable with, or even exceed, the first term at frequencies for which σ and ϵ may still be regarded as constants. In a field of a single frequency ω, the ratio of the second term to the first is $\epsilon\omega/4\pi\sigma$. If this ratio is small, the body behaves as an ordinary conductor of conductivity σ. At frequencies $\omega \gg 4\pi\sigma/\epsilon$, it behaves as a dielectric with dielectric constant ϵ.

In a homogeneous medium with constant ϵ and μ, equations (56.3)–(56.5) and (56.9) become

$$\operatorname{div}\mathbf{E} = 0, \qquad \operatorname{div}\mathbf{H} = 0, \tag{56.11}$$

$$\mathbf{curl}\,\mathbf{E} = -\frac{\mu}{c}\frac{\partial \mathbf{H}}{\partial t}, \qquad \mathbf{curl}\,\mathbf{H} = \frac{\epsilon}{c}\frac{\partial \mathbf{E}}{\partial t}. \tag{56.12}$$

Eliminating **E** in the usual manner, we obtain

$$\mathbf{curl}\,\mathbf{curl}\,\mathbf{H} = \frac{\epsilon}{c}\frac{\partial}{\partial t}\mathbf{curl}\,\mathbf{E} = -\frac{\epsilon\mu}{c^2}\frac{\partial^2 \mathbf{H}}{\partial t^2},$$

and, since $\mathbf{curl}\,\mathbf{curl}\,\mathbf{H} = \mathbf{grad}\operatorname{div} H - \triangle\mathbf{H} = -\triangle\mathbf{H}$, we reach the wave equation

$$\triangle\mathbf{H} - \frac{\epsilon\mu}{c^2}\frac{\partial^2 \mathbf{H}}{\partial t^2} = 0.$$

A similar equation for **E** can be obtained by eliminating **H**. We see that the velocity of propagation of electromagnetic waves in a homogeneous dielectric is

$$c/\sqrt{(\epsilon\mu)}. \tag{56.13}$$

The electromagnetic energy flux density in a dielectric is given by the same formula as in a metal:

$$\mathbf{S} = c\mathbf{E} \times \mathbf{H}/4\pi. \tag{56.14}$$

This is easily seen by calculating div **S**. Using equations (56.4) and (56.9), we obtain

$$\begin{aligned} \operatorname{div}\mathbf{S} &= \frac{c}{4\pi}(\mathbf{H}\cdot\mathbf{curl}\,\mathbf{E} - \mathbf{E}\cdot\mathbf{curl}\,\mathbf{H}) \\ &= -\frac{1}{4\pi}\left(\mathbf{E}\cdot\frac{\partial\mathbf{D}}{\partial t} + \mathbf{H}\cdot\frac{\partial\mathbf{B}}{\partial t}\right) = -\frac{\partial U}{\partial t}, \end{aligned} \tag{56.15}$$

in accordance with the expression $dU = (\mathbf{E}\cdot d\mathbf{D}+\mathbf{H}\cdot d\mathbf{B})/4\pi$ for the differential of the internal energy of a dielectric at given density and entropy.

The general requirements of relativistic invariance have the result that the energy flux density must be the same, apart from a factor c^2, as the space density of the field momentum,† which is therefore

$$\mathbf{E} \times \mathbf{H}/4\pi c. \tag{56.16}$$

This expression must, in particular, be used in determining the forces on a dielectric in a variable electromagnetic field. The force **f** per unit volume may be calculated from the stress tensor σ_{ik}: $f_i = \partial\sigma_{ik}/\partial x_k$. Here, however, it must be remembered that σ_{ik} is the momentum flux density, which includes the momentum of both the matter and the electromagnetic field. If **f** is taken as the force on the medium, the rate of change of the field momentum per unit volume must be subtracted:

$$f_i = \frac{\partial\sigma_{ik}}{\partial x_i} - \frac{\partial}{\partial t}\frac{(\mathbf{E}\times\mathbf{H})_i}{4\pi c}. \tag{56.17}$$

In a constant field the last term is zero, and so this question did not arise previously.

Since the field varies "slowly", the stress tensor may be taken to have the same value as in a constant field. For instance, in a fluid dielectric, σ_{ik} is given by the sum of the electric part (15.9) and the magnetic part (34.2). In differentiating these expressions with respect to the co-ordinates we must use the fact that the equations **curl E** = 0, **curl H** = 0 for a constant field (in the absence of currents) are replaced by equations (56.12). The result is

$$\begin{aligned} \mathbf{f} = &-\mathbf{grad}\,p_0 - \frac{E^2}{8\pi}\mathbf{grad}\,\epsilon + \mathbf{grad}\left[\rho\left(\frac{\partial\epsilon}{\partial\rho}\right)_T\frac{E^2}{8\pi}\right] - \frac{H^2}{8\pi}\mathbf{grad}\,\mu + \\ &+ \mathbf{grad}\left[\rho\left(\frac{\partial\mu}{\partial\rho}\right)_T\frac{H^2}{8\pi}\right] + \frac{\epsilon\mu - 1}{4\pi c}\frac{\partial}{\partial t}(\mathbf{E}\times\mathbf{H}). \end{aligned} \tag{56.18}$$

† This follows from the symmetry of the four-dimensional energy-momentum tensor; see *The Classical Theory of Fields*, §4–7, Addison-Wesley Press, Cambridge (Mass.), 1951; Pergamon Press, London, 1959.

§57. The electrodynamics of moving dielectrics

The motion of a medium results in an interaction between the electric and magnetic fields. Such phenomena for conductors have been discussed in §49; we shall now discuss them for dielectrics. Here we are in practice concerned with the phenomena occurring in moving media when external electric or magnetic fields are present. It should be emphasised that they are in no way related to the appearance of fields as a result of the motion itself (§§35, 50).

Our starting point in §49 was the formulae giving the transformation of the field when the frame of reference is changed. There it was sufficient to know the general formulae for the transformation of electric and magnetic fields in a vacuum, the averaging of which gives immediately the formulae for the transformation of **E** and **B**. In dielectrics the problem is considerably more complex, because the electromagnetic field is described by a greater number of quantities.

In the motion of macroscopic bodies, the velocities involved must in practice be small compared with the velocity of light. To obtain the necessary approximate transformation formulae, however, it is simplest to use the exact relativistic formulae which hold for all velocities.

In the electrodynamics of the field in a vacuum, the components of the electric and magnetic field vectors **e** and **h** are actually components of an antisymmetrical four-dimensional tensor (or "four-tensor") of rank two.† The same is true of **E** and **B**, which are the mean values of **e** and **h**. Thus there is a four-tensor F_{ik} whose components are given by‡

$$F_{ik} = \begin{bmatrix} 0 & B_z & -B_y & -iE_x \\ -B_z & 0 & B_x & -iE_y \\ B_y & -B_x & 0 & -iE_z \\ iE_x & iE_y & iE_z & 0 \end{bmatrix}. \tag{57.1}$$

Using this tensor, the first two Maxwell's equations,

$$\operatorname{div} \mathbf{B} = 0, \qquad \mathbf{curl}\,\mathbf{E} = -(1/c)\,\partial\mathbf{B}/\partial t, \tag{57.2}$$

can be written in the four-dimensional form

$$\frac{\partial F_{ik}}{\partial x_l} + \frac{\partial F_{kl}}{\partial x_i} + \frac{\partial F_{li}}{\partial x_k} = 0. \tag{57.3}$$

This shows the relativistic invariance of the equations. The applicability of equations (57.2) to moving bodies is evident, since they are obtained directly from the exact microscopic Maxwell's equations by replacing **e** and **h** by their averaged values **E** and **B**.

† See *The Classical Theory of Fields*, §§3–9, 4–1.

‡ In the present section (but not in the Problems) the tensor suffixes take the values 1, 2 3, 4, corresponding to the four-dimensional co-ordinates $x_1 = x$, $x_2 = y$, $x_3 = z$, $x_4 = ict$.

The second pair of Maxwell's equations

$$\operatorname{div}\mathbf{D} = 0, \qquad \mathbf{curl}\,\mathbf{H} = (1/c)\,\partial\mathbf{D}/\partial t \tag{57.4}$$

also retain their form in moving media. This is seen from the arguments given in §56, in which we used only general properties of bodies (e.g. that the total charge is zero), equally valid for moving bodies and bodies at rest. However, the relations between **D** and **E**, and **B** and **H**, need not be the same as in bodies at rest.

Since they are valid for bodies both at rest and in motion, equations (57.4) must be unaltered by the Lorentz transformation. For a field in a vacuum, the vectors **D** and **H** are the same as **E** and **B**, and the relativistic invariance of the second pair of Maxwell's equations appears in the fact that they also can be written in four-dimensional form, using the same tensor F_{ik}: $\partial F_{ik}/\partial x_k = 0$.† Hence it is clear that, to ensure the relativistic invariance of equations (57.4), it is necessary that the components of the vectors **D** and **H** should be transformed as the components of a four-tensor exactly similar to F_{ik}, which we denote by H_{ik}:

$$H_{ik} = \begin{bmatrix} 0 & H_z & -H_y & -iD_x \\ -H_z & 0 & H_x & -iD_y \\ H_y & -H_x & 0 & -iD_z \\ iD_x & iD_y & iD_z & 0 \end{bmatrix}. \tag{57.5}$$

Using this tensor, we can write equations (57.4) in the form

$$\partial H_{ik}/\partial x_k = 0. \tag{57.6}$$

Having elucidated that the quantities **E, D, H, B** form four-dimensional tensors, we have also ascertained the law of their transformation from one frame of reference to another. However, we are interested rather in the relations between the quantities in a moving medium, which generalise the relations $\mathbf{D} = \epsilon\mathbf{E}$ and $\mathbf{B} = \mu\mathbf{H}$ valid in a medium at rest.

We denote by u_i the velocity four-vector of the medium; its components are related to the three-dimensional velocity **v** by

$$u_{1,2,3} = v_{x,y,z}\Big/c\sqrt{\left(1-\frac{v^2}{c^2}\right)}, \qquad u_4 = i\Big/\sqrt{\left(1-\frac{v^2}{c^2}\right)}.$$

From this four-vector and the four-tensors F_{ik} and H_{ik} we form combinations which become **E** and **D** in a medium at rest. These combinations are the four-vectors $F_{ik}u_k$ and $H_{ik}u_k$; for $\mathbf{v} = 0$ their time components are

† See *The Classical Theory of Fields*, §4–5.

zero and their space components are **E** and **D** respectively. The four-dimensional generalisation of the equation $\mathbf{D} = \epsilon\mathbf{E}$ is therefore evidently†

$$H_{ik}u_k = \epsilon F_{ik}u_k. \tag{57.7}$$

Similarly, we see that the generalisation of $\mathbf{B} = \mu\mathbf{H}$ is the four-dimensional equation

$$F_{ik}u_l + F_{kl}u_i + F_{li}u_k = \mu(H_{ik}u_l + H_{kl}u_i + H_{li}u_k). \tag{57.8}$$

Returning from the four-dimensional to the three-dimensional notation, we derive from these two equations the vector relations‡

$$\begin{aligned} \mathbf{D} + \mathbf{v} \times \mathbf{H}/c &= \epsilon(\mathbf{E} + \mathbf{v} \times \mathbf{B}/c), \\ \mathbf{B} + \mathbf{E} \times \mathbf{v}/c &= \mu(\mathbf{H} + \mathbf{D} \times \mathbf{v}/c). \end{aligned} \tag{57.9}$$

These formulae, first derived by H. MINKOWSKI (1908), are exact in the sense that no assumption has yet been made concerning the magnitude of the velocity. If the ratio v/c is assumed small the equations can be solved for **D** and **B** as far as terms of the first order to give

$$\mathbf{D} = \epsilon\mathbf{E} + (\epsilon\mu - 1)\mathbf{v} \times \mathbf{H}/c, \tag{57.10}$$

$$\mathbf{B} = \mu\mathbf{H} + (\epsilon\mu - 1)\mathbf{E} \times \mathbf{v}/c. \tag{57.11}$$

These formulae, together with Maxwell's equations (57.2) and (57.4), form the basis for the electrodynamics of dielectrics in motion.

The boundary conditions on Maxwell's equations are also somewhat modified. From the equations $\operatorname{div} \mathbf{D} = 0$, $\operatorname{div} \mathbf{B} = 0$ the continuity of the normal components of the inductions follows as before:

$$D_{n1} = D_{n2}, \qquad B_{n1} = B_{n2}. \tag{57.12}$$

The conditions on the tangential components of the fields are most simply obtained by changing from the fixed frame of reference K to another, K', which moves with the surface element considered, whose velocity along the normal **n** we denote by v_n. The usual conditions, namely that $\mathbf{E}'_t$ and $\mathbf{H}'_t$ are continuous, hold in the frame K'. By the relativistic transformation formulae,|| these are equivalent to the continuity of the tangential components of the vectors $\mathbf{E}+\mathbf{v}\times\mathbf{B}/c$ and $\mathbf{H}-\mathbf{v}\times\mathbf{D}/c$. Taking the components perpendicular to **n** and using equations (57.12), we obtain the required boundary conditions:

$$\begin{aligned} \mathbf{n} \times (\mathbf{E}_2 - \mathbf{E}_1) &= v_n(\mathbf{B}_2 - \mathbf{B}_1)/c, \\ \mathbf{n} \times (\mathbf{H}_2 - \mathbf{H}_1) &= -v_n(\mathbf{D}_2 - \mathbf{D}_1)/c. \end{aligned} \tag{57.13}$$

† It should be noted that, by writing down relations involving only the local value of the velocity, we neglect slight effects due to the possibility of a velocity gradient, such as gyromagnetic effects (§35).

‡ If either of the relations $\mathbf{D} = \epsilon\mathbf{E}$ and $\mathbf{B} = \mu\mathbf{H}$ does not hold in the medium at rest, the corresponding relation (57.9) is replaced by a different functional relation between the vector sums on the two sides of the equation.

|| See *The Classical Theory of Fields*, §3–10.

If we substitute here the expressions (57.10) and (57.11), and neglect terms of higher order in v/c, we obtain

$$\begin{aligned} \mathbf{n} \times (\mathbf{E}_2 - \mathbf{E}_1) &= v_n(\mu_2 - \mu_1)\mathbf{H}_t/c, \\ \mathbf{n} \times (\mathbf{H}_2 - \mathbf{H}_1) &= -v_n(\epsilon_2 - \epsilon_1)\mathbf{E}_t/c. \end{aligned} \tag{57.14}$$

In this approximation the values of **H** and **E** on the two sides of the surface need not be distinguished on the right-hand sides of equations (57.14).

If the body moves so that its surface moves tangentially to itself (e.g. a solid of revolution rotating about its axis), then $v_n = 0$. Only in this case do the boundary conditions (57.13) or (57.14) reduce to the usual conditions that $\mathbf{E}_t$ and $\mathbf{H}_t$ are continuous.

PROBLEMS

PROBLEM 1. A dielectric sphere rotates uniformly in a vacuum in a uniform constant magnetic field $\mathfrak{H}$. Determine the resulting electric field near the sphere.

SOLUTION. In calculating the resulting electric field, the magnetic field may be taken to be the same as for a sphere at rest, since an allowance for the reciprocal effect of the magnetic field variation would give corrections of a higher order of smallness. Within the sphere, the magnetic field has the uniform value $\mathbf{H}^{(i)} = 3\mathfrak{H}/(2+\mu)$; cf. (8.2).

Since the rotation is steady, the resulting electric field is constant and, like any constant electric field, has a potential: $\mathbf{E} = -\mathbf{grad}\,\phi$. Outside the sphere, the potential satisfies the equation $\triangle\phi^{(e)} = 0$; inside the sphere, it satisfies

$$\triangle\phi^{(i)} = 2(\epsilon\mu-1)\mathbf{\Omega}\cdot\mathbf{H}^{(i)}/c\epsilon, \tag{1}$$

where $\mathbf{\Omega}$ is the angular velocity. The latter equation is obtained from $\operatorname{div}\mathbf{D} = 0$ by substituting for **D** the expression (57.10) with $\mathbf{v} = \mathbf{\Omega}\times\mathbf{r}$. The condition that the normal component of **D** is continuous at the surface of the sphere gives

$$-\epsilon\left[\frac{\partial\phi^{(i)}}{\partial r}\right]_{r=a} + \frac{\epsilon\mu-1}{c}a[\mathbf{\Omega}\cdot\mathbf{H}^{(i)} - (\mathbf{\Omega}\cdot\mathbf{n})(\mathbf{H}^{(i)}\cdot\mathbf{n})] = -\left[\frac{\partial\phi^{(e)}}{\partial r}\right]_{r=a}. \tag{2}$$

Here a is the radius of the sphere and **n** a unit radial vector.

From the symmetry of the sphere, the required electric field is determined by only two constant vectors, $\mathbf{\Omega}$ and $\mathfrak{H}$. From the components of these vectors we can form a bilinear scalar $\mathfrak{H}\cdot\mathbf{\Omega}$ and a bilinear tensor $\mathfrak{H}_i\Omega_k + \mathfrak{H}_k\Omega_i - \frac{2}{3}\delta_{ik}\mathfrak{H}\cdot\mathbf{\Omega}$, the sum of whose diagonal terms is zero. Accordingly, we seek the field potential outside the sphere in the form

$$\phi^{(e)} = \frac{1}{6}D_{ik}\frac{\partial^2}{\partial x_i \partial x_k}\left(\frac{1}{r}\right) = \frac{1}{2}D_{ik}\frac{n_i n_k}{r^3}, \tag{3}$$

where D_{ik} is a constant tensor (with $D_{ii} = 0$), the electric quadrupole moment tensor of the sphere.† No term of the form constant/r can appear in $\phi^{(e)}$, since such a term would give a non-zero total electric flux through a surface surrounding the sphere, whereas the sphere is uncharged. The field potential inside the sphere is sought in the form

$$\phi^{(i)} = \frac{r^2}{2a^5}D_{ik}n_i n_k + \frac{\epsilon\mu-1}{3c\epsilon}\mathbf{\Omega}\cdot\mathbf{H}^{(i)}(r^2-a^2). \tag{4}$$

The first term is the solution of the homogeneous equation $\triangle\phi = 0$, and the coefficient is chosen so as to give continuity of the potential, and therefore of $\mathbf{E}_t$, at the surface of the sphere. Substituting (3) and (4) in (2), we obtain

$$D_{ik} = -\frac{a^5}{c}\frac{3(\epsilon\mu-1)}{(3+2\epsilon)(2+\mu)}[\mathfrak{H}_i\Omega_k + \mathfrak{H}_k\Omega_i - \tfrac{2}{3}\delta_{ik}\mathfrak{H}\cdot\mathbf{\Omega}]. \tag{5}$$

† See *The Classical Theory of Fields*, §5–6.

Thus a quadrupole electric field is formed near the rotating sphere, and the quadrupole moment of the sphere is given by formula (5).† In particular, if the axis of rotation (the z-axis) is parallel to the external field, D_{ik} has only the diagonal components

$$D_{zz} = -\frac{a^5}{c}\frac{4(\epsilon\mu-1)}{(3+2\epsilon)(2+\mu)}\mathfrak{H}\Omega, \qquad D_{xx} = D_{yy} = -\tfrac{1}{2}D_{zz}.$$

PROBLEM 2. A magnetised sphere rotates uniformly in a vacuum about its axis, which is parallel to the direction of magnetisation. Determine the resulting electric field near the sphere.‡

SOLUTION. The magnetic field inside the sphere is uniform, and is expressed in terms of the constant magnetisation $\mathbf{M}$ by the equations $\mathbf{B}^{(i)}+2\mathbf{H}^{(i)} = 0$ (cf. (8.1)) and $\mathbf{B}^{(i)}-\mathbf{H}^{(i)} = 4\pi\mathbf{M}$, whence $\mathbf{B}^{(i)} = 8\pi\mathbf{M}/3$, $\mathbf{H}^{(i)} = -4\pi\mathbf{M}/3$. The second of formulae (57.9) does not hold in this case, because the formula $\mathbf{B} = \mu\mathbf{H}$ is not valid for a ferromagnetic at rest; from the first of (57.9) we have, inside the sphere,

$$\begin{aligned}\mathbf{D} &= \epsilon\mathbf{E}+\epsilon\mathbf{v}\times\mathbf{B}/c-\mathbf{v}\times\mathbf{H}/c\\ &= \epsilon\mathbf{E}+4\pi(2\epsilon+1)\mathbf{v}\times\mathbf{M}/3c.\end{aligned}$$

The potential of the resulting electric field outside the sphere satisfies the equation $\triangle\phi^{(e)} = 0$, and that inside the sphere satisfies $\triangle\phi^{(i)} = 8\pi(2\epsilon+1)M\Omega/3c\epsilon$.

The boundary condition that D_n is continuous at the surface of the sphere gives

$$-\epsilon\left[\frac{\partial\phi^{(i)}}{\partial r}\right]_{r=a}+\frac{4\pi(2\epsilon+1)}{3c}a\Omega M\sin^2\theta = -\left[\frac{\partial\phi^{(e)}}{\partial r}\right]_{r=a},$$

where θ is the angle between the normal $\mathbf{n}$ and the direction of $\mathbf{\Omega}$ and $\mathbf{M}$ (the z-axis). We seek $\phi^{(e)}$ and $\phi^{(i)}$ in the forms

$$\phi^{(e)} = \frac{D_{ik}n_in_k}{2r^3} = \frac{D_{zz}}{4r^3}(3\cos^2\theta-1),$$

$$\phi^{(i)} = \frac{r^2}{4a^5}D_{zz}(3\cos^2\theta-1)+\frac{4\pi(2\epsilon+1)}{9c\epsilon}M\Omega(r^2-a^2).$$

From the boundary condition we obtain the following expressions for the electric quadrupole moment of the rotating sphere:

$$D_{zz} = -\frac{4(2\epsilon+1)}{3c(2\epsilon+3)}a^2\Omega\mathcal{M}, \qquad D_{xx} = D_{yy} = -\tfrac{1}{2}D_{zz},$$

where $\mathcal{M}$ is the total magnetic moment of the sphere. For a metal sphere we must take $\epsilon\to\infty$, giving

$$D_{zz} = -4\Omega\mathcal{M}a^2/3c.$$

§58. The dispersion of the dielectric permeability

Let us now go on to study the important subject of rapidly varying electromagnetic fields, whose frequencies are not restricted to be small in comparison with the frequencies which characterise the establishment of the electric and magnetic polarisation of the substances concerned.

An electromagnetic field variable in time must necessarily be variable in space also. For a frequency ω, the spatial periodicity is characterised by a

† Similarly, a quadruple magnetic field occurs near a sphere rotating in a uniform electric field. The magnetic quadrupole moment is given by (5) if the sign is changed and ϵ, μ, $\mathfrak{H}$ are replaced by μ, ϵ, $\mathfrak{E}$ respectively.

‡ If the direction of magnetisation is not the same as that of the axis of rotation, the problem is considerably changed, since the sphere then emits electromagnetic waves.

wavelength $\lambda \sim c/\omega$. As the frequency increases, λ eventually becomes comparable with the atomic dimensions a. The macroscopic description of the field is thereafter invalid.

The question may arise whether there is any frequency range in which, on the one hand, dispersion phenomena are important but, on the other hand, the macroscopic formulation still holds good. It is easy to see that such a range must exist. The most rapid manner of establishment of the electric or magnetic polarisation in matter is the electronic mechanism. Its relaxation time is of the order of the atomic time a/v, where v is the velocity of the electrons in the atom. Since $v \ll c$, even the wavelength $\lambda \sim ac/v$ corresponding to these times is large compared with a.

In what follows we shall assume the condition $\lambda \gg a$ to hold.† It must be borne in mind, however, that this condition may not be sufficient: for metals at low temperatures there is a range of frequencies in which the macroscopic theory is inapplicable, although the inequality $c/\omega \gg a$ is satisfied (see §67).

The formal theory given below is equally applicable to metals and to dielectrics. At frequencies corresponding to the motion of the electrons within the atoms (*optical frequencies*) and at higher frequencies, there is, indeed, not even a quantitative difference in the properties of metals and dielectrics.

It is clear from the discussion in §56 that Maxwell's equations

$$\operatorname{div}\mathbf{D} = 0, \qquad \operatorname{div}\mathbf{B} = 0, \tag{58.1}$$

$$\mathbf{curl}\,\mathbf{E} = -(1/c)\,\partial\mathbf{B}/\partial t, \qquad \mathbf{curl}\,\mathbf{H} = (1/c)\,\partial\mathbf{D}/\partial t \tag{58.2}$$

remain formally the same in arbitrary variable electromagnetic fields. These equations are, however, largely useless until the relations between the quantities **D**, **B**, **E** and **H** which appear in them have been established. At the high frequencies at present under consideration, these relations bear no resemblance to those which are valid in the static case and which we have used for variable fields in the absence of dispersion.

First of all, the principal property of these relations, namely the dependence of **D** and **B** only on the values of **E** and **H** at the instant considered, no longer holds good. In the general case of an arbitrary variable field, the values of **D** and **B** at a given instant are not determined only by the values of **E** and **H** at that instant. On the contrary, they depend in general on the values of $\mathbf{E}(t)$ and $\mathbf{H}(t)$ at every previous instant. This expresses the fact that the establishment of the electric or magnetic polarisation of the matter cannot keep up with the change in the electromagnetic field. The frequencies at which dispersion phenomena first appear may be completely different for the electric and the magnetic properties of the substance.

---

† The effects (called the *natural optical activity*) resulting from terms of the next order in the small ratio a/λ will be considered in §83.

In the present section we shall refer to the dependence of **D** on **E**; the specific features of the dispersion of magnetic properties will be discussed in §60.

The polarisation vector **P** has been introduced in §6 by means of the definition $\bar{\rho} = -\mathrm{div}\,\mathbf{P}$, ρ being the true (microscopic) charge density. This equation expresses the electric neutrality of the body as a whole, and together with the condition $\mathbf{P} = 0$ outside the body it shows that the total electric moment of the body is $\int \mathbf{P}\,dV$. This derivation is evidently valid for variable as well as for constant fields. Thus in any variable field, even if dispersion is present, the vector $\mathbf{P} = (\mathbf{D}-\mathbf{E})/4\pi$ retains its physical significance: it is the electric moment per unit volume.

In rapidly varying fields, the field strengths involved are in practice always fairly small. Hence the relation between **D** and **E** can always be taken to be linear.† The most general linear relation between $\mathbf{D}(t)$ and the values of the function $\mathbf{E}(t)$ at all previous instants can be written in the integral form

$$\mathbf{D}(t) = \mathbf{E}(t) + \int_0^\infty f(\tau)\mathbf{E}(t-\tau)\,d\tau. \tag{58.3}$$

It is convenient to separate the term $\mathbf{E}(t)$, for reasons which will become evident later. In equation (58.3) $f(\tau)$ is a function of time and of the properties of the medium. By analogy with the electrostatic formula $\mathbf{D} = \epsilon\mathbf{E}$, we write the relation (58.3) in the symbolic form $\mathbf{D} = \hat{\epsilon}\mathbf{E}$, where $\hat{\epsilon}$ is a linear integral operator whose effect is shown by (58.3).

Any variable field can be resolved by a Fourier expansion into a series of components of a single frequency, in which all quantities depend on time through the factor $e^{-i\omega t}$. For such fields the relation (58.3) between **D** and **E** becomes

$$\mathbf{D} = \epsilon(\omega)\mathbf{E}, \tag{58.4}$$

where the function $\epsilon(\omega)$ is defined as

$$\epsilon(\omega) = 1 + \int_0^\infty f(\tau)e^{i\omega\tau}\,d\tau. \tag{58.5}$$

Thus, for periodic fields, we can regard the dielectric permeability (the coefficient of proportionality between **D** and **E**) as a function of the frequency as well as of the properties of the medium. The dependence of ϵ on the frequency is called its *dispersion law*.

---

† Here we assume that **D** depends linearly on **E** alone, and not on **H**. In a constant field, a linear dependence of **D** on **H** is excluded by the requirement of invariance with respect to a change in the sign of the time. In a variable field, this condition no longer applies, and a linear relation between **D** and **H** is possible if the substance possesses symmetry of various kinds. It is, however, a small effect of the order of a/λ, and is indeed the effect mentioned in the last footnote.

The function $\epsilon(\omega)$ is in general complex. We denote its real and imaginary parts by ϵ' and ϵ'':

$$\epsilon(\omega) = \epsilon'(\omega) + i\epsilon''(\omega). \tag{58.6}$$

From the definition (58.5) we see at once that

$$\epsilon(-\omega) = \epsilon^*(\omega). \tag{58.7}$$

Separating the real and imaginary parts, we have

$$\epsilon'(-\omega) = \epsilon'(\omega), \qquad \epsilon''(-\omega) = -\epsilon''(\omega). \tag{58.8}$$

Thus ϵ' is an even function of the frequency, and ϵ'' is an odd function.

For frequencies which are small compared with those at which the dispersion is large, we can expand $\epsilon(\omega)$ as a power series in ω. The expansion of the even function $\epsilon'(\omega)$ includes only even powers, and that of the odd function $\epsilon''(\omega)$ includes only odd powers. In the limit as $\omega \to 0$, the function $\epsilon(\omega)$ in dielectrics tends, of course, to the electrostatic dielectric constant, which we here denote by ϵ_0. In dielectrics, therefore, the expansion of $\epsilon'(\omega)$ begins with the constant term ϵ_0, while that of $\epsilon''(\omega)$ begins, in general, with a term in ω.

The function $\epsilon(\omega)$ at low frequencies can also be discussed for metals, if it is defined in such a way that, in the limit $\omega \to 0$, the equation

$$\mathbf{curl\,H} = (1/c)\,\partial\mathbf{D}/\partial t$$

becomes the equation

$$\mathbf{curl\,H} = 4\pi\sigma\mathbf{E}/c$$

for a constant field in a conductor. Comparing the two equations, we see that for $\omega \to 0$ we must have $\partial\mathbf{D}/\partial t \to 4\pi\sigma\mathbf{E}$. But, in a periodic field, $\partial\mathbf{D}/\partial t = -i\omega\epsilon\mathbf{E}$, and we thus obtain the following expression for $\epsilon(\omega)$ in the limit of low frequencies:

$$\epsilon(\omega) = 4\pi i\sigma/\omega. \tag{58.9}$$

Thus the expansion of the function $\epsilon(\omega)$ in conductors begins with an imaginary term in $1/\omega$, which is expressed in terms of the ordinary conductivity σ for constant currents.† The next term in the expansion of $\epsilon(\omega)$ is a real constant, although for metals this constant does not have the same electrostatic significance as it does for dielectrics.‡

Moreover, this term of the expansion may again be devoid of significance if the effects of the spatial non-uniformity of the field of the electromagnetic wave appear before those of its periodicity in time.

---

† The imaginary part of the function $\epsilon(\omega)$ is sometimes represented in the form (58.9) for all frequencies; this amounts to introducing a new function $\sigma(\omega)$, which has no physical significance apart from its relationship to $\epsilon''(\omega)$.

‡ To avoid misunderstanding, we should point out a slight change in notation in comparison with §56. In equation (56.10) for poor conductors, $\epsilon(\omega)$ is $(4\pi i\sigma/\omega) + \epsilon$.

In superconductors there is always considerable non-uniformity, resulting from the smallness of the "penetration depth" of the magnetic field. It is not yet clear whether the concept of the dielectric permeability $\epsilon(\omega)$ has any meaning for superconductors.

§59. The dielectric permeability at very high frequencies

In the limit as $\omega \to \infty$, the function $\epsilon(\omega)$ tends to unity. This is evident from simple physical considerations: when the field changes sufficiently rapidly, the polarisation processes responsible for the difference between the field **E** and the induction **D** cannot occur at all.

It is possible to establish the limiting form of the function $\epsilon(\omega)$ at high frequencies, which is valid for all bodies, whether metals or dielectrics. The field frequency is assumed large compared with the "frequencies" of the motion of all, or at least the majority, of the electrons in the atoms forming the body. When this condition holds, we can calculate the polarisation of the substance by regarding the electrons as free and neglecting their interaction with one another and with the nuclei of the atoms.

The velocities v of the motion of the electrons in the atoms are small compared with the velocity of light. Hence the distances v/ω which they traverse during one period of the electromagnetic wave are small compared with the wavelength c/ω. For this reason we can assume the wave field uniform in determining the velocity acquired by an electron in that field.

The equation of motion is $m\,d\mathbf{v}'/dt = e\mathbf{E} = e\mathbf{E}_0 e^{-i\omega t}$, where e and m are the electron charge and mass, and $\mathbf{v}'$ is the additional velocity acquired by the electron in the wave field. Hence $\mathbf{v}' = ie\mathbf{E}/m\omega$. The displacement $\mathbf{r}$ of the electron due to the field is given by $\dot{\mathbf{r}} = \mathbf{v}'$, and therefore $\mathbf{r} = -e\mathbf{E}/m\omega^2$. The polarisation **P** of the body is the dipole moment per unit volume. Summing over all electrons, we find $\mathbf{P} = \Sigma e\mathbf{r} = -e^2 N\mathbf{E}/m\omega^2$, where N is the number of electrons in all the atoms in unit volume of the substance. By the definition of the electric induction, we have $\mathbf{D} = \epsilon\mathbf{E} = \mathbf{E} + 4\pi\mathbf{P}$. We thus have the formula

$$\epsilon(\omega) = 1 - 4\pi N e^2/m\omega^2. \tag{59.1}$$

The range of frequencies over which this formula is applicable begins, in practice, at the far ultra-violet for light elements and at the X-ray region for heavier elements.†

§60. The dispersion of the magnetic permeability

Unlike the dielectric polarisability, the magnetic susceptibility ceases to have any physical meaning at relatively low frequencies. To take account of the deviation of $\mu(\omega)$ from unity would then be an unwarrantable refinement.

---

† If $\epsilon(\omega)$ is to retain the significance which it has in Maxwell's equations, the frequency must also satisfy the condition $\omega \ll c/a$. We shall see later (§97), however, that the expression (59.1) can be allotted a certain physical significance even at higher frequencies.

To show this, let us investigate to what extent the physical meaning of the quantity $\mathbf{M} = (\mathbf{B}-\mathbf{H})/4\pi$, as being the magnetic moment per unit volume, is maintained in a variable field. The magnetic moment of a body is, by definition, the integral

$$\frac{1}{2c}\int \mathbf{r} \times \overline{\rho\mathbf{v}}\, \mathrm{d}V. \tag{60.1}$$

The mean value of the microscopic current density is related to the mean field by equation (56.7):

$$\mathbf{curl\, B} = \frac{4\pi}{c}\overline{\rho\mathbf{v}} + \frac{1}{c}\frac{\partial \mathbf{E}}{\partial t}. \tag{60.2}$$

Subtracting the equation $\mathbf{curl\, H} = (1/c)\partial\mathbf{D}/\partial t$, we obtain

$$\overline{\rho\mathbf{v}} = c\,\mathbf{curl\, M} + \partial\mathbf{P}/\partial t. \tag{60.3}$$

The integral (60.1) can, as shown in §27, be put in the form $\int\mathbf{M}\,\mathrm{d}V$ only if $\overline{\rho\mathbf{v}} = c\,\mathbf{curl\, M}$ and $\mathbf{M} = 0$ outside the body.

Thus the physical meaning of $\mathbf{M}$, and therefore of the magnetic susceptibility, depends on the possibility of neglecting the term $\partial\mathbf{P}/\partial t$ in (60.3). Let us see to what extent the conditions can be fulfilled which make this neglect permissible.

For a given frequency, the most favourable conditions for measuring the susceptibility are those where the body is as small as possible (to increase the space derivatives in $\mathbf{curl\, M}$) and the electric field is as weak as possible (to reduce $\mathbf{P}$). The field of an electromagnetic wave does not satisfy the latter condition, because $E \sim H$. Let us therefore consider a variable field, say in a solenoid, with the body under investigation placed on the axis. The electric field is due only to induction by the variable magnetic field, and the order of magnitude of E inside the body can be obtained by estimating the terms in the equation $\mathbf{curl\, E} = -(1/c)\partial\mathbf{B}/\partial t$, whence $E/l \sim \omega H/c$ or $E \sim (\omega l/c)H$, where l is the dimension of the body. Putting $\epsilon - 1 \sim 1$, we have $\partial P/\partial t \sim \omega E \sim \omega^2 lH/c$. For the space derivatives of the magnetic moment $\mathbf{M} = \chi\mathbf{H}$ we have $|c\,\mathbf{curl\, M}| \sim c\chi H/l$. If $|\partial\mathbf{P}/\partial t|$ is small compared with $|c\,\mathbf{curl\, M}|$, we must have

$$l^2 \ll \chi c^2/\omega^2. \tag{60.4}$$

It is evident that the concept of magnetic susceptibility can be meaningful only if this inequality allows dimensions of the body which are (at least) just macroscopic, i.e. if it is compatible with the inequality $l \gg a$, where a is the atomic dimension. This condition is certainly not fulfilled for the optical frequency range; for such frequencies, the magnetic susceptibility is always $\sim v^2/c^2$, where v is the electron velocity in the atom;† but the optical

† The relaxation times for any paramagnetic or ferromagnetic processes are certainly large in comparison with the optical periods.

frequencies themselves are $\sim v/a$, and therefore the right-hand side of the inequality (60.4) is $\sim a^2$.

Thus there is certainly no meaning in using the magnetic susceptibility from optical frequencies onward, and in discussing such phenomena we must put $\mu = 1$. To distinguish between **B** and **H** in this frequency range would be an over-refinement. Actually, the same is true for many phenomena even at frequencies well below the optical range.

§61. The field energy in dispersive media

The formula

$$\mathbf{S} = c\mathbf{E} \times \mathbf{H}/4\pi \tag{61.1}$$

for the energy flux density remains valid in variable electromagnetic fields, even if dispersion is present. This is evident from the arguments given at the end of §29: on account of the continuity of the tangential components of **E** and **H**, formula (61.1) follows from the condition that the normal component of **S** is continuous at the boundary of the body and the validity of a similar formula in the vacuum outside the body.

The rate of change of the energy in unit volume of the body is div **S**. Using Maxwell's equations, we can write this expression as

$$-\operatorname{div}\mathbf{S} = \frac{1}{4\pi}\left(\mathbf{E}\cdot\frac{\partial \mathbf{D}}{\partial t} + \mathbf{H}\cdot\frac{\partial \mathbf{B}}{\partial t}\right); \tag{61.2}$$

see (56.15). In a dielectric medium without dispersion, when ϵ and μ are real constants, this quantity can be regarded as the rate of change of the electromagnetic energy

$$U = (\epsilon \mathbf{E}^2 + \mu \mathbf{H}^2)/8\pi, \tag{61.3}$$

which has an exact thermodynamic significance: it is the difference between the internal energy per unit volume with and without the field, the density and entropy remaining unchanged.

In the presence of dispersion, no such simple interpretation is possible. Moreover, in the general case of arbitrary dispersion, the electromagnetic energy cannot be rationally defined as a thermodynamic quantity. This is because the presence of dispersion in general signifies a dissipation of energy, i.e. a dispersive medium is also an absorbing medium.

To determine this dissipation, let us consider an electromagnetic field of a single frequency. By averaging with respect to time the expression (61.2), we find the steady rate of change of the energy, and this is the mean quantity Q of heat evolved per unit time and volume.

Since the expression (61.2) is quadratic in the fields, all quantities must be written in real form. If, as is convenient for a field of a single frequency, we take **E** and **H** to be complex, then in (61.2) we must substitute for **E** and $\partial\mathbf{D}/\partial t$ respectively $\frac{1}{2}(\mathbf{E}+\mathbf{E}^*)$ and $\frac{1}{2}(-i\omega\epsilon\mathbf{E}+i\omega\epsilon^*\mathbf{E}^*)$, and similarly for **H** and $\partial\mathbf{B}/\partial t$. On averaging with respect to time, the products $\mathbf{E}\cdot\mathbf{E}$ and $\mathbf{E}^*\cdot\mathbf{E}^*$, which contain factors $e^{\mp 2i\omega t}$, give zero, leaving

$$Q = \frac{i\omega}{16\pi}[(\epsilon^* - \epsilon)\mathbf{E}\cdot\mathbf{E}^* + (\mu^* - \mu)\mathbf{H}\cdot\mathbf{H}^*] = \frac{\omega}{8\pi}(\epsilon''|\mathbf{E}|^2 + \mu''|\mathbf{H}|^2).$$

This expression can also be written

$$Q = \omega(\epsilon''\overline{\mathbf{E}^2} + \mu''\overline{\mathbf{H}^2})/4\pi, \tag{61.4}$$

where $\mathbf{E}$ and $\mathbf{H}$ are the real fields, and the bar denotes an average with respect to time.

This important formula shows that the absorption (dissipation) of energy is determined by the imaginary parts of ϵ and μ. The two terms in (61.4) are called the *electric* and *magnetic losses* respectively. On account of the law of increase of entropy, the sign of these losses is determinate: the dissipation of energy is accompanied by the evolution of heat, i.e. $Q > 0$. It therefore follows from (61.4) that the imaginary parts of ϵ and μ are always positive:

$$\epsilon'' > 0, \qquad \mu'' > 0 \tag{61.5}$$

for all substances and at all frequencies.† The signs of the real parts of ϵ and μ for $\omega \neq 0$ are subject to no physical restriction.

Any non-steady process in an actual body is to some extent thermodynamically irreversible. The electric and magnetic losses in a variable electromagnetic field therefore always occur to some extent, however slight. That is, the functions $\epsilon''(\omega)$ and $\mu''(\omega)$ are not exactly zero for any frequency other than zero. We shall see in §62 that this statement is of fundamental importance, although it does not exclude the possibility of only very small losses in certain frequency ranges. Such ranges, in which ϵ'' and μ'' are very small in comparison with ϵ' and μ', are called *transparency ranges*. It is possible to neglect the absorption in these ranges and to introduce the concept of the internal energy of the body in the electromagnetic field, in the same sense as in a constant field. To determine this quantity, it is not sufficient to consider a field of only a single frequency, since the strict periodicity results in no steady accumulation of electromagnetic energy. Let us therefore consider a field whose components have frequencies in a narrow range about some mean value ω_0. The field strengths can be written

$$\mathbf{E} = \mathbf{E}_0(t)e^{-i\omega_0 t}, \qquad \mathbf{H} = \mathbf{H}_0(t)e^{-i\omega_0 t}, \tag{61.6}$$

† Strictly speaking, this statement applies to bodies which, in the absence of the variable field, are in thermodynamic equilibrium; we assume this condition to hold. If the body is not in thermal equilibrium, then Q may in principle be negative. The second law of thermodynamics requires only a net increase in entropy as a result of the effects of the variable electromagnetic field and of the absence of thermodynamic equilibrium, the latter effect being independent of the presence of the field. A hypothetical example of such a body is one in which all the atoms have been excited artificially (i.e. otherwise than by spontaneous thermal excitation).

where $\mathbf{E}_0(t)$ and $\mathbf{H}_0(t)$ are functions of time which vary only slowly in comparison with the factor $e^{-i\omega_0 t}$. The real parts of these expressions are to be substituted on the right-hand side of (61.2), and we then average with respect to time over the period $2\pi/\omega_0$, which is small compared with the time of variation of the factors $\mathbf{E}_0$ and $\mathbf{H}_0$.

The first term in (61.2), with $\mathbf{E}$ written in complex form, is

$$\tfrac{1}{2}(\mathbf{E}+\mathbf{E}^*)\cdot\tfrac{1}{2}(\dot{\mathbf{D}}+\dot{\mathbf{D}}^*)/4\pi,$$

and similarly for the second term. The products $\mathbf{E}\cdot\dot{\mathbf{D}}$ and $\mathbf{E}^*\cdot\dot{\mathbf{D}}^*$ vanish when averaged over time, and can therefore be ignored, leaving

$$\frac{1}{16\pi}\left(\mathbf{E}\cdot\frac{\partial\mathbf{D}^*}{\partial t}+\mathbf{E}^*\cdot\frac{\partial\mathbf{D}}{\partial t}\right). \tag{61.7}$$

We write the derivative $\partial\mathbf{D}/\partial t$ as $\hat{f}\mathbf{E}$, where $\hat{f}$ is the operator $\partial\hat{\epsilon}/\partial t$, and ascertain the effect of this operator on a function of the form (61.6). If $\mathbf{E}_0$ were a constant, we should have simply $\hat{f}\mathbf{E} = f(\omega)\mathbf{E}$, where $f(\omega) = -i\omega\epsilon(\omega)$. We expand the function $\mathbf{E}_0(t)$ as a series of Fourier components $\mathbf{E}_{0\alpha}e^{-i\alpha t}$, with constant $\mathbf{E}_{0\alpha}$. Since $\mathbf{E}_0(t)$ varies only slowly, this series will include only components with $\alpha \ll \omega_0$. We can therefore put

$$\begin{aligned}\hat{f}\mathbf{E}_{0\alpha}e^{-i(\omega_0+\alpha)} &= f(\alpha+\omega_0)\mathbf{E}_{0\alpha}e^{-i(\omega_0+\alpha)t}\\ &\cong f(\omega_0)\mathbf{E}_{0\alpha}e^{-i(\omega_0+\alpha)t}+\alpha\frac{df(\omega_0)}{d\omega_0}\mathbf{E}_{0\alpha}e^{-i(\omega_0+\alpha)t}.\end{aligned}$$

Summing the Fourier components, we have

$$\hat{f}\mathbf{E}_0(t)e^{-i\omega_0 t} = f(\omega_0)\mathbf{E}_0 e^{-i\omega_0 t}+i\frac{df(\omega_0)}{d\omega_0}\frac{\partial\mathbf{E}_0}{\partial t}e^{-i\omega_0 t}.$$

Omitting henceforward the suffix 0 to ω, we thus obtain

$$\frac{\partial\mathbf{D}}{\partial t} = -i\omega\epsilon(\omega)\mathbf{E}+\frac{d(\omega\epsilon)}{d\omega}\frac{\partial\mathbf{E}_0}{\partial t}e^{-i\omega t}. \tag{61.8}$$

Substituting this expression in (61.7) and neglecting the imaginary part of $\epsilon(\omega)$ gives

$$\frac{1}{16\pi}\frac{d(\omega\epsilon)}{d\omega}\left(\mathbf{E}_0^*\cdot\frac{\partial\mathbf{E}_0}{\partial t}+\mathbf{E}_0\cdot\frac{\partial\mathbf{E}_0^*}{\partial t}\right) = \frac{1}{16\pi}\frac{d(\omega\epsilon)}{d\omega}\frac{d}{dt}(\mathbf{E}\cdot\mathbf{E}^*),$$

since $\mathbf{E}\cdot\mathbf{E}^* = \mathbf{E}_0\cdot\mathbf{E}_0^*$. Adding a similar expression involving the magnetic field, we conclude that the steady rate of change of the energy in unit volume is given by $d\bar{U}/dt$, where

$$\bar{U} = \frac{1}{16\pi}\left[\frac{d(\omega\epsilon)}{d\omega}\mathbf{E}\cdot\mathbf{E}^*+\frac{d(\omega\mu)}{d\omega}\mathbf{H}\cdot\mathbf{H}^*\right]. \tag{61.9}$$

In terms of the real fields **E** and **H** this expression can be written

$$\bar{U} = \frac{1}{8\pi}\left[\frac{\mathrm{d}(\omega\epsilon)}{\mathrm{d}\omega}\overline{E^2} + \frac{\mathrm{d}(\omega\mu)}{\mathrm{d}\omega}\overline{H^2}\right]. \tag{61.10}$$

This is the required result: $\bar{U}$ is the mean value of the electromagnetic part of the internal energy per unit volume of a transparent medium. If there is no dispersion, ϵ and μ are constants, and (61.10) becomes the mean value of (61.3), as it should.

If the external supply of electromagnetic energy to the body is cut off, the absorption which is always present (even though very small) ultimately converts the energy $\bar{U}$ entirely into heat. Since, by the law of increase of entropy, there must be evolution and not absorption of heat, we must have $\bar{U} > 0$. It therefore follows, by (61.9), that the inequalities $\mathrm{d}(\omega\epsilon)/\mathrm{d}\omega > 0$, $\mathrm{d}(\omega\mu)/\mathrm{d}\omega > 0$ must hold. In reality, these conditions are necessarily fulfilled, by virtue of more stringent inequalities always satisfied by the functions $\epsilon(\omega)$ and $\mu(\omega)$ in transparency ranges (see §64).†

Considerable interest attaches to the determination of the (time) average stress tensor giving the forces on matter in a variable electromagnetic field. This problem is meaningful for both absorbing and non-absorbing media, whereas that concerning the internal energy can be proposed only if absorption is neglected. The corresponding formulae, however, have not yet been derived.

§62. The relation between the real and imaginary parts of $\epsilon(\omega)$

The function $f(\tau)$ in (58.3) is finite for all values of τ, including zero.‡ For dielectrics it tends to zero as $\tau \to \infty$. This simply expresses the fact that the value of $\mathbf{D}(t)$ at any instant cannot be appreciably affected by the values of $\mathbf{E}(t)$ at remote instants. The physical agency underlying the integral relation (58.3) consists in the processes of the establishment of the electric polarisation. Hence the range of values in which the function $f(\tau)$ differs appreciably from zero is of the order of the relaxation time which characterises these processes.

The above statements are true also of metals, the only difference being that the function $f(\tau) - 4\pi\sigma$, rather than $f(\tau)$ itself, tends to zero as $\tau \to \infty$. This difference arises because the passage of a steady conduction current, though it does not cause any actual change in the physical state of the metal, in our equations leads formally to the presence of an induction **D** such that

† The sum of the inequalities (64.1) and (64.2) shows, in fact, that the derivative $\mathrm{d}(\omega\epsilon)/\mathrm{d}\omega$ always exceeds unity.

‡ It was to ensure this that the term $\mathbf{E}(t)$ was separated in (58.3), since otherwise the function $f(\tau)$ would have a delta-function singularity at $\tau = 0$.

$(1/c)\partial\mathbf{D}/\partial t = 4\pi\sigma\mathbf{E}/c$ or

$$\mathbf{D}(t) = \int_{-\infty}^{t} 4\pi\sigma\mathbf{E}(\tau)\,d\tau = 4\pi\sigma\int_{0}^{\infty}\mathbf{E}(t-\tau)\,d\tau.$$

We have defined the function $\epsilon(\omega)$ by

$$\epsilon(\omega) = 1 + \int_{0}^{\infty} e^{i\omega\tau} f(\tau)\,d\tau. \tag{62.1}$$

It is possible to derive some very general relations concerning this function by using the methods of the theory of functions of a complex variable. To do so, we regard ω as a complex variable ($\omega = \omega' + i\omega''$), and ascertain the properties of the function $\epsilon(\omega)$ in the upper half of the ω-plane. From the definition (62.1) and the above-mentioned properties of the function $f(\tau)$, it follows that $\epsilon(\omega)$ is a one-valued regular function everywhere in the upper half-plane. For, when $\omega'' > 0$, the integrand in (62.1) includes the exponentially decreasing factor $e^{-\omega''\tau}$ and, since the function $f(\tau)$ is finite throughout the region of integration, the integral converges. The function $\epsilon(\omega)$ has no singularity on the real axis ($\omega'' = 0$), except possibly at the origin (where, for metals, $\epsilon(\omega)$ has a simple pole).†

It is useful to notice that the conclusion that $\epsilon(\omega)$ is regular in the upper half-plane is, physically, a consequence of the causality principle. The integration in (58.3) is, on account of this principle, taken only over times previous to t, and the region of integration in formula (62.1) therefore extends from 0 to ∞ rather than from $-\infty$ to ∞.

It is evident also from the definition (62.1) that

$$\epsilon(-\omega^*) = \epsilon^*(\omega). \tag{62.2}$$

This generalises the relation (58.7) for real ω. In particular, for purely imaginary ω we have $\epsilon(i\omega'') = \epsilon^*(i\omega'')$, i.e. the function $\epsilon(\omega)$ is real on the imaginary axis:

$$\operatorname{im}\epsilon = 0 \quad \text{for} \quad \omega = i\omega''. \tag{62.3}$$

It should be emphasised that the property (62.2) merely expresses the fact that the operator relation $\mathbf{D} = \hat{\epsilon}\mathbf{E}$ must give real values of $\mathbf{D}$ for real $\mathbf{E}$. If the function $\mathbf{E}(t)$ is given by the real expression

$$\mathbf{E} = \mathbf{E}_0 e^{-i\omega t} + \mathbf{E}_0^* e^{i\omega^* t}, \tag{62.4}$$

† In the lower half-plane, the definition (62.1) is invalid, since the integral diverges. Hence the function $\epsilon(\omega)$ can be defined in the lower half-plane only as the analytical continuation of formula (62.1) from the upper half-plane, and in general has singularities.

The function $\epsilon(\omega)$ has a physical as well as a mathematical significance in the upper half-plane: it gives the relation between $\mathbf{D}$ and $\mathbf{E}$ for fields whose amplitude increases as $e^{\omega'' t}$. In the lower half-plane, this physical interpretation is not possible, if only because the presence of a field which is damped as $e^{-|\omega''|t}$ implies an infinite field for $t \to -\infty$.

then, applying the operator $\hat{\epsilon}$ to each term, we have

$$\mathbf{D} = \epsilon(\omega)\mathbf{E}_0 e^{-i\omega t} + \epsilon(-\omega^*)\mathbf{E}_0{}^* e^{i\omega^* t},$$

and the condition for this to be real is just (62.2).

According to the results of §61, the imaginary part of $\epsilon(\omega)$ is positive for positive real $\omega = \omega'$, i.e. on the right-hand half of the real axis. Since, by (62.2), im $\epsilon(-\omega') = -$im $\epsilon(\omega')$, the imaginary part of $\epsilon(\omega)$ is negative on the left-hand half of this axis. Thus

$$\text{im}\,\epsilon \gtrless 0 \quad \text{for} \quad \omega = \omega' \gtrless 0. \tag{62.5}$$

At $\omega = 0$, im ϵ changes sign, passing through zero for dielectrics and through infinity for metals. This is the only point on the real axis for which im $\epsilon(\omega)$ can vanish.

When ω tends to infinity in any manner in the upper half-plane, $\epsilon(\omega)$ tends to unity. This has been shown in §59 for the case where ω tends to infinity along the real axis. The general result is seen from formula (62.1): if $\omega \to \infty$ in such a way that $\omega'' \to \infty$, the integral in (62.1) vanishes because of the factor $e^{-\omega''\tau}$ in the integrand, while if ω'' remains finite but $|\omega'| \to \infty$ the integral vanishes because of the oscillating factor $e^{i\omega'\tau}$.

The above properties of the function $\epsilon(\omega)$ are sufficient to prove the following theorem: the function $\epsilon(\omega)$ does not take real values at any finite point in the upper half-plane except on the imaginary axis, where it decreases monotonically from $\epsilon_0 > 1$ (for dielectrics) or from $+\infty$ (for metals) at $\omega = i0$ to 1 at $\omega = i\infty$. Hence, in particular, it follows that the function $\epsilon(\omega)$ has no zeros in the upper half-plane.

We shall not pause to prove this theorem, because it is identical with a general theorem concerning the "generalised susceptibility" (and the properties of $\epsilon(\omega)$ enumerated above exhibit a similar analogy).† For the same reason, the function $\epsilon(\omega)$ satisfies the general relations between the real and imaginary parts of the generalised susceptibility. We shall repeat here the derivation of these relations, in order to emphasise certain differences between dielectrics and metals.

Let us take some real value ω_0 of ω, and integrate the expression $(\epsilon-1)/(\omega-\omega_0)$ round the contour C shown in Fig. 29. This contour in-

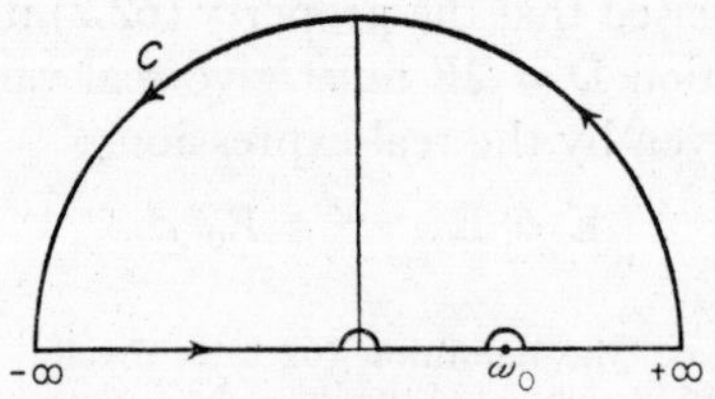

FIG. 29

† See *Statistical Physics*, §122, Pergamon Press, London, 1958. The generalised susceptibility $\alpha(\omega)$ used there corresponds to $\epsilon(\omega) - 1$, which vanishes as $\omega \to \infty$.

cludes the whole of the real axis, indented upwards at the point $\omega = \omega_0 > 0$, and also at the point $\omega = 0$ if the latter is (as in metals) a pole of the function $\epsilon(\omega)$, and is completed by a semicircle of infinite radius. At infinity $\epsilon \to 1$, and the function $(\epsilon-1)/(\omega-\omega_0)$ therefore tends to zero more rapidly than $1/\omega$. The integral

$$\int_C \frac{\epsilon - 1}{\omega - \omega_0} d\omega \tag{62.6}$$

consequently converges; since $\epsilon(\omega)$ is regular in the upper half-plane, and the point $\omega = \omega_0$ has been excluded from the region of integration, the function $(\epsilon-1)/(\omega-\omega_0)$ is analytic everywhere inside the contour C, and the integral is therefore zero.

The integral along the semicircle at infinity is also zero. We pass round the point ω_0 along a semicircle whose radius $\rho \to 0$. The direction of integration is clockwise, and the contribution to the integral is $-i\pi[\epsilon(\omega_0)-1]$. If the function $\epsilon(\omega)$ pertains to a dielectric, the indentation at the origin is unnecessary, and we therefore have

$$\lim_{\rho \to 0}\left\{ \int_{-\infty}^{-\rho+\omega_0} \frac{\epsilon - 1}{\omega - \omega_0} d\omega + \int_{\rho+\omega_0}^{\infty} \frac{\epsilon - 1}{\omega - \omega_0} d\omega \right\} - i\pi[\epsilon(\omega_0) - 1] = 0.$$

The expression in the braces is the integral from $-\infty$ to ∞, taken as a principal value. Thus we have

$$P\int_{-\infty}^{\infty} \frac{\epsilon - 1}{\omega - \omega_0} d\omega - i\pi[\epsilon(\omega_0) - 1] = 0. \tag{62.7}$$

Here the variable of integration ω takes only real values. We replace it by x, call the given real value ω instead of ω_0, and write the function $\epsilon(\omega)$ of the real variable ω, as in §58, in the form $\epsilon(\omega) = \epsilon'(\omega)+i\epsilon''(\omega)$. Taking the real and imaginary parts of (62.7), we obtain the following two formulae:

$$\epsilon'(\omega) - 1 = \frac{1}{\pi} P\int_{-\infty}^{\infty} \frac{\epsilon''(x)}{x - \omega} dx, \tag{62.8}$$

$$\epsilon''(\omega) = -\frac{1}{\pi} P\int_{-\infty}^{\infty} \frac{\epsilon'(x) - 1}{x - \omega} dx, \tag{62.9}$$

first derived by H. A. Kramers and R. de L. Kronig (1927). It should be emphasised that the only important property of the function $\epsilon(\omega)$ used in the proof is that it is regular in the upper half-plane.† Hence we can say that Kramers and Kronig's formulae, like this property of $\epsilon(\omega)$, are a direct consequence of the causality principle.

Using the fact that $\epsilon''(x)$ is an odd function, we can rewrite (62.8) as

$$\epsilon'(\omega) - 1 = \frac{1}{\pi} P \int_0^\infty \frac{\epsilon''(x)}{x - \omega} dx + \frac{1}{\pi} P \int_0^\infty \frac{\epsilon''(x)}{x + \omega} dx$$

$$= \frac{2}{\pi} P \int_0^\infty \frac{x\epsilon''(x)}{x^2 - \omega^2} dx. \tag{62.10}$$

If a metal is concerned, the function $\epsilon(\omega)$ has a pole at the point $\omega = 0$, near which $\epsilon = 4\pi i\sigma/\omega$ (58.9). The passage along a semicircle round this point gives a further real term $-(4\pi\sigma/\omega_0)\pi$, which must be added to the left-hand side of equation (62.7). Thus formula (62.9) becomes

$$\epsilon''(\omega) = -\frac{1}{\pi} P \int_{-\infty}^\infty \frac{\epsilon'(x) - 1}{x - \omega} dx + \frac{4\pi\sigma}{\omega}, \tag{62.11}$$

but (62.8) and (62.10) remain unchanged. A further remark is also necessary as regards metals. We have said at the end of §58 that there may be ranges of frequency for metals in which the function $\epsilon(\omega)$ becomes physically meaningless on account of the spatial non-uniformity of the field. In the formulae given here, however, the integration must be taken over all frequencies. In such cases $\epsilon(\omega)$ must be taken, in the frequency ranges concerned, as the function obtained by solving the formal problem of the behaviour of the body in a fictitious uniform periodic electric field (and not in the necessarily non-uniform field of the electromagnetic wave).

Formula (62.10) is of particular importance: it makes possible a calculation of the function $\epsilon'(\omega)$ if the function $\epsilon''(\omega)$ is known even approximately (for example, empirically) for a given body. It is important to note that, for any function $\epsilon''(\omega)$ satisfying the physically necessary condition $\epsilon'' > 0$ for $\omega > 0$, formula (62.10) gives a function $\epsilon'(\omega)$ consistent with all physical requirements, i.e. one which is in principle possible (the sign and magnitude of ϵ' are subject to no general physical restrictions). This makes it possible to use formula (62.10) even when the function $\epsilon''(\omega)$ is approximate. Formula (62.9), on the other hand, does not give a physically possible function $\epsilon''(\omega)$ for an arbitrary choice of the function $\epsilon'(\omega)$, since the condition that $\epsilon''(\omega) > 0$ is not necessarily fulfilled.

---

† The property $\epsilon \to 1$ as $\omega \to \infty$ is not important: if the limit $\epsilon(\infty)$ were other than unity, we should simply take $\epsilon - \epsilon(\infty)$ in place of $\epsilon - 1$, with corresponding obvious changes in formulae (62.8), (62.9).

In dispersion theory the expression for $\epsilon'(\omega)$ is customarily written in the form

$$\epsilon'(\omega) - 1 = -\frac{4\pi e^2}{m} P \int_0^\infty \frac{f(x)}{\omega^2 - x^2}\,dx, \tag{62.12}$$

where e and m are the charge and mass of the electron, and $f(\omega)\,d\omega$ is called the *oscillator strength* (or "number of dispersion electrons") in the frequency range $d\omega$. According to (62.10), this quantity is related to $\epsilon''(\omega)$ by

$$f(\omega) = \frac{m}{2\pi^2 e^2}\,\omega\epsilon''(\omega). \tag{62.13}$$

For metals, $f(\omega)$ tends to a finite limit as $\omega \to 0$.

For sufficiently large ω, x^2 can be neglected in comparison with ω^2 in the integrand in (62.10). Then

$$\epsilon'(\omega) - 1 = -\frac{2}{\pi\omega^2}\int_0^\infty x\epsilon''(x)\,dx.$$

For the dielectric constant at high frequencies, on the other hand, formula (59.1) holds, and a comparison shows that

$$\frac{m}{2\pi^2 e^2}\int_0^\infty \omega\epsilon''(\omega)\,d\omega = \int_0^\infty f(\omega)\,d\omega = N, \tag{62.14}$$

where N is the total number of electrons per unit volume.

If $\epsilon''(\omega)$ is regular at $\omega = 0$, we can take the limit $\omega \to 0$ in formula (62.10), obtaining

$$\epsilon'(0) - 1 = \frac{2}{\pi}\int_0^\infty \frac{\epsilon''(x)}{x}\,dx. \tag{62.15}$$

If the point $\omega = 0$ is a singularity of $\epsilon''(\omega)$ (as in metals), the limit of the integral (62.10) as $\omega \to 0$ is not what is obtained by simply deleting the term in ω. To calculate the limit, we must first replace $\epsilon''(x)$ in the integrand by $\epsilon''(x) - 4\pi\sigma/x$; the value of the integral is unchanged, because

$$P\int_0^\infty \frac{dx}{x^2 - \omega^2} \equiv 0.$$

For a dielectric, formula (62.15) can be rewritten as

$$\epsilon_0 - 1 = \frac{4\pi e^2 N}{m}\overline{\omega^{-2}}, \tag{62.16}$$

where the bar denotes averaging with respect to the "number of oscillators":

$$\overline{\omega^{-2}} = \frac{1}{N}\int_0^\infty \frac{f(\omega)}{\omega^2}\,d\omega.$$

The expression (62.16) may be useful in estimating ϵ_0.

The following formula† relates the values of $\epsilon(\omega)$ on the upper half of the imaginary axis to those of $\epsilon''(\omega)$ on the real axis:

$$\epsilon(i\omega) - 1 = \frac{2}{\pi}\int_0^\infty \frac{x\epsilon''(x)}{x^2+\omega^2}\,dx. \tag{62.17}$$

Integrating this relation over all ω, we obtain

$$\int_0^\infty [\epsilon(i\omega) - 1]\,d\omega = \int_0^\infty \epsilon''(\omega)\,d\omega. \tag{62.18}$$

All the above results are applicable, apart from slight changes, to the magnetic permeability $\mu(\omega)$. The differences are due principally to the fact that the function $\mu(\omega)$ ceases to be physically meaningful at relatively low frequencies. Hence, for example, Kramers and Kronig's formula must be applied to $\mu(\omega)$ as follows. We consider not an infinite but a finite range of ω (from 0 to ω_1), which extends only to frequencies where μ is still meaningful but no longer variable, so that its imaginary part may be taken as zero; let the real quantity $\mu(\omega_1)$ be denoted by μ_1. Then formula (62.10) must be written as

$$\mu'(\omega) - \mu_1 = \frac{2}{\pi}P\int_0^{\omega_1} \frac{x\mu''(x)}{x^2-\omega^2}\,dx. \tag{62.19}$$

Unlike ϵ_0, the value μ_0 of $\mu(0)$ may be either less than or greater than unity. The variation of $\mu(\omega)$ along the imaginary axis is again a monotonic decrease, from μ_0 to $\mu_1 < \mu_0$.

---

† See *Statistical Physics*, formula (122.19).

§63. A plane wave of a single frequency

Maxwell's equations (58.2) for a wave of a single frequency are

$$i\omega\mu(\omega)\mathbf{H} = c\,\mathbf{curl}\,\mathbf{E}, \qquad i\omega\epsilon(\omega)\,\mathbf{E} = -c\,\mathbf{curl}\,\mathbf{H}. \tag{63.1}$$

These equations as they stand are complete, since equations (58.1) follow from (63.1) and so do not require separate consideration. Assuming the medium homogeneous, and eliminating **H** from equations (63.1), we obtain the second-order equation

$$\triangle\mathbf{E} + \epsilon\mu(\omega^2/c^2)\mathbf{E} = 0; \tag{63.2}$$

elimination of **E** gives a similar equation for **H**.

Let us consider a plane electromagnetic wave propagated in an infinite homogeneous medium. In a plane wave in a vacuum, the space dependence of the field is given by a factor $e^{i\mathbf{k}\cdot\mathbf{r}}$, with a real wave vector **k**. In considering wave propagation in matter, however, it is in general necessary to take **k** complex: $\mathbf{k} = \mathbf{k}'+i\mathbf{k}''$, where the vectors $\mathbf{k}'$ and $\mathbf{k}''$ are real.

Taking **E** and **H** as proportional to $e^{i\mathbf{k}\cdot\mathbf{r}}$, and carrying out the differentiation with respect to the co-ordinates in equations (63.1), we obtain

$$\omega\mu\mathbf{H} = c\mathbf{k}\times\mathbf{E}, \qquad \omega\epsilon\mathbf{E} = -c\mathbf{k}\times\mathbf{H}. \tag{63.3}$$

Eliminating **E** and **H** from these two equations, we obtain for the square of the wave vector

$$k^2 \equiv k'^2 - k''^2 + 2i\mathbf{k}'\cdot\mathbf{k}'' = \epsilon\mu\omega^2/c^2. \tag{63.4}$$

We see that **k** can be real only if ϵ and μ are real and positive. Even then, however, **k** may still be complex if $\mathbf{k}'\cdot\mathbf{k}'' = 0$; we shall meet with such a case in discussing total reflection in §66.

It must be borne in mind that, in the general case of complex **k**, the term "plane wave" is purely conventional. Putting $e^{i\mathbf{k}\cdot\mathbf{r}} = e^{i\mathbf{k}'\cdot\mathbf{r}}e^{-\mathbf{k}''\cdot\mathbf{r}}$, we see that the planes perpendicular to the vector $\mathbf{k}'$ are planes of constant phase. The planes of constant amplitude, however, are those perpendicular to $\mathbf{k}''$, the direction in which the wave is damped. The surfaces on which the field itself is constant are in general not planes at all. Such waves are called *inhomogeneous plane waves*, in contradistinction to ordinary "homogeneous" plane waves.

The general relation between the electric and magnetic field components is given by formulae (63.3). In particular, taking the scalar product of these formulae with **k**, we obtain

$$\mathbf{k}\cdot\mathbf{E} = 0, \qquad \mathbf{k}\cdot\mathbf{H} = 0, \tag{63.5}$$

and, squaring either and using (63.4),

$$\mathbf{E}^2 = \mu\mathbf{H}^2/\epsilon. \tag{63.6}$$

It must be remembered, however, that because all three vectors **k**, **E** and **H** are complex these formulae do not in general have the same evident significance as when the vectors are real.

We shall not give the cumbersome relations valid in the general case, but consider only the most important particular cases. Especially simple results are obtained for a wave propagated without damping in a non-absorbing (transparent) homogeneous medium. The wave vector is real, and its magnitude is

$$k = \sqrt{(\epsilon\mu)}\omega/c = n\omega/c, \tag{63.7}$$

where $n = \sqrt{(\epsilon\mu)}$ is called the *refractive index* of the medium. The electric and magnetic fields are both in a plane perpendicular to the vector $\mathbf{k}$ (a pure transverse wave); they are mutually perpendicular, and are related by

$$\mathbf{H} = \sqrt{(\epsilon/\mu)}\mathbf{l} \times \mathbf{E}, \tag{63.8}$$

where $\mathbf{l}$ is a unit vector in the direction of $\mathbf{k}$. Hence it follows that $\epsilon E^2 = \mu H^2$, but this does not mean (as it would in the absence of dispersion) that the electric and magnetic energies in the wave are equal, since these energies are given by different expressions (namely, the two terms in formula (61.10)).

The velocity u with which the wave is propagated in the medium is given by the familiar expression for the group velocity:†

$$u = \frac{\mathrm{d}\omega}{\mathrm{d}k} = \frac{c}{\mathrm{d}(n\omega)/\mathrm{d}\omega}. \tag{63.9}$$

It is easy to verify that

$$u = \bar{S}/\bar{U}, \tag{63.10}$$

in accordance with its significance as the velocity of transfer of energy in the wave packet; here $\bar{U}$ is the energy density given by formula (61.9), and

$$\bar{S} = \frac{c}{8\pi}\sqrt{\frac{\epsilon}{\mu}}\mathbf{E}\cdot\mathbf{E}^* \tag{63.11}$$

is the mean value of the Poynting vector. In the absence of dispersion, when the refractive index is independent of frequency, the expression (63.9) becomes simply c/n; cf. (56.13).

Next, let us consider a more general case, the propagation of an electromagnetic wave in an absorbing medium, the wave vector having a definite direction (i.e. $\mathbf{k}'$ and $\mathbf{k}''$ being parallel). Then the wave is literally plane, since the surfaces of constant field in it are planes perpendicular to the direction of propagation (a *homogeneous plane wave*).

In this case we can introduce the "length" k of the wave vector, given by $\mathbf{k} = k\mathbf{l}$ ($\mathbf{l}$ being a unit vector in the direction of $\mathbf{k}'$ and $\mathbf{k}''$), and from (63.4) we have $k = \sqrt{(\epsilon\mu)}\omega/c$. The complex quantity $\sqrt{(\epsilon\mu)}$ is usually written in the form $n+i\kappa$, with real n and κ, so that

$$k = \sqrt{(\epsilon\mu)}\omega/c = (n + i\kappa)\omega/c. \tag{63.12}$$

† When considerable absorption occurs, the group velocity cannot be used, since in an absorbing medium wave packets are not propagated but rapidly "ironed out".

The quantity n is called the *refractive index* of the medium, and κ the *absorption coefficient*; the latter gives the rate of damping of the wave during its propagation. It should be emphasised, however, that the damping of the wave need not be due to true absorption: dissipation of energy occurs only when ϵ and μ are complex, but κ is different from zero if ϵ and μ are real and of opposite sign.

We may express n and κ in terms of the real and imaginary parts of the dielectric constant (taking $\mu = 1$). From the equation

$$n^2 - \kappa^2 + 2in\kappa = \epsilon = \epsilon' + i\epsilon''$$

we have $n^2 - \kappa^2 = \epsilon'$, $2n\kappa = \epsilon''$. Solving these equations for n and κ, we have†

$$\begin{aligned} n &= \sqrt{\{\tfrac{1}{2}[\epsilon' + \sqrt{(\epsilon'^2 + {}''\epsilon^2)}]\}}, \\ \kappa &= \sqrt{\{\tfrac{1}{2}[-\epsilon' + \sqrt{(\epsilon'^2 + \epsilon''^2)}]\}}. \end{aligned} \tag{63.13}$$

In particular, for metals and in the frequency range where formula (58.9) is valid, the imaginary part of ϵ is large compared with its real part, and is related to the conductivity by $\epsilon'' = 4\pi\sigma/\omega$; neglecting ϵ' in comparison with ϵ'', we find that n and κ are equal:

$$n = \kappa = \sqrt{(2\pi\sigma/\omega)}. \tag{63.14}$$

The relation between the fields **E** and **H** in this homogeneous plane wave is again given by formula (63.8), but ϵ and μ are now complex. The formula again shows that the two fields and the direction of propagation are mutually perpendicular. If $\mu = 1$, we write $\sqrt{\epsilon} = \sqrt{(n^2+\kappa^2)}\exp[i\tan^{-1}(\kappa/n)]$, which shows that the magnetic field is $\sqrt{(n^2+\kappa^2)}$ times the electric field in magnitude and $\tan^{-1}(\kappa/n)$ from it in phase; in particular, when (63.14) holds, the phase difference is $\frac{1}{4}\pi$.

PROBLEM

At a given instant $t = 0$ an electromagnetic perturbation occurs in some region of space. The perturbation is not maintained by external agencies, and is therefore damped in time. Find the damping decrement.

SOLUTION. We expand the initial perturbation as a Fourier integral with respect to the co-ordinates, and consider a component having a (real) wave vector $\mathbf{k}$. The time dependence of this component is given, for sufficiently large t, by a factor $e^{-i\omega t}$ with a complex "frequency" ω, which is to be determined; the damping decrement is $-\mathrm{im}\,\omega$.

From the equations $-\dot{\mathbf{H}}/c = \mathbf{curl}\,\mathbf{E} = i\mathbf{k}\times\mathbf{E}$, $\dot{\mathbf{D}}/c = \mathbf{curl}\,\mathbf{H} = i\mathbf{k}\times\mathbf{H}$ we have, eliminating $\mathbf{H}$,

$$\ddot{\mathbf{D}}/c^2 = \mathbf{k}\times(\mathbf{k}\times\mathbf{E}). \tag{1}$$

We take the direction of $\mathbf{k}$ as the x-axis. The "longitudinal" part of the perturbation therefore satisfies $\ddot{D}_x = 0$, whence $D_x = 0$.

---

† Since $\epsilon'' > 0$, the signs of n and κ must be the same, in accordance with the fact that the wave is damped in the direction of propagation. The choice of positive signs in (63.13) corresponds to a wave propagated in the positive x-direction.

The relation between D_x and E_x is of the form

$$E_x(t) = \hat{\epsilon}^{-1}D_x = \int_{-\infty} F(t-\tau)D_x(\tau)\,\mathrm{d}\tau; \tag{2}$$

cf. §58. Since we have $D_x(\tau) = 0$ for $\tau > 0$, it follows that

$$E_x(t) = \int_{-\infty}^{0} F(t-\tau)D_x(\tau)\,\mathrm{d}\tau. \tag{3}$$

Hence we see that, for large t, the time dependence of E_x is given essentially by that of the function $F(t)$.

For a field of a single frequency, (2) gives

$$\frac{1}{\epsilon(\omega)} = \int_{0}^{\infty} F(x)e^{i\omega x}\,\mathrm{d}x,$$

or, conversely,

$$F(t) = \frac{1}{2\pi}\int_{-\infty}^{\infty} \frac{1}{\epsilon(\omega)}e^{-i\omega t}\,\mathrm{d}\omega.$$

To estimate this integral for large t, we displace the path of integration into the lower half-plane of ω, where the integrand decreases rapidly. The singularities of the function $1/\epsilon(\omega)$, i.e. the zeros and branch points of $\epsilon(\omega)$, must be excluded from the contour. The integral is then essentially proportional to $e^{-i\omega_0 t}$, where ω_0 is the singularity nearest the real axis. This gives the solution for the longitudinal part of the perturbation.

For the transverse components, we have from (1) $\ddot{D}_{y,z}/c^2+k^2E_{y,z} = 0$. A similar analysis gives the result that the required "frequency" ω_0 is in this case the zero or branch point of the function $\omega^2\epsilon(\omega)-c^2k^2$ which lies nearest the real axis.

§64. Transparent media

Let us apply the general formulae derived in §62 to media which absorb only slightly in a given range of frequencies, i.e. assuming that for these frequencies the imaginary part of the dielectric permeability may be neglected.

In such a case there is no need to take the principal value in formula (62.10), since the point $x = \omega$ does not in practice lie in the region of integration. The integral can then be differentiated in the usual way with respect to the parameter ω, giving

$$\frac{\mathrm{d}\epsilon}{\mathrm{d}\omega} = \frac{4\omega}{\pi}\int_{0}^{\infty} \frac{x\epsilon''(x)}{(\omega^2 - x^2)^2}\,\mathrm{d}x.$$

Since the integrand is positive throughout the region of integration, we conclude that

$$\mathrm{d}\epsilon(\omega)/\mathrm{d}\omega > 0, \tag{64.1}$$

i.e. if absorption is absent the dielectric constant is a monotonically increasing function of the frequency.

Similarly, in the same frequency range we obtain another inequality,

$$\frac{\mathrm{d}}{\mathrm{d}\omega}[\omega^2(\epsilon-1)] = \frac{4\omega}{\pi}\int_0^\infty \frac{x^3\epsilon''(x)}{(x^2-\omega^2)^2}\mathrm{d}x > 0,$$

or

$$\mathrm{d}\epsilon/\mathrm{d}\omega > 2(1-\epsilon)/\omega. \tag{64.2}$$

If $\epsilon < 1$, this inequality is more stringent than (64.1).

It may be noted that the inequalities (64.1) and (64.2) (together with the corresponding ones for $\mu(\omega)$) ensure that the inequality $u < c$ is satisfied by the velocity of propagation of waves. For example, if $\mu = 1$ we have $n = \sqrt{\epsilon}$ and, replacing ϵ by n^2 in (64.1) and (64.2),

$$\mathrm{d}(n\omega)/\mathrm{d}\omega > n, \qquad \mathrm{d}(n\omega)/\mathrm{d}\omega > 1/n. \tag{64.3}$$

Thus we obtain two inequalities for the velocity u (63.9): $u < c/n$ and $u < cn$, whence $u < c$ whether $n < 1$ or $n > 1$. These inequalities also show that $u > 0$, i.e. the group velocity is in the same direction as the wave vector. This is quite natural, even if not logically necessary.

Let us suppose that the weak absorption extends over a wide range of frequencies, from ω_1 to ω_2 ($\gg \omega_1$), and consider frequencies ω such that $\omega_1 \ll \omega \ll \omega_2$. The region of integration in (62.10) divides into two parts, $x < \omega_1$ and $x > \omega_2$. In the former region we can neglect x in comparison with ω, and in the latter region ω in comparison with x, in the denominator of the integrand:

$$\epsilon(\omega) = 1 + \frac{2}{\pi}\int_{\omega_2}^\infty \epsilon''(x)\frac{\mathrm{d}x}{x} - \frac{2}{\pi\omega^2}\int_0^{\omega_1} x\epsilon''(x)\,\mathrm{d}x, \tag{64.4}$$

i.e. the function $\epsilon(\omega)$ in this range is of the form $a - b/\omega^2$, where a and b are positive constants. The constant b can be expressed in terms of the "number of dispersion electrons" N_1 responsible for the absorption in the range from 0 to ω_1 (cf. (62.14)):

$$\epsilon(\omega) = a - 4\pi N_1 e^2/m\omega^2. \tag{64.5}$$

From this expression it follows, in particular, that, when the region of weak absorption is sufficiently wide, the dielectric permeability in general passes through zero. In this connection it should be recalled that a literally "transparent" medium is one in which $\epsilon(\omega)$ is not only real but also positive; if ϵ is negative, the wave is damped inside the medium, even though no true dissipation of energy occurs.

For the frequency at which $\epsilon = 0$ the induction $\mathbf{D}$ is zero identically, and Maxwell's equations admit a variable electric field satisfying the single equation $\mathbf{curl}\,\mathbf{E} = 0$, with zero magnetic field. In other words, longitudinal electric waves can occur. To determine their velocity of propagation, we must take into account the dispersion of the dielectric permeability not only in frequency, but also with respect to the wave vector. The value of ω for which $\epsilon = 0$ is also a function of the wave vector. If the medium is isotropic, the next term after the zero-order term in the expansion of the scalar function $\omega(\mathbf{k})$ for which $\epsilon[\omega(\mathbf{k})] = 0$ is proportional to k^2: $\omega = \omega_0 + \frac{1}{2}\alpha\mathbf{k}^2$. Hence the velocity of propagation is $\mathbf{u} = \partial\omega/\partial\mathbf{k} = \alpha\mathbf{k}$, and is proportional to the wave vector itself.

PROBLEM

A plane electromagnetic wave with a sharply defined forward front is incident normally on the boundary of a half-space ($x > 0$) occupied by a transparent medium with $\mu = 1$. Determine the structure of the front of the transmitted wave (A. SOMMERFELD and L. BRILLOUIN, 1914).

SOLUTION. Let the wave be incident on the boundary of the medium at time $t = 0$, so that at $x = 0$ the field (E or H) of the incident wave is $E = 0$ for $t < 0$, $E \sim e^{-i\omega_0 t}$ for $t > 0$. Expanding this field as a Fourier integral with respect to time, we reduce the problem to that of waves of various frequencies and infinite extent incident on the boundary. The amplitude of the Fourier component of frequency ω is proportional to

$$\int_0^\infty e^{i(\omega-\omega_0)\tau}\, d\tau.$$

When a wave of frequency ω is incident, the transmitted wave is of the form $a(\omega)\, e^{-i\omega t + i\omega nx/c}$, where the amplitude $a(\omega)$ is a slowly varying function of frequency. Hence the wave field in the medium in the present problem is

$$E \sim \int_{-\infty}^{\infty} d\omega\, a(\omega) e^{-i\omega t + i\omega nx/c} \int_0^\infty e^{i(\omega-\omega_0)\tau}\, d\tau.$$

In the region near the wave front, the important values of ω in this integral are those close to ω_0. Using a new variable $\xi = \omega - \omega_0$, we replace $a(\omega)$ by $a(\omega_0)$, and expand the exponent in powers of ξ. Omitting unimportant constants and phase factors, we have

$$E \sim \int_0^\infty \int_{-\infty}^{\infty} \exp\left\{i\xi\left(\tau - t + \frac{x}{u}\right) - \tfrac{1}{2}i\xi^2 x \frac{u'}{u^2}\right\} d\xi\, d\tau,$$

where $u = u(\omega_0)$ is the velocity of propagation (63.9), and $u' = [du/d\omega]_{\omega=\omega_0}$. Effecting the integration over ξ, we easily bring E to the form

$$E \sim \int_w^\infty e^{\mp i\eta^2}\, d\eta, \qquad w = (x - ut)/\sqrt{(2x|u'|)},$$

the sign in the exponent depending on that of u'. The intensity distribution near the wave front is given by

$$I \sim \left| \int_w^\infty e^{i\eta^2}\, d\eta \right|^2.$$

This expression is of the same form as that which gives the intensity distribution near the edge of the shadow in Fresnel diffraction.† For $w > 0$ the intensity decreases monotonically with increasing w, but for $w < 0$ it oscillates with decreasing amplitude about a constant value to which it tends as $w \to -\infty$.‡

† See *The Classical Theory of Fields*, §7–8.

‡ At large distances preceding the front here considered there are found "precursors" propagated with velocity c. These correspond to the high-frequency Fourier components, for which $\epsilon \to 1$.

CHAPTER X

THE PROPAGATION OF ELECTROMAGNETIC WAVES

§65. Geometrical optics

THE condition for geometrical optics† to be applicable is that the wavelength λ should be small in comparison with the characteristic dimension l of the problem. The relation between geometrical and wave optics is that, for $\lambda \ll l$, any quantity ϕ which describes the wave field (i.e. any component of **E** or **H**) is given by a formula of the type $\phi = ae^{i\psi}$ where the amplitude a is a slowly varying function of the co-ordinates and time, and the phase ψ is a large quantity which is "almost linear" in the co-ordinates and the time; it is called the *eikonal*, and is of great importance in geometrical optics. The time derivative of ψ gives the frequency of the wave:

$$\partial\psi/\partial t = -\omega, \tag{65.1}$$

and the space derivatives give the wave vector:

$$\mathbf{grad}\,\psi = \mathbf{k}, \tag{65.2}$$

and consequently the direction of the ray through any point in space.

For a steady wave of a single frequency, the frequency is a constant and the time dependence of the eikonal is given by a term $-\omega t$. We then introduce a function ψ_1 (also called the eikonal), such that

$$\psi = -\omega t + (\omega/c)\psi_1(x, y, z). \tag{65.3}$$

Then ψ_1 is a function of the co-ordinates only, and its gradient is

$$\mathbf{grad}\,\psi_1 = \mathbf{n}, \tag{65.4}$$

where $\mathbf{n}$ is a vector such that

$$\mathbf{k} = \omega\mathbf{n}/c. \tag{65.5}$$

The magnitude of $\mathbf{n}$ is equal to the refractive index n of the medium.‡ Hence the equation for the eikonal in ray propagation in a medium of refractive index $n(x, y, z)$ (a given function of the co-ordinates) is

$$|\mathbf{grad}\,\psi_1|^2 \equiv \left(\frac{\partial\psi_1}{\partial x}\right)^2 + \left(\frac{\partial\psi_1}{\partial y}\right)^2 + \left(\frac{\partial\psi_1}{\partial z}\right)^2 = n^2. \tag{65.6}$$

---

† See *The Classical Theory of Fields*, §7–1, Addison-Wesley Press, Cambridge (Mass.), 1951; Pergamon Press, London, 1959.

‡ Only transparent media are considered in geometrical optics.

The equation of ray propagation in a steady state can also be derived from *Fermat's principle*, according to which the integral $\int \mathbf{k}\cdot \mathrm{d}\mathbf{l}$ (or, equivalently, the integral $\psi_1 = \int \mathbf{n}\cdot\mathrm{d}\mathbf{l} = \int n\mathrm{d}l$) along the path of the ray between two given points A and B has a value less than for any other path between A and B. Equating to zero the variation of this integral, we have

$$\delta\psi_1 = \int_A^B (\delta n \mathrm{d}l + n\delta \mathrm{d}l) = 0.$$

Let $\delta\mathbf{r}$ be a displacement of the ray path under the variation. Then $\delta n = \delta\mathbf{r}\cdot\mathbf{grad}\, n$, $\delta\,\mathrm{d}l = \mathbf{l}\cdot\mathrm{d}\delta\mathbf{r}$, where $\mathbf{l}$ is a unit vector tangential to the ray. Substituting in $\delta\psi_1$ and integrating by parts in the second term (using the fact that $\delta\mathbf{r} = 0$ at A and B), we have

$$\delta\psi_1 = \int_A^B \delta\mathbf{r}\cdot\mathbf{grad}\, n\,\mathrm{d}l + \int_A^B n\mathbf{l}\cdot\mathrm{d}\delta\mathbf{r}$$

$$= \int_A^B \left(\mathbf{grad}\, n - \frac{\mathrm{d}(n\mathbf{l})}{\mathrm{d}l}\right)\cdot\delta\mathbf{r}\,\mathrm{d}l = 0.$$

Hence

$$\mathrm{d}(n\mathbf{l})/\mathrm{d}l = \mathbf{grad}\, n. \tag{65.7}$$

Expanding the derivative and putting $\mathrm{d}n/\mathrm{d}l = \mathbf{l}\cdot\mathbf{grad}\, n$, we obtain

$$\frac{\mathrm{d}\mathbf{l}}{\mathrm{d}l} = \frac{1}{n}[\mathbf{grad}\, n - \mathbf{l}(\mathbf{l}\cdot\mathbf{grad}\, n)]. \tag{65.8}$$

This is the equation giving the form of the rays.

We know from differential geometry that the derivative $\mathrm{d}\mathbf{l}/\mathrm{d}l$ along the ray is equal to $\mathbf{N}/R$, where $\mathbf{N}$ is the unit vector along the principal normal and R the radius of curvature. Taking the scalar product of both sides of (65.8) with $\mathbf{N}$, and using the fact that $\mathbf{N}$ and $\mathbf{l}$ are perpendicular, we have

$$\frac{1}{R} = \mathbf{N}\cdot\frac{\mathbf{grad}\, n}{n}; \tag{65.9}$$

the rays are therefore bent in the direction of increasing refractive index.

The velocity of propagation of rays in geometrical optics is in the direction of $\mathbf{l}$, and is given by the derivative

$$\mathbf{u} = \partial\omega/\partial\mathbf{k}. \tag{65.10}$$

This is also called the *group velocity*, the ratio ω/k being called the *phase velocity*. It must be remembered, however, that the latter is not the velocity of physical propagation of any quantity.

It is easy to derive also the equation which gives the rate of change of the radiation intensity along a ray. The intensity I is the magnitude of the (time) average Poynting vector. This vector, like the group velocity, is in the direction of $\mathbf{l}$: $\overline{\mathbf{S}} = I\mathbf{l}$. In a steady state, the mean field energy density is constant at any given point in space. The equation of conservation of energy is therefore div $\overline{\mathbf{S}} = 0$, or

$$\operatorname{div}(I\mathbf{l}) = 0. \tag{65.11}$$

This is the required equation.

Finally, let us consider how the direction of polarisation of linearly polarised radiation varies along a ray (S. M. Rytov, 1938). As we know from differential geometry, a curve in space (in this case, the ray) is characterised at every point by the mutually perpendicular unit vectors along the tangent ($\mathbf{l}$), the principal normal ($\mathbf{N}$) and the binormal ($\mathbf{b}$), which form the *natural trihedral*. Since the electromagnetic waves are transverse, the vectors $\mathbf{E}$ and $\mathbf{H}$ are always coplanar with $\mathbf{N}$ and $\mathbf{b}$.

Let the direction of $\mathbf{E}$ at some point on the ray be the same as that of $\mathbf{N}$, i.e. let $\mathbf{E}$ lie in the osculating plane (that of $\mathbf{N}$ and $\mathbf{l}$). The deviation of the curve from the osculating plane over a length $\mathrm{d}l$ is of the third order of smallness with respect to $\mathrm{d}l$. We can therefore say that, over a length $\mathrm{d}l$ of the ray, the vector $\mathbf{E}$ remains in the original osculating plane. The osculating plane at the other end of $\mathrm{d}l$ is inclined to the original one at an angle $\mathrm{d}\phi = \mathrm{d}l/T$, where T is the radius of torsion. This is therefore the angle turned through by the vector $\mathbf{E}$ relative to $\mathbf{N}$ in the normal plane. Thus, over a distance $\mathrm{d}l$ along the ray, the direction of polarisation rotates in the normal plane, its angle to the principal normal varying in accordance with the equation

$$\mathrm{d}\phi/\mathrm{d}l = 1/T. \tag{65.12}$$

In particular, when the torsion is zero, i.e. the ray is a plane curve, the direction of the vector $\mathbf{E}$ in the normal plane is constant, as is in any case evident from symmetry.

PROBLEM

Determine the velocity of propagation of light in a medium moving relative to the observer.

Solution. Let ω and $\mathbf{k}$ be the frequency and wave vector of the light wave in a fixed frame of reference K, and ω', $\mathbf{k}'$ the corresponding quantities in a frame K' moving with the medium at velocity $\mathbf{v}$ relative to K. In the first approximation with respect to v/c (the only one we shall consider), the motion perpendicular to $\mathbf{k}$ has no effect on the propagation of light, and so, without loss of generality, we can assume that $\mathbf{v}$ and $\mathbf{k}$ are in the same direction.

In the frame K' the medium is at rest, and ω' and k' are therefore related by

$$ck' = \omega' n(\omega'). \tag{1}$$

According to the relativistic transformation formulae† we have, as far as terms of the first

† See *The Classical Theory of Fields*, §6–4.

order in v/c, $\omega' = \omega - kv$, $k' = k - \omega v/c^2$. Substituting these expressions in (1) and expanding the function $n(\omega')$, we obtain to the same accuracy

$$k = n\frac{\omega}{c} + \frac{v\omega}{c^2}\left(1 - n\frac{\mathrm{d}(n\omega)}{\mathrm{d}\omega}\right), \tag{2}$$

where $n = n(\omega)$. The velocity of propagation (the group velocity) is therefore

$$u = u_0 + v\left(1 - \frac{u_0^2}{c^2}\right) - \frac{vn\omega}{c}\frac{\mathrm{d}u_0}{\mathrm{d}\omega}, \tag{3}$$

where $u_0 = c[\mathrm{d}(n\omega)/\mathrm{d}\omega]^{-1}$ is the velocity of propagation in a medium at rest. The phase velocity is

$$\frac{\omega}{k} = \frac{c}{n} + v\left(1 - \frac{1}{n^2} + \frac{\omega}{n}\frac{\mathrm{d}n}{\mathrm{d}\omega}\right).$$

The first two terms in (3) can also be obtained by simply applying the relativistic formula for the addition of velocities, and the third is a dispersion effect, first discussed by H. A. Lorentz.

§66. Reflection and refraction of electromagnetic waves

Let us consider the reflection and refraction of a plane electromagnetic wave (of a single frequency) at a plane boundary between two homogeneous media.† Medium 1, from which the wave is incident, is assumed transparent, but not (for the present) medium 2. Quantities pertaining to the incident and reflected waves will be distinguished by the suffixes 0 and 1 respectively, and those for the refracted wave by the suffix 2 (Fig. 30). The direction of the normal from the boundary plane into medium 2 is taken as the z-axis.

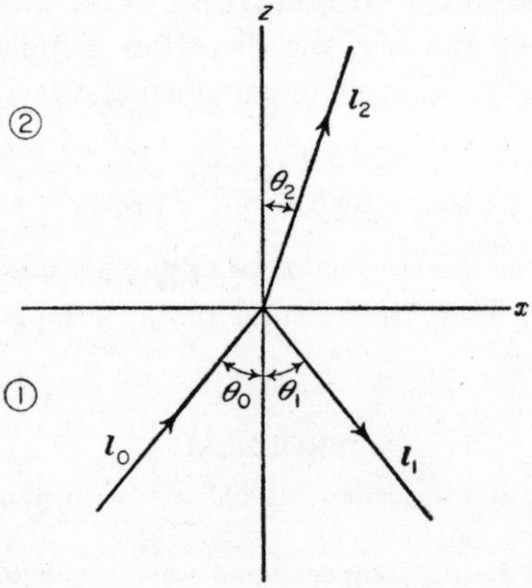

Fig. 30

Since there is complete homogeneity in the xy-plane, the dependence of the solution of the field equations on x and y must be the same in all space. The components k_x, k_y of the wave vector must therefore be the same for all three waves. Consequently, the directions of propagation of the three waves lie in one plane, which we take as the xz-plane.

† We take $\mu = 1$ in both media.

From the equations

$$k_{0x} = k_{1x} = k_{2x} \tag{66.1}$$

we find

$$\begin{aligned} k_{1z} &= -k_{0z} = -(\omega/c)\sqrt{\epsilon_1}\cos\theta_0, \\ k_{2z} &= \sqrt{[(\omega/c)^2\epsilon_2 - k_{0x}{}^2]} = (\omega/c)\sqrt{(\epsilon_2 - \epsilon_1\sin^2\theta_0)}. \end{aligned} \tag{66.2}$$

The vector $\mathbf{k}_0$ is, by definition, real, and so is $\mathbf{k}_1$. The quantity k_{2z}, however, is complex in an absorbing medium, and the sign of the root must be taken so that $\operatorname{im} k_{2z} > 0$, the refracted wave being damped towards the interior of medium 2.

If both media are transparent, equations (66.1) give the familiar laws of reflection and refraction:

$$\theta_1 = \theta_0, \qquad \frac{\sin\theta_2}{\sin\theta_0} = \sqrt{\frac{\epsilon_1}{\epsilon_2}} = \frac{n_1}{n_2}. \tag{66.3}$$

To determine the amplitudes of the reflected and refracted waves, we must use the boundary conditions at the surface of separation ($z = 0$), and we shall consider separately the two cases where the electric field $\mathbf{E}_0$ is in the plane of incidence and perpendicular to that plane; from the results we can obtain the solution for the general case, where $\mathbf{E}_0$ can be resolved into components in these two directions.

Let us first suppose that $\mathbf{E}_0$ is perpendicular to the plane of incidence. It is evident from symmetry that the same will be true of the fields $\mathbf{E}_1$ and $\mathbf{E}_2$ in the reflected and refracted waves. The vector $\mathbf{H}$ is in the xz-plane. The boundary conditions require† the continuity of $E_y = E$ and H_x; by (63.3) $H_x = -ck_zE_y/\omega$.

The field in medium 1 is the sum of the fields in the incident and reflected waves, so that we obtain the two equations $E_0+E_1 = E_2$, $k_{0z}(E_0-E_1)=k_{2z}E_2$. The exponential factors in E cancel because k_x (and therefore ω) is the same in all three waves. In what follows, $\mathbf{E}$ signifies the complex amplitude of a wave. The solution of the above equations gives *Fresnel's formulae*:

$$\begin{aligned} E_1 &= \frac{k_{0z} - k_{2z}}{k_{0z} + k_{2z}} E_0 = \frac{\sqrt{\epsilon_1}\cos\theta_0 - \sqrt{(\epsilon_2 - \epsilon_1\sin^2\theta_0)}}{\sqrt{\epsilon_1}\cos\theta_0 + \sqrt{(\epsilon_2 - \epsilon_1\sin^2\theta_0)}} E_0, \\ E_2 &= \frac{2k_{0z}}{k_{0z} + k_{2z}} E_0 = \frac{2\sqrt{\epsilon_1}\cos\theta_0}{\sqrt{\epsilon_1}\cos\theta_0 + \sqrt{(\epsilon_2 - \epsilon_1\sin^2\theta_0)}} E_0. \end{aligned} \tag{66.4}$$

† The boundary conditions on the normal components of $\mathbf{B}$ and $\mathbf{D}$ give nothing new in the present problem, because the equations $\operatorname{div}\mathbf{B} = 0$, $\operatorname{div}\mathbf{D} = 0$ are consequences of equations (63.1).

If both media are transparent, these formulae become, by (66.3),

$$E_1 = \frac{\sin(\theta_2 - \theta_0)}{\sin(\theta_2 + \theta_0)} E_0,$$
$$E_2 = \frac{2\cos\theta_0 \sin\theta_2}{\sin(\theta_2 + \theta_0)} E_0. \tag{66.5}$$

The case where **E** lies in the plane of incidence can be discussed similarly. Here it is more convenient to carry out the calculations for the magnetic field, which is perpendicular to the plane of incidence. A further two Fresnel's formulae are obtained:

$$H_1 = \frac{\epsilon_2 k_{0z} - \epsilon_1 k_{2z}}{\epsilon_2 k_{0z} + \epsilon_1 k_{2z}} H_0 = \frac{\epsilon_2 \cos\theta_0 - \sqrt{(\epsilon_1\epsilon_2 - \epsilon_1^2 \sin^2\theta_0)}}{\epsilon_2 \cos\theta_0 + \sqrt{(\epsilon_1\epsilon_2 - \epsilon_1^2 \sin^2\theta_0)}} H_0,$$
$$H_2 = \frac{2\epsilon_2 k_{0z}}{\epsilon_2 k_{0z} + \epsilon_1 k_{2z}} H_0 = \frac{2\epsilon_2 \cos\theta_0}{\epsilon_2 \cos\theta_0 + \sqrt{(\epsilon_1\epsilon_2 - \epsilon_1^2 \sin^2\theta_0)}} H_0. \tag{66.6}$$

If both media are transparent, these formulae may be written

$$H_1 = \frac{\tan(\theta_0 - \theta_2)}{\tan(\theta_0 + \theta_2)} H_0,$$
$$H_2 = \frac{\sin 2\theta_0}{\sin(\theta_0 + \theta_2)\cos(\theta_0 - \theta_2)} H_0. \tag{66.7}$$

The *reflection coefficient* R is defined as the ratio of the (time) average energy flux reflected from the surface to the incident flux. Each of these fluxes is given by the averaged z-component of the Poynting vector (63.11) for the wave in question,

$$R = \frac{\sqrt{\epsilon_1}\cos\theta_1 |\mathbf{E}_1|^2}{\sqrt{\epsilon_1}\cos\theta_0 |\mathbf{E}_0|^2} = \frac{|\mathbf{E}_1|^2}{|\mathbf{E}_0|^2}.$$

For normal incidence ($\theta = 0$) the two modes of polarisation are equivalent, and the reflection coefficient is given by

$$R = \left|\frac{\sqrt{\epsilon_1} - \sqrt{\epsilon_2}}{\sqrt{\epsilon_1} + \sqrt{\epsilon_2}}\right|^2. \tag{66.8}$$

This formula is valid whether the reflecting medium is transparent or not. If we put $\sqrt{\epsilon_2} = n_2 + i\kappa_2$, and if medium 1 is a vacuum ($\epsilon_1 = 1$), then

$$R = \frac{(n_2 - 1)^2 + \kappa_2^2}{(n_2 + 1)^2 + \kappa_2^2}. \tag{66.9}$$

The remaining discussion assumes that both media are transparent. The following general remark should be made first of all. The boundary between two different media is in reality not a geometrical surface but a thin transition layer. The validity of the formulae (66.1) does not rest on any assumptions concerning the nature of this layer. The derivation of Fresnel's formulae, on the other hand, is based on the use of the boundary conditions, and assumes that the thickness δ of the transition layer is small compared with the wavelength λ. The thickness δ is usually comparable with the distances between the atoms, which are always small compared with λ if the macroscopic description of the field is legitimate, and so the condition $\lambda \gg \delta$ is usually fulfilled. In the opposite limiting case the phenomenon of refraction is entirely different in character. For $\delta \gg \lambda$, geometrical optics is valid (λ being small compared with the dimensions of the inhomogeneities in the medium). In this case, therefore, the propagation of the wave can be regarded as the propagation of rays which undergo refraction in the transition layer but are not reflected from it. The reflection coefficient, therefore, would be zero.

Let us return now to Fresnel's formulae. In reflection from a transparent medium, the coefficients of proportionality between $\mathbf{E}_1$, $\mathbf{E}_2$ and $\mathbf{E}_0$ in these formulae are real.† This means that the wave phase either remains unchanged or changes by π, depending on the sign of the coefficients. In particular, the phase of the refracted wave is always the same as that of the incident wave. The reflection, on the other hand, may be accompanied by a change in phase.‡ For example, with normal incidence the phase of the wave is unchanged if $\epsilon_1 > \epsilon_2$, but if $\epsilon_1 < \epsilon_2$ the vectors $\mathbf{E}_1$ and $\mathbf{E}_0$ are in opposite directions, i.e. the wave phase changes by π.

The reflection coefficients for oblique incidence are, by (66.5) and (66.7),

$$R_\perp = \frac{\sin^2(\theta_2 - \theta_0)}{\sin^2(\theta_2 + \theta_0)}, \qquad R_\parallel = \frac{\tan^2(\theta_2 - \theta_0)}{\tan^2(\theta_2 + \theta_0)}. \tag{66.10}$$

Here, and in what follows, the suffixes $\perp$ and $\parallel$ refer to the cases where the field $\mathbf{E}$ is respectively perpendicular and parallel to the plane of incidence. The expressions (66.10) are unaltered when θ_2 and θ_0 are interchanged (but the phase of the reflected wave changes by π, as is seen from formulae (66.5) and (66.7)). The reflection coefficient for a wave incident from medium 1 at an angle θ_0 is therefore equal to that for a wave incident from medium 2 at an angle θ_2.

An interesting case is the reflection of light incident at an angle θ_0 such that $\theta_0 + \theta_2 = \frac{1}{2}\pi$ (the reflected and refracted rays being thus perpendicular). Let this angle be θ_p; $\sin\theta_p = \sin(\frac{1}{2}\pi - \theta_2) = \cos\theta_2$, and the law of refraction (66.3) gives

$$\tan\theta_p = \sqrt{(\epsilon_2/\epsilon_1)}. \tag{66.11}$$

† We ignore for the moment the possibility of total reflection (see below).

‡ Reflection from an absorbing medium leads in general to the appearance of elliptical polarisation. The explicit expressions for the amplitude and phase relations between the three waves are then extremely involved; they are given by J. A. Stratton, *Electromagnetic Theory*, Chapter IX, McGraw-Hill, New York, 1941.

For $\theta_0 = \theta_p$ we have $\tan(\theta_2+\theta_0) = \infty$, and $R_\parallel = 0$. Hence, whatever the direction of polarisation of light incident at this angle, the reflected light will be polarised so that the electric field is perpendicular to the plane of incidence. The reflected light is polarised in this way even when the incident light is natural: no component with any other polarisation is reflected. The angle θ_p is called the *angle of total polarisation* or the *Brewster angle*. It should be noticed that, whereas natural light can be totally polarised by reflection, this effect cannot be produced by refraction, whatever the angle of incidence.

The reflection and refraction of plane-polarised light always results in plane-polarised light, but the direction of polarisation is in general not the same as in the incident light. Let γ_0 be the angle between the direction of $\mathbf{E}_0$ and the plane of incidence, and γ_1, γ_2 the corresponding angles for the reflected and refracted waves. Using formulae (66.5) and (66.7), we easily obtain the relations

$$\tan\gamma_1 = -\frac{\cos(\theta_0-\theta_2)}{\cos(\theta_0+\theta_2)}\tan\gamma_0,$$
$$\tan\gamma_2 = \cos(\theta_0-\theta_2)\tan\gamma_0. \tag{66.12}$$

The angles γ_0, γ_1 and γ_2 are equal for all angles of incidence only in the obvious cases $\gamma_0 = 0$ and $\gamma_0 = \frac{1}{2}\pi$; they are also equal for normal incidence ($\theta_0 = \theta_2 = 0$) and for grazing incidence ($\theta_0 = \frac{1}{2}\pi$, in which case there is no refracted wave). In all other cases the formulae (66.12) give (by virtue of the inequalities $0 < \theta_0, \theta_2 < \frac{1}{2}\pi$ and, as we shall assume, $0 < \gamma_0 < \frac{1}{2}\pi$, $0 < \gamma_1, \gamma_2 < \pi$) the inequalities $\gamma_1 > \gamma_0$, $\gamma_2 < \gamma_0$. Thus the direction of $\mathbf{E}$ is turned away from the plane of incidence on reflection, but towards it on refraction.

A comparison of the two formulae (66.10) shows that, at all angles of incidence except $\theta_0 = 0$ or $\frac{1}{2}\pi$, $R_\parallel < R_\perp$. Hence, for example, when the incident light is natural the reflected light is partly polarised, and the predominant direction of the electric field is perpendicular to the plane of incidence. The refracted light is partly polarised, with the predominant direction of $\mathbf{E}$ lying in the plane of incidence.

The quantities $R_\parallel$ and $R_\perp$ depend quite differently on the angle of incidence. The coefficient $R_\perp$ increases monotonically with the angle θ_0 from the value (66.8) for $\theta_0 = 0$. The coefficient $R_\parallel$ takes the same value (66.8) for $\theta_0 = 0$, but as θ_0 increases $R_\parallel$ decreases to zero at $\theta_0 = \theta_p$ before monotonically increasing.

Here two distinct cases occur. If the reflection is from the "optically denser" medium, i.e. $\epsilon_2 > \epsilon_1$, then $R_\parallel$ and $R_\perp$ increase to the common value of unity at $\theta_0 = \frac{1}{2}\pi$ (grazing incidence). If, on the other hand, the reflecting medium is "optically less dense" ($\epsilon_2 < \epsilon_1$), both coefficients become equal to unity for $\theta_0 = \theta_r$, where

$$\sin\theta_r = \sqrt{(\epsilon_2/\epsilon_1)} = n_2/n_1; \tag{66.13}$$

θ_r is called the *angle of total reflection*. When $\theta_0 = \theta_r$ the angle of refraction $\theta_2 = \frac{1}{2}\pi$, i.e. the refracted wave is propagated along the surface separating the media.

Reflection from an optically less dense medium at angles $\theta_0 > \theta_r$ requires special consideration. In this case k_{2z} is purely imaginary (see (66.2)), i.e. the field is damped in medium 2. The damping of the wave without true absorption (i.e. dissipation of energy) signifies that the average energy flux from medium 1 into medium 2 is zero (by simple calculation it can easily be seen that the vector $\overline{\mathbf{S}}$ giving the average energy flux in medium 2 is in the x-direction). That is, all the energy incident on the boundary is reflected back into medium 1, so that the reflection coefficients are $R_\perp = R_\parallel = 1$. This phenomenon is called *total reflection*.† The equality of $R_\perp$ and $R_\parallel$ to unity can, of course, be obtained directly from Fresnel's formulae (66.4) and (66.6).

For $\theta_0 > \theta_r$ the proportionality coefficients between $\mathbf{E}_1$ and $\mathbf{E}_0$ become complex quantities, of the form $(a-ib)/(a+ib)$. The quantities $R_\perp$ and $R_\parallel$ are given by the squared moduli of these coefficients, which are equal to unity. The formulae give, besides the ratio of the magnitudes of the fields in the reflected and incident waves, the difference in their phases. For this purpose we write $E_{1\perp} = e^{-i\delta_\perp}E_{0\perp}$, $E_{1\parallel} = e^{-i\delta_\parallel}E_{0\parallel}$. Then‡

$$\begin{aligned} \tan\tfrac{1}{2}\delta_\perp &= \sqrt{(\epsilon_1 \sin^2\theta_0 - \epsilon_2)}/\sqrt{\epsilon_1}\cos\theta_0, \\ \tan\tfrac{1}{2}\delta_\parallel &= \sqrt{(\epsilon_1^2 \sin^2\theta_0 - \epsilon_1\epsilon_2)}/\epsilon_2\cos\theta_0. \end{aligned} \tag{66.14}$$

Thus total reflection involves a change in the wave phase which is in general different for the field components parallel and perpendicular to the plane of incidence. Hence, on reflection of a wave polarised in a plane inclined to the plane of incidence, the reflected wave will be elliptically polarised.‖ The phase difference $\delta = \delta_\perp - \delta_\parallel$ is easily found to be such that

$$\tan\tfrac{1}{2}\delta = \frac{\cos\theta_0\sqrt{(\epsilon_1\sin^2\theta_0 - \epsilon_2)}}{\sqrt{\epsilon_1}\sin^2\theta_0}. \tag{66.15}$$

The difference is zero only for $\theta_0 = \theta_r$ or $\theta_0 = \frac{1}{2}\pi$.

PROBLEMS

PROBLEM 1. Find the manner in which the reflection coefficient approaches unity near the angle of total reflection.

SOLUTION. We put $\theta_0 = \theta_r - \delta$, where δ is a small quantity, and expand $\sin\theta_0$ and $\cos\theta_0$ in formulae (66.10) in powers of δ. The result is

$$\begin{aligned} R_\perp &= 1 - 4\sqrt{(2\delta)}(n^2-1)^{-\frac{1}{2}}, \\ R_\parallel &= 1 - 4\sqrt{(2\delta)}n^2(n^2-1)^{-\frac{1}{2}}, \end{aligned}$$

where $n^2 = \epsilon_1/\epsilon_2 > 1$. The derivatives $dR/d\delta$ become infinite as $\delta^{-\frac{1}{2}}$ when $\delta \to 0$.

† It may be mentioned that the reflection coefficient is always equal to unity in reflection from a medium with ϵ real and negative. In such a medium there is again no true absorption, but the wave cannot penetrate into it.

‡ If $(a-ib)/(a+ib) = e^{-i\delta}$, then $\tan\frac{1}{2}\delta = b/a$.

‖ See *The Classical Theory of Fields*, §6–5.

PROBLEM 2. Find the reflection coefficient for almost grazing incidence of light from a vacuum on the surface of a body for which ϵ is almost unity.

SOLUTION. Formulae (66.10) give the same reflection coefficient:

$$R_{\perp} \cong R_{\parallel} \cong [\phi_0 - \sqrt{(\phi_0^2+\epsilon-1)}]^4/(\epsilon-1)^2,$$

where $\phi_0 = \frac{1}{2}\pi - \theta_0$.

PROBLEM 3. Determine the reflection coefficient for a wave incident from a vacuum on a medium for which both ϵ and μ are different from unity.

SOLUTION. Calculations entirely analogous to those given above furnish the result

$$R_{\perp} = \left|\frac{\mu \cos\theta_0 - \sqrt{(\epsilon\mu - \sin^2\theta_0)}}{\mu\cos\theta_0 + \sqrt{(\epsilon\mu-\sin^2\theta_0)}}\right|^2,$$

$$R_{\parallel} = \left|\frac{\epsilon \cos\theta_0 + \sqrt{(\epsilon\mu - \sin^2\theta_0)}}{\epsilon\cos\theta_0 + \sqrt{(\epsilon\mu-\sin^2\theta_0)}}\right|^2.$$

PROBLEM 4. A plane-parallel layer (region 2) lies between a vacuum (region 1) and an arbitrary medium (region 3). Light polarised parallel or perpendicular to the plane of incidence falls on the layer from the vacuum. Express the reflection coefficient R in terms of those for semi-infinite media of the substances in regions 2 and 3.

SOLUTION. We denote by A_0 and A_1 the amplitudes of the field (**E** or **H**, whichever is parallel to the layer) in the incident and reflected waves. The field in the layer consists of the refracted wave (amplitude A_2) and the wave reflected from region 3 (amplitude A_2'). The boundary condition between regions 1 and 2 gives

$$A_2' = a(A_1 - r_{12}A_0), \tag{1}$$

where a and r_{12} are constants. In reflection from a semi-infinite medium of the substance in region 2, A_2' is zero, and so from (1) we have $r_{12} = A_1/A_0$, i.e. r_{12} is the amplitude of reflection in that case. Another equation is obtained from (1) by interchanging A_1 and A_0 and replacing A_2' by A_2, which corresponds simply to a reversal of the z-component of the wave vector:

$$A_2 = a(A_0 - r_{12}A_1). \tag{2}$$

In region 3 there is only the transmitted wave, whose amplitude A_3 satisfies the conditions

$$A_2 e^{i\psi} = aA_3, \qquad A_2' e^{-i\psi} = -ar_{32}A_3 \tag{3}$$

analogous to (1), (2) with $A_1 = 0$. The exponential factors take account of the change in the wave phase over the thickness h of the layer, with

$$\psi = (\omega h/c)\sqrt{(\epsilon_2 - \sin^2\theta_0)}. \tag{4}$$

Eliminating A_3 from equations (3), we obtain

$$A_2' e^{-i\psi} = r_{23}A_2 e^{i\psi}, \tag{5}$$

where $r_{23} = -r_{32}$.

From equations (1), (2) and (5) we find the amplitude of reflection from the layer:

$$r = \frac{A_1}{A_0} = \frac{r_{12}e^{-2i\psi} + r_{23}}{e^{-2i\psi} + r_{12}r_{23}}, \tag{6}$$

and the reflection coefficient $R = |r|^2$. The significance of r_{23} is found from the fact that, for $h = 0$, r must be the amplitude of reflection r_{13} from a semi-infinite medium of the substance in region 3. Hence

$$r_{23} = (r_{12} - r_{13})/(r_{12}r_{13} - 1). \tag{7}$$

Formulae (6) and (7) give the required solution. It should be emphasised that their derivation involves no assumptions concerning the properties of regions 2 and 3, which may be either transparent or not.

If regions 2 and 3 are transparent, then ψ, r_{12} and r_{13} are all real, and r_{23} is the amplitude of reflection at the boundary between semi-infinite media of the substances in regions 2 and 3. From (6) we have

$$R = \frac{(r_{12}+r_{23})^2-4r_{12}r_{23}\sin^2\psi}{(r_{12}r_{23}+1)^2-4r_{12}r_{23}\sin^2\psi}. \tag{8}$$

As ψ varies, R varies between the limits $[(r_{12}+r_{23})/(r_{12}r_{23}+1)]^2$ and $[(r_{12}-r_{23})/(r_{12}r_{23}-1)]^2$. For normal incidence $r_{12} = (n_1-n_2)/(n_1+n_2)$, and r_{13} and r_{23} are given by similar relations. If $n_2^2 = n_1n_3$, then $r_{12} = r_{23}$, and R may be zero for some value of the thickness of the layer. If region 3 is a vacuum, then $r_{13} = 0$, $r_{23} = -r_{12}$, and (6) gives

$$r = \frac{r_{12}(e^{-2i\psi}-1)}{e^{-2i\psi}-r_{12}^2} = -\frac{\sinh i\psi}{\sinh[i\psi+\log(-r_{12})]}. \tag{9}$$

If also region 2 is transparent, we have

$$R = \frac{4R_{12}\sin^2\psi}{(1-R_{12})^2+4R_{12}\sin^2\psi}.$$

The transmission coefficient D for the layer (between vacua) is $1-R$ only if region 2 is transparent. Otherwise D must be calculated from equations (1)–(3), putting $r_{32} = r_{12}$. The amplitude of transmission d is

$$d = \frac{A_3}{A_0} = \frac{1-r_{12}^2}{e^{-i\psi}-r_{12}^2e^{i\psi}}, \tag{10}$$

and the transmission coefficient $D = |d|^2$.

PROBLEM 5. Determine the reflection and transmission coefficients for light incident normally on a slab with a very large complex dielectric permeability ϵ.

SOLUTION. In this case $r_{12} = (1-\sqrt{\epsilon})/(1+\sqrt{\epsilon}) \approx -(1-2/\sqrt{\epsilon})$, and formula (9) of Problem 4 gives $r = -[1-(2/\sqrt{\epsilon})\coth i\psi]^{-1}$, $\psi = \omega h\sqrt{\epsilon}/c$. If the slab is so thin that $\omega h/c \ll 1/\sqrt{|\epsilon|}$, then we can put $r = -[1+2ic/\epsilon\omega h]^{-1}$, and distinguish two cases:

$$\text{for } 1/|\epsilon| \ll \omega h/c \ll 1/\sqrt{|\epsilon|}, \qquad R = 1-4c\epsilon''/\omega h|\epsilon|^2,$$
$$\text{for } \omega h/c \ll 1/|\epsilon|, \qquad R = \omega^2h^2|\epsilon|^2/4c^2.$$

The transmission coefficient is, by formula (10),

$$\text{for } \omega h/c \sim 1/\sqrt{|\epsilon|}, \qquad d = -2/\sqrt{\epsilon}\sinh i\psi,$$
$$\text{for } \omega h/c \ll 1/\sqrt{|\epsilon|}, \qquad d = (1-i\epsilon\omega h/2c)^{-1}.$$

Again two cases can be distinguished:

$$\text{for } 1/|\epsilon| \ll \omega h/c \ll 1/\sqrt{|\epsilon|}, \qquad D = 4c^2/\omega^2h^2|\epsilon|^2,$$
$$\text{for } \omega h/c \ll 1/|\epsilon|, \qquad D = 1-\epsilon''\omega h/c.$$

§67. The surface impedance of metals

The dielectric permeability of metals is, in magnitude, large compared with unity at low frequencies (as $\omega \to 0$, it tends to infinity as $1/\omega$). The "wavelength" $\delta \sim c/\omega\sqrt{|\epsilon|}$ in metals† is then small compared with the wavelength $\lambda \sim c/\omega$ *in vacuo*. If δ (but not necessarily λ) is also small compared with the radii of curvature of the metal surface, the problem of the reflection of arbitrary electromagnetic waves from the metal can be considerably simplified.

† Large values of $\sqrt{\epsilon(\omega)}$ are almost always complex. The electromagnetic field is damped inside the body, so that the "wavelength" in the body is also the depth of penetration of the field. If $\epsilon(\omega)$ is expressed in terms of the conductivity by (58.9), the quantity δ is the same as the penetration depth used in §45.

The smallness of δ implies that the derivatives of the field components inside the metal along the normal to the surface are large compared with the tangential derivatives. The field inside the metal near the surface can therefore be regarded as the field of a plane wave, and hence the fields $\mathbf{E}_t$ and $\mathbf{H}_t$ are related by

$$\mathbf{E}_t = \sqrt{(\mu/\epsilon)}\mathbf{H} \times \mathbf{n}, \tag{67.1}$$

where $\mathbf{n}$ is a unit vector along the inward normal to the surface. Since $\mathbf{E}_t$ and $\mathbf{H}_t$ are continuous, their values outside the metal near the surface must be related in the same way. As M. A. LEONTOVICH (1948) has pointed out, the equation (67.1) may be used as a boundary condition in determining the field outside the metal. Thus the problem of determining the external electromagnetic field can be solved without considering the field inside the metal.

The quantity $\sqrt{(\mu/\epsilon)}$ is called the *surface impedance*† of the metal, and we denote it by $\zeta = \zeta' + i\zeta''$:

$$\zeta = \sqrt{(\mu/\epsilon)}. \tag{67.2}$$

In the frequency range where ϵ can be expressed in terms of the ordinary conductivity of the metal, we have

$$\zeta = (1-i)\sqrt{(\omega\mu/8\pi\sigma)}. \tag{67.3}$$

The (time) average energy flux through the surface of the metal is

$$\overline{\mathbf{S}} = (c/8\pi)\,\mathrm{re}\,(\mathbf{E}_t \times \mathbf{H}_t^*) = c\zeta'|\mathbf{H}_t|^2\mathbf{n}/8\pi. \tag{67.4}$$

This is the energy which enters the metal and is dissipated therein. Hence we see, in particular, that

$$\zeta' > 0. \tag{67.5}$$

This inequality determines the sign of the root in (67.2).

As the frequency increases, the depth of penetration δ becomes of the same order as the mean free path l of the conduction electrons.‡ In this case the spatial non-uniformity of the field renders impossible a macroscopic description of it in terms of the dielectric permeability ϵ, a fact first pointed out by H. LONDON (1940). It is remarkable that the condition $v/l \gg \omega$ (v being the velocity of the conduction electrons), which ensures the absence of dispersion of the conductivity and the equality of the latter to its value σ for a constant field, remains valid.

It is of importance to note that a boundary condition of the form

$$\mathbf{E} = \zeta\mathbf{H}_t \times \mathbf{n} \tag{67.6}$$

† This name is usually given to the quantity $4\pi\zeta/c$, but we find that convention less satisfactory.

‡ The mean free path depends considerably on the temperature of the metal. In practice, the temperatures considered are usually very low, in the helium range, and the phenomena under consideration occur in the range of very short radio waves.

still holds at such frequencies. The field inside the metal near the surface can again be regarded as a plane wave, although it is no longer described by the usual macroscopic Maxwell's equations. In such a wave the fields **E** and **H** must be linearly related, and the only possible linear relation between the axial vector **H** and the polar vector **E** is (67.6). The coefficient ζ in this formula is the only quantity characterising the metal which must be known in order to find the external electromagnetic field.

When the frequency increases further (usually into the infra-red region), the macroscopic description of the field again becomes possible, and ϵ is again meaningful. The reason is that, on absorbing a quantum $\hbar\omega$, a conduction electron acquires a large amount of energy, and its mean free path is therefore reduced, the inequality $l \ll \delta$ being consequently again fulfilled. The impedance ζ is again inversely proportional to $\sqrt{\epsilon}$.† In this frequency range the real part of $\epsilon(\omega)$ is negative, and its imaginary part is small. The inequality $l \ll \delta$ is the condition for both ϵ' and ϵ'' to be macroscopically significant. The macroscopic significance of the large quantity ϵ' alone, however, can be ensured by the fulfilment of the less stringent condition $v/\omega \ll \delta$, where v is the velocity of the conduction electrons in the metal. If this condition holds, the spatial inhomogeneity of the field may be neglected in considering the motion of the electrons.

The inequality $\zeta' > 0$ is always satisfied by the real part of the impedance. If formula (67.2) holds, we can also draw certain conclusions concerning the sign of ζ''. For example, if the dispersion of ϵ is more important than that of μ (i.e. if μ may be taken as real), the condition $\epsilon'' > 0$ gives $\zeta'\zeta'' < 0$ and, since $\zeta' > 0$, $\zeta'' < 0$. This is the most usual case. If the dispersion of ζ is determined by that of μ, however, a similar argument shows that $\zeta'' > 0$.

The concept of impedance can also be applied to superconductors. A characteristic property of superconductors is that the penetration depth δ is small even in the static case ($\omega = 0$). At fairly low frequencies the magnetic field distribution can be taken to be the same as the static distribution. To determine the electric field we use the equation $\mathbf{curl}\,\mathbf{E} = i\omega\mathbf{H}/c$, taking the z-axis along the outward normal to the surface of the superconductor. Neglecting the tangential derivatives in comparison with the large z-derivatives, we have $\partial E_x/\partial z = i\omega H_y/c$, and similarly for E_y. Integrating with respect to z through the body gives

$$E_x(0) = \frac{i\omega}{c}\int_{-\infty}^{0} H_y\,dz,$$

† It should be borne in mind, however, that equation (67.6) can be used as a boundary condition only while $|\epsilon|$ is large (i.e. ζ is small), and certainly does not hold at optical frequencies. We assume that $\mu \sim 1$, and so small ζ correspond to large $|\epsilon|$. If $\mu \gg 1$, the inequality $\delta \ll \lambda$ must be fulfilled if the boundary condition (67.6) is valid, and therefore we must have $\sqrt{(\mu\epsilon)} \gg 1$, so that $\zeta = \sqrt{(\mu/\epsilon)}$ may not be small.

$E_x(0)$ being the value of E_x for $z = 0$, i.e. at the surface of the body. We quantitatively define the penetration depth by the relation

$$\int_{-\infty}^{0} H_y \, dz = \delta H_y(0). \tag{67.7}$$

Then $E_x(0) = i\omega\delta H_y(0)/c$. Comparing this with the boundary condition (67.6), we find that the impedance of a superconductor (in the frequency range considered, which in practice extends to about the centimetre wavelength region) is given by

$$\zeta = -i\omega\delta/c. \tag{67.8}$$

This expression is the first term in an expansion of $\zeta(\omega)$ in powers of the frequency, and the expansion for superconductors thus begins with a term in ω. The next term, which is in ω^2 and real, is the first term in the expansion of ζ'.

The impedance $\zeta(\omega)$, regarded as a function of the complex variable ω, has many properties analogous to those of the function $\epsilon(\omega)$ (V. L. Ginzburg, 1954). The boundary condition, which for a wave of a single frequency has the form (67.6), must in general be taken as the operator relation

$$\mathbf{E}_t = \hat{\zeta}\mathbf{H}_t \times \mathbf{n}, \tag{67.9}$$

expressing the value of $\mathbf{E}_t$ at any instant in terms of the values of $\mathbf{H}_t$ at all previous instants (cf. §58). As in §62, it therefore follows that the function $\zeta(\omega)$ is regular in the upper half-plane of ω, including the real axis except for the point $\omega = 0$. The condition that $\mathbf{E}_t$ is real when $\mathbf{H}_t$ is real gives $\zeta(-\omega^*) = \zeta^*(\omega)$. Finally, since the energy dissipation is determined by the real part of $\zeta(\omega)$ (and not by the imaginary part as for $\epsilon(\omega)$), it follows that $\zeta'(\omega)$ is positive, and does not vanish for any real ω except $\omega = 0$. Arguments similar to those given in §62 then lead to the conclusion that $\text{re}\,\zeta(\omega) > 0$ throughout the upper half-plane. Hence, in particular, $\zeta(\omega)$ has no zeros in the upper half-plane.

The regularity of $\zeta(\omega)$ in the upper half-plane again leads to Kramers and Kronig's formulae. A particularly important formula is

$$\zeta''(\omega) = -\frac{1}{\pi} P \int_{-\infty}^{\infty} \frac{\zeta'(x) - 1}{x - \omega} \, dx.$$

Using the fact that $\zeta'(x)$ is even, we can also write

$$\zeta''(\omega) = -\frac{1}{\pi} P \int_{0}^{\infty} \frac{\zeta'(x) - 1}{x - \omega} \, dx + \frac{1}{\pi} P \int_{0}^{\infty} \frac{\zeta'(x) - 1}{x + \omega} \, dx$$

or

$$\zeta''(\omega) = -\frac{2\omega}{\pi} P \int_0^\infty \frac{\zeta'(x)}{x^2 - \omega^2} dx. \tag{67.10}$$

The term -1 in the numerator of the integrand may be omitted, since the principal value of the integral of $1/(x^2 - \omega^2)$ is zero.

The above statements concerning the function $\zeta(\omega)$ are, of course, equally applicable to the reciprocal function $1/\zeta(\omega)$; the operator $\hat{\zeta}^{-1}$ converts $\mathbf{E}_t$ into $\mathbf{H}_t \times \mathbf{n}$. In particular, (67.10) becomes

$$[\zeta^{-1}(\omega)]'' = -\frac{2\omega}{\pi} P \int_0^\infty \frac{[\zeta^{-1}(x)]'}{x^2 - \omega^2} dx. \tag{67.11}$$

For small ζ this formula may be more useful than (67.10). In the form (67.11), however, it is not applicable to superconductors, for which ζ^{-1}, according to (67.8), has a pole at $\omega = 0$. A simple modification in the derivation, analogous to that which changes (62.9) into (62.11), gives

$$[\zeta^{-1}(\omega)]'' = -\frac{2\omega}{\pi} P \int_0^\infty \frac{[\zeta^{-1}(x)]'}{x^2 - \omega^2} dx + \frac{c}{\omega\delta}. \tag{67.12}$$

To conclude this section we shall discuss, as an example of the use of the impedance, the reflection of a plane electromagnetic wave incident from a vacuum on the plane surface of a metal with surface impedance ζ. If the vector $\mathbf{E}$ is polarised perpendicular to the plane of incidence, the boundary condition (67.6) gives $E_0 + E_1 = \zeta(H_0 - H_1)\cos\theta_0 = \zeta(E_0 - E_1)\cos\theta_0$, the notation being the same as in §66. Hence, since ζ is small, we have $E_1/E_0 = -(1 - 2\zeta\cos\theta_0)$, and the reflection coefficient is

$$R_\perp = 1 - 4\zeta'\cos\theta_0. \tag{67.13}$$

If, on the other hand, $\mathbf{E}_0$ lies in the plane of incidence, the boundary condition in the form $\zeta\mathbf{H}_t = \mathbf{n} \times \mathbf{E}_t$ gives

$$\zeta(H_0 + H_1) = (E_0 - E_1)\cos\theta_0 = (H_0 - H_1)\cos\theta_0,$$

whence the reflection coefficient is

$$R_\parallel = \left|\frac{\cos\theta_0 - \zeta}{\cos\theta_0 + \zeta}\right|^2. \tag{67.14}$$

For angles of incidence not close to $\frac{1}{2}\pi$

$$R_\parallel = 1 - 4\zeta'\sec\theta_0. \tag{67.15}$$

If, on the other hand, $\phi_0 = \frac{1}{2}\pi - \theta_0 \ll 1$, then

$$R_{\parallel} = \left|\frac{\phi_0 - \zeta}{\phi_0 + \zeta}\right|^2. \tag{67.16}$$

This expression takes a minimum value $(|\zeta| - \zeta')/(|\zeta| + \zeta')$ for $\phi_0 = |\zeta|$.

Except for the special case (67.16), the reflection coefficient for a surface with small ζ is close to unity. A surface with $\zeta \to 0$ is "perfectly conducting" and also "perfectly reflecting". The boundary condition at such a surface is simply $\mathbf{E}_t = 0$, similarly to that for the electrostatic field at the surface of a conductor. In a variable field, however, the fulfilment of this condition necessarily implies that of a certain condition on the magnetic field: the equations $i\omega\mathbf{H}/c = \mathbf{curl}\,\mathbf{E}$ and $\mathbf{E}_t = 0$ on the surface imply that $H_n = 0$ there. Thus the normal component of the magnetic field must be zero on a perfectly conducting surface in a variable electromagnetic field. In this respect such a surface resembles the surface of a superconductor in a constant magnetic field.

PROBLEM

Determine the intensity of thermal radiation (of a given frequency) from a plane surface of small impedance.

SOLUTION. According to Kirchhoff's law, the intensity dI of thermal radiation into an element of solid angle do from an arbitrary surface is related to the intensity dI_0 of radiation from the surface of a black body by $dI = (1-R)\,dI_0$, where R is the reflection coefficient for natural light incident on the surface concerned. Calculating $R = \frac{1}{2}(R_{\perp}+R_{\parallel})$ from formulae (67.13) and (67.14) and using the isotropy of radiation from a black surface ($dI_0 = I_0\,do/2\pi$), we have

$$I = 2I_0\zeta' \int_0^{\frac{1}{2}\pi} \left\{1 + \frac{1}{\cos^2\theta + 2\zeta'\cos\theta + \zeta'^2 + \zeta''^2}\right\} \cos\theta \sin\theta \, d\theta.$$

Effecting the integration and omitting terms of higher order in ζ, we find

$$\frac{I}{I_0} = \zeta'\left[\log\frac{1}{\zeta'^2 + \zeta''^2} + 1 - \frac{2\zeta'}{\zeta''}\tan^{-1}\frac{\zeta''}{\zeta'}\right].$$

In particular, for a metal whose impedance is given by formula (67.3) ($\mu = 1$), we have

$$\frac{I}{I_0} = \sqrt{\frac{\omega}{8\pi\sigma}}\left[\log\frac{4\pi\sigma}{\omega} + 1 - \frac{1}{2}\pi\right].$$

§68. The propagation of waves in an inhomogeneous medium

Let us consider the propagation of electromagnetic waves in a medium which is electrically inhomogeneous but isotropic.† In Maxwell's equations $\mathbf{curl}\,\mathbf{E} = i\omega\mathbf{H}/c$, $\mathbf{curl}\,\mathbf{H} = -i\epsilon\omega\mathbf{E}/c$ (we put everywhere $\mu = 1$), ϵ is a

† For a discussion of wave propagation in an anisotropic medium in a constant magnetic field see YA. L. AL'PERT, V. L. GINZBURG and E. L. FEĬNBERG, *The Propagation of Radio Waves* (*Rasprostranenie radiovoln*), Moscow and Leningrad, 1953.

function of the co-ordinates. Substituting for **H** from the first equation in the second, we obtain for **E** the equation

$$\triangle \mathbf{E} + (\epsilon\omega^2/c^2)\mathbf{E} - \mathbf{grad}\,\mathrm{div}\,\mathbf{E} = 0. \tag{68.1}$$

Elimination of **E** gives for **H** the equation

$$\triangle \mathbf{H} + (\epsilon\omega^2/c^2)\mathbf{H} + (1/\epsilon)\,\mathbf{grad}\,\epsilon \times \mathbf{curl}\,\mathbf{H} = 0. \tag{68.2}$$

These equations are considerably simplified in the "one-dimensional" case, where ϵ varies only in one direction in space. We take this direction as the z-axis, and consider a wave whose direction of propagation lies in the xz-plane. In such a wave all quantities are independent of y, and the uniformity of the medium in the x-direction means that the dependence on x can be taken as being through a factor $e^{i\kappa x}$, with κ a constant. For $\kappa = 0$ the field depends only on z, i.e. we have a wave passing *normally* through a layer of matter in which $\epsilon = \epsilon(z)$. If $\kappa \neq 0$, the wave is said to pass *obliquely*.

For $\kappa \neq 0$ two independent cases of polarisation must be distinguished. In one, the vector **E** is perpendicular to the plane of propagation of the wave (i.e. it is in the y-direction), and the magnetic field **H** accordingly lies in that plane. Equation (68.1) becomes

$$\frac{\partial^2 E}{\partial z^2} + \left(\frac{\epsilon\omega^2}{c^2} - \kappa^2\right)E = 0. \tag{68.3}$$

In the other case, the field **H** is in the y-direction, and **E** lies in the plane of propagation. Here it is more convenient to start from equation (68.2), which gives

$$\frac{\partial}{\partial z}\left(\frac{1}{\epsilon}\frac{\partial H}{\partial z}\right) + \left(\frac{\omega^2}{c^2} - \frac{\kappa^2}{\epsilon}\right)H = 0. \tag{68.4}$$

We shall call these two types of wave *E waves* and *H waves* respectively.

The equations can be solved in a general form in the important case where the conditions of propagation approximate to those of geometrical optics. In what follows we shall assume that the function $\epsilon(z)$ is real.† In equation (68.3) the quantity $2\pi/\sqrt{f}$, where $f(z) = \epsilon k^2 - \kappa^2$, plays the part of a "wavelength" in the z-direction. The approximation of geometrical optics corresponds to the inequality

$$\frac{\mathrm{d}}{\mathrm{d}z}\frac{1}{\sqrt{f}} \ll 1, \tag{68.5}$$

† Equation (68.3) bears a formal resemblance to Schrödinger's equation for one-dimensional motion of a particle in quantum mechanics, and the approximation of geometrical optics corresponds to the quasi-classical case. Here we shall give the final results; their derivation may be found in *Quantum Mechanics*, Chapter VII, Pergamon Press, London, 1958.

and the two independent solutions of equation (68.3) are of the form

$$\frac{\text{constant}}{f^{\frac{1}{4}}} e^{\pm i\int\sqrt{f}\,dz}. \tag{68.6}$$

The condition (68.5) is certainly not fulfilled near any point where $f = 0$. Let $z = 0$ be such a point, with $f > 0$ for $z < 0$ and $f < 0$ for $z > 0$. At sufficiently great distances on either side of $z = 0$, the solution of equation (68.3) is of the form (68.6), but to establish the relation between the coefficients in the solutions for $z > 0$ and $z < 0$ it is necessary to examine the exact solution of equation (68.3) near $z = 0$. In the neighbourhood of this point, $f(z)$ can be expanded as a power series in $z: f = -\alpha z$. The solution of the equation $d^2E/dz^2 - \alpha z E = 0$ which is finite for all z is

$$E = (A/\alpha^{1/6})\Phi(\alpha^{\frac{1}{3}}z), \tag{68.7}$$

where

$$\Phi(\xi) = \frac{1}{\sqrt{\pi}}\int\limits_0^\infty \cos\left(\tfrac{1}{3}u^3 + u\xi\right) du$$

is the *Airy function*; we everywhere omit the factor $e^{-i\omega t + i\kappa x}$ in E. The asymptotic form of the solution of equation (68.3) for large $|z|$ is

$$E = \frac{A}{f^{\frac{1}{4}}}\cos\left(\int\limits_0^z \sqrt{f}\,dz + \tfrac{1}{4}\pi\right) \quad \text{for } z < 0,$$

$$E = \frac{A}{2|f|^{\frac{1}{4}}}\exp\left(-\int\limits_0^z \sqrt{|f|}\,dz\right) \quad \text{for } z > 0, \tag{68.8}$$

with the same coefficient A as in (68.7). The first of these expressions represents the stationary wave obtained by superposing the wave incident in the positive z-direction and the wave reflected from the plane $z = 0$. The amplitudes of these waves are both equal to $\frac{1}{2}A/f^{\frac{1}{4}}$, i.e. the reflection coefficient is unity. Only an exponentially damped field penetrates into the region $z > 0$.

As the reflection point is approached, the wave amplitude increases, as is shown by the factor $f^{\frac{1}{4}}$ in the denominators in (68.8). To determine the field in the immediate vicinity of that point, the expression (68.7) must be used. This function decreases monotonically into the region $z > 0$ and oscillates in the region $z < 0$, the successive maxima of $|E|$ continually decreasing. The first and highest maximum is reached at $\alpha^{\frac{1}{3}}z = -1{\cdot}02$, and its value is $E = 0{\cdot}949A\alpha^{-1/6}$.

So far we have spoken of solutions for E waves. It is easy to see that, in the approximation of geometrical optics, entirely similar formulae are valid for H waves. If we substitute in equation (68.4) $H = u\sqrt{\epsilon}$, the derivatives of ϵ appear as products with u, but not with u'; neglecting therefore the terms containing these derivatives, which are small by (68.5), we obtain for the function $u(z)$ the equation

$$\frac{\mathrm{d}^2u}{\mathrm{d}z^2}+\left(\frac{\epsilon\omega^2}{c^2}-\kappa^2\right)u = 0,$$

which is of the same form as (68.3). Hence the formulae for H differ from (68.6)–(68.8) only by a factor $\sqrt{\epsilon}$.

A curious difference in the behaviour of the two types of wave occurs when an obliquely incident wave ($\kappa \neq 0$) is reflected from a layer in which $\epsilon(z)$ passes through zero. The reflection takes place from the plane on which $f(z) = \epsilon k^2-\kappa^2 = 0$, i.e. the wave "does not reach" the plane where $\epsilon = 0$. The E wave penetrates beyond the latter plane only as an exponentially damped field. When an H wave is reflected, however, there is superposed on a similar damped field a strong local field near the plane on which $\epsilon = 0$ (see Problem 1).†

PROBLEMS

PROBLEM 1. Determine the electric field near the point where $\epsilon = 0$ when an obliquely ($\kappa \neq 0$) incident H wave is reflected.

SOLUTION. Let $\epsilon = 0$ at the point $z = 0$. Near this point, we write $\epsilon = az$, and equation (68.4) takes the form

$$\frac{\mathrm{d}^2H}{\mathrm{d}z^2}-\frac{1}{z}\frac{\mathrm{d}H}{\mathrm{d}z}+(ak^2z-\kappa^2)H = 0.$$

According to the general theory of linear differential equations, one of the solutions of this equation, which we call $H_1(z)$, has no singularity at $z = 0$, and its expansion in powers of z begins with z^2:

$$H_1(z) = z^2+\frac{1}{8}\kappa^2z^4-\frac{1}{15}ak^2z^5+\dots.$$

The other independent solution has a logarithmic singularity, and its expansion is

$$H_2(z) = H_1(z)\log\kappa z+\frac{2}{\kappa^2}-\frac{2k^2a}{3\kappa^2}z^3+\dots.$$

The field $H(z)$ is made up of these two solutions, and therefore tends to a constant H_0, say, as $z \to 0$. The leading terms in the electric field components are

$$E_x = -\frac{i}{\epsilon k}\frac{\partial H}{\partial z} \cong -\frac{i\kappa^2H_0}{ak}\log\kappa z,$$

$$E_z = \frac{i}{\epsilon k}\frac{\partial H}{\partial x} = -\frac{\kappa}{\epsilon k}H \cong -\frac{\kappa H_0}{akz},$$

and become infinite as $z \to 0$. In reality, of course, the absorption which must be present in the medium, even though slight (i.e. the fact that the imaginary part of ϵ is not exactly

† It should be noted that this point is a singularity of equation (68.4), and the approximation of geometrical optics is therefore invalid near it, even though $f(z)$ does not vanish and the condition (68.5) may hold.

zero), means that the field attains large but not infinite values compared with the weak field in the adjoining regions.

PROBLEM 2. A "surface" H wave can be propagated along a plane boundary between two media whose dielectric permeabilities ϵ_1 and $-|\epsilon_2|$ are of opposite signs. The wave is damped in both media. Determine the relation between the frequency and the wave number.

SOLUTION. We take the boundary surface as the xy-plane, the wave being propagated in the x-direction and the field $\mathbf{H}$ being in the y-direction. Let the half-space $z > 0$ contain the medium with the positive permeability ϵ_1, and the half-space $z < 0$ that with the negative permeability ϵ_2. We seek the field in the wave damped as $z \to \pm\infty$ in the form

$$H_1 = H_0 e^{ikx-\kappa_1 z}, \qquad \kappa_1 = \sqrt{(k^2-\omega^2\epsilon_1/c^2)} \qquad \text{for } z > 0,$$
$$H_2 = H_0 e^{ikx+\kappa_2 z}, \qquad \kappa_2 = \sqrt{(k^2+\omega^2|\epsilon_2|/c^2)} \qquad \text{for } z < 0,$$

where k, κ_1 and κ_2 are real. The boundary condition that $H_y = H$ is continuous is already satisfied, and the continuity condition on E_x gives $(1/\epsilon_1)\,\partial H_1/\partial z = (1/\epsilon_2)\,\partial H_2/\partial z$ for $z = 0$, or $\kappa_1/\epsilon_1 = \kappa_2/|\epsilon_2|$. This equation can be satisfied if $\epsilon_1 < |\epsilon_2|$ (and if $\epsilon_1\epsilon_2 < 0$, as has been assumed). The relation between k and ω is $k^2 = \omega^2\epsilon_1|\epsilon_2|/c^2(|\epsilon_2|-\epsilon_1)$.

It is easily seen that "surface" E waves cannot be propagated.

§69. The reciprocity principle

The emission of electromagnetic waves (of a single frequency) from a source consisting of a thin wire in an arbitrary medium is described by the equations

$$\mathbf{curl}\,\mathbf{E} = i\omega\mathbf{B}/c, \qquad \mathbf{curl}\,\mathbf{H} = -i\omega\mathbf{D}/c + 4\pi\mathbf{j}_{ex}/c, \tag{69.1}$$

where $\mathbf{j}_{ex}$ is the density of periodic currents flowing in the wire which are extraneous to the medium.

Let two different sources (of the same frequency) be placed in the medium; we denote by the suffixes 1 and 2 the fields due to these sources separately. The medium may be inhomogeneous and anisotropic. The only assumption which we shall make concerning the properties of the medium is that the linear relations $D_i = \epsilon_{ik}E_k$, $B_i = \mu_{ik}H_k$ hold, the tensors ϵ_{ik} and μ_{ik} being symmetrical. Under these conditions it is possible to derive a relation between the fields of the two sources and the extraneous currents in them.

We take the scalar products of the two equations $\mathbf{curl}\,\mathbf{E}_1 = ik\mathbf{B}_1$, $\mathbf{curl}\,\mathbf{H}_1 = -ik\mathbf{D}_1 + 4\pi\mathbf{j}_{ex,1}/c$ with $\mathbf{H}_2$ and $\mathbf{E}_2$ respectively, and of the corresponding equations for $\mathbf{E}_2$ and $\mathbf{H}_2$ with $-\mathbf{H}_1$ and $-\mathbf{E}_1$. Adding all four together, we obtain

$$(\mathbf{H}_2\cdot\mathbf{curl}\,\mathbf{E}_1 - \mathbf{E}_1\cdot\mathbf{curl}\,\mathbf{H}_2) + (\mathbf{E}_2\cdot\mathbf{curl}\,\mathbf{H}_1 - \mathbf{H}_1\cdot\mathbf{curl}\,\mathbf{E}_2)$$
$$= (i\omega/c)(\mathbf{B}_1\cdot\mathbf{H}_2 - \mathbf{H}_1\cdot\mathbf{B}_2) + (i\omega/c)(\mathbf{E}_1\cdot\mathbf{D}_2 - \mathbf{D}_1\cdot\mathbf{E}_2) +$$
$$+ (4\pi/c)(\mathbf{j}_{ex,1}\cdot\mathbf{E}_2 - \mathbf{j}_{ex,2}\cdot\mathbf{E}_1).$$

But $\mathbf{B}_1\cdot\mathbf{H}_2 = \mu_{ik}H_{1k}H_{2i} = \mathbf{H}_1\cdot\mathbf{B}_2$, and $\mathbf{E}_1\cdot\mathbf{D}_2 = \mathbf{D}_1\cdot\mathbf{E}_2$, so that the first two terms on the right-hand side are zero. The left-hand side can be transformed by a formula of vector analysis, and the result is

$$\operatorname{div}[\mathbf{E}_1\times\mathbf{H}_2 - \mathbf{E}_2\times\mathbf{H}_1] = (4\pi/c)(\mathbf{j}_{ex,1}\cdot\mathbf{E}_2 - \mathbf{j}_{ex,2}\cdot\mathbf{E}_1).$$

We integrate this equation over all space; the integral on the left-hand side can be transformed into one over an infinitely remote surface, and is zero.

Thus we have

$$\int \mathbf{j}_{\text{ex},1}\cdot\mathbf{E}_2\,\mathrm{d}V_1 = \int \mathbf{j}_{\text{ex},2}\cdot\mathbf{E}_1\,\mathrm{d}V_2. \tag{69.2}$$

The integrals are taken only over the volumes of sources 1 and 2 respectively, since the currents $\mathbf{j}_{\text{ex},1}$ and $\mathbf{j}_{\text{ex},2}$ are zero elsewhere. Since the wires are thin, the effect of each on the field of the other may be neglected, and therefore $\mathbf{E}_1$ and $\mathbf{E}_2$ in formula (69.2) are the fields due to each of the two sources at the position of the other. Formula (69.2) is the required relation; it is called the *reciprocity theorem.*

If the dimensions of the sources are small compared with the wavelength and with the distance between them, this formula can be simplified. The field of each source varies only slightly over the dimensions of the other, and in (69.2) we can take $\mathbf{E}_1$ and $\mathbf{E}_2$ outside the integrals and replace them by $\mathbf{E}_1(2)$ and $\mathbf{E}_2(1)$, 1 and 2 signifying the positions of the two sources:

$$\mathbf{E}_2(1)\cdot\int \mathbf{j}_{\text{ex},1}\,\mathrm{d}V_1 = \mathbf{E}_1(2)\cdot\int \mathbf{j}_{\text{ex},2}\,\mathrm{d}V_2.$$

The integral $\int \mathbf{j}_{\text{ex}}\,\mathrm{d}V$ is just the time derivative of the total dipole moment $\mathscr{P}$ of the source. Since $\dot{\mathscr{P}} = -i\omega\mathscr{P}$, we have finally

$$\mathbf{E}_2(1)\cdot\mathscr{P}_1 = \mathbf{E}_1(2)\cdot\mathscr{P}_2. \tag{69.3}$$

This form of the reciprocity theorem applies, of course, only to dipole emission. If the dipole moment of the source is zero, or very small, the approximation made in going from the general formula (69.2) to (69.3) is inadequate; see Problem 1.

PROBLEMS

PROBLEM 1. Derive the reciprocity theorem for quadrupole emitters and for magnetic dipole emitters.

SOLUTION. If $\int \mathbf{j}_{\text{ex}}\,\mathrm{d}V = 0$, the next terms in the expansion must be taken in the integrals (69.2):

$$\begin{aligned}\int \mathbf{j}_1\cdot\mathbf{E}_2\,\mathrm{d}V_1 &\cong \frac{\partial E_{2i}}{\partial x_k}\int x_k j_{1i}\,\mathrm{d}V_1\\ &= \frac{1}{4}\left(\frac{\partial E_{2i}}{\partial x_k}+\frac{\partial E_{2k}}{\partial x_i}\right)\int (x_k j_{1i}+x_i j_{1k})\,\mathrm{d}V_1+\\ &\quad+\frac{1}{4}\left(\frac{\partial E_{2i}}{\partial x_k}-\frac{\partial E_{2k}}{\partial x_i}\right)\int (x_k j_{1i}-x_i j_{1k})\,\mathrm{d}V_1;\end{aligned}$$

we omit the suffix ex for brevity. The quadrupole moment tensor and the magnetic moment tensor are defined by

$$\dot{D}_{ik} = -i\omega D_{ik} = \int [3(x_i j_k+x_k j_i)-2\delta_{ik}\mathbf{r}\cdot\mathbf{j}]\,\mathrm{d}V,$$

$$\mathscr{M} = \frac{1}{2c}\int \mathbf{r}\times\mathbf{j}\,\mathrm{d}V.$$

Using the equation $\mathbf{curl}\,\mathbf{E} = i\omega\,\mathbf{B}/c$ and assuming that ϵ = constant near the sources (and so $\operatorname{div}\mathbf{E} = 0$), we obtain

$$\int \mathbf{j}_1\cdot\mathbf{E}_2\,\mathrm{d}V = -\frac{i\omega}{12}\left(\frac{\partial E_{2i}}{\partial x_k}+\frac{\partial E_{2k}}{\partial x_i}\right)D_{1,ik}+i\omega\mathbf{B}_2(1)\cdot\mathscr{M}_1.$$

Hence we see that for quadrupole emitters the reciprocity theorem is

$$\left(\frac{\partial E_{2i}^{(1)}}{\partial x_k}+\frac{\partial E_{2k}^{(1)}}{\partial x_i}\right)D_{1,ik}=\left(\frac{\partial E_{1i}^{(2)}}{\partial x_k}+\frac{\partial E_{1k}^{(2)}}{\partial x_i}\right)D_{2,ik},$$

and for magnetic dipole emitters

$$\mathbf{B}_2(1)\cdot\mathcal{M}_1=\mathbf{B}_1(2)\cdot\mathcal{M}_2.$$

PROBLEM 2. Determine the intensity of emission from a dipole source immersed in a homogeneous isotropic medium as a function of the permeabilities ϵ and μ of the medium.

SOLUTION. By substituting $\mathbf{E}=\sqrt{(\mu/\epsilon)}\mathbf{E}'$, $\mathbf{H}=\mathbf{H}'$, $\omega=\omega'/\sqrt{(\epsilon\mu)}$, equations (69.1) are brought to the form $\mathbf{curl}\,\mathbf{E}'=i\omega'\mathbf{H}'/c$, $\mathbf{curl}\,\mathbf{H}'=-i\omega'\mathbf{E}'/c+4\pi\mathbf{j}_{ex}/c$, which do not involve ϵ or μ. The solution of these equations for dipole emission gives a vector field potential in the wave region† $\mathbf{A}'=(1/cR_0)\int\mathbf{j}_{ex}\,dV$, where R_0 is the distance from the source; the phase factors are omitted, since they do not affect the calculation of the intensity. Hence we see that, for given $\mathbf{j}_{ex}$, we can put $\mathbf{A}'=\mathbf{A}_0$, where the suffix 0 signifies the value for the source field in a vacuum. The values of $\mathbf{H}'$ and $\mathbf{E}'$ are

$$\mathbf{H}'=i\mathbf{k}'\times\mathbf{A}'=i\sqrt{(\epsilon\mu)}\mathbf{k}\times\mathbf{A}_0=\sqrt{(\epsilon\mu)}\mathbf{H}_0,\qquad \mathbf{E}'=\mathbf{H}'.$$

Hence $\mathbf{H}=\sqrt{(\epsilon\mu)}\mathbf{H}_0$, $\mathbf{E}=\mu\mathbf{E}_0$ and $I=I_0\mu^{3/2}\epsilon^{1/2}$. This is the required solution.

§70. Electromagnetic oscillations in hollow resonators

Let us consider the electric field in a hollow evacuated resonator with perfectly conducting walls. The equations of the field (of a single frequency) in the vacuum are

$$\mathbf{curl}\,\mathbf{E}=i\omega\mathbf{H}/c,\qquad \mathbf{curl}\,\mathbf{H}=-i\omega\mathbf{E}/c. \tag{70.1}$$

The boundary conditions on the surface of a perfect conductor (i.e. one whose impedance $\zeta=0$) are

$$\mathbf{E}_t=0,\qquad H_n=0. \tag{70.2}$$

To solve the problem, it suffices to consider either **E** or **H**. For instance, eliminating **H** from equations (70.1), we find that **E** satisfies the wave equation

$$\triangle\mathbf{E}+(\omega^2/c^2)\mathbf{E}=0, \tag{70.3}$$

together with the equation

$$\operatorname{div}\mathbf{E}=0, \tag{70.4}$$

which does not follow from (70.3). Solving these equations with the boundary condition $\mathbf{E}_t=0$, we find the field **E**, and then **H** can be derived from the first of (70.1). The boundary condition $H_n=0$ is automatically satisfied.

When the shape and size of the cavity are given, equations (70.3) and (70.4) have solutions only for certain values of ω, called the *eigenfrequencies* of the electromagnetic oscillations of the resonator concerned.‡ For $\zeta=0$

† See *The Classical Theory of Fields*, §9–2.

‡ The formulae for a resonator filled with a non-absorbing dielectric for which ϵ and μ differ from unity are obtained from those for an evacuated resonator by replacing ω, **E** and **H** by $\omega\sqrt{(\epsilon\mu)}$, $\sqrt{\epsilon}\mathbf{E}$ and $\sqrt{\mu}\mathbf{H}$ respectively. This is seen from the fact that the transformation just given converts equations (70.1) into the correct Maxwell's equations for the medium: $\mathbf{curl}\,\mathbf{E}=i\omega\mu\mathbf{H}/c$, $\mathbf{curl}\,\mathbf{H}=-i\omega\epsilon\mathbf{E}/c$. In particular, the presence of the medium reduces each eigenfrequency by a factor $\sqrt{(\epsilon\mu)}$.

the electromagnetic field does not penetrate into the metal, and no loss occurs there. All the characteristic oscillations are therefore undamped, and all the eigenfrequencies are real. The latter are infinite in number, and the order of magnitude of the lowest eigenfrequency ω_1 is c/l, where l is the linear dimension of the cavity. This follows immediately from dimensional considerations, since l is the only dimensional parameter characterising the problem if the shape of the resonator is given. The high eigenfrequencies ($\omega \gg c/l$) lie very close together, and the number of them per unit range of ω is $V\omega^2/2\pi^2c^3$, which depends on the volume V of the resonator but not on its shape.†

The (time) average values of the electric and magnetic field energies in the resonator are respectively $\frac{1}{2}\int(|\mathbf{E}|^2/8\pi)\,\mathrm{d}V$ and $\frac{1}{2}\int(|\mathbf{H}|^2/8\pi)\,\mathrm{d}V$. We shall show that they are equal. Using the first equation (70.1), we write $\int \mathbf{H}\cdot\mathbf{H}^*\,\mathrm{d}V = (c^2/\omega^2)\int \mathbf{curl}\,\mathbf{E}\cdot\mathbf{curl}\,\mathbf{E}^*\,\mathrm{d}V$. The second integral can be integrated by parts:

$$\int \mathbf{curl}\,\mathbf{E}\cdot\mathbf{curl}\,\mathbf{E}^*\,\mathrm{d}V = \oint \mathbf{curl}\,\mathbf{E}^*\cdot\mathrm{d}\mathbf{f}\times\mathbf{E} + \int \mathbf{E}\cdot\mathbf{curl}\,\mathbf{curl}\,\mathbf{E}^*\,\mathrm{d}V.$$

Since $\mathbf{E}_t = 0$ on the boundary of the volume considered, the surface integral is zero, leaving

$$\begin{aligned}\int|\mathbf{H}|^2\,\mathrm{d}V &= \frac{c^2}{\omega^2}\int \mathbf{E}\cdot\mathbf{curl}\,\mathbf{curl}\,\mathbf{E}^*\,\mathrm{d}V \\ &= -(c^2/\omega^2)\int \mathbf{E}\cdot\triangle\mathbf{E}^*\,\mathrm{d}V\end{aligned}$$

or, by (70.3),

$$\int|\mathbf{H}|^2\,\mathrm{d}V = \int|\mathbf{E}|^2\,\mathrm{d}V. \qquad (70.5)$$

This completes the proof.‡

Undamped oscillations in a resonator are obtained if the impedance of its walls is assumed to be zero. Let us now ascertain the effect on the eigenfrequencies if the impedance of the walls is small but not zero.

The (time) average energy dissipated in the walls of the resonator in unit time can be calculated as the flux of energy into the walls from the electromagnetic field in the cavity. Using the boundary condition (67.6) on the surface of a body with impedance ζ, we write the normal component of the energy flux density as $\bar{S}_n = (c/8\pi)\,\mathrm{re}\,(\mathbf{E}_t\times\mathbf{H}_t^*) = c\zeta'|\mathbf{H}_t|^2/8\pi$, where ζ' is the real part of ζ. In this expression, which already contains the small factor ζ', we can as a first approximation take $\mathbf{H}$ to be the field obtained

---

† See *The Classical Theory of Fields*, §6–9.

‡ By $\mathbf{E}$ and $\mathbf{H}$ we always mean the fields corresponding to a particular eigenfrequency. It is not difficult to show that the fields corresponding to two different eigenfrequencies ω_a and ω_b are orthogonal:

$$\int\mathbf{E}_a\cdot\mathbf{E}_b^*\,\mathrm{d}V = \int\mathbf{H}_a\cdot\mathbf{H}_b^*\,\mathrm{d}V = 0.$$

by solving the problem with $\zeta = 0$. The total energy dissipated is given by the integral

$$\frac{c}{8\pi}\oint \zeta'|\mathbf{H}|^2\,\mathrm{d}f, \tag{70.6}$$

taken over the internal surface of the resonator. The field amplitude is damped in time with a decrement obtained by dividing (70.6) by twice the total energy of the field, namely $\frac{1}{2}\int(|\mathbf{E}|^2+|\mathbf{H}|^2)\,\mathrm{d}V/8\pi = \int|\mathbf{H}|^2\,\mathrm{d}V/8\pi$.

The damping decrement is determined by the imaginary part $|\omega''|$ of the complex frequency $\omega = \omega'+i\omega''$.† Writing the formula in the complex form

$$\omega - \omega_0 = -\tfrac{1}{2}ic\frac{\oint\zeta|\mathbf{H}|^2\,\mathrm{d}f}{\int|\mathbf{H}|^2\,\mathrm{d}V}, \tag{70.7}$$

ω and ω_0 being the frequencies with and without allowance for ζ, we can determine not only the damping decrement but also the change in the eigenfrequencies themselves. The latter is seen to be determined by the imaginary part of ζ. We have mentioned in §67 that usually $\zeta'' < 0$, and the eigenfrequencies are then reduced.

In actual calculations, it may be more convenient to transform the volume integral in the denominator of (70.7) into one over the surface. The result is‡

$$\int|\mathbf{H}|^2\,\mathrm{d}V = \tfrac{1}{2}\oint(|\mathbf{H}|^2 - |\mathbf{E}|^2)\mathbf{r}\cdot\mathrm{d}\mathbf{f}. \tag{70.8}$$

PROBLEMS

PROBLEM 1. Determine the eigenfrequencies of a cuboidal resonator with perfectly conducting walls.

SOLUTION. We take the axes of x, y, z along three concurrent edges of the cuboid; let the lengths of these edges be a_1, a_2, a_3. The solutions of equations (70.3) and (70.4) which satisfy the boundary condition $\mathbf{E}_t = 0$ are

$$E_x = A_1 \cos k_x x \sin k y_y \sin k_z z \,.\, e^{-i\omega t} \tag{1}$$

† In radio engineering the *quality* of the resonator, defined as the ratio $\omega'/2|\omega''|$, is generally used instead of the damping decrement.

‡ Since the vector $\mathbf{H}$ is tangential to the surface, we have identically

$$\oint(\mathbf{H}\cdot\mathbf{H}^*)(\mathbf{r}\cdot\mathbf{df}) = \oint(\mathbf{H}\cdot\mathbf{H}^*)(\mathbf{r}\cdot\mathbf{df}) - \oint(\mathbf{H}\cdot\mathbf{r})(\mathbf{H}^*\cdot\mathbf{df}) - \oint(\mathbf{H}^*\cdot\mathbf{r})(\mathbf{H}\cdot\mathbf{df}).$$

The integrals on the right are transformed by putting $\mathbf{df} \to \mathrm{d}V\,\mathbf{grad}$, and using (70.1) we obtain

$$\oint(\mathbf{H}\cdot\mathbf{H}^*)(\mathbf{r}\cdot\mathbf{df}) = ik\int\mathbf{r}\cdot(\mathbf{H}\times\mathbf{E}^* - \mathbf{H}^*\times\mathbf{E})\,\mathrm{d}V + \int\mathbf{H}\cdot\mathbf{H}^*\,\mathrm{d}V.$$

Similarly, using the identity $\mathbf{r}\times(\mathbf{E}\times\mathbf{df}) = \mathbf{E}(\mathbf{r}\cdot\mathbf{df}) - (\mathbf{r}\cdot\mathbf{E})\,\mathbf{df} = 0$ (by the boundary condition $\mathbf{E}_t = 0$), we have

$$\begin{aligned}\oint(\mathbf{E}\cdot\mathbf{E}^*)(\mathbf{r}\cdot\mathbf{df}) &= -\oint(\mathbf{E}\cdot\mathbf{E}^*)(\mathbf{r}\cdot\mathbf{df}) + \oint(\mathbf{E}\cdot\mathbf{r})(\mathbf{E}^*\cdot\mathbf{df}) + \oint(\mathbf{E}^*\cdot\mathbf{r})(\mathbf{E}\cdot\mathbf{df})\\ &= ik\int\mathbf{r}\cdot(\mathbf{H}\times\mathbf{E}^* - \mathbf{H}^*\times\mathbf{E})\,\mathrm{d}V - \int\mathbf{E}\cdot\mathbf{E}^*\,\mathrm{d}V.\end{aligned}$$

Subtracting and using (70.5), we obtain formula (70.8).

and similarly for E_y, E_z, where

$$k_x = n_1\pi/a_1, \qquad k_y = n_2\pi/a_2, \qquad k_z = n_3\pi/a_3 \tag{2}$$

(n_1, n_2, n_3 being positive integers). The constants A_1, A_2, A_3 are related by

$$A_1k_x+A_2k_y+A_3k_z = 0, \tag{3}$$

and the eigenfrequencies are $\omega^2 = c^2(k_x^2+k_y^2+k_z^2)$.

The magnetic field is calculated from (1):

$$H_x = -(ic/\omega)(A_3k_y-A_2k_z) \sin k_xx \cos k_yy \cos k_zz \cdot e^{-i\omega t},$$

and similarly for H_y, H_z.

If two or all of the numbers n_1, n_2, n_3 are zero, $\mathbf{E} = 0$. Hence the lowest frequency corresponds to an oscillation in which one of these numbers is 0 and the other two are 1.

Since the relation (3) holds, the solution (1) (with given non-zero n_1, n_2, n_3) involves only two independent arbitrary constants, i.e. each eigenfrequency is doubly degenerate. The frequencies for which one of n_1, n_2, n_3 is zero are not degenerate.

PROBLEM 2. Determine the frequencies of electric dipole and magnetic dipole oscillations in a spherical resonator of radius a.

SOLUTION. In a stationary spherical electric dipole wave, the fields **E** and **H** are of the form†

$$\mathbf{E} = e^{-i\omega t} \mathbf{curl\,curl} \left(\frac{\sin kr}{r}\mathbf{b}\right), \qquad \mathbf{H} = -ike^{-i\omega t} \mathbf{curl} \left(\frac{\sin kr}{r}\mathbf{b}\right),$$

where $\mathbf{b}$ is a constant vector and $k = \omega/c$. The boundary condition $\mathbf{n}\times\mathbf{E} = 0$ at $r = a$ gives $\cot ka = (ka)^{-1}-ka$. The smallest root of this equation is $ka = 2{\cdot}74$. The frequency $\omega = 2{\cdot}74\ c/a$ is the lowest eigenfrequency of a spherical resonator.

In a stationary spherical magnetic dipole wave, we have

$$\mathbf{E} = ike^{-i\omega t} \mathbf{curl} \left(\frac{\sin kr}{r}\mathbf{b}\right), \qquad \mathbf{H} = e^{-i\omega t} \mathbf{curl\,curl} \left(\frac{\sin kr}{r}\mathbf{b}\right).$$

The boundary condition on **E** gives the equation $\tan ka = ka$, whose smallest root is $ka = 4{\cdot}49$.

§71. The propagation of electromagnetic waves in waveguides

A *waveguide* is a hollow pipe‡ of infinite length, i.e. a cavity infinite in one direction, whereas the resonators discussed in §70 are of finite volume. The characteristic oscillations in a resonator are stationary waves, but those in a waveguide are "stationary" only in the transverse directions; waves travelling in the direction along the pipe can be propagated.

Let us consider a straight waveguide of any (simply-connected) cross-section uniform along its length. We shall first suppose that the walls of the waveguide are perfectly conducting, and take the z-axis along the waveguide. In a travelling wave propagated in the z-direction, all quantities depend on z through a factor $\exp(ik_zz)$, with k_z a constant.

The electromagnetic waves possible in such a waveguide can be divided into two types: in one, $H_z = 0$, and in the other $E_z = 0$ (RAYLEIGH, 1897).

† See *The Classical Theory of Fields*, §9–6.

‡ The formulae below hold for an evacuated waveguide. Those for a waveguide filled with a non-absorbing dielectric are obtained by means of the transformation given in the first footnote to §70.

The former type, in which the magnetic field is purely transverse, are called *electric-type waves* or *E waves*. The latter, in which the electric field is purely transverse, are called *magnetic-type waves* or *H waves*.†

Let us first consider E waves. The x and y components of equations (70.1) give

$$\frac{\partial E_z}{\partial y} - ik_z E_y = i\frac{\omega}{c}H_x, \qquad -\frac{\partial E_z}{\partial x} + ik_z E_x = i\frac{\omega}{c}H\,,$$

$$ik_z H_y = i\frac{\omega}{c}E_x, \qquad ik_z H_x = -i\frac{\omega}{c}E_y.$$

Hence

$$E_x = \frac{ik_z}{\kappa^2}\frac{\partial E_z}{\partial x}, \qquad E_y = \frac{ik_z}{\kappa^2}\frac{\partial E_z}{\partial y},$$
$$H_x = -\frac{i\omega}{c\kappa^2}\frac{\partial E_z}{\partial y}, \qquad H_y = \frac{i\omega}{c\kappa^2}\frac{\partial E_z}{\partial x}, \tag{71.1}$$

where $\kappa^2 = (\omega^2/c^2) - k_z^2$. Thus, in an E wave, all the transverse components of **E** and **H** can be expressed in terms of the longitudinal component of the electric field. This component must be determined by solving the wave equation, which takes the two-dimensional form

$$\triangle_2 E_z + \kappa^2 E_z = 0 \tag{71.2}$$

($\triangle_2$ being the two-dimensional Laplacian). The boundary conditions for this equation are that the tangential components of **E** should vanish on the walls of the waveguide, and can be satisfied by putting

$$E_z = 0 \text{ on the circumference of the cross-section.} \tag{71.3}$$

According to formulae (71.1), the two-dimensional vector whose components are E_x, E_y is proportional to the two-dimensional gradient of E_z. When the condition (71.3) holds, therefore, the tangential component of **E** in the xy-plane is also zero.

Similarly, in an H wave the transverse components of **E** and **H** can be expressed in terms of the longitudinal component of the magnetic field:

$$H_x = \frac{ik_z}{\kappa^2}\frac{\partial H_z}{\partial x}, \qquad H_y = \frac{ik_z}{\kappa^2}\frac{\partial H_z}{\partial y},$$
$$E_x = \frac{i\omega}{c\kappa^2}\frac{\partial H_z}{\partial y}, \qquad E_y = -\frac{i\omega}{c\kappa^2}\frac{\partial H_z}{\partial x}. \tag{71.4}$$

† These types are also known as TM (transverse-magnetic) and TE (transverse-electric) waves.

The longitudinal field H_z is given by the solution of the equation

$$\triangle_2 H_z + \kappa^2 H_z = 0 \tag{71.5}$$

with the boundary condition

$$\partial H_z/\partial n = 0 \text{ on the circumference of the cross-section.} \tag{71.6}$$

According to formulae (71.4), this condition ensures that the normal component of **H** is zero.

Thus the problem of determining the electromagnetic field in a waveguide reduces to that of finding solutions of the two-dimensional wave equation $\triangle_2 f + \kappa^2 f = 0$, with the boundary condition $f = 0$ or $\partial f/\partial n = 0$ on the circumference of the cross-section. For a given cross-section, such solutions exist only for certain definite eigenvalues of the parameter κ^2.

For each eigenvalue κ^2 we have the relation

$$\omega^2 = c^2(k_z^2 + \kappa^2) \tag{71.7}$$

between the frequency ω and the wave number k_z of the wave. The velocity of propagation of the wave along the waveguide is given by the derivative

$$u_z = \frac{\partial\omega}{\partial k_z} = \frac{ck_z}{\sqrt{(k_z^2 + \kappa^2)}} = \frac{c^2 k_z}{\omega}. \tag{71.8}$$

For given κ, this varies from 0 to c when k_z varies from 0 to ∞.

The (time) average energy flux density along the waveguide is given by the z-component of the Poynting vector. A simple calculation, using formulae (71.1), gives for an E wave

$$\bar{S}_z = \frac{c}{8\pi}\,\mathrm{re}\,(\mathbf{E}\times\mathbf{H}^*)_z = \frac{\omega k_z}{8\pi\kappa^4}|\mathbf{grad}_2\,E_z|^2.$$

The total energy flux q is obtained by integrating $\bar{S}_z$ over the cross-section of the waveguide. We have

$$\int|\mathbf{grad}_2\,E_z|^2\,\mathrm{d}f = \oint E_z^*\frac{\partial E_z}{\partial n}\,\mathrm{d}l - \int E_z^*\triangle_2 E_z\,\mathrm{d}f.$$

The first integral is taken along the circumference of the cross-section, and is zero on account of the boundary condition $E_z = 0$. In the second integral we replace $\triangle_2 E_z$ by $-\kappa^2 E_z$, and the result is

$$q = \frac{\omega k_z}{8\pi\kappa^2}\int|E_z|^2\,\mathrm{d}f. \tag{71.9}$$

The expression obtained for an H wave is the same with H_z instead of E_z.

The electromagnetic energy density W (per unit length of the waveguide) may be calculated similarly. It is simpler, however, to derive W directly from q, since we must have $q = Wu_z$. From (71.8) and (71.9), therefore,

$$W = \frac{\omega^2}{8\pi\kappa^2 c^2}\int|E_z|^2\,\mathrm{d}f. \tag{71.10}$$

It follows from (71.7) that, for each type of wave (for a given value of κ^2) there is a minimum possible frequency, namely $c\kappa$. At lower frequencies the propagation of waves of the type concerned is not possible. There is a smallest eigenvalue $\kappa_{\min}$, which is not zero (see below). We therefore conclude that there is a frequency $\omega_{\min} = c\kappa_{\min}$ below which no waves can be propagated along the waveguide. The order of magnitude of $\omega_{\min}$ is c/a, where a is the transverse dimension of the pipe.

This statement is valid, however, only for waveguides in which the cross-section is simply connected (as we have hitherto assumed). When the cross-section is multiply connected,† the situation is quite different. In such waveguides not only the E and H waves described above but also another type of wave, whose frequency is subject to no restriction, can be propagated. Such waves (called *principal waves*) are characterised by the fact that $k_z = k$ (i.e. $\kappa = 0$); the velocity of propagation is equal to the velocity of light c. We shall derive the chief properties of such waves, and shall see why such waves cannot occur when the cross-section of the waveguide is simply connected.

All the field components in a principal wave satisfy the two-dimensional Laplace's equation, $\triangle_2 f = 0$. With the boundary condition $f = 0$, the only solution of this equation regular throughout the cross-section (whether or not multiply connected) is $f \equiv 0$. Hence we have $E_z = 0$ in a principal wave.

With the boundary condition $\partial f/\partial n = 0$, a regular solution is $f =$ constant. It is easy to see, however, that when f is H_z the constant must be zero (by a "constant", of course, we mean a quantity independent of x and y, and depending on z and t through the factor $\exp(ik_z z - i\omega t)$). For, integrating the equation

$$\operatorname{div}\mathbf{H} = \frac{\partial H_x}{\partial x} + \frac{\partial H_y}{\partial y} + \frac{i\omega}{c} H_z = 0$$

over the cross-section, we obtain $\oint H_n \, \mathrm{d}l + (i\omega/c) \int H_z \, \mathrm{d}f = 0$; since $H_n = 0$ on the circumference of the cross-section and H_z is constant over its area, it follows that $H_z = 0$.

Thus a principal wave is purely transverse. For $E_z = H_z = 0$, the x and y components of equations (70.1) give

$$H_x = -E_y, \qquad H_y = E_x, \tag{71.11}$$

i.e. the fields $\mathbf{E}$ and $\mathbf{H}$ are perpendicular and equal in magnitude. They are determined by the equations

$$\operatorname{div}\mathbf{E} = \frac{\partial E_x}{\partial x} + \frac{\partial E_y}{\partial y} = 0, \qquad (\mathbf{curl}\,\mathbf{E})_z = \frac{\partial E_y}{\partial x} - \frac{\partial E_x}{\partial y} = 0,$$

with the boundary condition $\mathbf{E}_t = 0$.

† For example, the space between two pipes one inside the other, or the space outside two parallel pipes.

We see that the dependence of **E**, and therefore of **H**, on x and y is given by the solution of a two-dimensional electrostatic problem: $\mathbf{E} = -\mathbf{grad}_2\,\phi$, where the potential ϕ satisfies the equation $\triangle_2\phi = 0$ with the boundary condition ϕ = constant. In a simply-connected region, this boundary condition means that ϕ = constant (and so $\mathbf{E} = 0$) is the only solution regular throughout the region. This shows that waves of this type cannot be propagated along a waveguide whose cross-section is simply connected. In a multiply-connected region, on the other hand, the constant in the boundary condition need not be the same on the various separate parts of the boundary, and so Laplace's equation has solutions which are not trivial. The electric-field distribution over the cross-section of the waveguide is the same as the two-dimensional electrostatic field between the plates of a condenser at a given potential difference.

So far we have assumed the walls of the waveguide to be perfectly conducting.† If the walls have a small but finite impedance, losses occur and the wave is therefore damped as it is propagated along the waveguide. The damping coefficient can be calculated in the same way as for the damping in time of electromagnetic oscillations in a resonator (§70).

The amount of energy dissipated in unit time per unit length of the walls of the waveguide is given by the integral $(c/8\pi)\zeta'\oint|\mathbf{H}|^2\,\mathrm{d}l$, taken along the circumference of the cross-section; **H** is the magnetic field calculated on the assumption that $\zeta = 0$. Dividing this expression by twice the energy flux q along the waveguide, we obtain the required damping coefficient α. With this definition, α gives the rate of damping of the wave amplitude, which decreases along the waveguide as $e^{-\alpha z}$.

Expressing all quantities in terms of E_z or H_z by means of formulae (71.1) or (71.4), we obtain the following formulae for the absorption coefficients: for an E wave

$$\alpha = \frac{\omega\zeta'}{2\kappa^2 k_z c}\frac{\oint|\mathbf{grad}_2 E_z|^2\,\mathrm{d}l}{\int|E_z|^2\,\mathrm{d}f} \tag{71.12}$$

and for an H wave

$$\alpha = \frac{c\kappa^2\zeta'}{2k_z\omega}\frac{\oint\{|H_z|^2 + (k_z^2/\kappa^4)|\mathbf{grad}_2 H_z|^2\}\,\mathrm{d}l}{\int|H_z|^2\,\mathrm{d}f}. \tag{71.13}$$

In an actual calculation it may be convenient to transform the surface integrals in the denominators into integrals along the circumference. The necessary formulae, whose derivation is similar to that of (70.8), are

$$\begin{aligned}\int|E_z|^2\,\mathrm{d}f &= \frac{1}{2\kappa^2}\oint(\mathbf{n}\cdot\mathbf{r})|\mathbf{grad}_2 E_z|^2\,\mathrm{d}l,\\ \int|H_z|^2\,\mathrm{d}f &= \frac{1}{2\kappa^2}\oint(\mathbf{n}\cdot\mathbf{r})\{\kappa^2|H_z|^2 - |\mathbf{grad}_2 H_z|^2\}\,\mathrm{d}l.\end{aligned} \tag{71.14}$$

† In particular, this assumption is necessary for a rigorous separation of waves with $E_z = 0$ and those with $H_z = 0$.

When $k_z \to 0$, i.e. the frequency $\omega \to c\kappa$, the expressions (71.12) and (71.13) become infinite, but they are then no longer applicable, because their derivation presupposes that κ is small compared with k_z.

Formulae (71.12) and (71.13) are not valid for a principal wave (in a waveguide with a multiply-connected cross-section), in which E_z, H_z and κ are all zero. In this case all the field components can be expressed in terms of the scalar potential ϕ. Using the fact that the fields **H** and $\mathbf{E} = -\mathbf{grad}_2\,\phi$ in a principal wave are perpendicular and equal in magnitude, we obtain the absorption coefficient

$$\alpha = \frac{\zeta' \oint |\mathbf{grad}_2\,\phi|^2\, \mathrm{d}l}{2\int |\mathbf{grad}_2\,\phi|^2\, \mathrm{d}f}. \tag{71.15}$$

The propagation of a principal wave along a waveguide can be relatively simply discussed when its absorption coefficient is not small (so that formula (71.15) is inapplicable) but the wavelength c/ω is large compared with the transverse dimension of the waveguide.

As has been mentioned, the transverse electric field in a principal wave at any instant corresponds to the electrostatic field in a condenser formed by the walls of the waveguide carrying equal and opposite charges. Let these charges be $\pm e(z)$ per unit length. They are related to the currents $\pm J(z)$ flowing on the walls by the "equation of continuity" $\partial e/\partial t = -\partial J/\partial z$, or, for a field of a single frequency, $i\omega e = \partial J/\partial z$. Next, let C be the capacity per unit length of the waveguide. The "potential difference" $\phi_2 - \phi_1$ between its walls is e/C; differentiating this with respect to z, we obtain the e.m.f. which maintains the current on the walls. (When absorption is present, the field is not purely transverse.) Equating the e.m.f. to ZJ, where Z is the impedance per unit length, we have

$$-\frac{\partial}{\partial z}\left(\frac{e}{C}\right) = ZJ$$

or

$$\frac{\partial}{\partial z}\left(\frac{1}{C}\frac{\partial J}{\partial z}\right) + i\omega ZJ = 0. \tag{71.16}$$

Substituting $Z = R - i\omega L/c^2$, where R and L are the resistance and self-inductance per unit length of the waveguide, we can return from the single-frequency current components to currents which are arbitrary functions of time. Assuming the capacity C to be constant along the waveguide, we arrive at the *telegrapher's equation*:

$$\frac{1}{C}\frac{\partial^2 J}{\partial z^2} - R\frac{\partial J}{\partial t} - \frac{L}{c^2}\frac{\partial^2 J}{\partial t^2} = 0. \tag{71.17}$$

If there is no resistance ($R = 0$), this equation reduces, as it should, to the wave equation with a velocity of wave propagation $\sqrt{(c^2/LC)} = c$.†

PROBLEMS

PROBLEM 1. Find the values of κ for waves propagated in a waveguide whose cross-section is a rectangle of sides a and b. Find the damping coefficients.

SOLUTION. In E waves‡ $E_z = \text{constant} \times \sin k_x x \sin k_y y$, where $k_x = n_1\pi/a$, $k_y = n_2\pi/b$, with n_1 and n_2 positive integers. In H waves $H_z = \text{constant} \times \cos k_x x \cos k_y y$, and one of n_1 and n_2 may be zero. In both types of wave $\kappa^2 = k_x^2 + k_y^2 = \pi^2(n_1^2/a^2 + n_2^2/b^2)$. The smallest value of κ corresponds to an H_{10} wave (the suffixes show the values of n_1 and n_2) and is $\kappa_{\text{min}} = \pi/a$ (we assume that $a > b$).

The damping coefficients are calculated from formulae (71.12) and (71.13) and are: for E waves $\alpha = 2\zeta'\omega(k_x^2 b + k_y^2 a)/c\kappa^2 k_z ab$, for $H_{n_1 0}$ waves

$$\alpha = \frac{\zeta'\omega}{ck_z ab}\left(a + \frac{2\kappa^2}{k^2}b\right),$$

and for $H_{n_1 n_2}$ waves ($n_1, n_2 \neq 0$)

$$\alpha = \frac{2c\kappa^2\zeta'}{\omega k_z ab}\left[a + b + \frac{k_z^2}{\kappa^4}(k_x^2 a + k_y^2 b)\right].$$

PROBLEM 2. The same as Problem 1, but for a waveguide whose cross-section is a circle of radius a.

SOLUTION. Solving the wave equation in polar co-ordinates r, ϕ, we have for E waves

$$E_z = \text{constant} \times J_n(\kappa r) \begin{matrix}\sin\\ \cos\end{matrix} n\phi$$

with the condition $J_n(\kappa a) = 0$, which gives the value of κ. In H waves the value of H_z is given by the same formula, but κ is determined by the condition $J_n'(\kappa a) = 0$. The smallest value of κ occurs for the H_1 wave, and is $\kappa_{\text{min}} = 1{\cdot}84/a$.

The damping coefficient is calculated from formulae (71.12)–(71.14). For E waves it is $\alpha = \omega\zeta'/cak_z$, and for H waves

$$\alpha = \frac{c\zeta'\kappa^2}{\omega k_z a}\left[1 + \frac{n^2\omega^2}{c^2\kappa^2(a^2\kappa^2 - n^2)}\right].$$

§72. The scattering of electromagnetic waves by small particles

Let us consider the scattering of electromagnetic waves by macroscopic particles whose dimensions are small compared with the wavelength $\lambda \sim c/\omega$ of the wave undergoing scattering (RAYLEIGH, 1871). When this condition holds, the electromagnetic field near the particle may be supposed uniform. Being in a uniform field periodic in time, each particle acquires definite electric and magnetic moments $\mathscr{P}$ and $\mathscr{M}$, whose dependence on time is given by factors of the form $e^{-i\omega t}$. The scattered wave can be described as being the result of emission by these variable moments. At distances R from

† The equation $LC = 1$ follows from the mathematical equivalence of the problems of determining $1/C$ and L for a given cross-section. The electric and magnetic fields between perfectly conducting surfaces are perpendicular and equal in magnitude (see (71.11)), and if this magnitude is given on the surfaces the charge density and the current density are respectively determined. Hence the coefficients of proportionality ($1/C$ and L) between the field energy and the squared charge and current respectively are the same.

‡ We everywhere omit the factor $\exp(ik_z z - i\omega t)$.

the particle which are large compared with λ (the wave region), the fields in the scattered wave are given by†

$$\mathbf{H}' = \frac{\omega^2}{c^2R}\{\mathbf{n}\times\mathscr{P} + \mathbf{n}\times(\mathscr{M}\times\mathbf{n})\},$$
$$\mathbf{E}' = \mathbf{H}'\times\mathbf{n}, \tag{72.1}$$

where the unit vector $\mathbf{n}$ gives the direction of scattering, and the values of $\mathscr{P}$ and $\mathscr{M}$ at the time $t-R/c$ must be taken. We denote the fields in the scattered wave by primed letters and those in the incident wave by unprimed letters. The (time) average intensity of radiation scattered into a solid angle do is $\mathrm{d}I = \frac{1}{2}c|\mathbf{H}'|^2R^2\,\mathrm{d}o/4\pi$; dividing by the energy flux density in the incident wave $c|\mathbf{H}|^2/8\pi = c|\mathbf{E}|^2/8\pi$, we obtain the *effective scattering cross-section.*

The calculation of $\mathscr{P}$ and $\mathscr{M}$ is particularly simple if the dimensions of the particle are small in comparison not only with λ but also with the "wave-length" δ corresponding to the frequency ω in the material of the particle. In this case we can calculate the polarisability of the particle from the formulae for an external uniform static field, the only difference being, of course, that the values taken for ϵ and μ are those corresponding to the given frequency ω, and not the static values. If, as usually happens, μ is close to unity, the magnetic dipole term in formula (72.1) may be omitted.

For a spherical particle of volume V we have (see (8.9))

$$\mathscr{P} = V\alpha\mathbf{E}, \qquad \alpha = 3(\epsilon-1)/4\pi(\epsilon+2), \tag{72.2}$$

and the effective scattering cross-section is

$$\mathrm{d}\sigma = (\omega/c)^4|\alpha|^2V^2\sin^2\theta\,\mathrm{d}o, \tag{72.3}$$

where θ is the angle between the scattering direction $\mathbf{n}$ and the direction of the electric field $\mathbf{E}$ in the linearly polarised incident wave. The total effective cross-section is

$$\sigma = 8\pi|\alpha|^2\omega^4V^2/3c^4. \tag{72.4}$$

The frequency dependence of the effective cross-section is determined by the factor ω^4 and by the polarisability. At frequencies so low that α shows no dispersion, the scattering is proportional to ω^4. It may be noted also that the effective cross-section is proportional to the square of the volume of the particle.

If the incident wave is unpolarised (natural light) then the differential effective cross-section must be obtained by averaging (72.3) over all directions of the vector $\mathbf{E}$ in a plane perpendicular to the direction of propagation of the incident wave (i.e. perpendicular to its wave vector $\mathbf{k}$). Denoting by ϑ

† See *The Classical Theory of Fields*, §9–12.

and ϕ the polar angle and the azimuth of the direction of **n** relative to **k** (ϕ being measured from the plane of **k** and **E**), we have $\cos\theta = \sin\vartheta\cos\phi$ (Fig. 31), so that

$$d\sigma = (\omega/c)^4|\alpha|^2V^2(1-\sin^2\vartheta\cos^2\phi)\,do. \tag{72.5}$$

On averaging over ϕ, we obtain the following formula for the effective cross-section for scattering of an unpolarised wave:†

$$d\sigma = \tfrac{1}{2}(\omega/c)^4|\alpha|^2V^2(1+\cos^2\vartheta)\,do, \tag{72.6}$$

where ϑ is the angle between the directions of incidence and scattering.

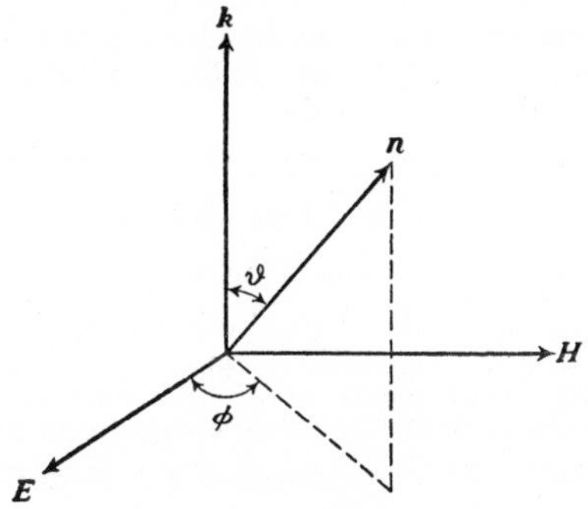

FIG. 31

From formula (72.5) we can easily find the degree of depolarisation of the scattered light. To do so, we notice that, for a given direction of **E**, **E**′ lies in the plane of **E** and **n**. The direction of the electric field **E**′ in the scattered wave therefore lies in the plane of **k** and **n** (the *plane of scattering*) or perpendicular to that plane, according as the azimuth ϕ of the vector **E**, measured from the plane of **k** and **n**, is 0 or $\frac{1}{2}\pi$. Let $I_\parallel$ and $I_\perp$ be the intensities of scattered radiation having these two polarisations. The degree of depolarisation is defined as the ratio of the smaller to the larger of these quantities. By (72.5) we have

$$I_\parallel/I_\perp = \cos^2\vartheta. \tag{72.7}$$

If the scattering particle has a large dielectric permeability,

$$\delta \sim c/\omega\sqrt{|\epsilon|} \ll \lambda.$$

The dimensions of the particle may then be small compared with λ but not small compared with δ. In the first approximation with respect to $1/\epsilon$, the electric moment of the particle may be calculated as simply the moment of a conductor ($\epsilon \to \infty$) in a uniform constant external field. In calculating the magnetic moment, however, the induced currents in the particle are of

† For future reference we may note the formula $\overline{\sin^2\theta} = \frac{1}{2}(1+\cos^2\vartheta)$.

importance, and the problem cannot be taken as static; instead, we must seek a solution of equation (63.2) (with $\mu = 1$):

$$\triangle \mathbf{H} + \epsilon\omega^2\mathbf{H}/c^2 = 0 \tag{72.8}$$

which becomes the field of the incident wave far from the particle. The magnetic and electric moments are of the same order of magnitude, and both terms in formula (72.1) must be retained. The angular distribution and amount of scattering are different from those discussed above (see Problem 2).

PROBLEMS

PROBLEM 1. Linearly polarised light is scattered by randomly oriented small particles whose electric polarisability tensor has three different principal values. Determine the depolarisation coefficient for the scattered light.

SOLUTION. Neglecting, as above, the magnetic moment, we have from (72.1)

$$\mathbf{E}' = (\omega^2/c^2R)(\mathbf{n}\times\mathscr{P})\times\mathbf{n}.$$

The required depolarisation coefficient is given by the ratio of the principal values of the two-dimensional tensor $I_{\alpha\beta} = \overline{E'_\alpha E'_\beta{}^*}$, where the bar denotes an averaging over orientations of the scattering particle for a given direction of scattering **n**, and the suffixes α and β take two values in the plane perpendicular to **n**.† It is more convenient, however, to average the three-dimensional tensor $\mathscr{P}_i\mathscr{P}_k{}^*$ and then project it on the plane perpendicular to **n**; these components of the tensor $\overline{\mathscr{P}_i\mathscr{P}_k{}^*}$ are proportional to the corresponding components $I_{\alpha\beta}$. Substituting $\mathscr{P}_i = \alpha_{ik}E_{ik}$, we have

$$\overline{\mathscr{P}_i\mathscr{P}_k{}^*} = \overline{\alpha_{il}\alpha_{km}{}^*}E_lE_m{}^*.$$

In effecting the averaging we use the formula

$$\overline{\alpha_{ik}\alpha_{lm}{}^*} = A\delta_{ik}\delta_{lm} + B(\delta_{il}\delta_{km} + \delta_{im}\delta_{kl}).$$

This is the most general tensor of rank four which is symmetrical in i, k and l, m and contains only scalar constants. These constants are determined from two equations obtained by contracting the tensor, firstly with respect to i, k and l, m, secondly with respect to i, l and k, m. They are

$$A = \frac{2|\alpha_{ii}|^2 - |\alpha_{ik}|^2}{15} = \frac{1}{15}\{|\alpha_1|^2 + |\alpha_2|^2 + |\alpha_3|^2 + 4\,\mathrm{re}(\alpha_1\alpha_2{}^* + \alpha_1\alpha_3{}^* + \alpha_2\alpha_3{}^*)\},$$

$$B = \frac{3|\alpha_{ik}|^2 - |\alpha_{ii}|^2}{30} = \frac{1}{15}\{|\alpha_1|^2 + |\alpha_2|^2 + |\alpha_3|^2 - \mathrm{re}(\alpha_1\alpha_2{}^* + \alpha_1\alpha_3{}^* + \alpha_2\alpha_3{}^*)\},$$

where α_1, α_2, α_3 are the principal values of the tensor α_{ik}.

In a linearly polarised wave, the field amplitude $\mathbf{E}^{(i)}$ (we omit the time factor $e^{-i\omega t}$) can always be defined so as to be real. Then we have

$$\overline{\mathscr{P}_i\mathscr{P}_k{}^*} = (A+B)E_iE_k + B\delta_{ik}E^2. \tag{1}$$

Let the z-axis be in the direction of **n**, and the xz-plane contain the directions of **n** and **E**; these axes are the principal axes of the tensor $I_{\alpha\beta}$. Taking the appropriate components of the tensor (1), we find the depolarisation coefficient $I_y/I_x = B/[(A+B)\sin^2\theta + B]$, where θ is the angle between **E** and **n**.

PROBLEM 2. Determine the effective cross-section for scattering by a sphere of radius a, for which ϵ is large; it is assumed that $\lambda \gg a \sim \delta$.

† See *The Classical Theory of Fields*, §6–7.

SOLUTION. The problem of calculating the magnetic moment acquired by a sphere with given ϵ (and $\mu = 1$) in a variable magnetic field **H** is the same as that solved in §45, Problem 1, except that k in the formulae derived there must be replaced by $\omega\sqrt{\epsilon}/c$. Thus $\mathscr{M} = -a^3\gamma\mathbf{H}$, where

$$\gamma = \frac{1}{2}\left(1+\frac{3}{ka}\cot ka - \frac{3}{(ka)^2}\right).$$

The electric moment can be calculated, in the first approximation with respect to $1/\epsilon$, as simply the moment of a conducting ($\epsilon \to \infty$) sphere in a uniform constant electric field: $\mathscr{P} = a^3\mathbf{E}$.

Taking into account the fact that **E** and **H** are perpendicular, we have after a simple calculation, using (72.1), the following formula for the effective scattering cross-section:

$$d\sigma = (a^6\omega^4/c^4)\{|\gamma|^2\cos^2\phi+\sin^2\phi-(\gamma+\gamma^*)\cos\vartheta+\cos^2\vartheta(\cos^2\phi+|\gamma|^2\sin^2\phi)\}\,do,$$

where ϕ and ϑ are the angles shown in Fig. 31. In scattering of unpolarised light we have

$$d\sigma = (a^6\omega^4/c^4)\{\tfrac{1}{2}[1+|\gamma|^2][1+\cos^2\vartheta]-(\gamma+\gamma^*)\cos\vartheta\}\,do,$$

and the degree of depolarisation of the scattered light is $I_\parallel/I_\perp = |(\gamma-\cos\vartheta)/(1-\gamma\cos\vartheta)|^2$. The total scattering cross-section is $\sigma = 8\pi a^6\omega^4(1+|\gamma|^2)/3c^4$.

In the limit $ka \to \infty$ (i.e. when $\lambda \gg a \gg \delta$) we have $\gamma = \frac{1}{2}$, corresponding to scattering by a perfectly reflecting sphere into which neither the electric nor the magnetic field penetrates.

§73. The absorption of electromagnetic waves by small particles

The scattering of electromagnetic waves by particles is accompanied by absorption. The effective absorption cross-section is given by the ratio of the mean energy Q dissipated in a particle per unit time to the incident energy flux density. To calculate Q we can use the formula

$$Q = -\mathscr{P}\cdot\dot{\mathfrak{E}} - \mathscr{M}\cdot\dot{\mathfrak{H}}, \tag{73.1}$$

where $\mathscr{P}$ and $\mathscr{M}$ are the total electric and magnetic moments of the particle, and the external fields $\mathfrak{E}$ and $\mathfrak{H}$ are replaced by the fields **E** and **H** in the scattered wave; cf. (45.21).

Using the complex representation of quantities, we can write (see the penultimate footnote to §45)

$$Q = -\tfrac{1}{2}\,\mathrm{re}(\mathscr{P}\cdot\dot{\mathbf{E}}^* + \mathscr{M}\cdot\dot{\mathbf{H}}^*) = \tfrac{1}{2}\omega V(\alpha_e'' + \alpha_m'')|\mathbf{E}|^2,$$

where α_e and α_m are the electric and magnetic polarisabilities of the particle. Dividing by the incident energy flux, we obtain

$$\sigma = 4\pi\omega V(\alpha_e'' + \alpha_m'')/c. \tag{73.2}$$

Let us apply this formula to absorption by a sphere of radius $a \ll \lambda$, assuming it non-magnetic ($\mu = 1$). The nature of the absorption depends considerably on the magnitude of the dielectric permeability.

If ϵ is small, then we have both $a \ll \lambda$ and $a \ll \delta$. In this case the magnetic polarisability may be neglected in comparison with the electric polarisability. With the latter given by (72.2), we have

$$\sigma = 12\pi\omega a^3\epsilon''/c[(\epsilon' + 2)^2 + (\epsilon'')^2]. \tag{73.3}$$

If, on the other hand, $|\epsilon| \gg 1$, the electric part of the absorption becomes small, and the magnetic absorption may be important even if we still have

$\delta \gg a$. When this last condition holds (i.e. $|ka| \ll 1$), the magnetic polarisability is $\alpha_m = (ka)^2/40\pi = a^2\omega^2\epsilon/40\pi c^2$ and the effective absorption cross-section is

$$\sigma = \frac{12\pi\omega a^3\epsilon''}{c}\left(\frac{1}{|\epsilon|^2} + \frac{\omega^2 a^2}{90c^2}\right). \tag{73.4}$$

When ϵ increases further, the electric part of the absorption becomes small compared with the magnetic part. In the limit $\delta \ll a$ (i.e. $|ka| \gg 1$, $\cot ka \to -i$) we have $\alpha_m = 9i/8\pi ka = 9ic\zeta/8\pi\omega a$, where $\zeta = 1/\sqrt{\epsilon}$ is the surface impedance of the sphere. Hence

$$\sigma = 6\pi a^2\zeta''. \tag{73.5}$$

It may be noticed that this formula could have been obtained more directly, without using the general expression for the magnetic polarisability $\alpha_m(\omega)$ of the sphere. When ζ is small, the energy dissipation Q can be calculated by "integrating" the mean Poynting vector (67.4) over the surface of the sphere, the distribution of the magnetic field over the surface being given by the solution (42.3) of the problem of a superconducting ($\zeta = 0$) sphere in a uniform magnetic field.

Knowing the effective absorption cross-section of the sphere, we can immediately determine the intensity of the thermal radiation emitted from the sphere. According to Kirchhoff's law,† the intensity dI in a frequency range $d\omega$ is given in terms of $\sigma(\omega)$ by $dI = 4\pi c\sigma(\omega)e_0(\omega)\,d\omega$, where $e_0(\omega) = \hbar\omega^3/4\pi^3c^3\,[\exp(\hbar\omega/T)-1]$ is the spectral density of black-body radiation per unit volume and unit solid angle.

§74. Diffraction by a wedge

The ordinary approximate theory of diffraction‡ is based on the assumption that the deviations from geometrical optics are small. It is thereby assumed, firstly, that all dimensions are large compared with the wavelength; this applies both to dimensions of bodies (screens) or apertures and to distances of bodies from the points of emission and observation of the light. Secondly, only small angles of diffraction are considered, i.e. the distribution of light is examined only in directions close to the edge of the geometrical shadow. Under these conditions, the actual optical properties of the substances involved are of no importance; all that matters is that they are opaque.

If these conditions are not fulfilled, the solution of the diffraction problem requires an exact solution of the wave equation, taking into account the appropriate boundary conditions on the surfaces of the bodies, which depend on their properties. The finding of such solutions offers exceptional mathematical difficulties, and has been effected for only a small number of problems. A simplifying assumption is usually made concerning the properties

† See *Statistical Physics*, §60, Pergamon Press, London, 1958.
‡ See *The Classical Theory of Fields*, §§7–7 to 7–9.

of the body at which the diffraction occurs, namely that it is perfectly conducting, and therefore perfectly reflecting.

The following remark may be made here. It might seem reasonable to solve the diffraction problem on the assumption that the surface of the body is "black", i.e. completely absorbs light incident on it. In reality, however, such an assumption concerning the body in stating the exact problem of diffraction would involve a contradiction. The reason is that, if the substance of the body is strongly absorbing, the coefficient of reflection is not small but, on the contrary, almost unity (see §67)). Hence a reflection coefficient close to zero implies a weakly absorbing substance and a thickness of the body which is large compared with the wavelength. In the exact theory of diffraction, parts of the surface of the body at a distance from its edge of the order of the wavelength are necessarily of importance; but the thickness of the body near its edge is always small, so that the assumption that it is "black" is certainly untenable.

Considerable theoretical interest attaches to the exact solution (first obtained by A. Sommerfeld, 1894) of the problem of diffraction at the edge of a perfectly conducting wedge bounded by two intersecting semi-infinite planes. A complete exposition of the very complex mathematical theory, which involves the use of special devices, is beyond the scope of this book. Here we shall give, for reference, the final results.†

We take the edge of the wedge as the z-axis in a system of cylindrical co-ordinates r, ϕ, z. The front surface (OA in Fig. 32) corresponds to

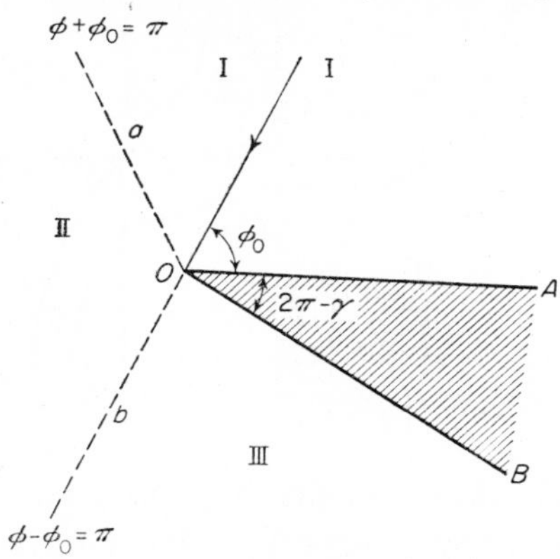

Fig. 32

† A detailed account of the calculations is given by A. Sommerfeld, *Optics*, Academic Press, New York, 1954; P. Frank and R. von Mises, *Differential and Integral Equations in Physics* (*Differential- und Integralgleichungen der Physik*), part 2, Chapter XX, 2nd ed., Vieweg, Brunswick, 1935. Another method of solution, due to M. I. Kontorovich and N. N. Lebedev, is given by G. A. Grinberg, *Selected Problems in the Mathematical Theory of Electric and Magnetic Phenomena* (*Izbrannye voprosy matematicheskoĭ teorii élektricheskikh i magnitnykh yavleniĭ*), Chapter XXII, Moscow, 1948.

A modified solution for diffraction of a cylindrical wave emitted by a line source parallel to the edge of the wedge has been given by H. S. Carslaw, *Proceedings of the London Mathematical Society* **30,** 121, 1899.

$\phi = 0$, and the rear surface (OB) to $\phi = \gamma$, where $2\pi - \gamma$ is the angle of the wedge, the region outside it being $0 < \phi < \gamma$. Let a plane wave of a single frequency and unit amplitude be incident in the $r\phi$-plane on the front surface at an angle ϕ_0 to the surface; by symmetry, it is sufficient to consider angles $\phi_0 < \frac{1}{2}\gamma$. We shall distinguish two independent modes of polarisation of the incident wave, and therefore of the diffracted wave also: the edge of the wedge (the z-axis) may be parallel to either **E** or **H**. The letter u will denote E_z and H_z respectively.

The electromagnetic field is then given in all space by the formula (the time factor $e^{-i\omega t}$ being everywhere omitted)

$$u(r, \phi) = v(r, \phi - \phi_0) \mp v(r, \phi + \phi_0), \tag{74.1}$$

where the upper and lower signs correspond to the polarisations with **E** and **H** respectively in the z-direction, and the function $v(r, \psi)$ is given by the complex integral

$$v(r, \psi) = \frac{1}{2\gamma} \int_C e^{-ikr\cos\zeta} \frac{d\zeta}{1 - e^{-i\pi(\zeta+\psi)/\gamma}}, \tag{74.2}$$

where $k = \omega/c$. The path of integration C in the ζ-plane consists of the two loops C_1 and C_2 shown in Fig. 33. The ends of these loops are at infinity

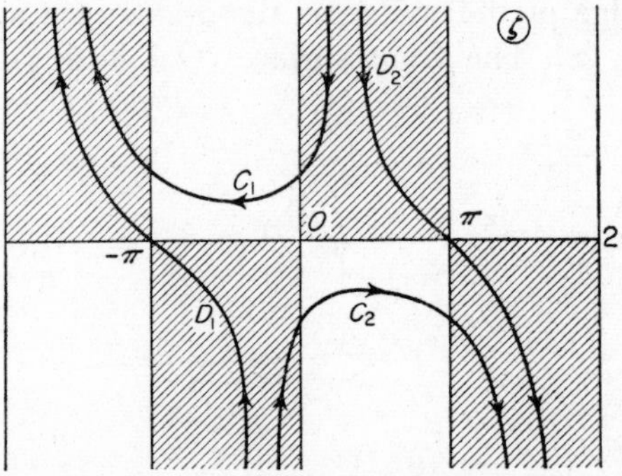

FIG. 33

in parts of the ζ-plane (shaded in Fig. 33) where im $\cos\zeta < 0$, and so the factor $e^{-ikr\cos\zeta}$ tends to zero at infinity. The integrand in (74.2) has poles on the real ζ-axis at the points $\zeta = -\psi + 2n\gamma$, where n is any integer. The integration may be taken along a path $D = D_1 + D_2$ (Fig. 33) instead of C, adding to the integral the residues of the integrand at the poles, if any, in the range $-\pi \leqslant \zeta \leqslant \pi$. We write v as

$$v(r, \psi) = v_0(r, \psi) + v_d(r, \psi), \tag{74.3}$$

where v_d is the integral (74.2) taken along the path D, and v_0 is the contribution from the residues at these poles. Each pole gives rise to a term $\exp[-ikr\cos(\psi - 2n\gamma)]$ in v_0, which represents either the incident wave or one of the waves reflected from the surface of the wedge in accordance with the laws of geometrical optics. The function v_d represents the diffractive distortion of the wave. The field at distances from the edge of the wedge large compared with the wavelength is of the greatest interest. When $kr \gg 1$, the asymptotic formula†

$$v_d(r, \psi) = \frac{\pi}{\gamma\sqrt{(2\pi kr)}} e^{i(kr+\frac{1}{4}\pi)} \frac{\sin(\pi^2/\gamma)}{\cos(\pi^2/\gamma) - \cos(\pi\psi/\gamma)} \tag{74.4}$$

holds, provided that the angle ψ satisfies the condition

$$[\cos(\pi^2/\gamma) - \cos(\pi\psi/\gamma)]^2 \gg 1/kr. \tag{74.5}$$

The dependence on r of the function v_d, and therefore of the field $u_d(r, \phi) = v_d(r, \phi-\phi_0) \mp v_d(r, \phi+\phi_0)$, is given by a factor $e^{ikr}/\sqrt{r}$, i.e. this field resembles a cylindrical wave emitted by the edge of the wedge.

In the form given above, (74.1)–(74.5) are valid for any angles γ and ϕ_0. The more detailed discussion of these formulae will be effected on the assumption (for definiteness) that the angles ϕ_0 and γ are so related ($\gamma > \pi+\phi_0$) that, in geometrical optics, two boundaries are formed: the boundary Ob of the complete shadow (region III in Fig. 32), and the boundary Oa of the "shadow" of the wave reflected from the surface OA.‡

In regions I, II, III the function $u_0(r, \phi) = v_0(r, \phi-\phi_0) \mp v_0(r, \phi+\phi_0)$ has the following forms:

$$\left.\begin{aligned} \text{Region I:}\ u_0 &= e^{-ikr\cos(\phi-\phi_0)} \mp e^{-ikr\cos(\phi+\phi_0)}, \\ \text{Region II:}\ u_0 &= e^{-ikr\cos(\phi-\phi_0)}, \\ \text{Region III:}\ u_0 &= 0. \end{aligned}\right\} \tag{74.6}$$

These expressions, which do not vanish as $kr \to \infty$, describe the incident (region II) or incident and reflected (region I) waves, undistorted by diffraction. The diffractive distortion of the field is given by formula (74.4), but the condition (74.5) ceases to hold when ψ approaches π and the difference $|\psi-\pi|$ is no longer large compared with $1/\sqrt{(kr)}$.

The values $\phi \mp \phi_0 = \pi$ correspond to the geometrical boundaries of the shadow; for $\phi-\phi_0 = \pi$ we have the boundary of the complete shadow, and for $\phi+\phi_0 = \pi$ that of the shadow of the reflected wave. In the immediate neighbourhood of these values a different asymptotic expression must be used, which is valid if the inequality $|\psi-\pi| \ll 1$ holds. This condition,

---

† The next terms in this asymptotic expansion have been given by W. Pauli, *Physical Review* **54**, 924, 1938.

‡ In Fig. 32, $\phi_0 < \frac{1}{2}\pi$. If $\phi_0 > \frac{1}{2}\pi$, the boundary Oa lies to the right of the direction of the incident wave.

If $\gamma < \pi + \phi_0$, there is no region of complete shadow, and reflection (single or multiple) takes place from both sides of the wedge.

together with $kr \gg 1$, ensures the validity of the usual approximate theory of Fresnel diffraction.† Accordingly we have near the boundary Ob of the complete shadow the asymptotic expression

$$u(r,\phi) = e^{-ikr\cos(\phi-\phi_0)}\frac{1-i}{\sqrt{(2\pi)}}\int\limits_{-\infty}^{w} e^{i\eta^2}\,d\eta, \qquad (74.7)$$

$$w = -(\phi-\phi_0-\pi)\sqrt{(\tfrac{1}{2}kr)}.$$

Similarly, near the boundary Oa of the "shadow" of the reflected wave

$$u(r,\phi) = e^{-ikr\cos(\phi-\phi_0)} + e^{-ikr\cos(\phi+\phi_0)}\frac{1-i}{\sqrt{(2\pi)}}\int\limits_{-\infty}^{w} e^{i\eta^2}\,d\eta,$$

$$w = -(\phi+\phi_0-\pi)\sqrt{(\tfrac{1}{2}kr)}. \qquad (74.8)$$

In this approximation the diffraction pattern is independent of the angle of the wedge and of the direction of polarisation of the wave.

The ranges of applicability of formulae (74.4) and (74.7), (74.8) partly overlap. For example, near the boundary of the complete shadow the common range of applicability is given by

$$1 \gg |\phi-\phi_0-\pi| \gg 1/\sqrt{(kr)},$$

and in this range

$$u(r,\phi) = u_0(r,\phi) + \frac{1}{\sqrt{(2\pi kr)}}e^{i(kr+\frac{1}{4}\pi)}\frac{1}{\phi-\phi_0-\pi}, \qquad (74.9)$$

with u_0 given by (74.6). This expression can be obtained from (74.7) by using the asymptotic formulae for the Fresnel integral with large $|w|$:

$$\int\limits_{-\infty}^{w} e^{i\eta^2}\,d\eta = (1+i)\sqrt{(\tfrac{1}{2}\pi)} + e^{iw^2}/2iw \quad \text{for } w > 0,$$

$$\int\limits_{-\infty}^{w} e^{i\eta^2}\,d\eta = e^{iw^2}/2iw \quad \text{for } w < 0.$$

§75. Diffraction by a plane screen

The exact formula (74.2) for diffraction by a wedge can be brought to a comparatively simple form in the particular case of diffraction by a half-

---

† See *The Classical Theory of Fields*, §7–8.

plane ($\gamma = 2\pi$).† The complex integral in (74.2) can be reduced to a Fresnel integral:

$$v(r, \psi) = \frac{1}{\sqrt{\pi}} e^{-i(kr\cos\psi + \frac{1}{4}\pi)} \int_{-\infty}^{w} e^{i\eta^2} \mathrm{d}\eta,$$

$$w = \sqrt{(2kr)} \cos \tfrac{1}{2}\psi. \tag{75.1}$$

This formula holds for any values of r and ψ. For $kr \gg 1$ and angles $|\psi - \pi| \gg 1/\sqrt{(kr)}$ the asymptotic expression

$$v_d(r, \psi) = -e^{i(kr + \frac{1}{4}\pi)} \frac{1}{2\sqrt{(2\pi kr)} \cos \frac{1}{2}\psi} \tag{75.2}$$

(formula (74.4) with $\gamma = 2\pi$) holds.‡

Using formula (75.2), the solution of the problem of diffraction by a plane perfectly conducting screen of any shape can be obtained in closed form. The only assumptions are that the dimensions of the screen and the distance from it are large compared with the wavelength, and that the angles of diffraction are moderately large (this region overlaps the region of small angles in which the ordinary Fresnel-diffraction formulae are valid). The result is in the form of an integral along the edge of the screen, analogously to the expression of the diffraction field, in the ordinary approximate theory,|| as an integral over a surface spanning the aperture in a screen. We shall not pause to give the calculations here.

In the exact theory of diffraction by plane perfectly conducting screens, there is a theorem (due to L. I. Mandel'shtam and M. A. Leontovich) in some ways analogous to Babinet's theorem in the approximate theory.

Let us consider a plane screen with an aperture of any shape, and take the plane of the screen as $z = 0$. Let an electromagnetic wave be incident from the side $z < 0$, and let $\mathbf{E}_0$, $\mathbf{H}_0$ be the total fields in the incident wave and the wave which would be reflected from the screen if there were no aperture. We assume the field continued beyond the screen ($z > 0$). Since $H_z = 0$, $\mathbf{E}_t = 0$ for $z = 0$ (by the boundary conditions at a perfectly conducting surface), the values of $\mathbf{E}_0$ and $\mathbf{H}_0$ for $z > 0$ and $z < 0$ are related by

$$\begin{aligned} E_{0z}(x, y, z) &= E_{0z}(x, y, -z), & \mathbf{E}_{0t}(x, y, z) &= -\mathbf{E}_{0t}(x, y, -z), \\ H_{0z}(x, y, z) &= -H_{0z}(x, y, -z), & \mathbf{H}_{0t}(x, y, z) &= \mathbf{H}_{0t}(x, y, -z). \end{aligned} \tag{75.3}$$

Next, let $\mathbf{E}'$ and $\mathbf{H}'$ be the fields which would occur if a flat plate corresponding to the aperture in size, shape and position, and having infinite

---

† See the references quoted in the second footnote to §74.

‡ Yu. V. Vandakurov (*Zhurnal éksperimental'noĭ i teoreticheskoĭ fiziki* **26**, 3, 1954) has obtained the exact solution of the three-dimensional problem of the diffraction by a half-plane of electromagnetic waves emitted from an arbitrarily oriented electric or magnetic dipole at a finite distance from the edge of the half-plane.

|| See *The Classical Theory of Fields*, §7–7.

magnetic permeability, were placed in the field $\mathbf{E}_0$, $\mathbf{H}_0$. Then the solution of the diffraction problem for the aperture in the screen is given by

$$\begin{aligned} \mathbf{E} &= \tfrac{1}{2}(\mathbf{E}_0 + \mathbf{E}'), \qquad \mathbf{H} = \tfrac{1}{2}(\mathbf{H}_0 + \mathbf{H}') \quad \text{for } z < 0, \\ \mathbf{E} &= \tfrac{1}{2}(\mathbf{E}_0 - \mathbf{E}'), \qquad \mathbf{H} = \tfrac{1}{2}(\mathbf{H}_0 - \mathbf{H}') \quad \text{for } z > 0. \end{aligned} \tag{75.4}$$

To show this, we notice that the fields $\mathbf{E}'$, $\mathbf{H}'$ have the same symmetry (expressed by formulae (75.3)) as the fields $\mathbf{E}_0$, $\mathbf{H}_0$. They therefore satisfy on the plane $z = 0$ the conditions

$$\begin{aligned} &\mathbf{E}'_t = 0, \qquad H'_z = 0 \qquad \text{outside the aperture,} \\ &\mathbf{E}'_{t1} = -\mathbf{E}'_{t2}, \qquad H'_{z1} = -H'_{z2} \quad \text{on the aperture,} \end{aligned}$$

the suffixes 1 and 2 corresponding to $z \to 0\pm$. They also satisfy the further conditions

$$E'_z = 0, \qquad \mathbf{H}'_t = 0 \text{ on the aperture,}$$

since the boundary conditions on the surface of a body with $\mu = \infty$ are obtained from those for a perfectly conducting body ($\epsilon = \infty$) by interchanging **E** and **H**. Hence it is clear that the fields (75.4) satisfy the necessary conditions $\mathbf{E}_t = 0$, $H_z = 0$ on the surface of the screen ($z \to 0-$) outside the aperture, and are continuous on the aperture. Finally, since $\mathbf{E}'$, $\mathbf{H}'$ tend to $\mathbf{E}_0$, $\mathbf{H}_0$ at infinity, the fields (75.4) tend to $\mathbf{E}_0$, $\mathbf{H}_0$ as $z \to -\infty$ and to zero as $z \to +\infty$. They therefore satisfy all the conditions of the problem. This proves the theorem.

Thus the problem of diffraction by an aperture in a screen with $\epsilon = \infty$ is equivalent to a problem of diffraction by a complementary screen with $\mu = \infty$.

PROBLEMS

PROBLEM 1. A plane wave of a single frequency is incident normally on a slit cut in a perfectly conducting screen, the width $2a$ of the slit being large compared with the wavelength. Determine the distribution of light intensity beyond the slit, at large distances from it and for large angles of diffraction.

SOLUTION. For $a \gg \lambda$, the diffraction field beyond the slit can be regarded as a superposition of fields arising from independent diffraction at each of the two edges of the slit and determined by means of the asymptotic formula (75.2). When the distances $AP = r_1$ and $BP = r_2$ from the edges of the slit to the point of observation (Fig. 34) are large compared with a, we can put, in the factors e^{ikr_1} and e^{ikr_2}, $r_1 = r - a\sin\chi$, $r_2 = r + a\sin\chi$, and elsewhere $r_1 \cong r_2 \cong r$; the angles between the z-axis and AP, OP, BP can all be taken as the angle of diffraction χ.

The result is

$$u = \frac{e^{i(kr+\frac{1}{4}\pi)}}{\sqrt{(2\pi kr)}}\left\{\frac{\sin(ka\sin\chi)}{\sin\frac{1}{2}\chi} \pm i\frac{\cos(ka\sin\chi)}{\cos\frac{1}{2}\chi}\right\}.$$

Hence the intensity of light diffracted into an angle $d\chi$ is (relative to the total intensity of light incident on the slit)

$$\begin{aligned} dI &= \frac{1}{4\pi ka}\left\{\left[\frac{\sin(ka\sin\chi)}{\sin\frac{1}{2}\chi}\right]^2 + \left[\frac{\cos(ka\sin\chi)}{\cos\frac{1}{2}\chi}\right]^2\right\} d\chi \\ &= \frac{ka}{\pi}\left\{\left[\frac{\sin(ka\sin\chi)}{ka\sin\chi}\right]^2 \cos\chi + \frac{1}{[2ka\cos\frac{1}{2}\chi]^2}\right\} d\chi. \end{aligned}$$

For small χ this expression becomes the formula for Fraunhofer diffraction by the slit:

$$\mathrm{d}I = \frac{1}{\pi ka}\frac{\sin^2 ka\chi}{\chi^2}\,\mathrm{d}\chi.$$

PROBLEM 2. A plane wave is incident on a perfectly conducting plane with a circular aperture whose radius a is small compared with the wavelength. Determine the intensity of diffracted light passing through the aperture (RAYLEIGH, 1897).

SOLUTION. As stated above, this problem is equivalent to that of diffraction by a circular disc with $\mu = \infty$, and, since $a \ll \lambda$, we have the case of scattering by a small particle. According to §72, in order to solve the latter problem it is necessary to determine the static electric and magnetic polarisabilities of the disc. The field $\mathbf{E}_0$ is perpendicular to the plane of the disc, and the boundary condition $E'_z = 0$ is formally identical with the condition in electrostatics at the boundary of a body with $\epsilon = 0$. The field $\mathbf{H}_0$ is parallel to the disc, and the boundary condition $\mathbf{H}'_t = 0$ corresponds to a magnetostatic problem with $\mu = \infty$. Hence the electric and magnetic moments of the disc are (see §4, Problem 4, and §42, Problem) $\mathscr{P} = -2a^3\mathbf{E}_0/3\pi$, $\mathscr{M} = 4a^3\mathbf{H}_0/3\pi$. In going to the problem of diffraction by an aperture we must, in accordance with formulae (75.4), divide these expressions by 2 and then substitute them in the scattering formula (72.1).

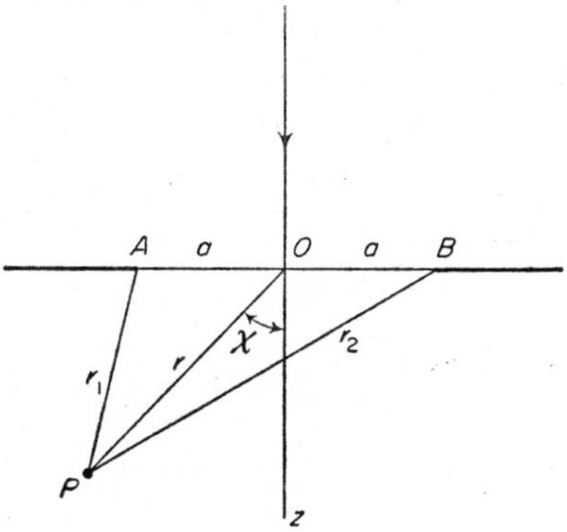

FIG. 34

Thus the intensity of radiation diffracted into a solid angle do is†

$$\mathrm{d}I = \frac{c}{4\pi}\frac{\omega^4 a^6}{9\pi^2 c^4}\{\mathbf{n}\times\mathbf{E}_0 - 2\mathbf{n}\times(\mathbf{H}_0\times\mathbf{n})\}\;\mathrm{d}o$$

$$= \frac{c}{4\pi}\frac{\omega^4 a^6}{9\pi^2 c^4}\{(\mathbf{n}\times\mathbf{E}_0)^2 + 4(\mathbf{n}\times\mathbf{H}_0)^2 + 4\mathbf{n}\cdot\mathbf{H}_0\times\mathbf{E}_0\}\;\mathrm{d}o.$$

The total diffracted intensity is obtained by integration over a hemisphere, and is

$$I = \frac{c}{4\pi}\frac{4\omega^4 a^6}{27\pi c^4}(E_0^2 + 4H_0^2).$$

The "effective diffraction cross-section" may be defined as the ratio of the intensity of diffracted radiation to the energy flux density in the incident wave $cE^2/4\pi$ (letters without suffixes refer to the incident wave). Two modes of polarisation of the incident wave may be distinguished:

(a) the vector $\mathbf{E}$ in the incident wave is perpendicular to the plane of incidence (the xz-plane), i.e. it is parallel to the plane of the screen (the xy-plane). The sum of the fields in the incident and reflected waves at the surface of the screen is

$$E_0 = 0, \qquad H_{0x} = 2H\cos\alpha = 2E\cos\alpha$$

† The factor $e^{-i\omega t}$ is omitted; $\mathbf{E}$ and $\mathbf{H}$ are real.

(α being the angle of incidence). Hence

$$d\sigma = \frac{16a^6\omega^4}{9\pi^2c^4}\cos^2\alpha\,(1-\sin^2\vartheta\cos^2\phi)\,do,$$

where ϑ is the angle between the direction of diffraction $\mathbf{n}$ and the normal to the screen (the z-axis), and ϕ is the azimuth of the vector $\mathbf{n}$ with respect to the plane of incidence. The total cross-section is $\sigma = (64\omega^4a^6/27\pi c^4)\cos^2\alpha$.

(b) the vector $\mathbf{E}$ lies in the plane of incidence. Then $E_0 = E_{0z} = -2E\sin\alpha$, $= H_{0y} = 2H = 2E$. The differential effective cross-section is

$$d\sigma = \frac{16a^6\omega^4}{9\pi^2c^4}\cos^2\vartheta+\sin^2\vartheta\,(\cos^2\phi+\tfrac{1}{4}\sin^2\alpha)-\sin\vartheta\sin\alpha\cos\phi\}\,do,$$

and the total cross-section is $\sigma = (64\omega^4a^6/27\pi c^4)(1+\frac{1}{4}\sin^2\alpha)$.

For natural incident light $\sigma = (64\omega^4a^6/27\pi c^4)(1-\frac{3}{8}\sin^2\alpha)$.

CHAPTER XI

ELECTROMAGNETIC WAVES IN ANISOTROPIC MEDIA

§76. The dielectric permeability of crystals

THE properties of an anisotropic medium with respect to electromagnetic waves are defined by the tensors $\epsilon_{ik}(\omega)$ and $\mu_{ik}(\omega)$, which give the relation between the inductions and the fields:† $D_i = \epsilon_{ik}(\omega)E_k$, $B_i = \mu_{ik}(\omega)H_k$. In what follows we shall, for definiteness, consider the electric field and the tensor ϵ_{ik}; all the results obtained are valid for the tensor μ_{ik} also.

As $\omega \rightarrow 0$, the ϵ_{ik} tend to their static values, which have been shown in §13 to be symmetrical with respect to i and k. The proof was thermodynamical, and therefore holds only for states of thermodynamic equilibrium. In a variable field, a substance is of course not in equilibrium, and the proof in §13 is consequently invalid. To ascertain the properties of the tensor ϵ_{ik} we must use the generalised principle of the symmetry of the kinetic coefficients.

It is easy to see that the components of the tensor ϵ_{ik} come under the general definition of the quantities α_{ab}:‡ the rate of change of the energy in a variable electric field is given by the integral

$$\int \frac{1}{4\pi}\mathbf{E}\cdot\frac{\partial \mathbf{D}}{\partial t}\,\mathrm{d}V. \tag{76.1}$$

A comparison with SP (124.7) shows that, if the components of the vector **E** at each point are taken as the quantities x_a, the corresponding quantities f_a will be the components of **D**. (The suffix a takes a continuous series of values, denumerating both the components of the vectors and the points in the body.) The coefficients α_{ab} are then the components of the tensor $\epsilon^{-1}{}_{ik}$. The symmetry properties of ϵ_{ik} are, of course, identical with those of its inverse.

It should be noted that the components of the polarisability tensor for the whole body, i.e. the coefficients in the equations $\mathscr{P}_i = V\alpha_{ik}\mathfrak{E}_k$, also come under the general definition. For the rate of change of the energy of a body placed in a variable external field $\mathfrak{E}$ is

$$-\mathscr{P}\cdot\mathrm{d}\mathfrak{E}/\mathrm{d}t. \tag{76.2}$$

† It should be recalled that these quantities refer to the variable fields in the wave; the possible presence of a constant induction (in a pyroelectric or ferromagnetic crystal) is irrelevant to this discussion.

‡ See *Statistical Physics*, §124, Pergamon Press, London, 1958. Formulae in this book will be referred to by means of the prefix SP.

Hence we see that, if the x_a are the three components of the vector $\mathscr{P}$, then the corresponding f_a are those of the vector $\mathfrak{E}$, so that the coefficients α_{ab} are in this case $V\alpha_{ik}$.

Thus we can use the generalised principle of the symmetry of the kinetic coefficients (SP (124.13)) to deduce that the tensor ϵ_{ik} is symmetrical:

$$\epsilon_{ik} = \epsilon_{ki}. \tag{76.3}$$

Here it is assumed that the body is not in an external magnetic field.†

Repeating for the anisotropic case the derivation of formula (61.4), we find that the electric losses are given by

$$\frac{i\omega}{8\pi}(\epsilon_{ik}{}^* - \epsilon_{ki})E_i E_k{}^*. \tag{76.4}$$

The condition that absorption is absent is $\epsilon_{ik}{}^* = \epsilon_{ki} = \epsilon_{ik}$, i.e. the ϵ_{ik} must be real, as in an isotropic medium.

When absorption is absent, the internal electromagnetic energy per unit volume can be defined as shown in §61. The formula for an anisotropic medium corresponding to (61.9) is

$$\bar{U} = \frac{1}{16\pi}\frac{\mathrm{d}}{\mathrm{d}\omega}(\omega\epsilon_{ik})E_i{}^* E_k. \tag{76.5}$$

In §67 we used the surface impedance ζ, in terms of which the boundary conditions at the surface of a metal can be formulated even if the dielectric permeability is no longer meaningful. At the surface of an anisotropic body the boundary condition corresponding to (67.6) is

$$E_\alpha = \zeta_{\alpha\beta}(\mathbf{H} \times \mathbf{n})_\beta, \tag{76.6}$$

where $\zeta_{\alpha\beta}(\omega)$ is a two-dimensional tensor on the surface of the body. It should be borne in mind that the value of this tensor depends, in general, on the crystallographic direction of the surface concerned.

The energy flux into the body is $(c/4\pi)\mathbf{E}\times\mathbf{H}\cdot\mathbf{n} = (c/4\pi)\mathbf{E}\cdot\mathbf{H}\times\mathbf{n} = (c/4\pi)E_\alpha(\mathbf{H}\times\mathbf{n})_\alpha$. (Here **E** and **H** are real.) Hence we see that if, in applying the principle of the symmetry of the kinetic coefficients, we take the components E_α as the x_a, then the corresponding f_a will be $-(\mathbf{H}\times\mathbf{n})_\alpha$, i.e. f_a will be $-(i/\omega)(\mathbf{H}\times\mathbf{n})_\alpha$ (returning to the complex form). The coefficients α_{ab} are therefore the same, apart from a factor, as the components $\zeta_{\alpha\beta}$, and we conclude that

$$\zeta_{\alpha\beta} = \zeta_{\beta\alpha} \tag{76.7}$$

in the absence of an external magnetic field.

† The properties of the tensor ϵ_{ik} in the presence of an external magnetic field will be discussed in §82.

PROBLEM

Express the components of the tensor $\zeta_{\alpha\beta}$ in terms of those of $\eta_{\alpha\beta} \equiv \epsilon^{-1}{}_{\alpha\beta}$, assuming that the latter exists and that the body is non-magnetic ($\mu_{ik} = \delta_{ik}$).

SOLUTION. In an anisotropic medium, the equation $\zeta^2 = 1/\epsilon$ (67.2) becomes $\zeta_{\alpha\gamma}\zeta_{\gamma\beta} = \eta_{\alpha\beta}$. In components this gives†

$$\zeta_{11}^2+\zeta_{12}\zeta_{21} = \eta_{11}, \qquad \zeta_{22}^2+\zeta_{12}\zeta_{21} = \eta_{22},$$
$$\zeta_{12}(\zeta_{11}+\zeta_{22}) = \eta_{12}, \qquad \zeta_{21}(\zeta_{1}+\zeta_{22}) = \eta_{21}.$$

The solution of these equations is

$$\zeta_{12} = \eta_{12}/\xi, \qquad \zeta_{21} = \eta_{21}/\xi,$$
$$\zeta_{11} = [\eta_{11} \pm \sqrt{(\eta_{11}\eta_{22}-\eta_{12}\eta_{21})}]/\xi, \qquad \zeta_{22} = [\eta_{22} \pm \sqrt{(\eta_{11}\eta_{22}-\eta_{12}\eta_{21})}]/\xi,$$
$$\xi^2 = \eta_{11}+\eta_{22} \pm 2\sqrt{(\eta_{1122}-\eta_{12}\eta_{21})}.$$

The choice of signs is determined by the condition that the absorption of energy must be positive.

§77. A plane wave in an anisotropic medium

In studying the optics of anisotropic bodies (crystals) we shall take only the most important case, where the medium may be supposed non-magnetic and transparent in a given range of frequencies. Accordingly, the relation between the electric and magnetic fields and inductions is

$$D_i = \epsilon_{ik}E_k, \qquad \mathbf{B} = \mathbf{H}. \tag{77.1}$$

The components of the dielectric tensor ϵ_{ik} are all real, and its principal values are positive.

Maxwell's equations for the field of a wave of a single frequency ω are

$$i\omega\mathbf{H} = c\,\mathbf{curl}\,\mathbf{E}, \qquad i\omega\mathbf{D} = -c\,\mathbf{curl}\,\mathbf{H}. \tag{77.2}$$

In a plane wave propagated in a transparent medium all quantities are proportional to $e^{i\mathbf{k}\cdot\mathbf{r}}$, with a real wave vector $\mathbf{k}$. Effecting the differentiation with respect to the co-ordinates, we obtain

$$\omega\mathbf{H}/c = \mathbf{k}\times\mathbf{E}, \qquad \omega\mathbf{D}/c = -\mathbf{k}\times\mathbf{H}. \tag{77.3}$$

Hence we see, first of all, that the three vectors **k, D, H** are mutually perpendicular. Moreover, **H** is perpendicular to **E**, and so the three vectors **D, E, k,** being all perpendicular to **H**, must be coplanar. Fig. 35 shows the relative position of all these vectors. With respect to the direction of the wave vector **D** and **H** are transverse, but **E** is not. The diagram shows also the direction of the energy flux **S** in the wave. It is given by the vector product **E**×**H**, i.e. it is perpendicular to both **E** and **H**. The direction of **S** is not the same as that of **k**, unlike what happens for an isotropic medium.

† We do not assume $\zeta_{12} = \zeta_{21}$, and thereby allow for the presence of an external magnetic field.

Clearly the vector **S** is coplanar with **E**, **D** and **k**, and the angle between **S** and **k** is equal to that between **E** and **D**.

We can define a vector **n** by

$$\mathbf{k} = \omega \mathbf{n}/c. \tag{77.4}$$

The magnitude of this vector in an anisotropic medium depends on its direction, whereas in an isotropic medium $n = \sqrt{\epsilon}$ depends only on the frequency.† Using (77.4), we can write the fundamental formulae (77.3) as

$$\mathbf{H} = \mathbf{n} \times \mathbf{E}, \qquad \mathbf{D} = -\mathbf{n} \times \mathbf{H}. \tag{77.5}$$

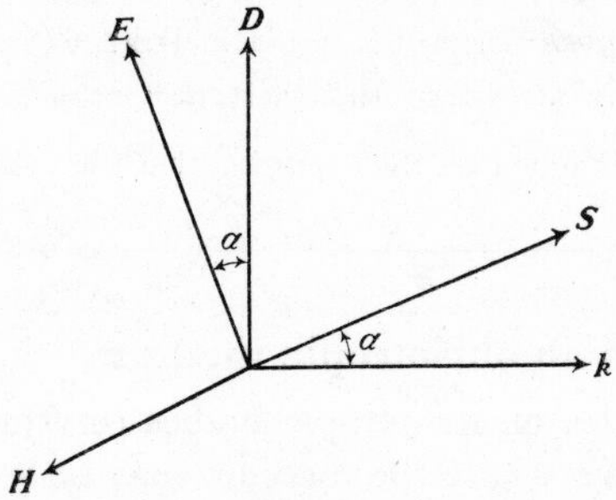

FIG. 35

The energy flux vector in a plane wave is

$$\mathbf{S} = c\mathbf{E} \times \mathbf{H}/4\pi = (c/4\pi)\{E^2\mathbf{n} - (\mathbf{E}\cdot\mathbf{n})\mathbf{E}\}; \tag{77.6}$$

in this formula **E** and **H** are real.

So far we have not used the relation (77.1) which involves the constants ϵ_{ik} characterising the material. This relation, together with equations (77.5), determines the function $\omega(\mathbf{k})$.

Substituting the first equation (77.5) in the second, we have

$$\mathbf{D} = \mathbf{n} \times (\mathbf{E} \times \mathbf{n}) = n^2\mathbf{E} - (\mathbf{n}\cdot\mathbf{E})\mathbf{n}. \tag{77.7}$$

If we equate the components of this vector to $\epsilon_{ik}E_k$ in accordance with (77.1), we obtain three linear homogeneous equations for the three components of **E**: $n^2E_i - n_in_kE_k = \epsilon_{ik}E_k$ or

$$(n^2\delta_{ik} - n_in_k - \epsilon_{ik})E_k = 0. \tag{77.8}$$

The compatibility condition for these equations is that the determinant of their coefficients should vanish:

$$|n^2\delta_{ik} - n_in_k - \epsilon_{ik}| = 0. \tag{77.9}$$

In practice, this determinant is conveniently evaluated by taking as the axes of x, y, z the principal axes of the tensor ϵ_{ik} (called the *principal dielectric axes*). Let the principal values of the tensor be $\epsilon^{(x)}$, $\epsilon^{(y)}$, $\epsilon^{(z)}$.

† The magnitude n is still called the *refractive index*, although it no longer bears the same simple relation to the law of refraction as in isotropic bodies.

Then a simple calculation gives

$$n^2(\epsilon^{(x)}n_x^2 + \epsilon^{(y)}n_y^2 + \epsilon^{(z)}n_z^2) - [n_x^2\epsilon^{(x)}(\epsilon^{(y)} + \epsilon^{(z)}) + \\ + n_y^2\epsilon^{(y)}(\epsilon^{(x)} + \epsilon^{(z)}) + n_z^2\epsilon^{(z)}(\epsilon^{(x)} + \epsilon^{(y)})] + \epsilon^{(x)}\epsilon^{(y)}\epsilon^{(z)} = 0. \quad (77.10)$$

The sixth-order terms cancel when the determinant is expanded; this is, of course, no accident and is due ultimately to the fact that the wave has two, not three, independent directions of polarisation.

Equation (77.10), called *Fresnel's equation*, is one of the fundamental equations of crystal optics. It determines implicitly the dispersion relation, i.e. the frequency as a function of the wave vector. (It should be recalled that the principal values $\epsilon^{(i)}$ are functions of frequency, and so are, in some cases (see §79), the directions of the principal axes of the tensor ϵ_{ik}.) For waves of a single frequency, however, ω, and therefore all the $\epsilon^{(i)}$, are usually given constants, and equation (77.10) then gives the magnitude of the wave vector as a function of its direction. When the direction of $\mathbf{n}$ is given, (77.10) is a quadratic equation, for n^2, with real coefficients. Hence two different magnitudes of the wave vector correspond, in general, to each direction of $\mathbf{n}$.

Equation (77.10) (with constant coefficients $\epsilon^{(i)}$) defines in the co-ordinates n_x, n_y, n_z the "wave-vector surface".† In general this is a surface of the fourth order, whose properties will be discussed in detail in the following sections. Here we shall mention some general properties of this surface.

We first introduce another quantity characterising the propagation of light in an anisotropic medium. The direction of the light rays (in geometrical optics) is given by the group velocity vector $\partial\omega/\partial\mathbf{k}$. In an isotropic medium, the direction of this vector is always the same as that of the wave vector, but in an anisotropic medium the two do not in general coincide. The rays may be characterised by a vector $\mathbf{s}$, whose direction is that of the group velocity, while its magnitude is given by

$$\mathbf{n}\cdot\mathbf{s} = 1. \quad (77.11)$$

We shall call $\mathbf{s}$ the *ray vector*. Its significance is as follows.

Let us consider a beam of rays (of a single frequency) propagated in all directions from some point. The value of the eikonal (which is, apart from a factor ω/c, the wave phase; see §65) at any point is given by the integral $\int \mathbf{n}\cdot d\mathbf{l}$ taken along the ray. Using the vector $\mathbf{s}$ which determines the direction of the ray, we can put $\psi = \int\mathbf{n}\cdot d\mathbf{l} = \int(\mathbf{n}\cdot\mathbf{s}/s)\, dl = \int dl/s$. In a homogeneous medium, s is constant along the ray, so that $\psi = L/s$, where L is the length of the ray segment concerned. Hence we see that, if a segment equal (or proportional) to s is taken along each ray from the centre, the resulting surface is such that the phase of the rays is the same at every point. This is called the *ray surface*.

† A much less convenient concept called the "surface of normals" or "surface of indices" has often been used; it is obtained by taking a point at a distance $1/n$ (instead of n) in each direction.

The wave-vector surface and the ray surface are in a certain dual relationship. Let the equation of the wave-vector surface be written $f(k_x, k_y, k_z, \omega) = 0$. Then the components of the group velocity vector are

$$\frac{\partial \omega}{\partial k_i} = -\frac{\partial f / \partial k_i}{\partial f / \partial \omega}, \tag{77.12}$$

i.e. they are proportional to the derivatives $\partial f / \partial k_i$, or, what is the same thing (since the derivatives are taken for constant ω), to the derivatives $\partial f / \partial n_i$. The components of the ray vector, therefore, are also proportional to $\partial f / \partial n_i$.† But the vector $\partial f / \partial \mathbf{n}$ is normal to the surface $f = 0$. Thus we conclude that the direction of the ray vector of a wave with given $\mathbf{n}$ is that of the normal at the corresponding point of the wave-vector surface.

It is easy to see that the reverse is also true: the normal to the ray surface gives the direction of the corresponding wave vectors. For the equation $\mathbf{s} \cdot \delta \mathbf{n} = 0$, where $\delta \mathbf{n}$ is an arbitrary infinitesimal change in $\mathbf{n}$ (for given ω), i.e. the vector of an infinitesimal displacement on the surface, expresses the fact that $\mathbf{s}$ is perpendicular to the wave-vector surface. Differentiating (again for given ω) the equation $\mathbf{n} \cdot \mathbf{s} = 1$, we obtain $\mathbf{n} \cdot \delta \mathbf{s} + \mathbf{s} \cdot \delta \mathbf{n} = 0$, and therefore $\mathbf{n} \cdot \delta \mathbf{s} = 0$, which proves the above statement.

This relation between the surfaces of $\mathbf{n}$ and $\mathbf{s}$ can be made more precise. Let $\mathbf{n}_0$ be the radius vector of a point on the wave-vector surface, and $\mathbf{s}_0$ the corresponding ray vector. The equation (in co-ordinates n_x, n_y, n_z) of the tangent plane at this point is $\mathbf{s}_0 \cdot (\mathbf{n} - \mathbf{n}_0) = 0$, which states that $\mathbf{s}_0$ is perpendicular to any vector $\mathbf{n} - \mathbf{n}_0$ in the plane. Since $\mathbf{s}_0$ and $\mathbf{n}_0$ are related by $\mathbf{s}_0 \cdot \mathbf{n}_0 = 1$, we can write the equation as

$$\mathbf{s}_0 \cdot \mathbf{n} = 1. \tag{77.13}$$

Hence it follows that $1/s_0$ is the length of the perpendicular from the origin to the tangent plane to the wave-vector surface at the point $\mathbf{n}_0$.

Conversely, the length of the perpendicular from the origin to the tangent plane to the ray surface at a point $\mathbf{s}_0$ is $1/n_0$.

To ascertain the location of the ray vector relative to the field vectors in the wave, we notice that the group velocity is always in the same direction as the (time) average energy flux vector. For let us consider a wave packet, occupying a small region of space. When the packet moves, the energy concentrated in it must evidently move with it, and the direction of the

---

† Differentiating the left-hand side of equation (77.10) with respect to n_i and determining from the condition $\mathbf{n} \cdot \mathbf{s} = 1$ the proportionality coefficient between s_i and $\partial f / \partial n_i$, we obtain the following relations between the components of $\mathbf{s}$ and $\mathbf{n}$:

$$s_x = n_x \frac{\epsilon^{(x)}(\epsilon^{(y)} + \epsilon^{(z)}) - 2\epsilon^{(x)} n_x^2 - (\epsilon^{(x)} + \epsilon^{(y)}) n_y^2 - (\epsilon^{(x)} + \epsilon^{(z)}) n_z^2}{2\epsilon^{(x)}\epsilon^{(y)}\epsilon^{(z)} - n_x^2 \epsilon^{(x)}(\epsilon^{(y)} + \epsilon^{(z)}) - n_y^2 \epsilon^{(y)}(\epsilon^{(x)} + \epsilon^{(z)}) - n_z^2 \epsilon^{(z)}(\epsilon^{(x)} + \epsilon^{(y)})}, \tag{77.12a}$$

and similarly for s_y, s_z.

energy flux is therefore the same as the direction of the velocity of the packet, i.e. the group velocity.†

Since the Poynting vector is perpendicular to **H** and **E**, the same is true of **s**:

$$\mathbf{s}\cdot\mathbf{H} = 0, \qquad \mathbf{s}\cdot\mathbf{E} = 0. \tag{77.14}$$

A direct calculation, using formulae (77.5), (77.11) and (77.14), gives

$$\mathbf{H} = \mathbf{s}\times\mathbf{D}, \qquad \mathbf{E} = -\mathbf{s}\times\mathbf{H}. \tag{77.15}$$

For example, $\mathbf{s}\times\mathbf{H} = \mathbf{s}\times(\mathbf{n}\times\mathbf{E}) = \mathbf{n}(\mathbf{s}\cdot\mathbf{E})-\mathbf{E}(\mathbf{n}\cdot\mathbf{s}) = -\mathbf{E}$.

If we compare formulae (77.15) and (77.5), we see that they differ by the interchange of

$$\mathbf{E} \text{ and } \mathbf{D}, \qquad \mathbf{n} \text{ and } \mathbf{s}, \qquad \epsilon_{ik} \text{ and } \epsilon^{-1}{}_{ik} \tag{77.16}$$

(the relation $\mathbf{n}\cdot\mathbf{s} = 1$ remaining valid, of course). The last of these pairs must be included in order that the relation (77.1) between **D** and **E** should remain valid. Thus the following useful rule may be formulated: an equation valid for one set of quantities can be converted into one valid for another set by means of the interchanges (77.16).

In particular, the application of this rule to (77.10) gives immediately an analogous equation for **s**:

$$s^2(\epsilon^{(y)}\epsilon^{(z)}s_x^2 + \epsilon^{(x)}\epsilon^{(z)}s_y^2 + \epsilon^{(x)}\epsilon^{(y)}s_z^2) -$$
$$- [s_x^2(\epsilon^{(y)} + \epsilon^{(z)}) + s_y^2(\epsilon^{(x)} + \epsilon^{(z)}) + s_z^2(\epsilon^{(x)} + \epsilon^{(y)})] + 1 = 0. \tag{77.17}$$

This equation gives the form of the ray surface. Like the wave-vector surface, it is of the fourth order. When the direction of **s** is given, (77.17) is a quadratic equation for s^2, which in general has two different real roots. Thus two rays with different wave vectors can be propagated in any direction in the crystal.

Let us now consider the polarisation of waves propagated in an anisotropic medium. Equations (77.8), from which Fresnel's equation has been derived, are unsuitable for this, because they involve the field **E**, whereas it is the induction **D** which is transverse (to the given **n**) in the wave. In order to take account immediately of the fact that **D** is transverse, we use for the time being a new co-ordinate system with one axis in the direction

† It is easy to demonstrate mathematically that the group velocity is in the same direction as the Poynting vector. Differentiating formulae (77.5) (for given ω), we obtain

$$\delta\mathbf{D} = \delta\mathbf{H}\times\mathbf{n} + \mathbf{H}\times\delta\mathbf{n}, \qquad \delta\mathbf{H} = \mathbf{n}\times\delta\mathbf{E} + \delta\mathbf{n}\times\mathbf{E}.$$

We take the scalar product of the first equation with **E** and of the second with **H**, obtaining

$$\mathbf{E}\cdot\delta\mathbf{D} = \mathbf{H}\cdot\delta\mathbf{H} + \mathbf{E}\times\mathbf{H}\cdot\delta\mathbf{n}, \qquad \mathbf{H}\cdot\delta\mathbf{H} = \mathbf{D}\cdot\delta\mathbf{E} + \mathbf{E}\times\mathbf{H}\cdot\delta\mathbf{n}.$$

But $\mathbf{D}\cdot\delta\mathbf{E} = \epsilon_{ik}E_k\delta E_i = \mathbf{E}\cdot\delta\mathbf{D}$, and so, adding the two equations, we have $\mathbf{E}\times\mathbf{H}\cdot\delta\mathbf{n} = 0$, i.e. the vector $\mathbf{E}\times\mathbf{H}$ is normal to the wave-vector surface. This is the required result.

The result thus obtained relates to the instantaneous, as well as to the average, energy flux. In this proof, however, the symmetry of the tensor ϵ_{ik} is vital. The result is therefore not valid in the above form for media in which ϵ_{ik} is not symmetrical (*gyrotropic* media, §82). The statement is still valid, however, for the average value of the Poynting vector.

of the wave vector, and denote the two transverse axes by Greek suffixes, which take the values 1 and 2. The transverse components of equation (77.7) give $D_\alpha = n^2 E_\alpha$; substituting $E_\alpha = \epsilon^{-1}{}_{\alpha\beta} D_\beta$, where $\epsilon^{-1}{}_{\alpha\beta}$ is a component of the tensor inverse to ϵ_{ik}, we have $D_\alpha - n^2 \epsilon^{-1}{}_{\alpha\beta} D_\beta = 0$, or

$$\left(\frac{1}{n^2}\delta_{\alpha\beta} - \epsilon^{-1}{}_{\alpha\beta}\right) D_\beta = 0. \qquad (77.18)$$

The condition for the two equations ($\alpha = 1, 2$) in the two unknowns D_1, D_2 to be compatible is that their determinant should be zero. This condition is, of course, the same as Fresnel's equation, which was written in the original co-ordinates x, y, z. We now see also, however, that the vectors **D** corresponding to the two values of n are along the principal axes of the symmetrical two-dimensional tensor of rank two $\epsilon^{-1}{}_{\alpha\beta}$. According to general theorems it follows that these two vectors are perpendicular. Thus, in the two waves with the wave vector in the same direction, the electric induction vectors are linearly polarised in two perpendicular planes.

Equations (77.18) have a simple geometrical interpretation. Let us draw the tensor ellipsoid corresponding the tensor $\epsilon^{-1}{}_{ik}$, returning to the principal dielectric axes, i.e. the surface

$$\epsilon^{-1}{}_{ik} x_i x_k = \frac{x^2}{\epsilon^{(x)}} + \frac{y^2}{\epsilon^{(y)}} + \frac{z^2}{\epsilon^{(z)}} = 1 \qquad (77.19)$$

(Fig. 36). Let this ellipsoid be cut by a plane through its centre perpendicular to the given direction of **n**. The section is in general an ellipse; the lengths of its axes determine the values of n, and their directions determine the directions of the oscillations, i.e. the vectors **D**.

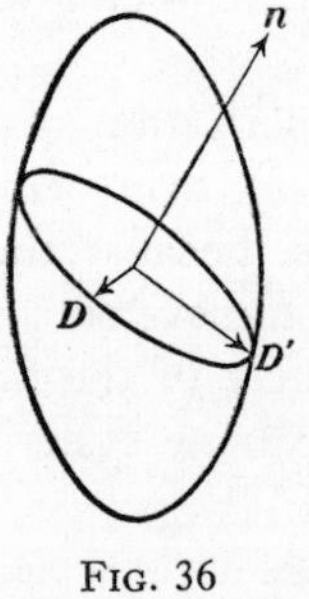

FIG. 36

From this construction (with, in general, $\epsilon^{(x)}$, $\epsilon^{(y)}$, $\epsilon^{(z)}$ different) we see at once, in particular, that, if the wave vector is in (say) the x-direction, the directions of polarisation (**D**) will be the y and z directions. If the vector **n** lies in one of the co-ordinate planes, e.g. the xy-plane, one of the directions of polarisation is also in that plane, and the other is in the z-direction.

The polarisations of two waves with the ray vector in the same direction have entirely similar properties. Instead of the directions of the induction

D, we must now consider those of the vector **E**, which is transverse to **s**, and equations (77.18) are replaced by the analogous equations

$$\left(\frac{1}{s^2}\delta_{\alpha\beta} - \epsilon_{\alpha\beta}\right)E_\beta = 0. \tag{77.20}$$

The geometrical construction is here based on the tensor ellipsoid

$$\epsilon_{ik}x_i x_k = \epsilon^{(x)}x^2 + \epsilon^{(y)}y^2 + \epsilon^{(z)}z^2 = 1, \tag{77.21}$$

corresponding to the tensor ϵ_{ik} itself (called the *Fresnel ellipsoid*).

It should be emphasised that plane waves propagated in an anisotropic medium are completely linearly polarised in certain planes. In this respect the optical properties of anisotropic media are very different from those of isotropic media. A plane wave propagated in an isotropic medium is in general elliptically polarised, and is linearly polarised only in particular cases. This important difference arises because the case of complete isotropy of the medium is in a sense one of degeneracy, in which a single wave vector corresponds to two directions of polarisation, whereas in an anisotropic media there are in general two different wave vectors (in the same direction). The two linearly polarised waves propagated with the same value of **n** combine to form one elliptically polarised wave.

§78. Optical properties of uniaxial crystals

The optical properties of a crystal depend primarily on the symmetry of its dielectric tensor ϵ_{ik}. In this respect all crystals fall under three types: cubic, uniaxial and biaxial (see §13). In a crystal of the cubic system $\epsilon_{ik} = \epsilon\delta_{ik}$, i.e. the three principal values of the tensor are equal, and the directions of the principal axes are arbitrary. As regards their optical properties, therefore, cubic crystals are no different from isotropic bodies.

The uniaxial crystals include those of the rhombohedral, tetragonal and hexagonal systems. Here one of the principal axes of the tensor ϵ_{ik} coincides with the axis of symmetry of the third, fourth or sixth order respectively; in optics, this axis is called the *optical axis* of the crystal, and in what follows we shall take it as the z-axis, denoting the corresponding principal value of ϵ_{ik} by $\epsilon_\parallel$. The directions of the other two principal axes, in a plane perpendicular to the optical axis, are arbitrary, and the corresponding principal values, which we denote by $\epsilon_\perp$, are equal.

If in Fresnel's equation (77.10) we put $\epsilon^{(x)} = \epsilon^{(y)} = \epsilon_\perp$, $\epsilon^{(z)} = \epsilon_\parallel$, the left-hand side is a product of two quadratic factors:

$$(n^2 - \epsilon_\perp)[\epsilon_\parallel n_z^2 + \epsilon_\perp(n_x^2 + n_y^2) - \epsilon_\perp\epsilon_\parallel] = 0.$$

In other words, the quartic equation gives the two quadratic equations

$$n^2 = \epsilon_\perp, \tag{78.1}$$

$$\frac{n_z^2}{\epsilon_\perp} + \frac{n_x^2 + n_y^2}{\epsilon_\parallel} = 1. \tag{78.2}$$

Geometrically, this signifies that the wave-vector surface, which is in general of the fourth order, becomes two separate surfaces, a sphere and an ellipsoid. Fig. 37 shows a cross-section of these surfaces. Two cases are possible: if $\epsilon_\perp > \epsilon_\parallel$, the sphere lies outside the ellipsoid, but if $\epsilon_\perp < \epsilon_\parallel$ it lies inside. In the first case we speak of a *negative uniaxial crystal*, and in the second case of a *positive* one. The two surfaces touch at opposite poles on the n_z-axis. The direction of the optical axis therefore corresponds to only one value of the wave vector.

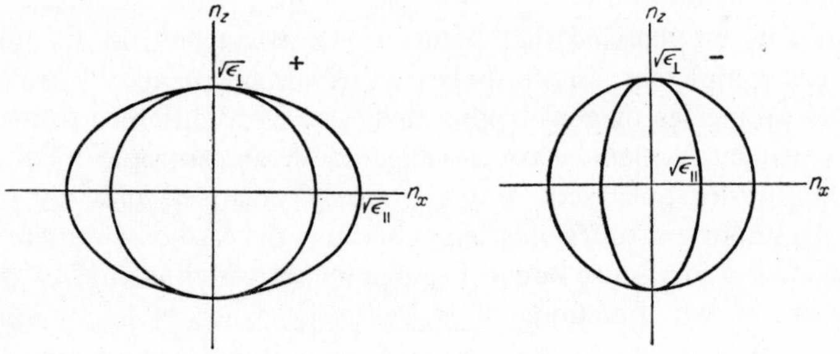

FIG. 37

The ray surface is exactly similar in form. By the rule (77.16), its equation is obtained from (78.1) and (78.2) by replacing **n** by **s** and ϵ by $1/\epsilon$:

$$s^2 = 1/\epsilon_\perp, \tag{78.3}$$

$$\epsilon_\perp s_z^2 + \epsilon_\parallel(s_x^2 + s_y^2) = 1. \tag{78.4}$$

In a positive crystal the ellipsoid lies within the sphere, and in a negative one outside.

Thus we see that two types of wave can be propagated in a uniaxial crystal. With respect to one type, called *ordinary waves*, the crystal behaves like an isotropic body of refractive index $n = \sqrt{\epsilon_\perp}$. The magnitude of the wave vector is $\omega n/c$ whatever its direction, and the direction of the ray vector is that of **n**.

In waves of the second type, called *extraordinary waves*, the magnitude of the wave vector depends on the angle θ which it makes with the optical axis. By (78.2)

$$\frac{1}{n^2} = \frac{\sin^2\theta}{\epsilon} + \frac{\cos^2\theta}{\epsilon_\perp}. \tag{78.5}$$

The ray vector in an extraordinary wave is not in the same direction as the wave vector, but is coplanar with that vector and the optical axis, their common plane being called the *principal section* for the given **n**. Let this be the zx-plane; the ratio of the derivatives of the left-hand side of (78.2) with respect to n_z and n_x gives the direction of the ray vector: $s_x/s_z = \epsilon_\perp n_x/\epsilon_\parallel n_z$. Thus the angle θ' between the ray vector and the optical axis and the angle θ satisfy the simple relation

$$\tan\theta' = (\epsilon_\perp/\epsilon_\parallel)\tan\theta. \tag{78.6}$$

The directions of **n** and **l** are the same only for waves propagated along or perpendicular to the optical axis.

The problem of the directions of polarisation of the ordinary and extraordinary waves is very easily solved. It is sufficient to observe that the four vectors **E**, **D**, **s** and **n** are always coplanar. In the extraordinary wave **s** and **n** are not in the same direction, but lie in the same principal section. This wave is therefore polarised so that the vectors **E** and **D** lie in the same principal section as **s** and **n**. The vectors **D** in the ordinary and extraordinary waves with the same direction of **n** (or **E**, with the same direction of **s**) are perpendicular. Hence the polarisation of the ordinary wave is such that **E** and **D** lie in a plane perpendicular to the principal section.

An exception is formed by waves propagated in the direction of the optical axis. In this direction there is no difference between the ordinary and the extraordinary wave, and so their polarisations combine to give a wave which is, in general, elliptically polarised.

The refraction of a plane wave incident on the surface of a crystal is different from refraction at a boundary between two isotropic media. The laws of refraction and reflection are again obtained from the continuity of the component $\mathbf{n}_t$ of the wave vector which is tangential to the plane of separation. The wave vectors of the refracted and reflected waves therefore lie in the plane of incidence. In a crystal, however, two different refracted waves are formed, a phenomenon known as *double refraction*. They correspond to the two possible values of the normal component n_n which satisfy Fresnel's equation for a given tangential component $\mathbf{n}_t$. It should also be remembered that the observed direction of propagation of the rays is determined not by the wave vector but by the ray vector **s**, whose direction is different from that of **n** and in general does not lie in the plane of incidence.

In a uniaxial crystal, ordinary and extraordinary refracted waves are formed. The ordinary wave is entirely analogous to the refracted wave in isotropic bodies; in particular, its ray vector (which is in the same direction as its wave vector) lies in the plane of incidence. The ray vector of the extraordinary wave in general does not lie in the plane of incidence.

PROBLEMS

PROBLEM 1. Find the direction of the extraordinary ray when light incident from a vacuum is incident on a surface of a uniaxial crystal which is perpendicular to its optical axis.

SOLUTION. In this case the refracted ray lies in the plane of incidence, which we take as the xz-plane, with the z-axis normal to the surface. The x-component of the wave vector $n_x = \sin\vartheta$ (ϑ being the angle of incidence) is continuous; the component n_z for the refracted wave is found from (78.2):

$$n_z = \sqrt{\left(\epsilon_\perp - \frac{\epsilon_\perp}{\epsilon_\parallel}\sin^2\vartheta\right)}.$$

The direction of the refracted ray is given by (78.6):

$$\tan\vartheta' = \frac{\epsilon_\perp}{\epsilon_\parallel}\frac{n_x}{n_z} = \frac{\sqrt{\epsilon_\perp}\sin\vartheta}{\sqrt{[\epsilon_\parallel(\epsilon_\parallel - \sin^2\vartheta)]}},$$

where ϑ' is the angle of refraction.

PROBLEM 2. Find the direction of the extraordinary ray when light is incident normally on a surface of a uniaxial crystal at any angle to the optical axis.

SOLUTION. The refracted ray lies in the xz-plane, which passes through the normal to the surface (the z-axis) and the optical axis. Let α be the angle between these axes. The ray vector **s**, whose components are proportional to the derivatives of the left-hand side of equation (78.2) with respect to the corresponding components of **n**, is proportional to

$$\frac{\mathbf{n}}{\epsilon_{\parallel}}+(\mathbf{n}\cdot\mathbf{l})\mathbf{l}\left(\frac{1}{\epsilon_{\perp}}-\frac{1}{\epsilon_{\parallel}}\right),$$

where **l** is a unit vector in the direction of the optical axis. In the present case the wave vector **n** is in the z-direction, so that

$$s_x \sim \cos\alpha \sin\alpha\left(\frac{1}{\epsilon_{\perp}}-\frac{1}{\epsilon_{\parallel}}\right), \qquad s_z \sim \frac{\sin^2\alpha}{\epsilon_{\parallel}}+\frac{\cos^2\alpha}{\epsilon_{\perp}}.$$

Hence we find

$$\tan\vartheta' = \frac{s_x}{s_z} = \frac{(\epsilon_{\parallel}-\epsilon_{\perp})\sin 2\alpha}{\epsilon_{\parallel}+\epsilon_{\perp}+(\epsilon_{\parallel}-\epsilon_{\perp})\cos 2\alpha}.$$

§79. Biaxial crystals

In biaxial crystals the three principal values of the tensor ϵ_{ik} are all different. The crystals of the triclinic, monoclinic and rhombic systems are of this type. In those of the triclinic system, the position of the principal dielectric axes is unrelated to any specific crystallographic direction; in particular, it varies with frequency, as do all the components ϵ_{ik}. In crystals of the monoclinic system, one of the principal dielectric axes is crystallographically fixed; it coincides with the second-order axis of symmetry, or is perpendicular to the plane of symmetry. The position of the other two principal axes depends on the frequency. Finally, in crystals of the rhombic system, the position of all three principal axes is fixed: they must coincide with the three mutually perpendicular second-order axes of symmetry.

The study of the optical properties of biaxial crystals involves the consideration of Fresnel's equation (77.10) in its general form. We shall assume for definiteness that

$$\epsilon^{(x)} < \epsilon^{(y)} < \epsilon^{(z)}. \tag{79.1}$$

To ascertain the form of the fourth-order surface defined by equation (77.10), let us begin by finding its intersections with the co-ordinate planes. Putting in equation (77.10) $n_z = 0$, we find that the left-hand side is the product of two factors:

$$(n^2-\epsilon^{(z)})(\epsilon^{(x)}n_x^2+\epsilon^{(y)}n_y^2-\epsilon^{(x)}\epsilon^{(y)}) = 0.$$

Hence we see that the section by the xy-plane consists of the circle

$$n^2 = \epsilon^{(z)} \tag{79.2}$$

and the ellipse

$$\frac{n_x^2}{\epsilon^{(y)}}+\frac{n_y^2}{\epsilon^{(x)}} = 1, \tag{79.3}$$

and by the assumption (79.1) the ellipse lies inside the circle. Similarly we find that the sections by the yz and xz planes are also composed of an ellipse and a circle; in the yz-plane the ellipse lies outside the circle, and in the xz-plane they intersect. Thus the wave-vector surface intersects itself, and is as shown in Fig. 38, where one octant is drawn.

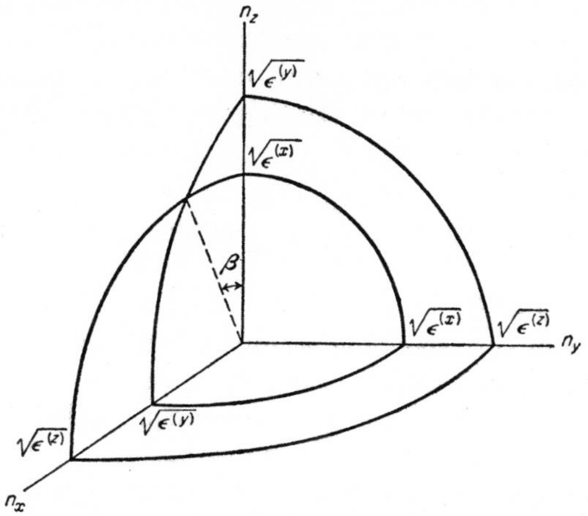

FIG. 38

This surface has four singular points of self-intersection, one in each quadrant of the xz-plane. The singular points of a surface whose equation is $f(n_x, n_y, n_z) = 0$ are given by the vanishing of all three first derivatives of the function f. Differentiating the left-hand side of (77.10), we obtain the equations

$$\left.\begin{aligned} n_x[\epsilon^{(x)}(\epsilon^{(y)}+\epsilon^{(z)}) - \epsilon^{(x)}n^2 - (\epsilon^{(x)}n_x^2+\epsilon^{(y)}n_y^2+\epsilon^{(z)}n_z^2)] &= 0, \\ n_y[\epsilon^{(y)}(\epsilon^{(x)}+\epsilon^{(z)}) - \epsilon^{(y)}n^2 - (\epsilon^{(x)}n_x^2+\epsilon^{(y)}n_y^2+\epsilon^{(z)}n_z^2)] &= 0, \\ n_z[\epsilon^{(z)}(\epsilon^{(x)}+\epsilon^{(y)}) - \epsilon^{(z)}n^2 - (\epsilon^{(x)}n_x^2+\epsilon^{(y)}n_y^2+\epsilon^{(z)}n_z^2)] &= 0; \end{aligned}\right\} \quad (79.4)$$

the equation (77.10) itself must, of course, be satisfied also. Since we know that the required directions of $\mathbf{n}$ lie in the xz-plane, we put $n_y = 0$, and the two remaining equations give immediately†

$$n_x^2 = \frac{\epsilon^{(z)}(\epsilon^{(y)} - \epsilon^{(x)})}{\epsilon^{(z)} - \epsilon^{(x)}}, \qquad n_z^2 = \frac{\epsilon^{(x)}(\epsilon^{(z)} - \epsilon^{(y)})}{\epsilon^{(z)} - \epsilon^{(x)}}. \quad (79.5)$$

The directions of these vectors $\mathbf{n}$ are inclined to the z-axis at an angle β such that

$$\frac{n_x}{n_z} = \pm \tan\beta = \pm \sqrt{\frac{\epsilon^{(z)}(\epsilon^{(y)} - \epsilon^{(x)})}{\epsilon^{(x)}(\epsilon^{(z)} - \epsilon^{(y)})}}. \quad (79.6)$$

† It is easy to see that the solution thus found is the only real solution of equations (79.4). If none of n_x, n_y, n_z is zero, the three equations (79.4) are inconsistent: they then involve only two unknowns, namely n^2 and $\epsilon^{(x)}n_x^2 + \epsilon^{(y)}n_y^2 + \epsilon^{(z)}n_z^2$. If n_x or n_z is zero the solutions are imaginary.

This formula determines lines in two directions in the xz-plane, each of which passes through two opposite singular points and is at an angle β to the z-axis. These lines are called the *optical axes* or *binormals* of the crystal; one of them is shown dashed in Fig. 38. The directions of the optical axes are evidently the only ones for which the wave vector has only one magnitude.†

The properties of the ray surface are entirely similar. To derive the corresponding formulae, it is sufficient to replace $\mathbf{n}$ by $\mathbf{s}$ and ϵ by $1/\epsilon$. In particular, there are two *optical ray axes* or *biradials*, also lying in the xz-plane and at an angle γ to the z-axis, where

$$\tan\gamma = \sqrt{\frac{\epsilon^{(y)} - \epsilon^{(x)}}{\epsilon^{(z)} - \epsilon^{(y)}}} = \sqrt{\frac{\epsilon^{(x)}}{\epsilon^{(z)}}}\tan\beta. \tag{79.7}$$

Since $\epsilon^{(x)} < \epsilon^{(z)}$, $\gamma < \beta$.

The directions of corresponding vectors $\mathbf{n}$ and $\mathbf{s}$ are given by the general formulae (77.12a). Their directions are the same only for waves propagated along one of the co-ordinate axes (i.e. the principal dielectric axes). If $\mathbf{n}$ lies in one of the co-ordinate planes, $\mathbf{s}$ lies in that plane also. This rule, however, is subject to an important exception for wave vectors in the direction of the optical axes.

When the values of $\mathbf{n}$ given by (79.5) are substituted in formulae (77.12a), the components of $\mathbf{s}$ take the indeterminate form 0/0. The origin and meaning of this indeterminacy are quite evident from the following geometrical considerations. Near a singular point, the inner and outer parts of the wave-vector surface are cones with a common vertex. At the vertex, which is the singular point itself, the direction of the normal to the surface becomes indeterminate; and the direction of $\mathbf{s}$ as given by formulae (77.12a) is just the direction of the normal. In fact the wave vector along the binormal corresponds to an infinity of ray vectors, whose directions occupy a certain conical surface, called the *cone of internal conical refraction.*

To determine this cone of rays, we could investigate the directions of the normals near the singular point. It is more informative, however, to use a geometrical construction from the ray surface.

Fig. 39 shows one quadrant of the intersection of the ray surface with the xz-plane (continuous curves), and also the intersection of the wave-vector surface, on a different scale. The line OS is the biradial, and ON the binormal. Let $\mathbf{n}_N$ be the wave vector corresponding to the point N. It is easy to see that the singular point N on the wave-vector surface corresponds to a singular tangent plane to the ray surface. This plane is perpendicular to ON, and touches the ray surface not at one point but along a curve, which is found to be a circle. In Fig. 39 the trace of this plane is shown by ab. This follows at once from the geometrical correspondence between the wave-vector

† In the tensor ellipsoid (77.19) the binormals are the directions perpendicular to the circular sections of the ellipsoid. An ellipsoid has two such sections.

surface and the ray surface (§77): if the tangent plane is drawn at any point $\mathbf{s}$ of the ray surface, then the perpendicular from the origin to this plane is in the same direction as the wave vector $\mathbf{n}$ corresponding to $\mathbf{s}$, and its length is $1/n$. In our case there must be an infinity of vectors $\mathbf{s}$ corresponding to the single value $\mathbf{n} = \mathbf{n}_N$; hence the points on the ray surface which represent these vectors $\mathbf{s}$ must lie in one tangent plane, which is perpendicular to $\mathbf{n}_N$. Thus in Fig. 39 the triangle *Oab* is the section of the cone of internal conical refraction by the *xz*-plane.

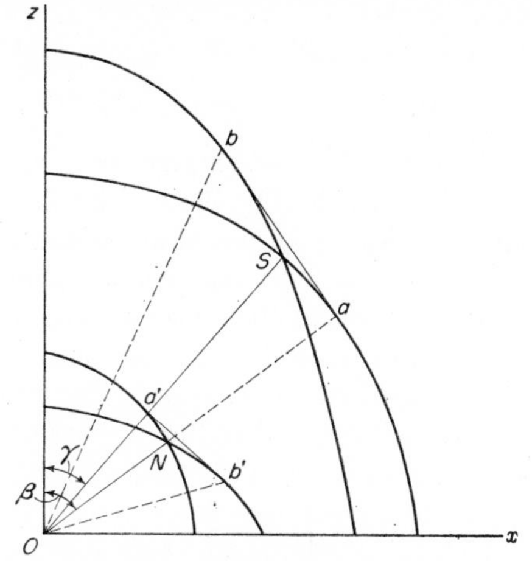

FIG. 39

There is no especial difficulty in carrying out a quantitative calculation corresponding to this geometrical picture, but we shall not do so here, and give only the final formulae. The equations of the circle in which the cone of refraction cuts the ray surface are

$$(\epsilon^{(z)} - \epsilon^{(x)})s_y^2 + \\ + \{s_x\sqrt{[\epsilon^{(x)}(\epsilon^{(z)} - \epsilon^{(y)})]} - s_z\sqrt{[\epsilon^{(z)}(\epsilon^{(y)} - \epsilon^{(x)})]}\} \times \\ \times \left(s_x\sqrt{\frac{\epsilon^{(z)} - \epsilon^{(y)}}{\epsilon^{(x)}}} - s_z\sqrt{\frac{\epsilon^{(y)} - \epsilon^{(x)}}{\epsilon^{(z)}}}\right) = 0, \tag{79.8}$$

$$s_x\sqrt{[\epsilon^{(z)}(\epsilon^{(y)} - \epsilon^{(x)})]} + s_z\sqrt{[\epsilon^{(x)}(\epsilon^{(z)} - \epsilon^{(y)})]} = \sqrt{[\epsilon^{(z)} - \epsilon^{(x)}]}. \tag{79.9}$$

The first of these equations is the equation of the cone of refraction if s_x, s_y, s_z are regarded as three independent variables. The second is the equation of the tangent plane to the ray surface. In particular, for $s_y = 0$ equation (79.8) gives the two equations

$$\frac{s_x}{s_z} = \sqrt{\frac{\epsilon^{(z)}(\epsilon^{(y)} - \epsilon^{(x)})}{\epsilon^{(x)}(\epsilon^{(z)} - \epsilon^{(y)})}}, \qquad \frac{s_x}{s_z} = \sqrt{\frac{\epsilon^{(x)}(\epsilon^{(y)} - \epsilon^{(x)})}{\epsilon^{(z)}(\epsilon^{(z)} - \epsilon^{(y)})}},$$

which determine the directions of the extreme rays (respectively *Oa* and *Ob* in Fig. 39) in the section by the xz-plane. The former is along the binormal (cf. (79.6)), which is perpendicular to the tangent *ab*.

Similar results hold for the wave vectors corresponding to a given ray vector. The vector $\mathbf{s}$ along the biradial corresponds to an infinity of wave vectors, whose directions occupy the *cone of external conical refraction.* In Fig. 39 the triangle $Oa'b'$ is the section of this cone by the xz-plane. The corresponding formulae are again obtained by substituting $\mathbf{n}$ for $\mathbf{s}$ and $1/\epsilon$ for ϵ in the formulae (79.8), (79.9), and are

$$\epsilon^{(y)}(\epsilon^{(z)}-\epsilon^{(x)})n_y^2+[n_x\sqrt{(\epsilon^{(z)}-\epsilon^{(y)})}-n_z\sqrt{(\epsilon^{(y)}-\epsilon^{(x)})}]\times$$
$$\times[n_x\epsilon^{(x)}\sqrt{(\epsilon^{(z)}-\epsilon^{(y)})}-n_z\epsilon^{(z)}\sqrt{(\epsilon^{(y)}-\epsilon^{(x)})}]=0,$$
$$n_x\sqrt{(\epsilon^{(y)}-\epsilon^{(x)})}+n_z\sqrt{(\epsilon^{(z)}-\epsilon^{(y)})}=\sqrt{[\epsilon^{(y)}(\epsilon^{(z)}-\epsilon^{(x)})]}.$$

In observations of the internal conical refraction† we can use a flat plate cut perpendicular to the binormal (Fig. 40). The surface of the plate is covered by a diaphragm of small aperture, which selects a narrow beam from a plane light wave (i.e. one whose wave vector is in a definite direction) incident on the plate. The wave vector in the wave transmitted into the plate is in the direction of the binormal, and so the rays are on the cone of internal refraction. The wave vector in the wave leaving the other side of the plate is the same as in the incident wave, and so the rays are on a circular cylinder.

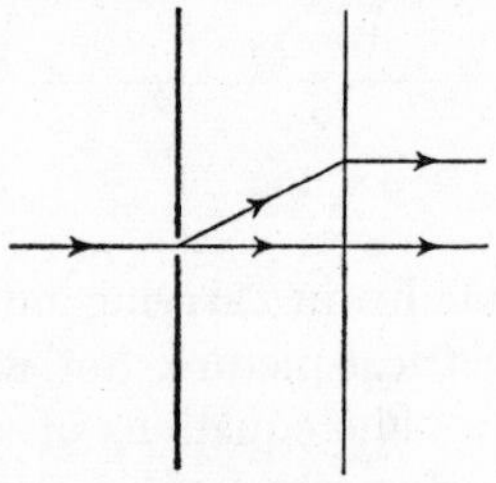

Fig. 40

To observe the external conical refraction, the plate must be cut perpendicular to the biradial, and both its surfaces must be covered by diaphragms having small apertures in exactly opposite positions. When the plate is illuminated by a convergent beam (i.e. one containing rays with all possible values of $\mathbf{n}$), the diaphragms admit to the plate rays with $\mathbf{s}$ along the biradial, and therefore with directions of $\mathbf{n}$ occupying the surface of the cone of external conical refraction. The light leaving the second aperture is therefore on a conical surface, although this does not exactly coincide with the cone of external refraction, on account of the refraction on leaving the plate.

The laws of refraction at the surface of a biaxial crystal for an arbitrary direction of incidence are extremely complex, and we shall not pause to discuss

† We shall describe only the principle of the experiment.

them here,† but only mention that, unlike what happens for a uniaxial crystal, both refracted waves are "extraordinary" and, in particular, the rays of neither lie in the plane of incidence.

§80. Double refraction in an electric field

An isotropic body becomes optically anisotropic when placed in a constant electric field. This anisotropy may be regarded as the result of a change in the dielectric constant due to the constant field. Although this change is relatively very slight, it is important here because it leads to a qualitative change in the optical properties of bodies.

In this section we denote by **E** the constant electric field in the body,‡ and expand the dielectric tensor ϵ_{ik} in powers of **E**. In an isotropic body in the zero-order approximation, we have $\epsilon_{ik} = \epsilon^{(0)}\delta_{ik}$. There can be no terms in ϵ_{ik} which are of the first order in the field, since in an isotropic body there is no constant vector with which a tensor of rank two linear in **E** could be constructed. The next terms in the expansion of ϵ_{ik} must therefore be quadratic in the field. From the components of the vector **E** we can form two symmetrical tensors of rank two, $E^2\delta_{ik}$ and E_iE_k. The former does not alter the symmetry of the tensor $\epsilon^{(0)}\delta_{ik}$, and the addition of it amounts to a small correction in the scalar constant $\epsilon^{(0)}$, which evidently does not result in optical anisotropy and is therefore of no interest. Thus we arrive at the following form of the dielectric tensor as a function of the field:

$$\epsilon_{ik} = \epsilon^{(0)}\delta_{ik} + \alpha E_iE_k, \tag{80.1}$$

where α is a scalar constant.

One of the principal axes of this tensor coincides with the direction of the electric field, and the corresponding principal value is

$$\epsilon_{\parallel} = \epsilon^{(0)} + \alpha E^2. \tag{80.2}$$

The other two principal values are both equal to

$$\epsilon_{\perp} = \epsilon^{(0)}, \tag{80.3}$$

and the position of the corresponding principal axes in a plane perpendicular to the field is arbitrary. Thus an isotropic body in an electric field behaves optically as a uniaxial crystal (the *Kerr effect*).

The change in optical symmetry in an electric field may occur in a crystal also (for example, an optically uniaxial crystal may become biaxial, and a cubic crystal may cease to be optically isotropic), and here the effect may be of the first order in the field. This linear effect corresponds to a dielectric tensor of the form $\epsilon_{ik} = \epsilon_{ik}{}^{(0)} + \alpha_{ikl}E_l$, where the coefficients α_{ikl} form a tensor of rank three symmetrical in the suffixes i and k ($\alpha_{ikl} = \alpha_{kil}$). The

† A detailed account of the calculations may be found in the article by G. Szivessy, *Handbuch der Physik*, vol. XX, Chapter 11, Springer, Berlin, 1928.

‡ Not to be confused with the variable field of the wave, which is usually very weak.

symmetry of this tensor is the same as that of the piezoelectric tensor. The effect in question therefore occurs in the twenty crystal classes which admit piezoelectricity.

§81. Mechanical–optical effects

Besides the Kerr effect discussed in §80, there are other ways in which the optical symmetry of a medium can be changed by external agencies. These include, first of all, the effect of elastic deformations on the optical properties of solids. In particular, such deformations may render an isotropic solid body optically anisotropic. Such phenomena are described by the inclusion in $\epsilon_{ik}(\omega)$ of additional terms proportional to the components of the deformation tensor. The corresponding formulae are exactly the same as (16.1) and (16.6) for the static dielectric permeability, except that the coefficients are now functions of frequency. In the deformation of an isotropic body, for example, we have

$$\epsilon_{ik} = \epsilon^{(0)}\delta_{ik} + a_1 u_{ik} + a_2 u_{ll}\delta_{ik}. \tag{81.1}$$

The coefficients $a_1(\omega)$ and $a_2(\omega)$ are called *elastic–optical constants.*

Another case is the occurrence of optical anisotropy in a moving fluid. Here we do not refer to the relativistic effects described by the equations of §57; the effects to be considered are due to the presence of velocity gradients in the fluid. The corresponding general expression for the dielectric tensor is

$$\epsilon_{ik} = \epsilon^{(0)}\delta_{ik} + \lambda_1\left(\frac{\partial v_i}{\partial x_k} + \frac{\partial v_k}{\partial x_i}\right) + \lambda_2\left(\frac{\partial v_i}{\partial x_k} - \frac{\partial v_k}{\partial x_i}\right), \tag{81.2}$$

and represents the first terms in an expansion of ϵ_{ik} in powers of the derivatives of the velocity. In an incompressible fluid $\partial v_l/\partial x_l \equiv \operatorname{div} \mathbf{v} = 0$, and the last two terms in (81.2) give zero on contraction; $\epsilon^{(0)}$ is the dielectric permeability of the fluid at rest.† The second and third terms in (81.2) are respectively symmetrical and antisymmetrical in the suffixes i and k. For uniform rotation of the fluid we have $\mathbf{v} = \mathbf{\Omega}\times\mathbf{r}$, where $\mathbf{\Omega}$ is the angular velocity of rotation, and the symmetrical term is zero.‡

These phenomena are of practical importance only in such systems as suspensions and colloidal solutions of anisotropically shaped particles.

† To avoid misunderstanding, it should be emphasised that the symmetry relations discussed in *Statistical Physics* §124 (the generalised principle of symmetry of the kinetic coefficients) do not apply to the expression (81.2). These relations are derived on the assumption that the processes corresponding to the coefficients under consideration are the only cause of energy dissipation in the system. In the present case, however, besides the dissipation in the variable electromagnetic field in the wave, there is another mode of dissipation, which is unrelated to the field, namely the internal friction in the non-uniform fluid stream.

‡ See §82 for the optical properties resulting from the antisymmetrical part of the tensor ϵ_{ik}.

In this case the effect (called the *Maxwell effect*) is due primarily to the orienting of particles suspended in the fluid by the action of the velocity gradients. Since a uniform rotation cannot orient the particles, it follows that $\lambda_2 \ll \lambda_1$, and we can write simply

$$\epsilon_{ik} = \epsilon^{(0)}\delta_{ik} + \lambda_1\left(\frac{\partial v_i}{\partial x_k} + \frac{\partial v_k}{\partial x_i}\right). \tag{81.3}$$

§82. Magnetic–optical effects

In the presence of a constant magnetic field **H**,† the tensor ϵ_{ik} is no longer symmetrical. The generalised principle of symmetry of the kinetic coefficients given by SP (124.14) requires that

$$\epsilon_{ik}(\mathbf{H}) = \epsilon_{ki}(-\mathbf{H}). \tag{82.1}$$

The condition that absorption is absent requires that the tensor should be Hermitian:

$$\epsilon_{ik} = \epsilon_{ki}^{*}, \tag{82.2}$$

as is seen from (76.4), but not that it should be real. Equation (82.2) implies only that the real and imaginary parts of ϵ_{ik} must be respectively symmetrical and antisymmetrical:

$$\epsilon_{ik}' = \epsilon_{ki}', \qquad \epsilon_{ik}'' = -\epsilon_{ki}''. \tag{82.3}$$

Using (82.1), we have

$$\begin{aligned}\epsilon_{ik}'(\mathbf{H}) &= \epsilon_{ki}'(\mathbf{H}) = \epsilon_{ik}'(-\mathbf{H}),\\ \epsilon_{ik}''(\mathbf{H}) &= -\epsilon_{ki}''(\mathbf{H}) = -\epsilon_{ik}''(-\mathbf{H}),\end{aligned} \tag{82.4}$$

i.e. in a non-absorbing medium ϵ_{ik}' is an even function of **H**, and ϵ_{ik}'' an odd function.

The inverse tensor $\epsilon^{-1}{}_{ik}$ evidently has the same symmetry properties, and is more convenient for use in the following calculations. To simplify the notation we shall write‡

$$\epsilon^{-1}{}_{ik} = \eta_{ik} = \eta_{ik}' + i\eta_{ik}''. \tag{82.5}$$

Any antisymmetrical tensor of rank two is equivalent (dual) to some axial vector; let the vector corresponding to the tensor η_{ik}'' be **G**. Using the antisymmetrical unit tensor e_{ikl}, we can write the relation between the components η_{ik}'' and G_i as

$$\eta_{ik}'' = e_{ikl}G_l, \tag{82.6}$$

---

† Not to be confused with the weak variable field of the electromagnetic wave.
‡ Of course, η_{ik}' and η_{ik}'' are not the tensors inverse to ϵ_{ik}' and ϵ_{ik}''.

or, in components, $\eta_{xy}'' = G_z$, $\eta_{zx}'' = G_y$, $\eta_{yz}'' = G_x$. The relation $E_i = \eta_{ik}D_k$ between the electric field and induction becomes

$$E_i = (\eta_{ik}' + ie_{ikl}G_l)D_k = \eta_{ik}'D_k + i(\mathbf{D}\times\mathbf{G})_i. \tag{82.7}$$

A medium in which the relation between **E** and **D** is of this form is said to be *gyrotropic*.†

We may give a general discussion of the nature of waves propagated in an arbitrary gyrotropic medium, assumed anisotropic, with no restriction on the magnitude of the magnetic field.‡

We take the direction of the wave vector as the z-axis. Then equations (77.18) become

$$\left(\eta_{\alpha\beta} - \frac{1}{n^2}\delta_{\alpha\beta}\right)D_\beta = \left(\eta_{\alpha\beta}' + i\eta_{\alpha\beta}'' - \frac{1}{n^2}\delta_{\alpha\beta}\right)D_\beta = 0, \tag{82.8}$$

where the suffixes α, β take the values x, y. The directions of the x and y axes are taken along the principal axes of the two-dimensional tensor $\eta_{\alpha\beta}'$; and we denote the corresponding principal values of this tensor by $1/n_{01}^2$ and $1/n_{02}^2$. Then the equations become

$$\begin{aligned}\left(\frac{1}{n_{01}^2} - \frac{1}{n^2}\right)D_x + iG_zD_y &= 0,\\ -iG_zD_x + \left(\frac{1}{n_{02}^2} - \frac{1}{n^2}\right)D_y &= 0.\end{aligned} \tag{82.9}$$

The condition that the determinant of these equations vanishes gives an equation quadratic in n^2:

$$\left(\frac{1}{n^2} - \frac{1}{n_{01}^2}\right)\left(\frac{1}{n^2} - \frac{1}{n_{02}^2}\right) = G_z^2, \tag{82.10}$$

whose roots give the two values of n for a given direction of **n**:‖

$$\frac{1}{n^2} = \frac{1}{2}\left(\frac{1}{n_{01}^2} + \frac{1}{n_{02}^2}\right) \pm \sqrt{\left[\frac{1}{4}\left(\frac{1}{n_{01}^2} - \frac{1}{n_{02}^2}\right)^2 + G_z^2\right]}. \tag{82.11}$$

---

† The *gyration vector* is the vector **g** in the opposite relation

$$D_i = \epsilon_{ik}'E_k + i(\mathbf{E}\times\mathbf{g})_i. \tag{82.7a}$$

The coefficients in (82.7) and (82.7a) are related as follows (cf. §21, Problem):

$$\begin{aligned}\eta_{ik}' &= \{|\epsilon'|\epsilon'^{-1}_{ik} - g_ig_k\}/|\epsilon|,\\ G_i &= -\epsilon_{ik}'g_k/|\epsilon|,\end{aligned} \tag{82.7b}$$

where $|\epsilon|$ and $|\epsilon'|$ are the determinants of the tensors ϵ_{ik} and ϵ_{ik}'.

‡ The medium is again assumed non-magnetic with respect to the variable field of the electromagnetic wave, i.e. $\mu_{ik}(\omega) = \delta_{ik}$. This, however, does not exclude a constant field magnetising the medium (i.e. the static permeability may differ from unity).

The properties derived for $\epsilon_{ik}(\omega)$ are equally applicable to the tensor $\mu_{ik}(\omega)$ in a frequency range where the dispersion of the magnetic permeability is of importance.

‖ When there is no field, $\mathbf{G} = 0$ and $n = n_{01}$ or n_{02}. It should be remembered, however, that when the field is present n_{01} and n_{02} in equation (82.10) are not in general the values of n for $\mathbf{H} = 0$, since not only **G** but also the components η_{ik}' depend on the field.

Substituting these values in equations (82.9), we find the corresponding ratios D_y/D_x:

$$\frac{D_y}{D_x} = \frac{i}{G_z}\left\{\frac{1}{2}\left(\frac{1}{n_{01}^2}-\frac{1}{n_{02}^2}\right) \mp \sqrt{\left[\frac{1}{4}\left(\frac{1}{n_{01}^2}-\frac{1}{n_{02}^2}\right)^2 + G_z^2\right]}\right\}. \quad (82.12)$$

The purely imaginary value of the ratio D_y/D_x signifies that the waves are elliptically polarised, and the principal axes of the ellipses are the x and y axes. The product of the two values of the ratio is easily seen to be unity. Thus, if in one wave $D_y = i\rho D_x$, where the real quantity ρ is the ratio of the axes of the polarisation ellipse, then in the other wave $D_y = -iD_x/\rho$. This means that the polarisation ellipses of the two waves have the same axis ratio, but are 90° apart, and the directions of rotation are opposite (Fig. 41).†

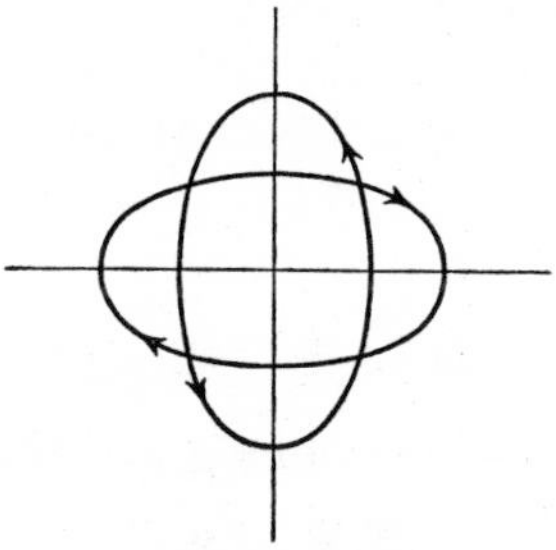

FIG. 41

The components G_i and η_{ik}' are functions of the magnetic field. If, as usually happens, the magnetic field is fairly weak, we can expand in powers of the field. The vector **G** is zero in the absence of the field, and so for a weak field we can put

$$G_i = f_{ik}H_k, \quad (82.13)$$

where f_{ik} is a tensor of rank two, in general not symmetrical. This dependence is in accordance with the general rule (82.4) whereby, in a transparent medium, the components of the antisymmetrical tensor η_{ik}'' (and ϵ_{ik}'') must be odd functions of **H**. The symmetrical components η_{ik}' are even functions of the magnetic field. The first correction terms (which do not appear in the absence of the field) in η_{ik}' are therefore quadratic in the field.‡

In the general case of an arbitrarily directed wave vector, the magnetic field has little effect on the propagation of light in the crystal, causing only

† If the vectors **D** in the two waves are denoted by $\mathbf{D}_1$ and $\mathbf{D}_2$, these relations may be written $\mathbf{D}_1 \cdot \mathbf{D}_2^* = D_{1x}D_{2x}^* + D_{1y}D_{2y}^* = 0$. This is a general property of the eigenvectors on reduction to the principal axes of a Hermitian tensor (in this case, the tensor $\eta_{\alpha\beta}'$).

‡ When second-order quantities are neglected, formulae (82.7b) reduce to the simpler forms

$$\eta_{ik}' = \epsilon'^{-1}{}_{ik}, \qquad G_i = -\epsilon_{ik}'g_k/|\epsilon'|. \quad (82.13a)$$

a slight ellipticity of the oscillations, with an axis ratio of the polarisation ellipse which is small (of the first order with respect to the field).

The directions of the optical axes (and neighbouring directions) form an exception. The two values of n are equal in the absence of the field when the wave vector is along one of these axes. The roots of equation (82.10) then differ from these values by first-order quantities,† and the resulting effects are analogous to those in isotropic bodies, which we shall now consider.

The magnetic–optical effect in isotropic bodies (and in crystals of the cubic system) is of particular interest on account of its nature and its comparatively large magnitude.

Neglecting second-order quantities, we have $\eta_{ik}' = \epsilon^{-1}\delta_{ik}$, where ϵ is the dielectric permeability of the isotropic medium in the absence of the magnetic field. The relation between **D** and **E** is

$$\mathbf{E} = \frac{1}{\epsilon}\mathbf{D} + i\mathbf{D} \times \mathbf{G}, \tag{82.14}$$

or

$$\mathbf{D} = \epsilon\mathbf{E} + i\mathbf{E} \times \mathbf{g}; \tag{82.15}$$

in the same approximation, the vectors **g** and **G** are related by

$$\mathbf{G} = -\mathbf{g}/\epsilon^2. \tag{82.16}$$

The dependence of **g** (or **G**) on the external field reduces in an isotropic medium to simple proportionality:

$$\mathbf{g} = f\mathbf{H}, \tag{82.17}$$

in which the scalar constant f may be either positive or negative.

In equation (82.10) we now have $n_{01} = n_{02} = n_0 = \sqrt{\epsilon}$, the refractive index in the absence of the field. Hence $1/n^2 = \mp G_z + 1/n_0^2$ or, to the same accuracy,

$$n_{\mp}^2 = n_0^2 \pm n_0^4 G_z = n_0^2 \mp g_z. \tag{82.18}$$

Since the z-axis is in the direction of **n**, we can write this formula, to the same accuracy, in the vector form

$$\left(\mathbf{n} \pm \frac{1}{2n_0}\mathbf{g}\right)^2 = n_0^2. \tag{82.19}$$

Hence we see that the wave-vector surface in this case consists of two spheres of radius n_0, whose centres are at distances $\pm g/2n_0$ from the origin in the direction of **G**.

† It should be noticed that the two roots of (82.10) do not become equal. The geometrical significance of this is that the two parts of the wave-vector surface are separated.

A different polarisation of the wave corresponds to each of the two values of n: we have

$$D_x = \mp iD_y, \tag{82.20}$$

where the signs correspond to those in (82.18). The equality of the magnitudes of D_x and D_y, and their phase difference of $\mp\frac{1}{2}\pi$, signify a circular polarisation of the wave, with the direction of rotation of the vector **D** respectively anticlockwise and clockwise looking along the wave vector (or, to use the customary expressions, with *right-hand* and *left-hand* polarisation respectively).

The difference between the refractive indices in the left-hand and right-hand polarised waves has the result that two circularly polarised refracted waves are formed at the surface of a gyrotropic body. This phenomenon is called *double circular refraction.*

Let a linearly polarised plane wave be incident normally on a slab of thickness l. We take the direction of incidence as the z-axis, and that of the vector $\mathbf{E}$ $(=\mathbf{D})$ in the incident wave as the x-axis. The linear oscillation can be represented as the sum of two circular oscillations with opposite directions of rotation, which are then propagated through the slab with different wave vectors $k_{\pm} = \omega n_{\pm}/c$. Arbitrarily taking the wave amplitude as unity, we have $D_x = \frac{1}{2}[\exp(ik_+z)+\exp(ik_-z)]$, $D_y = \frac{1}{2}i[-\exp(ik_+z)+\exp(ik_-z)]$, or, putting $k = \frac{1}{2}(k_+ + k_-)$ and $\kappa = \frac{1}{2}(k_+ - k_-)$,

$$D_x = \tfrac{1}{2}e^{ikz}(e^{i\kappa z} + e^{-i\kappa z}) = e^{ikz}\cos\kappa z,$$

$$D_y = \tfrac{1}{2}ie^{ikz}(-e^{i\kappa z} + e^{-i\kappa z}) = e^{ikz}\sin\kappa z.$$

When the wave leaves the slab we have $D_y/D_x = \tan\kappa l = \tan(l\omega g/2cn_0)$. Since this ratio is real, the wave remains linearly polarised, but the direction of polarisation is changed (the *Faraday effect*). The angle through which the plane of polarisation is rotated is proportional to the path traversed by the wave; the angle per unit length in the direction of the wave vector is $(\omega g/2cn_0)\cos\theta$, where θ is the angle between $\mathbf{n}$ and $\mathbf{g}$.

It should be noticed that, when the direction of the magnetic field is given, the direction of rotation of the plane of polarisation (with respect to the direction of $\mathbf{n}$) is reversed (left-hand becoming right-hand, and *vice versa*) when the sign of $\mathbf{n}$ is changed. If the ray traverses the same path twice in opposite directions, the total rotation of the plane of polarisation is therefore double the value resulting from a single traversal.

For $\theta = \frac{1}{2}\pi$ (the wave vector perpendicular to the magnetic field), the effect linear in the field given by formulae (82.18) disappears, in accordance with the general rule stated above that only the component of $\mathbf{g}$ in the direction of $\mathbf{n}$ affects the propagation of light. For angles θ close to $\frac{1}{2}\pi$ we must therefore take account of the terms proportional to the square of the field, and in particular these terms must be included in the tensor η_{ik}'. By virtue of the axial symmetry about the direction of the field, two principal values of the symmetrical tensor η_{ik}' are equal, as for a uniaxial crystal. We shall take the x-axis in the direction of the field, and denote by $\eta_{\parallel}$ and $\eta_{\perp}$ the principal values of η_{ik}' in the directions parallel and perpendicular to the magnetic field. The difference $\eta_{\parallel}-\eta_{\perp}$ is proportional to H^2.

Let us consider the purely quadratic effect (called the *Cotton–Mouton effect*) which occurs when **n** and **g** are perpendicular. In equations (82.9) and (82.10) we have $G_z = 0$, and $1/n_{01}^2$, $1/n_{02}^2$ are respectively $\eta_{\parallel}$, $\eta_{\perp}$. Thus in one wave we have $1/n^2 = \eta_{\parallel}$, $D_y = 0$; this wave is linearly polarised, and the vector **D** is parallel to the x-axis. In the other wave $1/n^2 = \eta_{\perp}$, $D_x = 0$, i.e. **D** is parallel to the y-axis. Let linearly polarised light be incident normally on a slab in a magnetic field parallel to its surface. The two components in the slab (with vectors **D** in the xz and yz planes) are propagated with different values of n. Consequently the light leaving the slab is elliptically polarised.

PROBLEMS

PROBLEM 1. Determine the directions of the rays when a ray incident from a vacuum is refracted at the surface of an isotropic body in a magnetic field.

SOLUTION. The direction of the ray vector **s** is given by the normal to the wave-vector surface. Differentiating the left-hand side of equation (82.19) with respect to the components of the vector **n**, we find that **s** is proportional to $\mathbf{n}\pm\mathbf{g}/2n_0$. The square of the latter expression is n_0^2, and so the unit vector in the direction of the ray is given by

$$\frac{\mathbf{s}}{s} = \frac{1}{n_0}\left(\mathbf{n}\pm\frac{1}{2n_0}\mathbf{g}\right). \tag{1}$$

Let the angle of incidence be θ. The refracted rays do not in general lie in the plane of incidence, and their directions are given by the angle θ' to the normal to the surface and the azimuth ϕ' measured from the plane of incidence. We take the latter as the xz-plane, with the z-axis perpendicular to the surface. The components n_x and n_y of the wave vector are unaltered by refraction. In the incident ray they are $n_x = \sin\theta$, $n_y = 0$. Substituting these values in (1), we find the x and y components of the unit vector $\mathbf{s}/s$, which give immediately the directions of the refracted rays:

$$\sin\theta'\cos\phi' = \frac{1}{n_0}\sin\theta\pm\frac{1}{2n_0^2}g_x,$$

$$\sin\theta'\sin\phi' = \pm\frac{1}{2n_0^2}g_y.$$

When the angle of incidence is not small, the azimuth ϕ' is small, and we can write

$$\phi' = \pm g_y/2n_0\sin\theta,$$

$$\sin\theta' = \frac{\sin\theta}{n_0}\pm\frac{g_x}{2n_0^2}.$$

For normal incidence ($\theta = 0$) we take the xz-plane through the vector **G**; then $\phi' = 0$, and $\theta' \cong \sin\theta' = \pm g_x/2n_0^2$. Although this formula does not involve g_z, it is not valid if $g_z = 0$, since the approximation linear in the field is inadequate when **n** and **g** are perpendicular.

PROBLEM 2. Determine the polarisation of the reflected light when a linearly polarised wave is incident normally from a vacuum on the surface of a body rendered anisotropic by a magnetic field.

SOLUTION. For normal incidence the direction of the wave vector is unaltered by the passage of the wave into the medium. In all three waves (incident, reflected and refracted) the vectors **H** are therefore parallel to the surface (the xy-plane). The electric vector **E** in the incident and reflected waves is also parallel to the xy-plane; in the refracted wave $E_z \neq 0$, but the relation between the x and y components of **E** and **H** is the same as in an isotropic body ($H_x = -nE_y$, $H_y = nE_x$). If the polarisation of the incident wave is the same as that of one of the two types of wave which can be propagated in the anisotropic medium concerned, with the given direction of **n**, then there is only one refracted wave, which has this polarisation. The problem is then formally identical with that of reflection from an isotropic body, and the fields $\mathbf{E}_1$ and $\mathbf{E}_0$ in the reflected and incident waves are related by

$$\mathbf{E}_1 = (1-n)\mathbf{E}_0/(1+n), \tag{1}$$

where n is the refractive index corresponding to this polarisation.

The linear polarisation can be regarded as resulting from the superposition of two circular polarisations with opposite directions of rotation. If $\mathbf{E}_0$ in the incident field is in the x-direction, we put $\mathbf{E}_0 = \mathbf{E}_0{}^+ + \mathbf{E}_0{}^-$, where $E_0{}^+{}_x = iE_0{}^+{}_y = \frac{1}{2}E_0$, $E_0{}^-{}_x = -iE_0{}^-{}_y = \frac{1}{2}E_0$. Using formula (1) for each wave, with $n_\pm$ given by (82.18), we obtain

$$E_{1x} = \tfrac{1}{2}E_0\left[\frac{1-n_+}{1+n_+} + \frac{1-n_-}{1+n_-}\right] \cong E_0\frac{1-n_0}{1+n_0},$$

$$E_{1y} = \tfrac{1}{2}iE_0\left[\frac{1-n_-}{1+n_-} - \frac{1-n_+}{1+n_+}\right] \cong iE_0\frac{g\cos\theta}{n_0(1+n_0)^2},$$

where θ is the angle between the direction of the incidence and the vector **g**. Hence we see that the reflected wave is elliptically polarised, the major axis of the ellipse being in the x-direction, and the ratio of the minor and major axes being $(g\cos\theta)/n_0(n_0{}^2-1)$.

PROBLEM 3. Determine the limiting form of the frequency dependence of the gyration vector at high frequencies.

SOLUTION. The calculations are similar to those in §59, except that the electron equation of motion must include the Lorentz force due to the constant external magnetic field **H**:

$$m\frac{d\mathbf{v}'}{dt} = e\mathbf{E}_0 e^{-i\omega t} + e\mathbf{v}'\times\mathbf{H}/c.$$

If $\omega \gg eH/mc$, this equation can be solved by successive approximations. As far as terms of the first order in **H** we have

$$\mathbf{v}' = \frac{ie}{m\omega}\mathbf{E} - \frac{e^2}{m^2\omega^2 c}\mathbf{E}\times\mathbf{H},$$

and the induction is then

$$\mathbf{D} = \epsilon(\omega)\mathbf{E} + if(\omega)\mathbf{E}\times\mathbf{H},$$

where $\epsilon(\omega)$ is given by (59.1) and $f(\omega) = -4\pi Ne^3/cm^2\omega^3$.

§83. Natural optical activity

The frequency dispersion of the dielectric (and magnetic) permeability results from the dependence of the macroscopic properties of matter on the time variation of the electromagnetic field. The dependence on its spatial variation has been ignored up to this point. The condition for this treatment to be valid is that the atomic dimension a should be small compared with the wavelength λ (see §58).

The inequality $a \ll \lambda$ is a necessary condition for the macroscopic theory to be applicable at all. When the quantities involving the small ratio a/λ are entirely neglected, however, certain kinds of effect are overlooked which make their appearance when the next terms in a/λ after the zero-order approximation are included. We shall now discuss these effects.

The expansion in powers of a/λ corresponds, in the macroscopic theory, to an expansion of the induction **D** in powers of the spatial derivatives of the field **E** as well as of **E** itself. Taking only the first-order terms, we must include terms proportional to the first powers of the first-order derivatives. For a field of a single frequency ω we can write the expansion as

$$D_i = \epsilon_{ik}^{(0)}E_k + \gamma_{ikl}\partial E_k/\partial x_l, \tag{83.1}$$

where $\epsilon_{ik}^{(0)}$ and γ_{ikl} are functions of frequency.

Before proceeding to investigate this expression, we should make the following remark. To the accuracy used here there is no physical significance in separating the mean value of the microscopic current density $\overline{\rho\mathbf{v}}$ into the two parts $\partial\mathbf{P}/\partial t$ and c **curl M**. In the present theory, therefore, it is appropriate to write Maxwell's equations as

$$\begin{aligned} \mathbf{curl}\,\mathbf{E} &= -\frac{1}{c}\frac{\partial \mathbf{B}}{\partial t}, \\ \mathbf{curl}\,\mathbf{B} &= \frac{1}{c}\frac{\partial \mathbf{D}}{\partial t}, \end{aligned} \tag{83.2}$$

without introducing **H** as well as the mean microscopic magnetic field $\bar{\mathbf{h}} = \mathbf{B}$. Instead, all terms resulting from the averaging of the microscopic currents are supposed included in the definition of **D**.

The symmetry properties of the tensor γ_{ikl} in (83.1) are determined by applying the generalised principle of symmetry of the kinetic coefficients, as was done in §76 for the tensor ϵ_{ik}. We saw in §76 that, if the components of the vector **E** at each point in the body are taken as the quantities x_a, then the corresponding f_a will be the components of the vector **D**. The presence of the spatial derivatives in the relations (83.1), however, interferes with the direct application of the symmetry principle, which is best used as follows. Let x_a and x'_a be two different sets of values of the x_a, and f_a, f'_a the corresponding sets of values of the f_a. By the symmetry ($\alpha_{ab} = \alpha_{ab}$) of the coefficients in the relations

$$x_a = \sum_b \alpha_{ab} f_b, \qquad x'_a = \sum_b \alpha_{ab} f'_b$$

we have

$$\sum_a x_a f'_a = \sum_a x'_a f_a. \tag{83.3}$$

In the present case, this equation takes the form $\int E_i D'_i \,\mathrm{d}V = \int E'_i D_i \,\mathrm{d}V$. Substituting (83.1) and using the known symmetry of $\epsilon^{(0)}_{ik}$, we obtain

$$\int \gamma_{ikl} E_i \frac{\partial E'_k}{\partial x_l}\,\mathrm{d}V = \int \gamma_{ikl} E'_i \frac{\partial E_k}{\partial x_l}\,\mathrm{d}V$$

or, integrating by parts on one side of the equation,

$$\int \gamma_{ikl} E_i \frac{\partial E'_k}{\partial x_l} \mathrm{d}V = -\int \gamma_{ikl} E_k \frac{\partial E'_i}{\partial x_l} \mathrm{d}V = -\int \gamma_{kil} E_i \frac{\partial E'_k}{\partial x_l} \mathrm{d}V.$$

Since the functions **E** and **E**$'$ are arbitrary, we therefore have the required symmetry property:

$$\gamma_{ikl} = -\gamma_{kil}. \tag{83.4}$$

We shall also suppose that no absorption takes place in the medium. Let us ascertain what conditions are thereby imposed on the tensor γ_{ikl}. The dissipation of energy in a periodic field is given by the (time) average value of the integral $-(1/4\pi)\int \mathbf{E}\cdot(\partial\mathbf{D}/\partial t)\,\mathrm{d}V$. Here **E** and **D** are real; if we use the complex representation, the integral to be averaged can be written

$$-\frac{1}{16\pi}\int\left(\mathbf{E}\cdot\frac{\partial \mathbf{D}^*}{\partial t} + \mathbf{E}^*\cdot\frac{\partial \mathbf{D}}{\partial t}\right)\mathrm{d}V = -\frac{i\omega}{16\pi}\int(\mathbf{E}\cdot\mathbf{D}^* - \mathbf{E}^*\cdot\mathbf{D})\,\mathrm{d}V.$$

Substituting (83.1) and using the fact that $\epsilon^{(0)}{}_{ik}$ is real in a transparent medium, we obtain

$$-\frac{i\omega}{16\pi}\int\left(\gamma_{ikl}{}^* E_i \frac{\partial E_k{}^*}{\partial x_l} - \gamma_{ikl} E_i{}^* \frac{\partial E_k}{\partial x_l}\right)\mathrm{d}V$$

$$= -\frac{i\omega}{16\pi}\int\left(\gamma_{ikl}{}^* E_i \frac{\partial E_k{}^*}{\partial x_l} + \gamma_{ikl} E_k \frac{\partial E_i{}^*}{\partial x_l}\right)\mathrm{d}V$$

$$= -\frac{i\omega}{16\pi}\int(\gamma_{ikl}{}^* + \gamma_{kil}) E_i \frac{\partial E_k{}^*}{\partial x_l}\mathrm{d}V.$$

This expression is zero identically if $\gamma_{ikl}{}^* = -\gamma_{kil} = \gamma_{ikl}$. Thus we conclude that, if absorption is absent, the tensor γ_{ikl} must be real.

For a plane wave, with wave vector $\mathbf{k} = \omega\mathbf{n}/c$, we have $\partial E_k/\partial x_l = i\omega E_k n_l/c$, so that $D_i = \epsilon_{ik}E_k$, where

$$\epsilon_{ik} = \epsilon^{(0)}{}_{ik} + i\omega\gamma_{ikl}n_l/c \tag{83.5}$$

is the dielectric permeability tensor, which now exhibits dispersion with respect to both frequency and wave vector.†

Instead of the antisymmetrical tensor of rank two $\gamma_{ikl}n_l$, we shall use the *gyration vector* **g**, which is dual to it. This vector is given by

$$\omega\gamma_{ikl}n_l/c = e_{ikl}g_l, \tag{83.6}$$

i.e.

$$\epsilon_{ik} = \epsilon^{(0)}{}_{ik} + ie_{ikl}g_l, \tag{83.7}$$

† When $\omega \to 0$ the quantities γ_{ikl}, which do not pertain to the expansion in powers of ω, tend to constants. The imaginary part of ϵ_{ik} therefore tends to zero as the first power of the frequency.

which is formally the same as the expression used in §82. The only difference is that in §82 the vector **g** depended only on the properties of the medium (and on the applied magnetic field), whereas here the gyration vector depends also on the wave vector of the field. According to (83.6) the components of this vector are linear functions of the components of **n**, i.e.

$$g_i = g_{ik}n_k. \qquad (83.8)$$

Substituting (83.8) in (83.6), we find $\omega\gamma_{ikl}n_l/c = e_{ikm}g_{ml}n_l$, or, since **n** is arbitrary,

$$\omega\gamma_{ikl}/c = e_{ikm}g_{ml}, \qquad (83.9)$$

which gives the relation between the components of the tensor γ_{ikl} of rank three and the pseudotensor g_{ik} of rank two.†

The particular crystallographic symmetry of the body places certain restrictions on the components of the tensor γ_{ikl} (or g_{ik}) and, in particular, may have the result that all the components are zero. For example, the tensor γ_{ikl} cannot exist in bodies having a centre of symmetry: when the sign of each co-ordinate is changed (inversion), all the components of a tensor of rank three (and of a pseudotensor of rank two) change sign, whereas by the symmetry of the body they must remain unchanged by this transformation.

Bodies in which the tensor g_{ik} is not zero are said to have *natural optical activity*. Thus the existence of optical activity certainly implies that the body has no centre of symmetry.

Let us first consider the natural optical activity of isotropic bodies. If a liquid or gas consists of a substance having no stereoisomer, it is symmetrical not only with respect to any rotation but also with respect to reflection (inversion) about any point, and can have no optical activity. Such activity can occur only in fluids having two stereoisomeric forms, and the two forms must be present in different quantities. The fluid then has no centre of symmetry.

In an isotropic body, and in crystals of the cubic system, the pseudotensor g_{ik} reduces to a pseudoscalar:

$$g_{ik} = f\delta_{ik}; \qquad (83.10)$$

the tensor γ_{ikl} is given in terms of f by $\gamma_{ikl} = cfe_{ikl}/\omega$. A pseudoscalar is a quantity which changes sign on inversion of the co-ordinates. The two stereoisomers are converted into one another by the operation of inversion, and so their values of f are the same with opposite signs.

Thus, in an optically active isotropic body, the gyration vector $\mathbf{g} = f\mathbf{n}$, and the relation between the electric induction and field in the wave is given by

$$\mathbf{D} = \epsilon^{(0)}\mathbf{E} + if\mathbf{E}\times\mathbf{n}. \qquad (83.11)$$

Since $\mathbf{D}\cdot\mathbf{n} = 0$, it follows that $\mathbf{E}\cdot\mathbf{n} = 0$. That is, in such a wave not only the induction **D** (as in any medium) but also the field **E** is transverse to the direction of **n**.

† In components $g_{xx} = \omega\gamma_{yzx}/c$, $g_{xy} = \omega\gamma_{yzy}/c$, $g_{yx} = \omega\gamma_{zxx}/c$, etc.

The change in the refractive index n when allowance is made for the natural optical activity is a small quantity. In determining this change we can therefore put $n = n_0 = \sqrt{\epsilon^{(0)}}$ in the small term $\mathbf{E}\times\mathbf{g}$ in (83.11). Then the problem of calculating the difference $n-n_0$ is formally identical with that considered in §82 of the change in n due to the magnetic field, except that $\mathbf{g}$ has a different meaning and is always parallel to $\mathbf{n}$ (the z-axis in §82). By analogy with (82.18) we can therefore derive immediately the equation

$$n_{\pm}^2 = n_0^2 \pm g = n_0^2 \pm f n_0. \tag{83.12}$$

These two values correspond (cf. (82.20)) to the following ratios of the two components of $\mathbf{E}$ (or $\mathbf{D}$):

$$E_x = \pm iE_y, \tag{83.13}$$

i.e. to waves which are left-hand and right-hand circularly polarised. It may also be noted that the magnitude of $\mathbf{n}$ is independent of its direction, and therefore the direction of $\mathbf{n}$ is the same as that of the ray vector $\mathbf{s}$.

Thus we see that the optical properties of a naturally active isotropic body resemble those of an inactive body in a magnetic field: it exhibits double circular refraction, and when a linearly polarised wave is propagated in it the plane of polarisation is rotated. The angle of rotation per unit path length of the ray is $\omega f/2c$.

The sign of the constant g, and therefore the direction of rotation, are opposite for the two stereoisomers, and we therefore speak of *dextrorotatory* and *laevorotatory* stereoisomers.

Unlike the rotation of the plane of polarisation in a magnetic field, the magnitude and sign of the rotation in naturally active substances do not depend on the direction of propagation of the ray. Hence, if a linearly polarised ray traverses the same path in a naturally active medium twice in opposite directions, the plane of polarisation is unchanged.

Let us now consider naturally active crystals. We shall not give here a systematic analysis of all possible cases of symmetry (see the Problem), but simply note that natural activity is impossible if a centre of symmetry is present, but possible if there is a plane of symmetry or a rotary-reflection axis. It should be emphasised that the conditions for the existence of natural activity in crystals are not the same as those which allow the existence of crystals in two mirror-image (*enantiomorphic*) forms; the latter conditions are more stringent, and require the absence of both a centre and a plane of symmetry. Thus a crystal can be optically active and yet be identical with its mirror image.

In a naturally active crystal (uniaxial or biaxial), when light is propagated with an arbitrary direction of the wave vector, we have essentially ordinary double refraction of linearly polarised waves; the allowance for the activity would amount to replacing the strictly linear polarisation by an elliptical polarisation with an axis ratio of the first order of smallness.

The only exception is formed by the directions of the optical axes, along which, if the activity is neglected, the two roots of Fresnel's equation coincide. In these directions the phenomenon of natural activity of crystals is analogous to that of isotropic bodies: double circular refraction of the first order occurs, with a corresponding rotation of the plane of polarisation of linearly polarised waves. These phenomena rapidly disappear as the wave vector deviates from the direction of the optical axis.

For a quantitative calculation of natural activity in crystals it is more convenient to use, not the expression giving **D** in terms of **E**, but the inverse, as in §82. As far as first-order quantities this is

$$E_i = \epsilon^{(0)-1}{}_{ik} D_k + (\mathbf{D} \times \mathbf{G})_i, \tag{83.14}$$

where the vector **G** is related to the **g** previously used by $G_i = -\epsilon^{(0)}{}_{ik} g_k / |\epsilon^{(0)}|$; see (82.13a). Owing to the formal correspondence between this expression and (82.7), the equations (82.9) and (82.10) are again valid. In these equations G_z is the component of **G** in the direction of **n**. If we write **G** in the form

$$G_i = G_{ik} n_k, \tag{83.15}$$

in analogy with (83.8), the component is proportional to

$$\mathbf{n} \cdot \mathbf{G} = G_{ik} n_i n_k. \tag{83.16}$$

This quadratic form determines the optical properties of a naturally active crystal. The tensor G_{ik} itself need not be symmetrical, but if it is separated into symmetrical and antisymmetrical parts the latter does not appear in the form (83.16). Thus we conclude that the tensor G_{ik} may be assumed symmetrical in discussing the optical properties of naturally active crystals.

PROBLEM

Find the restrictions imposed by crystal symmetry on the components of the tensor G_{ik}.

SOLUTION. Under any rotation, the pseudotensor G_{ik} behaves as a true tensor; in particular, the presence of an axis of symmetry of order higher than the second results, as for a true symmetrical tensor of rank two, in complete isotropy in a plane perpendicular to the axis. The behaviour of the pseudotensor G_{ik} under reflection is determined by the fact that it is dual to a true tensor of rank three: under any reflection which changes the sign of a given component of a true tensor of rank two, the corresponding component of G_{ik} remains unchanged, and *vice versa*. For example, on reflection in the *yz*-plane the components G_{xx}, G_{yy}, G_{zz}, G_{yz} change sign, but G_{xy}, G_{xz} do not.

We give below the non-vanishing components of the tensor G_{ik} for all crystal classes which allow natural activity. The *z*-axis is taken along the axis of symmetry of the third, fourth or sixth order or (in the classes C_2, C_{2v}) along the only second-order axis of symmetry or (in the class C_s) perpendicular to the plane of symmetry. When three mutually perpendicular axes of symmetry are present, they are the co-ordinate axes.

Class C_1: all.

Class C_2: G_{xx}, G_{yy}, G_{zz}, G_{xy}, the last of which may be made to vanish by a suitable choice of the *x* and *y* axes.

Class C_s: G_{xz}, G_{yz}, one of which may be made to vanish by a suitable choice of the *x* and *y* axes.

Class C_{2v}: G_{xy} (the *xz* and *yz* planes being planes of symmetry).

Class D_2: G_{xx}, G_{yy}, G_{zz}.

Classes C_3, C_4, C_6, D_3, D_4, D_6: $G_{xx} = G_{yy}$, G_{zz}.

Class S_4: $G_{xx} = -G_{yy}$, G_{xy}, one of which may be made to vanish by a suitable choice of the x and y axes.

Class D_{2d}: G_{xy} (the x and y axes being in vertical planes of symmetry).

Classes T, O: $G_{xx} = G_{yy} = G_{zz}$.

It may be noted that, in uniaxial crystals of the classes S_4 and D_{2d}, the scalar (83.16) is zero if the vector $\mathbf{n}$ is in the z-direction, since $G_{zz} = 0$. This means that in these crystals there is no natural-activity effect in the direction of the optical axis.

In a biaxial crystal of the class C_{2v} the optical axes are in one of the planes of symmetry. For vectors $\mathbf{n}$ lying in the xz or yz plane the scalar (83.16) is again identically zero, so that here also there is no effect in the direction of the optical axes. The only crystal class which allows rotation of the plane of polarisation along the optical axis but not enantiomorphism is the monoclinic class C_s.

CHAPTER XII

THE PASSAGE OF FAST PARTICLES THROUGH MATTER

§84. Ionisation losses by fast particles in matter: the non-relativistic case

A FAST charged particle, in passing through matter, ionises the atoms and thereby loses energy.† In gases, the ionisation losses can be regarded as being due to collisions between the fast particle and individual atoms. In a solid or liquid medium, however, several atoms interact simultaneously with the particle. The effect of this on the energy loss by the particle can be macroscopically regarded as resulting from the dielectric polarisation of the medium by the charge. Let us first consider this effect for non-relativistic velocities of the particle. We shall see that the polarisation of the medium then has only a slight effect on the losses. The derivation of this result is of interest because the method can be extended to other cases.

Let us first of all ascertain the conditions under which the phenomenon can be macroscopically considered. The spectral resolution of the field produced at a distance r from the path of a particle moving with velocity v consists chiefly of terms whose frequency is of the order v/r (the reciprocal of the "collision time"). The ionisation of an atom can be effected by field components of frequency $\omega \gtrsim \omega_0$, where ω_0 is some mean frequency corresponding to the motion of the majority of the electrons in the atom. The particle therefore interacts simultaneously with many atoms if v/ω_0 is large compared with the distances between the atoms. In solids and liquids these distances are of the same order of magnitude as the dimension a of the atoms themselves. Thus we obtain the condition $v \gg a\omega_0$, i.e. the velocity of the ionising particle must be large compared with the velocities of the atomic electrons (or at least of the majority of them).‡

Let us now determine the field produced by a charged particle moving through matter. In the non-relativistic case it is sufficient to consider only the electric field, defined by the scalar potential ϕ. This potential satisfies Poisson's equation

$$\hat{\epsilon}\triangle\phi = -4\pi e\delta(\mathbf{r}-\mathbf{v}t), \tag{84.1}$$

† We speak, as is customary, of "ionisation losses", but these are, of course, understood to include losses due to the excitation of atoms to discrete energy levels.

‡ The corresponding condition for the energy E of the particle is $E \gg MI/m$, where M is the mass of the particle, m that of the electron, and I some mean ionisation energy for the majority of the electrons in the atom.

in which the "dielectric constant" is written as an operator, and the expression $e\delta(\mathbf{r}-\mathbf{v}t)$ on the right-hand side is the density due to a point charge e moving with constant velocity $\mathbf{v}$.†

We expand ϕ as a Fourier space integral:

$$\phi = \int_{-\infty}^{\infty} \phi_{\mathbf{k}} \exp(i\mathbf{k}\cdot\mathbf{r})\, d\mathbf{k}. \tag{84.2}$$

Taking the Laplacian of this equation, we have

$$\triangle\phi = -\int_{-\infty}^{\infty} \phi_{\mathbf{k}} k^2 \exp(i\mathbf{k}\cdot\mathbf{r})\, d\mathbf{k},$$

whence it is seen that the Fourier component of $\triangle\phi$ is $(\triangle\phi)_{\mathbf{k}} = -k^2\phi_{\mathbf{k}}$.

Taking the Fourier component of equation (84.1) gives

$$\begin{aligned}\hat{\epsilon}(\triangle\phi)_{\mathbf{k}} &= -\frac{1}{(2\pi)^3}\int 4\pi e\delta(\mathbf{r}-\mathbf{v}t)\exp(-i\mathbf{k}\cdot\mathbf{r})\, dV \\ &= -\frac{e}{2\pi^2}\exp(-it\mathbf{v}\cdot\mathbf{k}).\end{aligned}$$

Thus $\hat{\epsilon}\phi_{\mathbf{k}} = (e/2\pi^2k^2)\exp(-it\mathbf{v}\cdot\mathbf{k})$, and $\phi_{\mathbf{k}}$ therefore depends on time through a factor $\exp(-it\mathbf{v}\cdot\mathbf{k})$. The operator $\hat{\epsilon}$ acting on a function $\exp(-i\omega t)$ multiplies it by $\epsilon(\omega)$. Hence

$$\phi_{\mathbf{k}} = \frac{e}{2\pi^2k^2\epsilon(\mathbf{k}\cdot\mathbf{v})}\exp(-it\mathbf{v}\cdot\mathbf{k}).$$

The Fourier components of the field and of the potential are related by $\mathbf{E}_{\mathbf{k}}\exp(i\mathbf{k}\cdot\mathbf{r}) = -\mathbf{grad}\,[\phi_{\mathbf{k}}\exp(i\mathbf{k}\cdot\mathbf{r})] = -i\mathbf{k}\phi_{\mathbf{k}}\exp(i\mathbf{k}\cdot\mathbf{r})$, or $\mathbf{E}_{\mathbf{k}} = -i\mathbf{k}\phi_{\mathbf{k}}$. Thus

$$\mathbf{E}_{\mathbf{k}} = -\frac{ie\mathbf{k}}{2\pi^2k^2\epsilon(\mathbf{k}\cdot\mathbf{v})}\exp(-it\mathbf{v}\cdot\mathbf{k}). \tag{84.3}$$

The total field strength is obtained by inverting the Fourier transform:

$$\mathbf{E} = \int_{-\infty}^{\infty} \mathbf{E}_{\mathbf{k}}\exp(i\mathbf{k}\cdot\mathbf{r})\, d\mathbf{k}. \tag{84.4}$$

The energy loss by the moving particle is just the work done by the force $e\mathbf{E}$ exerted on the particle by the field which it produces. Taking the value of the field at the point occupied by the particle, namely

---

† We assume that the particle moves in a straight line, and thereby neglect scattering, as is always permissible in problems of this type.

If the charge on the particle is ze, then all the formulae pertaining to energy loss in this and the following sections should be multiplied by z^2.

$\mathbf{r} = \mathbf{v}t$, we obtain in the integrand in (84.4) a factor $\exp(it\mathbf{v}\cdot\mathbf{k})$ which cancels with the factor $\exp(-it\mathbf{v}\cdot\mathbf{k})$ in the expression (84.3) for $\mathbf{E_k}$. Hence the force $\mathbf{F}$ is

$$\mathbf{F} = -\frac{ie^2}{2\pi^2}\int\limits_{-\infty}^{\infty}\frac{\mathbf{k}}{k^2\epsilon(\mathbf{k}\cdot\mathbf{v})}\mathrm{d}\mathbf{k}.$$

It is evident that the direction of the force $\mathbf{F}$ is opposite to that of the velocity $\mathbf{v}$; let the latter be the x-direction. Putting $k_x v = \omega$, $q = \sqrt{(k_y^2+k_z^2)}$ and replacing $\mathrm{d}k_y\mathrm{d}k_z$ by $2\pi q\,\mathrm{d}q$, we can write the magnitude of $\mathbf{F}$ as

$$F = \frac{ie^2}{\pi}\int\limits_{-\infty}^{\infty}\int\limits_{0}^{q_0}\frac{q\omega\,\mathrm{d}q\,\mathrm{d}\omega}{\epsilon(\omega)(q^2v^2+\omega^2)}. \tag{84.5}$$

The choice of q_0 is discussed below.

The following remark should be made concerning the integration with respect to ω in formula (84.5). As $\omega \to \infty$ the function $\epsilon(\omega) \to 1$, and the integral is logarithmically divergent. This happens because we ought to have subtracted from the field $\mathbf{E}$ the field which would be present if the particle were moving in a vacuum (i.e. if $\epsilon = 1$); this field evidently does not affect the energy lost by the particle in matter.

If this subtraction were effected, $1/\epsilon$ in the integrand of (84.5) would be diminished by unity, and the integral would converge. The same result can be obtained by taking the integration from $-R$ to $+R$ and then letting R tend to infinity. Since the function $\epsilon'(\omega)$ is even, the real part of the integrand is an odd function of the frequency, and gives zero. The integral of the imaginary part of the integrand converges.

In what follows we shall sometimes find it convenient to use the notation

$$1/\epsilon(\omega) = \eta(\omega) = \eta' + i\eta'', \tag{84.6}$$

with $\eta'(\omega)$ and $\eta''(\omega)$ respectively even and odd functions, and $\eta'' = -\epsilon''/|\epsilon|^2 < 0$. Formula (84.5) can be rewritten in the explicitly real form

$$F = \frac{2e^2}{\pi}\int\limits_{0}^{\infty}\int\limits_{0}^{q_0}\frac{q\omega|\eta''(\omega)|}{(q^2v^2+\omega^2)}\mathrm{d}q\,\mathrm{d}\omega. \tag{84.7}$$

The energy loss per unit path length is the work done by the force over that distance, which is just F; it is called the *stopping power* of the substance with respect to the particle.

According to the general rules of quantum mechanics, the Fourier component of the field whose wave vector is $\mathbf{k}$ transmits to the δ-electron released in ionisation a momentum $\hbar\mathbf{k}$. For sufficiently large q ($\gg \omega_0/v$) we have $k^2 = q^2+\omega^2/v^2 \approx q^2$, so that the momentum transferred is approximately $\hbar\mathbf{q}$. A given value of $\mathbf{q}$ corresponds to collisions with impact parameter $\sim 1/q$. Hence the condition for the macroscopic treatment to be valid is $1/q \gg a$. Accordingly, we take as the upper limit of integration a value q_0

such that $\omega_0/v \ll q_0 \ll 1/a$. The quantity $F(q_0)$ is the energy loss of a fast particle with transfer of momentum not exceeding $\hbar q_0$ to the atomic electron.

Integrating with respect to q in (84.7), we obtain

$$F(q_0) = \frac{2e^2}{\pi v^2}\int\limits_0^\infty \omega|\eta''(\omega)| \log\frac{q_0 v}{\omega}\,d\omega. \tag{84.8}$$

This formula cannot be further transformed in a general manner, but it can be written in a more convenient form as follows. We first calculate the integral

$$\int\limits_0^\infty \omega\eta''(\omega)\,d\omega = -\tfrac{1}{2}i\int\limits_{-\infty}^\infty (\omega/\epsilon)\,d\omega.$$

To do so, we notice that, if the integration is taken in the complex ω-plane along a contour consisting of the real axis and a very large semicircle σ in the upper half-plane, the integral is zero, since the integrand has no poles in the upper half-plane. For large values of ω, the function $\epsilon(\omega)$ is given by formula (59.1):

$$\epsilon(\omega) = 1 - \frac{4\pi e^2 N}{m\omega^2}. \tag{84.9}$$

The integration along the large semicircle σ can be carried out by using this formula, and the result is†

$$-\int\limits_0^\infty \omega\eta''(\omega)\,d\omega = -\frac{2\pi i N e^2}{m}\int\limits_\sigma \frac{d\omega}{\omega} = 2\pi^2 N e^2/m. \tag{84.10}$$

We define a mean frequency of the motion of the atomic electrons by

$$\log\bar{\omega} = \frac{\int\limits_0^\infty \omega\eta''(\omega)\log\omega\,d\omega}{\int\limits_0^\infty \omega\eta''(\omega)\,d\omega}$$

$$= \frac{m}{2\pi^2 N e^2}\int\limits_0^\infty \omega|\eta''(\omega)|\log\omega\,d\omega. \tag{84.11}$$

† This is the same as the value of the integral

$$\int\limits_0^\infty \omega\epsilon''(\omega)\,d\omega$$

(see (62.14)), as it should be, since, as $|\omega| \to \infty$, $|\epsilon| \to 1$ and $\eta'' \to -\epsilon''$.

Then formula (84.8) can be written

$$F(q_0) = (4\pi Ne^4/mv^2)\log(q_0 v/\bar{\omega}). \tag{84.12}$$

The following remark should be made here. It might seem from the form of (84.7) or (84.11) that the main contribution to the ionisation losses (84.12) comes from frequencies at which there is considerable absorption. This is not so; these formulae may contain a considerable contribution from ranges in which ϵ'' is small. The reason is that in such ranges the function $\epsilon(\omega) \approx \epsilon'(\omega)$ may pass through zero. It is seen from formula (84.5) that the zeros of $\epsilon(\omega)$ are poles of the integrand. In reality, of course, $\epsilon''(\omega)$ is not exactly zero, and so the zeros of $\epsilon(\omega)$ are not on the real axis but just below it. Hence, when the expression used for $\epsilon(\omega)$ is real and passes through zero, the contour must be indented upwards at the pole of the integrand, and so a contribution to the integral occurs. For example, if the function $\epsilon(\omega)$ is given by (64.5), the contribution to the retardation (84.12) from the poles $\pm\omega_1$ (where $\epsilon(\omega_1) = 0$) is easily seen, by direct calculation from (84.7), to be $(4\pi Ne^4/mv^2a^2)\log(q_1 v/\omega_1)$.

In order to find the energy loss $F(q_1)$ with transfer of momentum not exceeding some value $\hbar q_1 > \hbar q_0$, we must "join" formula (84.12) to that given by the quantum theory of collisions, corresponding to energy loss by collisions with single atoms. This can be done by using the fact that the ranges of applicability of the two formulae overlap. As we know from the theory of collisions, the energy loss with transfer of momentum in a range of $\hbar dq$ is

$$dF = (4\pi Ne^4/mv^2)\,dq/q, \tag{84.13}$$

and this formula is applicable (in the non-relativistic case) for any value of $q \gg \omega_0/v$ which is compatible with the laws of conservation of momentum and energy, provided that the energy transferred is small compared with the initial energy of the fast particle.† The energy loss with all values of q between q_0 and q_1 is accordingly $(4\pi Ne^4/mv^2)\log(q_1/q_0)$. When this quantity is added to formula (84.12), q_0 is replaced by q_1, so that

$$F(q_1) = (4\pi Ne^4/mv^2)\log(q_1 v/\bar{\omega}). \tag{84.14}$$

If a momentum $\hbar q_1$ large compared with the atomic momenta is given to an atomic electron, its energy is $E_1 = \hbar^2 q_1^2/2m$. Thus we can write

$$F(E_1) = (2\pi Ne^4/mv^2)\log(2mv^2 E_1/\hbar^2\bar{\omega}^2). \tag{84.15}$$

† See *Quantum Mechanics*, §121, Pergamon Press, London, 1958. The "effective retardation" used there differs from F by a factor N.

Formula (84.13) applies to collisions with free electrons. Its range of applicability as hitherto determined ($q \gg \omega_0/v$), however, extends to values of q for which the atomic electrons cannot be regarded as free. The condition for this is $q \gg \omega_0/v_0$, where v_0 is the order of magnitude of the velocity of the majority of the atomic electrons; the energy $\hbar^2 q^2/2m$ of the δ-electron is then large compared with atomic energies.

This formula gives the energy loss of a fast particle (an electron, for example) by ionisation with a transfer of energy not exceeding E_1. It differs from the usual formula derived from a microscopic discussion of collisions, neglecting interactions between atoms,† only by the definition of the "ionisation energy", which is here represented by $\hbar\bar{\omega}$. The mean (with respect to the electrons) ionisation energy of an atom is usually almost independent of its interaction with other atoms, being determined mainly by the electrons of the inner shells, which are almost unaffected by that interaction. Moreover, this quantity appears here only in a logarithm, and so the exact definition of it has even less effect on the magnitude of the energy loss.

The maximum energy which can be transmitted to an atomic electron in its interaction with a fast heavy particle is $2mv^2$, and is small compared with the original energy of the heavy particle.‡ Substituting this value for E_1 in (84.15), we obtain the total ionisation losses of a heavy particle:

$$F = (4\pi Ne^4/mv^2)\log(2mv^2/\hbar\bar{\omega}). \tag{84.16}$$

This differs from the usual formula|| only in the definition of the ionisation energy as $\hbar\bar{\omega}$.

§85. Ionisation losses by fast particles in matter: the relativistic case

At velocities comparable with that of light, the effect of the polarisation of the medium on its stopping power with respect to a fast particle may become very important even in gases.††

To derive the appropriate formulae, we use a method analogous to that used in §84, but it is now necessary to begin from the complete Maxwell's equations. When extraneous charges are present with volume density ρ_{ex}, and extraneous currents with density $\mathbf{j}_{ex}$, these equations are‡‡

$$\operatorname{div}\mathbf{H} = 0, \qquad \mathbf{curl}\,\mathbf{E} = -\frac{1}{c}\frac{\partial \mathbf{H}}{\partial t}, \tag{85.1}$$

$$\operatorname{div}\hat{\epsilon}\mathbf{E} = 4\pi\rho_{ex}, \qquad \mathbf{curl}\,\mathbf{H} = \frac{1}{c}\frac{\partial \hat{\epsilon}\mathbf{E}}{\partial t} + \frac{4\pi}{c}\mathbf{j}_{ex}. \tag{85.2}$$

In the present case the extraneous charge and current distribution are given by

$$\rho_{ex} = e\delta(\mathbf{r} - \mathbf{v}t), \qquad \mathbf{j}_{ex} = e\mathbf{v}\,\delta(\mathbf{r} - \mathbf{v}t). \tag{85.3}$$

---

† See *Quantum Mechanics*, formula (121.13).

‡ When a heavy particle collides with an electron, the maximum transferable momentum $\hbar q_{max}$ is small compared with the momentum Mv of the heavy particle. The change in the energy of this particle is therefore $\mathbf{v}\cdot\hbar\mathbf{q}$, and equating this to the electron energy we have $\hbar^2q^2/2m = \hbar\mathbf{v}\cdot\mathbf{q} \leqslant \hbar vq$, whence $\hbar q_{max} = 2mv$, $E_{1,max} = 2mv^2$.

|| See *Quantum Mechanics*, formula (122.10).

†† This effect was pointed out by E. Fermi (1940), who performed the calculation for the particular case of a gas whose atoms are regarded as harmonic oscillators. The general derivation given here is due to L. Landau.

‡‡ We put $\mu(\omega) \equiv 1$, since matter does not exhibit magnetic properties at the frequencies important as regards ionisation losses.

We introduce scalar and vector potentials, with the usual definitions:

$$\mathbf{H} = \mathbf{curl}\,\mathbf{A}, \qquad \mathbf{E} = -\frac{1}{c}\frac{\partial \mathbf{A}}{\partial t} - \mathbf{grad}\,\phi, \tag{85.4}$$

so that equations (85.1) are satisfied identically. The additional condition

$$\operatorname{div}\mathbf{A} + \frac{1}{c}\frac{\partial \hat{\epsilon}\phi}{\partial t} = 0 \tag{85.5}$$

is imposed on the potentials **A** and ϕ; this is a generalisation of the usual *Lorentz condition* in the theory of radiation. Then, substituting (85.4) in (85.2), we obtain the following equations for the potentials:

$$\begin{aligned} \triangle\mathbf{A} - \frac{\hat{\epsilon}}{c^2}\frac{\partial^2 \mathbf{A}}{\partial t^2} &= -\frac{4\pi}{c}e\mathbf{v}\,\delta(\mathbf{r}-\mathbf{v}t), \\ \hat{\epsilon}\left(\triangle\phi - \frac{\hat{\epsilon}}{c^2}\frac{\partial^2\phi}{\partial t^2}\right) &= -4\pi e\,\delta(\mathbf{r}-\mathbf{v}t). \end{aligned} \tag{85.6}$$

We expand **A** and ϕ as Fourier space integrals. Taking the Fourier components of equations (85.6), we have (cf. §84)

$$\begin{aligned} k^2\mathbf{A}_\mathbf{k} + \frac{\hat{\epsilon}}{c^2}\frac{\partial^2\mathbf{A}_\mathbf{k}}{\partial t^2} &= \frac{e\mathbf{v}}{2\pi^2 c}\exp(-it\mathbf{v}\cdot\mathbf{k}), \\ \hat{\epsilon}\left(k^2\phi_\mathbf{k} + \frac{\hat{\epsilon}}{c^2}\frac{\partial^2\phi_\mathbf{k}}{\partial t^2}\right) &= \frac{e}{2\pi^2}\exp(-it\mathbf{v}\cdot\mathbf{k}). \end{aligned}$$

Hence we see that $\mathbf{A}_\mathbf{k}$ and $\phi_\mathbf{k}$ depend on time through a factor $\exp(-it\mathbf{v}\cdot\mathbf{k})$. We again put $\omega = \mathbf{k}\cdot\mathbf{v} = k_x v$, and obtain

$$\begin{aligned} \mathbf{A}_\mathbf{k} &= \frac{e}{2\pi^2 c}\frac{\mathbf{v}}{k^2 - \omega^2\epsilon(\omega)/c^2}e^{-i\omega t}, \\ \phi_\mathbf{k} &= \frac{e}{2\pi^2\epsilon(\omega)}\frac{1}{k^2 - \omega^2\epsilon(\omega)/c^2}e^{-i\omega t}. \end{aligned} \tag{85.7}$$

The Fourier component of the electric field is

$$\mathbf{E}_\mathbf{k} = i\omega\mathbf{A}_\mathbf{k}/c - i\mathbf{k}\phi_\mathbf{k}. \tag{85.8}$$

From these formulae the force $\mathbf{F} = e\mathbf{E}$ acting on the particle is found in the same way as in §84.† Using the same notation, we now have

$$F = \frac{ie^2}{\pi}\int_{-\infty}^{\infty}\int_{0}^{q_0}\frac{\left(\dfrac{1}{v^2} - \dfrac{\epsilon}{c^2}\right)\omega q\,\mathrm{d}q\,\mathrm{d}\omega}{\epsilon\left[q^2 + \omega^2\left(\dfrac{1}{v^2} - \dfrac{\epsilon}{c^2}\right)\right]}. \tag{85.9}$$

† The magnetic force $e\mathbf{v}\times\mathbf{H}/c$ is seen by symmetry to be zero, and in any case is perpendicular to the velocity of the particle and so does no work on it.

As $c \to \infty$ this formula tends, of course, to (84.5).

Let us first carry out the integration with respect to frequency. In order to effect an integration in the complex ω-plane, we first ascertain the poles of the integrand in the upper half-plane. The function $\epsilon(\omega)$ has no singularity and no zero in this half-plane, and so the required poles can only be the zeros of the expression

$$\omega^2\left(\frac{\epsilon}{c^2}-\frac{1}{v^2}\right)-q^2.$$

We shall show that, for any value of the positive real quantity q^2, this expression vanishes for only one value of ω.

The proof is as follows. Let

$$f(\omega)\equiv\omega^2\left[\frac{\epsilon(\omega)}{c^2}-\frac{1}{v^2}\right].$$

We consider the integral

$$\frac{1}{2\pi i}\int\limits_C \frac{\mathrm{d}f(\omega)}{\mathrm{d}\omega}\frac{\mathrm{d}\omega}{f(\omega)-a},$$

taken along a contour C consisting of the real axis and a large semicircle (Fig. 42). The function $f(\omega)$ has no pole in the upper half-plane or on the real axis;† the integral in question therefore gives the number of zeros of the function $f(\omega)-a$ in the upper half-plane. To calculate its value, we write it as

$$\frac{1}{2\pi i}\int\limits_{C'}\frac{\mathrm{d}f}{f-a}. \tag{85.10}$$

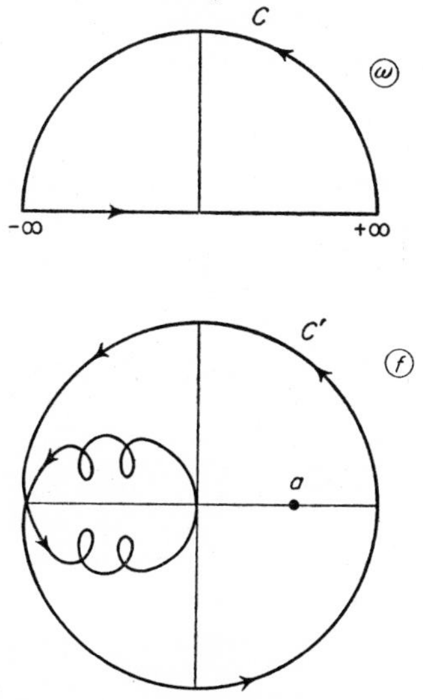

FIG. 42

† For metals $\epsilon(\omega)$ has a pole at $\omega = 0$, but $\omega^2\epsilon$ always tends to zero with ω.

For $\omega = 0$, $f = 0$. For positive real ω we have $\operatorname{im} f > 0$, and for negative real ω $\operatorname{im} f < 0$. At infinity f tends to $-\omega^2[(1/v^2)-(1/c^2)]$, and therefore f goes round a large circle when ω goes round the large semicircle. Hence we see that the path of integration C' in the f-plane is of the kind shown in Fig. 42. Let $a = q^2$ be a positive real number, as in Fig. 42. Then, in going round C', the argument of the complex number $f-a$ changes by 2π, and the integral (85.10) is equal to unity. This completes the proof.†

Furthermore, it is easy to see that this single root of the equation $f(\omega)-q^2 = 0$ lies on the imaginary ω-axis: for purely imaginary ω the function $f(\omega)$, like $\epsilon(\omega)$, is real and takes all values from 0 to ∞, including q^2.

Let us now return to the integral with respect to ω in (85.9):

$$\int\limits_{-\infty}^{\infty} \frac{\left(\dfrac{1}{\epsilon v^2}-\dfrac{1}{c^2}\right)\omega\,\mathrm{d}\omega}{q^2-\omega^2\left(\dfrac{\epsilon}{c^2}-\dfrac{1}{v^2}\right)}.$$

This can be written as the difference between the integral along the contour C and that along the large semicircle. The latter is $\int \mathrm{d}\omega/\omega = i\pi$, and the former is $2\pi i$ times the residue of the integrand at its only pole. Let $\omega(q)$ be the function defined by the equation

$$\omega^2\left(\frac{\epsilon}{c^2}-\frac{1}{v^2}\right) = q^2. \tag{85.11}$$

Then, since the residue of an expression $f(z)/\phi(z)$ at a pole $z = z_0$ is $f(z_0)/\phi'(z_0)$, the integral along C is

$$2\pi i\frac{\omega\left(\dfrac{1}{\epsilon v^2}-\dfrac{1}{c^2}\right)}{-\dfrac{\mathrm{d}}{\mathrm{d}\omega}\left[\omega^2\left(\dfrac{\epsilon}{c^2}-\dfrac{1}{v^2}\right)\right]} = 2\pi i\frac{\omega\left(\dfrac{1}{\epsilon v^2}-\dfrac{1}{c^2}\right)}{-\mathrm{d}q^2/\mathrm{d}\omega}.$$

Collecting these expressions and substituting in (85.9), we have

$$F = e^2\int\limits_0^{q_0}\left[\frac{\omega\left(\dfrac{1}{\epsilon v^2}-\dfrac{1}{c^2}\right)}{q\,\mathrm{d}q/\mathrm{d}\omega}+1\right]q\,\mathrm{d}q$$

† If a is negative the argument of $f-a$ changes by 4π on going round C', so that the integral (85.10) is equal to 2, i.e. the function $f(\omega)+|a|$ has two zeros in the upper half-plane.

or, replacing the integration with respect to q in the first term by one with respect to ω,

$$F = e^2 \int\limits_{\omega(0)}^{\omega(q_0)} \left[\frac{1}{v^2\epsilon(\omega)} - \frac{1}{c^2}\right]\omega\, d\omega + \tfrac{1}{2}e^2 q_0{}^2$$

$$= \frac{e^2}{v^2} \int\limits_{\omega(0)}^{\omega(q_0)} \left[\frac{1}{\epsilon(\omega)} - 1\right]\omega\, d\omega + \tfrac{1}{2}e^2 q_0{}^2 +$$

$$+ \tfrac{1}{2}e^2\left(\frac{1}{v^2} - \frac{1}{c^2}\right)[\omega^2(q_0) - \omega^2(0)]. \qquad (85.12)$$

Large values of q correspond to large absolute values ω of the root of equation (85.11). Using therefore the expression (84.9) for $\epsilon(\omega)$, we find

$$\omega^2(q_0) = -\frac{v^2}{\beta^2}\left(q_0{}^2 + \frac{4\pi N e^2}{mc^2}\right),$$

where we have put $\beta = \sqrt{[1-v^2/c^2]}$. Substitution in (85.12) gives

$$F = \frac{e^2}{v^2} \int\limits_{\omega(0)}^{ivq_0/\beta} \left[\frac{1}{\epsilon(\omega)} - 1\right]\omega\, d\omega - \frac{2\pi N e^4}{mc^2} - \frac{e^2\beta^2}{2v^2}\omega^2(0); \qquad (85.13)$$

in the integral, only the leading term ivq_0/β need be retained in $\omega(q_0)$.

The integration in (85.13) is over purely imaginary values of ω. We use the real variable $\omega'' \equiv \omega/i$, with the lower limit $\xi \equiv \omega(0)/i$, and again put $1/\epsilon = \eta$ (84.6). The required integral is

$$-\int\limits_{\xi}^{vq/\beta} [\eta(i\omega'') - 1]\omega''\, d\omega''.$$

The values of the function $\eta(\omega)$ on the imaginary axis can be expressed in terms of its imaginary part on the real axis:

$$\eta(i\omega'') - 1 = \frac{2}{\pi}\int\limits_0^\infty \frac{x\eta''(x)}{x^2 + \omega''^2}\, dx$$

(cf. (62.17)). Hence the integral is (if we neglect x in comparison with vq_0)

$$\frac{2}{\pi}\int\limits_0^\infty \int\limits_\xi^{vq_0/\beta} \frac{x|\eta''(x)|\omega''\, d\omega''\, dx}{x^2 + \omega''^2} = \frac{1}{\pi}\int\limits_0^\infty x|\eta''(x)| \log\frac{v^2 q_0{}^2}{\beta^2(x^2+\xi^2)}\, dx.$$

We substitute this result in (85.13), and for simplicity put

$$\log \Omega \equiv \overline{\tfrac{1}{2}\log(\omega^2+\xi^2)}, \tag{85.14}$$

where the bar denotes an averaging with weight $\omega|\eta''(\omega)|$, as in (84.11). Then

$$F(q_0) = \frac{4\pi Ne^4}{mv^2}\log\frac{q_0 v}{\beta\Omega} - \frac{2\pi Ne^4}{mc^2} + \frac{e^2\beta^2}{2v^2}\xi^2. \tag{85.15}$$

Two cases must be considered in the further examination of this formula. Let us first suppose that the medium is a dielectric, and that the velocity of the particle satisfies the condition

$$v^2 < c^2/\epsilon_0, \tag{85.16}$$

where $\epsilon_0 = \epsilon(0)$ is the electrostatic value of the dielectric permeability. On the imaginary axis the function $\epsilon(\omega)$ decreases monotonically from $\epsilon_0 > 1$ for $\omega = 0$ to 1 for $\omega = i\infty$. The expression on the left-hand side of equation (85.11) therefore increases monotonically from 0 to ∞, and for $q = 0$ (85.11) gives $\omega = 0$. Thus we must put $\xi = 0$ in (85.15); then Ω becomes the mean atomic frequency $\bar{\omega}$ (84.11), and

$$F(q_0) = \frac{4\pi Ne^4}{mv^2}\left[\log\frac{q_0 v}{\beta\bar{\omega}} - \frac{v^2}{2c^2}\right]. \tag{85.17}$$

For $v \ll c$ this formula becomes (84.12), as it should.

The value of q_0 is such that $q_0 \ll 1/a$, where a is the order of magnitude of the distances between the atoms (in solids and liquids equal to the dimension of the atoms). In order to extend the formula to higher values of the transferred momentum and energy, it must be "joined" to the formulae of the ordinary theory of collisions, as in §84, but the joining must now be carried out in two stages. First, using formula (84.13), we enter the range of q corresponding to energy transfers large compared with atomic energies but not yet relativistic. Formula (85.17) is unchanged in form, but now involves the δ-electron energy $\hbar^2 q^2/2m$. Calling this E_1, we have

$$F(E_1) = \frac{2\pi Ne^4}{mv^2}\left[\log\frac{2mv^2 E_1}{\beta^2\hbar^2\bar{\omega}^2} - \frac{v^2}{c^2}\right]. \tag{85.18}$$

We can now go on to the relativistic values of E_1 by using a formula of relativistic collision theory, according to which the stopping power with energy transfer between E' and $E'+\mathrm{d}E'$ is

$$(2\pi Ne^4/mv^2)\,\mathrm{d}E'/E' \tag{85.19}$$

if E' is small compared with the maximum transfer $E_{1,\max}$ compatible with the laws of conservation of momentum and energy for a collision between the fast particle concerned and a free electron. (In the non-relativistic case, this formula is the same as (84.13).) Since the integration of (85.19) gives a term in $\log E'$, it is clear that formula (85.18) is unchanged in form, and it is therefore valid for all $E_1 \ll E_{1,\max}$.

The maximum energy transfer to an electron from a heavy particle is† $E_{1,\max} \approx 2mv^2/\beta^2$. If $E_{1,\max}$ is small compared with the total energy E of the fast particle (i.e. if $E \ll M^2c^2/m$), the differential expression for the energy lost by free electrons is

$$\frac{2\pi Ne^4}{mv^2}\left(\frac{1}{E'}-\frac{\beta^2}{2mc^2}\right)\mathrm{d}E'$$

for all E', whatever the kind of heavy particle concerned. The energy loss additional to (85.18), with energy transfer from E_1 to $E_{1,\max}$ (with $E_1 \ll E_{1,\max}$) is then

$$\frac{2\pi Ne^4}{mv^2}\left(\log\frac{E_{1,\max}}{E_1}-\frac{\beta^2E_{1,\max}}{2mc^2}\right) = \frac{2\pi Ne^4}{mv^2}\left(\log\frac{2mv^2}{\beta^2E_1}-\frac{v^2}{c^2}\right). \tag{85.20}$$

Adding this to (85.18), we find the total stopping power with respect to the heavy particle:

$$F = \frac{4\pi Ne^4}{mv^2}\left(\log\frac{2mv^2}{\beta^2\hbar\bar{\omega}}-\frac{v^2}{c^2}\right). \tag{85.21}$$

Formulae (85.18) and (85.21) differ from those of the usual theory only in that the "ionisation energy" is $\hbar\bar{\omega}$.

Let us now turn to the second case, namely that where

$$v^2 > c^2/\epsilon_0, \tag{85.22}$$

which, in particular, always holds for metals, where $\epsilon_0 = \infty$. The expression $\omega^2(\epsilon/c^2-1/v^2)$ on the left-hand side of equation (85.11) then has two zeros on the imaginary ω-axis, one at $\omega = 0$ and the other at $\omega = i\xi$, where ξ is defined by

$$\epsilon(i\xi) = c^2/v^2. \tag{85.23}$$

In the range from 0 to $i\xi$ the expression $\omega^2(\epsilon/c^2-1/v^2)$ is negative, and for $|\omega| > \xi$ it takes all positive values from 0 to ∞. As $q \to 0$, therefore, the root of equation (85.11) in this case tends to ξ, which is the value to be substituted in (85.14) and (85.15).

Two limiting cases may be considered. If ξ is small compared with the atomic frequencies ω_0, then the last term in (85.15) may be neglected, and $\Omega \approx \bar{\omega}$. Thus we return to formula (85.17). The opposite limiting case, where $\xi \gg \omega_0$, is of particular interest. Since, for large ξ, the function $\epsilon(i\xi)$ tends to 1, it is evident from (85.23) that this case corresponds to ultra-relativistic velocities of the particle. Using formula (84.9) for $\epsilon(\omega)$, we can write equation (85.23) as $1+4\pi Ne^2/m\xi^2 = c^2/v^2$, whence

$$\xi^2 = 4\pi Ne^2v^2/mc^2\beta^2 \approx 4\pi Ne^2/m\beta^2.$$

† See *The Classical Theory of Fields*, §2–5, Addison-Wesley Press, Cambridge (Mass.), 1951; Pergamon Press, London, 1959.

As the velocity of the particle increases, the condition $\xi \gg \omega_0$ is ultimately fulfilled in any medium, i.e. whatever the electron density N (even in a gas). The velocity required is, however, the greater, the smaller N, i.e. the more rarefied the medium.

From (85.14) we then have simply $\Omega \approx \xi$. Putting also $v \approx c$, we find that the last two terms in (85.15) cancel, leaving

$$F(q_0) = (2\pi Ne^4/mc^2) \log (mc^2 q_0^2/4\pi Ne^2).$$

Extending this formula, in the same manner as above, to large values of the momentum and energy transfer, we find the following expression for the energy loss of an ultra-relativistic particle with an energy transfer not exceeding E_1 ($\ll E_{1,\max}$):

$$F(E_1) = (2\pi Ne^4/mc^2) \log (m^2c^2E_1/2\pi Ne^2\hbar^2). \tag{85.24}$$

This result is considerably different from that obtained in the ordinary collision theory, which neglects the polarisation of the medium. According to that theory, in the ultra-relativistic range the stopping power $F(E_1)$ continues to increase (through only logarithmically) with the energy of the particle. The polarisation of the medium results in a screening of the charge, and the increase in the losses is thereby finally stopped; it tends to the constant value (independent of β) given by formula (85.24).

For heavy particles a formula can also be derived for the total stopping power with any energy transfer up to $E_{1,\max}$ (if the latter is small compared with the energy of the particle itself). Again using the expression (85.20), in which we can now put $v = c$, we find

$$F = \frac{2\pi Ne^4}{mc^2}\left[\log\frac{m^3c^4}{\pi Ne^2\hbar^2\beta^2} - 1\right]. \tag{85.25}$$

We see that the total stopping power continues to increase with the velocity of the particle, owing to "close" collisions with a large energy transfer, for which the polarisation of the medium has no screening effect. This increase, however, is rather slower than that given by the theory when the polarisation is neglected.

It may also be noted that the presence of the electron density N in the argument of the logarithm in formulae (85.24) and (85.25) results in the following property of energy losses of ultra-relativistic particles: when such a particle passes through different substances containing the same number of electrons per unit surface area, the losses are smaller in media with larger N.

Finally, we may point out that a measurement of the energy losses of fast particles in matter makes possible, in principle, the determination of the function $\epsilon(i\xi)$ for the substance concerned. It is easy to show that the exact expression for F for the case (85.22) is such that

$$\frac{\mathrm{d}[(F - F_0)v^2]}{\mathrm{d}(v^2)} = -\frac{e^2\xi^2}{2c^2}, \tag{85.26}$$

where F_0 is the quantity given by formula (85.18) or (85.21). F is measured; the derivative $d(F_0v^2)/d(v^2)$ contains only the known quantities N and v, and can be calculated. Thus, using (85.26), each value of ξ can be related to a value of v, and the value of $\epsilon(i\xi)$ can then be calculated from (85.23).

§86. Cherenkov radiation

A charged particle moving in a transparent medium emits, in certain circumstances, an unusual type of radiation, first observed by P. A. CHERENKOV and S. I. VAVILOV, and theoretically interpreted by I. E. TAMM and I. M. FRANK (1937). It must be emphasised that this radiation is entirely unrelated to the bremsstrahlung which is almost always emitted by a rapidly moving electron. The latter radiation is emitted by the moving electron itself when it collides with atoms. The Cherenkov effect, however, involves radiation emitted by the medium under the action of the field of the particle moving in it. The distinction between the two types of radiation appears with particular clarity when the particle has a very large mass: the bremsstrahlung disappears, but the Cherenkov radiation is unaffected.

The wave vector and frequency of an electromagnetic wave propagated in a transparent medium are related by $k = n\omega/c$, where $n = \sqrt{\epsilon}$ is the refractive index, which is real.† We have seen that the frequency of the Fourier component of the field of a particle moving uniformly in the x-direction in a medium is related to the x-component of the wave vector by $\omega = k_xv$. If this component is a freely propagated wave, these two relations must be consistent. Since $k > k_x$, it follows that we must have

$$v > c/n(\omega). \tag{86.1}$$

Thus radiation of frequency ω occurs if the velocity of the particle exceeds the phase velocity of waves of that frequency in the medium concerned.

Let θ be the angle between the direction of motion of the particle and the direction of emission. We have $k_x = k \cos\theta = (n\omega/c)\cos\theta$ and, since $k_x = \omega/v$, we find that

$$\cos\theta = c/nv. \tag{86.2}$$

Thus a definite value of the angle θ corresponds to radiation of a given frequency. That is, the radiation of each frequency is emitted forwards, and is distributed over the surface of a cone of vertical angle 2θ, where θ is given by (86.2). The distributions of the radiation in angle and in frequency are thus related in a definite manner.

---

† We again suppose the medium isotropic and non-magnetic. The Cherenkov radiation in an anisotropic medium has been discussed by V. L. GINZBURG, *Zhurnal éksperimental'noĭ i teoreticheskoĭ fiziki* **10**, 608, 1940; A. A. KOLOMENSKIĬ, *Doklady Akademii Nauk SSSR* **86**, 1097, 1952; M. I. KAGANOV, *Zhurnal tekhnicheskoĭ fiziki* **23**, 507, 1953.

A review of various cases in the theory of Cherenkov radiation and an extensive bibliography is given by B. M. BOLOTOVSKIĬ, *Uspekhi fizicheskikh nauk* **62**, 201, 1957.

The emission of electromagnetic waves, if it occurs, involves a loss of energy by the moving particle. This loss forms part, through a small part, of the total losses calculated in §85.† In this sense the name "ionisation losses" is not quite accurate. We shall now find the corresponding part of the total losses, and thus determine the intensity of the Cherenkov radiation.

According to (85.9), the energy loss in the frequency interval $d\omega$ is

$$dF = -d\omega \frac{ie^2}{\pi} \sum \omega \left(\frac{1}{c^2} - \frac{1}{\epsilon v^2} \right) \int \frac{q\,dq}{q^2 - \omega^2 \left(\dfrac{\epsilon}{c^2} - \dfrac{1}{v^2} \right)},$$

where the summation is over terms with $\omega = \pm|\omega|$. We introduce as a new variable

$$\xi = q^2 - \omega^2 \left(\frac{\epsilon}{c^2} - \frac{1}{v^2} \right).$$

Then

$$dF = -d\omega \frac{ie^2}{2\pi} \sum \omega \left(\frac{1}{c^2} - \frac{1}{\epsilon v^2} \right) \int \frac{d\xi}{\xi}.$$

In integrating along the real ξ-axis we must pass round the singular point $\xi = 0$ (for which $q^2 + k_x{}^2 = k^2$) in some manner, which is determined by the fact that, although we suppose $\epsilon(\omega)$ real (the medium being transparent), it actually has a small imaginary part, which is positive for $\omega > 0$ and negative for $\omega < 0$. Accordingly, ξ has a small negative or positive imaginary part, and the path of integration ought to pass below or above the real axis respectively. This means that, when the path of integration is displaced to the real axis, we must pass below or above the singular point respectively. This gives a contribution to dF, and the real parts cancel in the sum. Indenting the path of integration with infinitesimal semicircles, we find

$$\Sigma \omega \int d\xi / \xi = 2i\pi\omega.$$

Thus the final formula is

$$dF = \frac{e^2}{c^2} \left(1 - \frac{c^2}{v^2 n^2} \right) \omega\, d\omega, \tag{86.3}$$

which gives the intensity of the radiation in a frequency interval $d\omega$. According to (86.2), this radiation is emitted in an angle interval

$$d\theta = \frac{c}{v n^2 \sin\theta} \frac{dn}{d\omega} d\omega. \tag{86.4}$$

† The bremsstrahlung is not included therein.

The total intensity of the radiation is obtained by integrating (86.3) over all frequencies for which the medium is transparent.

It is easy to determine the polarisation of the Cherenkov radiation. As we see from (85.7) the vector potential of the radiation field is parallel to the velocity **v**. The magnetic field $\mathbf{H}_\mathbf{k} = i\mathbf{k}\times\mathbf{A}_\mathbf{k}$ is therefore perpendicular to the plane containing **v** and the ray direction **k**. The electric field (in the "wave region") is perpendicular to the magnetic field, and therefore lies in that plane.

In connection with our discussion of the radiation emitted by a particle moving in matter, we may mention another effect whose existence has been deduced by V. L. GINZBURG and I. M. FRANK: a particle must emit radiation on passing from one medium to another. This "transition" radiation is in principle different from the Cherenkov radiation, in that it must occur for any velocity of the particle, not necessarily exceeding the phase velocity of light in the medium. It is also unrelated to the bremsstrahlung which also occurs when charged particles are incident on a surface separating two media. As with Cherenkov radiation, the distinction is particularly clear for a particle of infinite mass, for which the bremsstrahlung is zero but the transition radiation is not.†

† A simple derivation of the formulae for the transition radiation is given by G. M. GARIBYAN, *Zhurnal éksperimental'noĭ i teoreticheskoĭ fiziki* **33**, 1403, 1957; *Soviet Physics JETP* **6 (33)**, 1079, 1958.

CHAPTER XIII

ELECTROMAGNETIC FLUCTUATIONS

§87. Current fluctuations in linear circuits

WE MAY apply the general theory of fluctuations† to the interesting problem of current fluctuations in linear electric circuits, first considered by H. NYQUIST (1928).

The current fluctuations are free electrical oscillations in the conductor (i.e. they occur in the absence of any externally applied e.m.f.). In a closed linear circuit the oscillations of greatest interest are, of course, those in which a non-zero total current J flows in the conductor. In what follows we shall assume that the condition for a quasi-steady state holds: the dimensions of the circuit are small compared with the wavelength $\lambda \sim c/\omega$. Then the total current J is the same at every point in the circuit, and is a function of time only.

In order to find the spectral resolution of the current fluctuations, we take J as the quantity x which appears in the general formulae of SP §124. In order to ascertain the corresponding meaning of α, let us suppose that an external e.m.f. $\mathscr{E}$ acts on the circuit. Then the rate of dissipation of energy in the circuit is $Q = J\mathscr{E}$. A comparison with SP (124.7) shows that $\dot{f} = -\mathscr{E}$, or, if in this linear relation we take f and $\mathscr{E}$ proportional to $e^{-i\omega t}$, $\mathscr{E} = i\omega f$. But the current and the e.m.f. in a linear circuit are related by $\mathscr{E} = ZJ$, where $Z(\omega)$ is the impedance of the circuit; see §47. Hence $J = \mathscr{E}/Z = i\omega f/Z$, whence we conclude that $\alpha(\omega) = i\omega/Z(\omega)$. Its imaginary part is $\alpha'' = \mathrm{im}\,(i\omega/Z) = \omega R/|Z|^2$, where $R(\omega) \equiv \mathrm{re}\, Z(\omega)$. The formulae below do not depend on the particular nature of the phenomena which result in the dispersion of the circuit resistance.

From SP (123.8) we now find for the required current fluctuations

$$(J^2)_\omega = \frac{\hbar\omega}{2\pi|Z|^2} R \coth\frac{\hbar\omega}{2T}. \tag{87.1}$$

This formula can be written in another form by regarding the current fluctuation as the result of a "random" e.m.f. $\mathscr{E}_\omega = Z(\omega)J_\omega$. This is given by

$$(\mathscr{E}^2)_\omega = \frac{\hbar\omega}{2\pi} R(\omega) \coth\frac{\hbar\omega}{2T}. \tag{87.2}$$

† See *Statistical Physics*, §123, Pergamon Press, London, 1958. Sections and formulae in this book will be referred to by means of the prefix SP.

In the classical case ($\hbar\omega \ll T$) we have

$$(\mathscr{E}^2)_\omega = TR(\omega)/\pi. \tag{87.3}$$

§88. Electromagnetic field fluctuations

The electromagnetic quantities **E**, **H**, . . . which appear in macroscopic electrodynamics are obtained by an averaging process, which can be regarded as consisting of two operations. If we take, for clarity, the classical view, then we have the averaging over a physically infinitesimal volume, the particles in that volume being in fixed positions, followed by the averaging with respect to the motion of the particles. In considering electromagnetic fluctuations we are concerned with the oscillations in time of quantities averaged over physically infinitesimal volumes, and the quantities discussed below will be of this kind.

It should be noted that, if we take the quantum view, we can consider the volume average of the operator of a quantity, but not that of the quantity itself, and the second stage in the averaging consists in determining the expectation value of this operator by the use of quantum probabilities. Strictly speaking, therefore, the quantities **E**, **H**, . . . mentioned below should be regarded as operators of quantum mechanics, but this does not affect the final results, and to simplify the formulae we shall regard **E**, **H**, . . . as classical quantities.

As a result of fluctuations in the position and motion of the charges in a body, spontaneous local electric and magnetic moments occur in it; let the values of these moments per unit volume be respectively $\mathbf{K}/4\pi$ and $\mathbf{L}/4\pi$. They are in a sense analogous to the spontaneous polarisation of pyroelectrics and the spontaneous magnetisation of ferromagnetics, but of course differ in that they give zero on averaging. The relation between the induction and the field for these electric and magnetic fluctuations is given by

$$D_i = \hat{\epsilon}_{ik} E_k + K_i, \qquad B_i = \hat{\mu}_{ik} H_k + L_i, \tag{88.1}$$

and their "Fourier components" are

$$\begin{aligned} D_{i\omega} &= \epsilon_{ik}(\omega) E_{k\omega} + K_{i\omega}, \\ B_{i\omega} &= \mu_{ik}(\omega) H_{k\omega} + L_{i\omega}. \end{aligned} \tag{88.2}$$

Maxwell's equations are

$$(\mathbf{curl}\,\mathbf{E}_\omega)_i = (i\omega/c)(\mu_{ik} H_{k\omega} + L_{i\omega}), \tag{88.3}$$

$$(\mathbf{curl}\,\mathbf{H}_\omega)_i = -(i\omega/c)(\epsilon_{ik} E_{k\omega} + K_{i\omega}). \tag{88.4}$$

We call **K** and **L** the *extraneous fluctuating inductions*, but this name is, of course, conventional and refers to the way in which these quantities are formally defined rather than to their physical nature.

In order to use the general formulae derived in SP §124 we must establish the relations between the electromagnetic quantities under consideration and the quantities x_a, f_a which appear in the general theory. This is done as follows. We suppose, in a purely formal manner, that the quantities **K** and **L** are not spontaneously arising moments but the result of an external action, namely the placing of certain extraneous electric charges and currents in the body, and calculate the consequent change in the energy of the body.

To do this we observe that the equation of conservation of energy, in the form which follows from Maxwell's equations, is

$$\int \frac{1}{4\pi}\left\{\mathbf{E}\cdot\frac{\partial \mathbf{D}}{\partial t} + \mathbf{H}\cdot\frac{\partial \mathbf{B}}{\partial t}\right\} \mathrm{d}V = -\frac{c}{4\pi}\oint \mathbf{E}\times\mathbf{H}\cdot \mathrm{d}\mathbf{f},$$

or, substituting from (88.1),

$$\int \frac{1}{4\pi}\left\{E_i\frac{\partial}{\partial t}(\hat{\epsilon}_{ik}E_k) + H_i\frac{\partial}{\partial t}(\hat{\mu}_{ik}H_k)\right\}$$

$$= -\frac{c}{4\pi}\oint \mathbf{E}\times\mathbf{H}\cdot \mathrm{d}\mathbf{f} - \frac{1}{4\pi}\int\left\{\mathbf{E}\cdot\frac{\partial \mathbf{K}}{\partial t} + \mathbf{H}\cdot\frac{\partial \mathbf{L}}{\partial t}\right\}\mathrm{d}V.$$

Hence we see that the change in energy due to the "external action" considered is

$$-\frac{1}{4\pi}\int\left\{\mathbf{E}\cdot\frac{\partial \mathbf{K}}{\partial t} + \mathbf{H}\cdot\frac{\partial \mathbf{L}}{\partial t}\right\}\mathrm{d}V. \tag{88.5}$$

In SP §124 we considered a discrete series of fluctuating quantities x_a, whereas here we have a continuous series (the values of the fields at every point in the body). We shall evade this unimportant difficulty in a purely formal manner, by dividing the volume of the body into small but finite portions ΔV and taking some mean values of the fields in each portion; the passage to infinitesimal portions will be made in the final formulae. Thus the integral in (88.5) is replaced by the sum

$$-\frac{1}{4\pi}\sum\left\{\mathbf{E}\cdot\frac{\partial \mathbf{K}}{\partial t} + \mathbf{H}\cdot\frac{\partial \mathbf{L}}{\partial t}\right\}\Delta V,$$

taken over all the portions ΔV.

Comparing this expression with SP (124.7), we see that, if the x_a are taken to be the components of the vectors $\mathbf{E}\Delta V/4\pi$, $\mathbf{H}\Delta V/4\pi$ in each portion ΔV, then the corresponding f_a will be the components of the vectors **K** and **L**:

$$\begin{aligned} x_a &\to \mathbf{E}\Delta V/4\pi, \qquad && \mathbf{H}\Delta V/4\pi; \\ f_a &\to \mathbf{K}, && \mathbf{L}. \end{aligned} \tag{88.6}$$

The relations SP (124.11)

$$f_{a\omega} = \sum_b \alpha^{-1}{}_{ab}(\omega)x_{b\omega}, \tag{88.7}$$

which give the relation between f_ω and x_ω, correspond to Maxwell's equations (88.3), (88.4), and so we have

$$\begin{aligned} K_{i\omega} &= -\epsilon_{ik}E_{k\omega} + (ic/\omega)(\mathbf{curl}\,\mathbf{H}_\omega)_i, \\ L_{i\omega} &= -\mu_{ik}H_{k\omega} - (ic/\omega)(\mathbf{curl}\,\mathbf{E}_\omega)_i. \end{aligned} \tag{88.8}$$

The coefficients $\alpha^{-1}{}_{ab}$ are found by comparing (88.8) with (88.7), using the definitions (88.6); the suffixes a and b denumerate both the components of the vectors **E**, **H** and the portions ΔV.

The curl operators in (88.8) are to be regarded as difference operators, defined with respect to a discrete set of points (say the centres of the portions ΔV). The actual form of these operators is, however, of no importance, since it is here sufficient to note that the operators acting on $\mathbf{H}_\omega$ and $\mathbf{E}_\omega$ in (88.8) are purely imaginary and differ only in sign. This means that the relations $\alpha^{-1}{}_{ab} = (\alpha^{-1}{}_{ba})^*$ are satisfied by the coefficients $\alpha^{-1}{}_{ab}$ which relate the values of **K** and **L** at a given point to those of **H** and **E** respectively at various points.

According to the general formula SP (124.12) it therefore follows at once that

$$(K_{i1}L_{k2})_\omega = 0, \tag{88.9}$$

where the suffixes 1 and 2 signify that the quantities are taken at the points $\mathbf{r}_1$ and $\mathbf{r}_2$ respectively. Formula (88.9) is valid whether $\mathbf{r}_1 = \mathbf{r}_2$ or not.

Next, from the first equation (88.8), using (88.6), we see that the coefficients $\alpha^{-1}{}_{ab}$ which relate $K_{i\omega}$ and $E_{k\omega}$ are $-\epsilon_{ik}\,4\pi/\Delta V$ if $\mathbf{K}_\omega$ and $\mathbf{E}_\omega$ refer to the same point in space, and zero otherwise. By SP (124.12) we therefore have

$$(K_{i1}K_{k2})_\omega = 0 \qquad (\mathbf{r}_1 \neq \mathbf{r}_2),$$

$$(K_iK_k)_\omega = i\hbar(\epsilon_{ki}{}^* - \epsilon_{ik})\frac{1}{\Delta V}\coth(\hbar\omega/2T).$$

Passing now to the limit $\Delta V \to 0$, we can evidently write both these formulae together as

$$(K_{i1}K_{k2})_\omega = i\hbar(\epsilon_{ki}{}^* - \epsilon_{ik})\,\delta(\mathbf{r}_2 - \mathbf{r}_1)\coth(\hbar\omega/2T), \tag{88.10}$$

where $\mathbf{r}_1$ and $\mathbf{r}_2$ refer to any two points in the body. In what follows we shall assume that the body is not in an external magnetic field. Then $\epsilon_{ik} = \epsilon_{ki}$, and (88.10) can be written

$$(K_{i1}K_{k2})_\omega = 2\hbar\epsilon_{ik}''\,\delta(\mathbf{r}_2 - \mathbf{r}_1)\coth(\hbar\omega/2T). \tag{88.11}$$

In an entirely similar manner we may derive the formula

$$(L_{i1}L_{k2})_\omega = 2\hbar\mu_{ik}''\,\delta(\mathbf{r}_2 - \mathbf{r}_1)\coth(\hbar\omega/2T). \tag{88.12}$$

Thus the fluctuations of the "extraneous" inductions at two points in the body are correlated only in the limit when the two points coincide ($\mathbf{r}_2 \to \mathbf{r}_1$). This limit, of course, must be taken in the macroscopic sense, and the above statement really means that the correlation extends only to distances comparable with the dimension of the atoms. It is most important to observe that the correlation formulae for the extraneous inductions do not depend on the shape of the body; in this sense the formulae are universally valid.

Formulae (88.11) and (88.12) can be put in another form for fairly low frequencies (the *quasi-static* range), when the tensor ϵ_{ik} can be expressed in terms of the constant (frequency-independent) conductivity tensor σ_{ik} by

$$\epsilon_{ik} = 4\pi i\sigma_{ik}/\omega. \tag{88.13}$$

We then introduce the quantity $\mathbf{j} = (1/4\pi)\partial\mathbf{K}/\partial t$, or

$$\mathbf{j}_\omega = -i\omega\mathbf{K}_\omega/4\pi. \tag{88.14}$$

The significance of this quantity is seen from the resulting form of equation (88.4):

$$(\mathbf{curl}\,\mathbf{H}_\omega)_i = (4\pi/c)(\sigma_{ik}E_{k\omega} + j_{i\omega}). \tag{88.15}$$

From this we find that the total fluctuation of the current density is $\sigma_{ik}E_k+j_i$, so that the vector $\mathbf{j}$ is the "extraneous" current which is not related to the electric field $\mathbf{E}$. For frequencies at which (88.13) holds and not too low temperatures we have $T \gg \hbar\omega$, so that $\coth(\hbar\omega/2T) \approx 2T/\hbar\omega$. Formula (88.11) thus becomes

$$(j_{i1}j_{k2})_\omega = (T/\pi)\sigma_{ik}\,\delta(\mathbf{r}_2 - \mathbf{r}_1). \tag{88.16}$$

Formula (88.16) was derived, in another manner, by M. A. Leontovich and S. M. Rytov (1952), and formulae (88.11) and (88.12) by S. M. Rytov (1953). Together with equations (88.3) and (88.4), these equations in principle solve the problem of calculating the electromagnetic fluctuations in any body. The solution proceeds as follows. Regarding $\mathbf{K}_\omega$ and $\mathbf{L}_\omega$ as known functions of the co-ordinates, we solve equations (88.3), (88.4) for $\mathbf{E}_\omega$ and $\mathbf{H}_\omega$, taking into account the appropriate boundary conditions: the tangential components of $\mathbf{E}_\omega$ and $\mathbf{H}_\omega$ are continuous at the surface of the body (outside the body, of course, $\mathbf{K} = \mathbf{L} = 0$, but $\mathbf{E}$ and $\mathbf{H}$ are not zero). We thus obtain $\mathbf{E}_\omega$ and $\mathbf{H}_\omega$ as linear functionals of $\mathbf{K}_\omega$ and $\mathbf{L}_\omega$. Accordingly, any quantity quadratic (or bilinear) in $\mathbf{E}_\omega$ and $\mathbf{H}_\omega$ can be expressed in terms of quadratic functionals of $\mathbf{K}_\omega$ and $\mathbf{L}_\omega$, and the mean values are calculated from formulae (88.11), (88.12); $\mathbf{K}_\omega$ and $\mathbf{L}_\omega$ do not appear in the final result.

As an example, let us consider electromagnetic fluctuations in an infinite isotropic medium (S. M. Rytov, 1953). We assume the magnetic permeability of the medium to be unity. Then $\mu'' = 0$, and we must put $\mathbf{L} = 0$ also. Thus equations (88.3) and (88.4) become

$$\begin{aligned}\mathbf{curl}\,\mathbf{E}_\omega &= i\omega\mathbf{H}_\omega/c,\\ \mathbf{curl}\,\mathbf{H}_\omega &= -i\omega(\epsilon\mathbf{E}_\omega + \mathbf{K}_\omega)/c,\end{aligned} \tag{88.17}$$

and

$$(K_{i1}K_{k2})_\omega = 2\hbar\epsilon''\,\delta_{ik}\,\delta(\mathbf{r}_2 - \mathbf{r}_1)\coth(\hbar\omega/2T). \tag{88.18}$$

We write $\mathbf{K}_\omega$ as a spatial Fourier integral:

$$\mathbf{K}_\omega(\mathbf{r}) = \int_{-\infty}^{\infty} \mathbf{g}_\omega(\mathbf{p}) \exp(i\mathbf{p}\cdot\mathbf{r})\, d\mathbf{p}. \tag{88.19}$$

Then

$$\mathbf{g}_\omega(\mathbf{p}) = \frac{1}{(2\pi)^3} \int_{-\infty}^{\infty} \mathbf{K}_\omega(\mathbf{r}) \exp(-i\mathbf{p}\cdot\mathbf{r})\, d\mathbf{r},$$

$$\mathbf{g}_\omega^*(\mathbf{p}) = \mathbf{g}_{-\omega}(-\mathbf{p}).$$

Let us determine the correlation function for the components $\mathbf{g}_\omega(\mathbf{p})$. To do so, we write the product $g_{i\omega}(\mathbf{p})g_{k\omega'}(\mathbf{p}')$ as a double integral:

$$g_{i\omega}(\mathbf{p})g_{k\omega'}(\mathbf{p}') = \frac{1}{(2\pi)^6} \int_{-\infty}^{\infty}\int_{-\infty}^{\infty} K_{i\omega}(\mathbf{r}_1)K_{k\omega'}(\mathbf{r}_2) \exp[-i(\mathbf{p}\cdot\mathbf{r}_1 + \mathbf{p}'\cdot\mathbf{r}_2)]\, d\mathbf{r}_1\, d\mathbf{r}_2.$$

Averaging by means of the formula

$$\overline{K_{i\omega}(\mathbf{r}_1)K_{k\omega'}(\mathbf{r}_2)} = (K_{i1}K_{k2})_\omega\, \delta(\omega + \omega'),$$

substituting (88.18) and effecting the integration over either $\mathbf{r}_1$ or $\mathbf{r}_2$, we obtain, on account of the factor $\delta(\mathbf{r}_2 - \mathbf{r}_1)$ in the integrand,

$$\overline{g_{i\omega}(\mathbf{p})g_{k\omega'}(\mathbf{p}')} = 2\hbar\epsilon''\, \delta(\omega + \omega')\, \delta_{ik} \coth(\hbar\omega/2T) \times \\ \times \frac{1}{(2\pi)^6} \int_{-\infty}^{\infty} \exp[-i(\mathbf{p} + \mathbf{p}')\cdot\mathbf{r}]\, d\mathbf{r}$$

or, finally,

$$\overline{g_{i\omega}(\mathbf{p})g_{k\omega'}(\mathbf{p}')} = \frac{\hbar}{4\pi^3}\epsilon''\, \delta_{ik}\, \delta(\omega + \omega')\, \delta(\mathbf{p} + \mathbf{p}') \coth(\hbar\omega/2T). \tag{88.20}$$

Equations (88.17) may be solved by Fourier's method. As well as representing $\mathbf{K}_\omega$ as the integral (88.19), we put

$$\mathbf{E}_\omega = \int_{-\infty}^{\infty} \mathbf{a}(\mathbf{p}) \exp(i\mathbf{p}\cdot\mathbf{r})\, d\mathbf{p},$$

$$\mathbf{H}_\omega = \frac{1}{k} \int_{-\infty}^{\infty} \mathbf{p} \times \mathbf{a} \exp(i\mathbf{p}\cdot\mathbf{r})\, d\mathbf{p}.$$

Then the first equation (88.17) is satisfied, and substitution in the second equation gives $\mathbf{p}\times(\mathbf{p}\times\mathbf{a}) = -k^2(\epsilon\mathbf{a}+\mathbf{g})$, whence

$$\mathbf{a} = [k^2\epsilon\mathbf{g} - (\mathbf{p}\cdot\mathbf{g})\mathbf{p}]/\epsilon(p^2 - \epsilon k^2).$$

Using this expression and formula (88.20), we obtain for the correlation of the Fourier components of the electric field

$$\overline{a_{i\omega}(\mathbf{p})a_{k\omega'}(\mathbf{p}')} = \frac{\hbar\epsilon''}{4\pi^3|\epsilon|^2}\delta(\mathbf{p}+\mathbf{p}')\,\delta(\omega+\omega')\coth\frac{\hbar\omega}{2T}\times$$
$$\times\frac{k^4|\epsilon|^2\,\delta_{ik} - p_ip_k[k^2(\epsilon+\epsilon^*) - p^2]}{|p^2 - k^2\epsilon|^2}. \qquad (88.21)$$

Finally, the spatial correlation of the fluctuation of the electric field is obtained by inverting the Fourier transformation:

$$\overline{E_{i\omega}(\mathbf{r}_1)E_{k\omega'}{}^*(\mathbf{r}_2)}$$
$$= \int_{-\infty}^{\infty}\int_{-\infty}^{\infty}\overline{a_{i\omega}(\mathbf{p})a_{k\omega'}(\mathbf{p}')}\exp\,[i(\mathbf{p}\cdot\mathbf{r}_1 + \mathbf{p}'\cdot\mathbf{r}_2)]\,d\mathbf{p}\,d\mathbf{p}'.$$

One integration can be effected immediately, because of the delta function in (88.21). To carry out the second integration we must expand (88.21) in partial fractions, and then use the formulae

$$\int_{-\infty}^{\infty}\frac{\exp\,(i\mathbf{p}\cdot\mathbf{r})}{p^2+\kappa^2}d\mathbf{p} = 2\pi^2\frac{e^{-\kappa r}}{r},$$

$$\int_{-\infty}^{\infty}\frac{p_ip_k\exp\,(i\mathbf{p}\cdot\mathbf{r})}{p^2+\kappa^2}d\mathbf{p} = -2\pi^2\frac{\partial^2}{\partial x_i\partial x_k}\left(\frac{e^{-\kappa r}}{r}\right).$$

The first of these is obtained by taking the Fourier component of the well-known relation

$$(\triangle - \kappa^2)\frac{e^{-\kappa r}}{r} = -4\pi\delta(\mathbf{r}), \qquad (88.22)$$

and the second by differentiating the first.

The result is

$$(E_{i1}E_{k2})_\omega = \frac{\hbar}{4\pi i}\coth\frac{\hbar\omega}{2T}\left\{\frac{k^2}{r}(e^{-kr\sqrt{-\epsilon}} - e^{-kr\sqrt{-\epsilon^*}})\,\delta_{ik} + \right.$$
$$\left. + \frac{1}{|\epsilon|^2}\frac{\partial^2}{\partial x_i\partial x_k}\left[\frac{1}{r}(\epsilon^*e^{-kr\sqrt{-\epsilon}} - \epsilon e^{-kr\sqrt{-\epsilon^*}})\right]\right\}, \qquad (88.23)$$

where $r = |\mathbf{r}_2 - \mathbf{r}_1|$, and the root $\sqrt{-\epsilon}$ is taken with the sign for which $\mathrm{re}\sqrt{-\epsilon} > 0$. In particular, contracting with respect to the suffixes i and k and using the relation (88.22), we find

$$(\mathbf{E}_1 \cdot \mathbf{E}_2)_\omega = \frac{\hbar}{4\pi i} \coth\frac{\hbar\omega}{2T}\left\{\frac{2k^2}{r}(e^{-kr\sqrt{-\epsilon}} - e^{-kr\sqrt{-\epsilon^*}}) + \right.$$
$$\left. + \frac{8\pi i\epsilon''}{|\epsilon|^2}\delta(\mathbf{r})\right\}. \qquad (88.24)$$

We can similarly calculate the correlation of the various components $\mathbf{H}_\omega$, both among themselves and with the $\mathbf{E}_\omega$, but shall not pause to do so here.

§89. Black-body radiation in a transparent medium

The presence of the factors ϵ'' and μ'' in formulae (88.11) and (88.12) emphasises the relation between electromagnetic fluctuations and absorption in a medium. If we take the limit as $\epsilon'' \to 0$ (with $\epsilon' > 0$) in formulae (88.23) and (88.24), the result is not zero. This arises from a difference in the order of passage to two limits, those of infinite medium and zero ϵ''. Since, in an infinite medium, any non-zero value of ϵ'', no matter how small, causes absorption, the result obtained by passing to the limits in our order pertains to a transparent medium in which, as in any actual medium, there is in fact some absorption.

For example, let us find the limiting form of formula (88.24). To do so, we note that, for small ϵ'', $\sqrt{-\epsilon} = \sqrt{(-\epsilon' - i\epsilon'')} \approx -i\sqrt{\epsilon'}(1 + \frac{1}{2}i\epsilon''/\epsilon')$, $\sqrt{-\epsilon^*} = \sqrt{(-\epsilon' + i\epsilon'')} \approx i\sqrt{\epsilon'}(1 - \frac{1}{2}i\epsilon''/\epsilon')$. The choice of signs is determined by the condition that the real part should be positive. In the limit $\epsilon'' \to 0$, therefore,

$$(\mathbf{E}_1 \cdot \mathbf{E}_2)_\omega = \frac{\omega^2\hbar}{\pi c^2}\frac{\sin \omega n r/c}{r}\coth\frac{\hbar\omega}{2T},$$

where $n = \sqrt{\epsilon}$ is the refractive index. Since there is no delta-function term, this expression remains finite when $\mathbf{r}_1 = \mathbf{r}_2$:

$$(\mathbf{E}^2)_\omega = (\omega^3\hbar n/\pi c^3)\coth(\hbar\omega/2T). \qquad (89.1)$$

The spectral density of the electric field energy per unit volume is (cf. (61.10) and SP (118.6))

$$\frac{1}{8\pi}2(\mathbf{E}^2)_\omega\frac{\mathrm{d}(n^2\omega)}{\mathrm{d}\omega}.$$

Substituting (89.1), we have

$$\frac{\omega^3\hbar n}{4\pi^2 c^3}\frac{\mathrm{d}(n^2\omega)}{\mathrm{d}\omega}\coth\frac{\hbar\omega}{2T}.$$

The mean square of the magnetic field can be calculated similarly. It is found that $(\mathbf{H}^2)_\omega = \epsilon(\mathbf{E}^2)_\omega$, and so the magnetic energy is

$$\frac{1}{8\pi} 2(\mathbf{H}^2)_\omega = \frac{\omega^3 \hbar n^3}{4\pi^2 c^3} \coth\frac{\hbar\omega}{2T}.$$

We shall not give the detailed calculations here, since the final result which is obtained below is in any case obvious.

Thus the total spectral density of the electromagnetic energy density in the fluctuation fields is

$$\frac{\omega^3\hbar}{4\pi^2c^3}\left(n\frac{\mathrm{d}(n^2\omega)}{\mathrm{d}\omega} + n^3\right)\coth\frac{\hbar\omega}{2T}$$
$$= \left(\tfrac{1}{2}\hbar\omega + \frac{\hbar\omega}{e^{\hbar\omega/T}-1}\right)\frac{\omega^2n^2}{\pi^2c^3}\frac{\mathrm{d}}{\mathrm{d}\omega}(n\omega).$$

The first term in the parentheses relates to the zero-order oscillations of the field; the second term gives the energy of thermodynamic-equilibrium electromagnetic radiation in a transparent medium (i.e. the energy of black-body radiation):

$$\frac{\hbar\omega}{e^{\hbar\omega/T}-1}\frac{\omega^2n^2}{\pi^2c^3}\frac{\mathrm{d}}{\mathrm{d}\omega}(n\omega). \tag{89.2}$$

This formula could also be obtained, without considering fluctuations, by an appropriate generalisation of Planck's formula for black-body radiation in a vacuum. According to this formula, the energy of black-body radiation per unit volume having wave-vector components in an interval $\mathrm{d}k_x$, $\mathrm{d}k_y$, $\mathrm{d}k_z$ is

$$\frac{\hbar\omega}{e^{\hbar\omega/T}-1}\cdot\frac{2\mathrm{d}k_x\mathrm{d}k_y\mathrm{d}k_z}{(2\pi)^3};$$

the factor 2 arises because of the two directions of polarisation. To obtain the spectral energy density, we must replace $\mathrm{d}k_x\,\mathrm{d}k_y\,\mathrm{d}k_z$ by $4\pi k^2\,\mathrm{d}k$ and substitute $k = \omega/c$. To go from a vacuum to a transparent medium it is sufficient to put $k = n\omega/c$ instead of $k = \omega/c$, i.e. $k^2\,\mathrm{d}k = k^2(\mathrm{d}k/\mathrm{d}\omega)\,\mathrm{d}\omega = (\omega^2n^2/c^3)\,\mathrm{d}(n\omega)/\mathrm{d}\omega$, which gives formula (89.2). It should be noted that this formula remains valid even if $\mu \neq 1$, provided that n is interpreted as $\sqrt{(\epsilon\mu)}$.

§90. Forces of molecular attraction between solid bodies

The theory of electromagnetic fluctuations can be used to calculate the forces of interaction between any two macroscopic bodies whose surfaces are a very short distance apart (E. M. Lifshitz, 1954). In what follows we assume only that this distance is large compared with those between the atoms. In this case the problem can be treated macroscopically.

We may consider the interaction between bodies as resulting from the fluctuations of the electromagnetic field which always occur in an absorbing medium and also outside it. If the space between the surfaces is a vacuum, this means of interaction is evidently the only one.

Let us regard the interacting bodies as two media occupying half-spaces with plane parallel boundaries at a distance l apart. The fluctuations of the electromagnetic field in the two media and in the space between them can be found by solving equations (88.17)† with the appropriate boundary conditions (continuity of the tangential components of $\mathbf{E}_\omega$ and $\mathbf{H}_\omega$) at the two surfaces. The solution is most conveniently effected by expanding the required functions (and the quantity $\mathbf{K}_\omega$) as Fourier integrals with respect to the transverse co-ordinates y, z (the x-axis being normal to the surfaces); this gives a system of linear inhomogeneous ordinary differential equations to determine the fields as functions of x. Solving these equations, we obtain integral expressions for $\mathbf{E}_\omega$ and $\mathbf{H}_\omega$, whose integrands contain the "external" fluctuation fields $\mathbf{K}1_\omega$ and $\mathbf{K}2_\omega$ in the two media. Actually, it is sufficient to obtain the explicit forms of $\mathbf{E}_\omega$ and $\mathbf{H}_\omega$ in the space between the media, since the mutual attraction force F_ω per unit area of either surface can be calculated as the xx-component of the Maxwell stress tensor, statistically averaged in accordance with formula (88.18). Since the calculations involve only the spectral components of the fields, the required total attraction force F must be obtained by integrating F_ω over all frequencies.‡

The calculations are somewhat laborious; we shall not go through them here, but give only the final result. The force is||

$$F = \frac{\hbar}{2\pi^2 c^3}\,\mathrm{re}\int\limits_0^\infty \int p^2\omega^3 \coth\frac{\hbar\omega}{2T}\left\{\left[\frac{(s_1+p)(s_2+p)}{(s_1-p)(s_2-p)}e^{-2ip\omega l/c}-1\right]^{-1}+\right.$$

$$\left.+\left[\frac{(s_1+\epsilon_1 p)(s_2+\epsilon_2 p)}{(s_1-\epsilon_1 p)(s_2-\epsilon_2 p)}e^{-2ip\omega l/c}-1\right]^{-1}\right\}\mathrm{d}p\,\mathrm{d}\omega, \qquad (90.1)$$

where $\epsilon_1(\omega)$, $\epsilon_2(\omega)$ are the dielectric permeabilities of the two media, and

$$s_1 = \sqrt{[\epsilon_1(\omega)-1+p^2]}, \qquad s_2 = \sqrt{[\epsilon_2(\omega)-1+p^2]}, \qquad (90.2)$$

the signs of the roots being taken so that the imaginary parts of s_1 and s_2 are positive.†† The paths of integration are shown in Fig. 43a. The integra-

† The magnetic permeabilities of the two bodies are assumed to be unity.

‡ The value of F_ω resulting from the calculation includes a term which diverges on integration with respect to ω. This term, however, is independent of l, and represents the pressure exerted on the surface by the black-body radiation in the vacuum. In an actual problem these forces act on all sides of a body and cancel out, so that the term in question does not relate to the mutual attraction under consideration, and must be omitted.

|| See E. M. Lifshitz, *Zhurnal éksperimental'noĭ i teoreticheskoĭ fiziki* **29**, 94, 1955; *Soviet Physics JETP* **2**, 73, 1956.

†† Since the imaginary part of the radicand (ϵ'') is positive, im $s > 0$ implies re $s > 0$.

tion with respect to ω is over real values from 0 to ∞; that with respect to p is along the real axis from 1 to 0, and thence along the imaginary axis to $i\infty$.

If the temperature of the bodies may be taken as zero (see below), $\coth(\hbar\omega/2T)$ in (90.1) is replaced by unity. We shall begin by discussing formula (90.1) for this particular case.

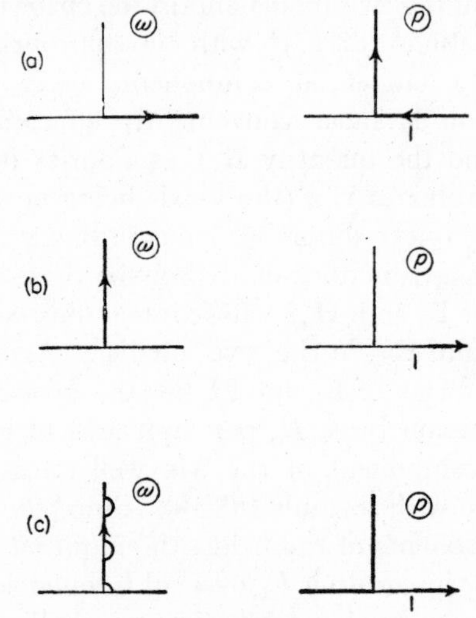

FIG. 43

Both the complex form of (90.1) and the appearance of the expression $e^{-2ip\omega l/c}$, which oscillates on the real part of the path of integration with respect to p, are inconvenient. The latter fact, in particular, hampers the calculation of the integral for large values of l, when the oscillation becomes very rapid. This difficulty can be removed by appropriate changes in the paths of integration in the planes of the complex variables ω and p: they must be displaced in such a way that the integration with respect to p is taken over only real values, and that with respect to ω over only imaginary ones (Fig. 43b). Then the exponent $-2ip\omega l/c$ is always real.†

The result is the following expression for the interaction force (when $T = 0$):

$$F = \frac{\hbar}{2\pi^2 c^3}\int_0^\infty\int_1^\infty p^2\xi^3\left\{\left[\frac{(s_1+p)(s_2+p)}{(s_1-p)(s_2-p)}e^{2p\xi l/c}-1\right]^{-1}+\right.$$

$$\left.+\left[\frac{(s_1+\epsilon_1 p)(s_2+\epsilon_2 p)}{(s_1-\epsilon_1 p)(s_2-\epsilon_2 p)}e^{2p\xi l/c}-1\right]^{-1}\right\}\mathrm{d}p\,\mathrm{d}\xi. \tag{90.3}$$

† This transformation is permissible if there is some way of simultaneously displacing both paths without passing through a pole of the integrand. A detailed investigation, using the properties of the function $\epsilon(\omega)$ given in §62, shows that this is so.

Here we have put $\omega = i\xi$ for imaginary ω; ϵ_1 and ϵ_2 denote the real functions $\epsilon_1(i\xi)$ and $\epsilon_2(i\xi)$. The sign re has been omitted, since the expression (90.3) is evidently real. This formula makes possible, in principle, a calculation of the force F for any distance l if the functions $\epsilon(i\xi)$ for the two bodies are known. These functions can be expressed in terms of the imaginary part of $\epsilon(\omega)$ for real ω, by formula (62.17). Thus we can say that the law of interaction of the bodies is entirely determined when the functions $\epsilon''(\omega)$ in them are given.

Let us consider the limiting case of distances l which are small compared with the wavelengths λ_0 of greatest importance in the absorption spectra of the bodies. The temperatures which occur in solids and liquids are always small compared with the important values of $\hbar\omega \sim \hbar\omega_0$ (where $\omega_0 \sim 2\pi c/\lambda_0$). Hence we can assume that $T = 0$ and use formula (90.3).

On account of the exponentially increasing factor $e^{2p\xi l/c}$ in the denominators in the integrand, the main contribution to the integral with respect to p comes from values such that $p\xi l/c \sim 1$. Then $p \gg 1$, and hence we can put $s_1 \approx s_2 \approx p$ in determining the leading terms. In this approximation the first term in square brackets in (90.3) is zero. The second term gives

$$F = \frac{\hbar}{16\pi^2 l^3} \int_0^\infty \int_0^\infty \frac{x^2\,dx\,d\xi}{\left(\dfrac{\epsilon_1+1}{\epsilon_1-1}\right)\left(\dfrac{\epsilon_2+1}{\epsilon_2-1}\right)e^x - 1}, \tag{90.4}$$

where the new variable of integration $x = 2p\xi l/c$, and the lower limit of integration $2\xi l/c$ has been replaced in this approximation by zero.

Formula (90.4) gives the force of attraction in the limiting case of small l. It is inversely proportional to the cube of the distance. The function $\epsilon(i\xi)-1$ decreases monotonically to zero with increasing ξ. Values of ξ exceeding some ξ_0 therefore make no important contribution to the integral; the condition for l to be small is $l \ll c/\xi_0$.

We shall show how the passage to the limit of the interaction between individual atoms is made in (90.4). To do so, we formally assume both media to be so rarefied that the differences $\epsilon_1 - 1$ and $\epsilon_2 - 1$ are almost zero, and (90.4) gives with sufficient accuracy

$$F = \frac{\hbar}{64\pi^2 l^3} \int_0^\infty \int_0^\infty x^2 e^{-x}(\epsilon_1 - 1)(\epsilon_2 - 1)\,dx\,d\xi$$

$$= \frac{\hbar}{32\pi^2 l^3} \int_0^\infty [\epsilon_1(i\xi) - 1][\epsilon_2(i\xi) - 1]\,d\xi.$$

Expressing $\epsilon(i\xi)$ in terms of $\epsilon''(\omega)$ on the real axis by (62.17) we obtain

$$\int_0^\infty [\epsilon_1(i\xi) - 1][\epsilon_2(i\xi) - 1]\, d\xi$$

$$= \frac{4}{\pi^2}\int_0^\infty\int_0^\infty\int_0^\infty \frac{\omega_1\omega_2\epsilon_1''(\omega_1)\epsilon_2''(\omega_2)}{(\omega_1^2+\xi^2)(\omega_2^2+\xi^2)}\, d\xi\, d\omega_1\, d\omega_2$$

$$= \frac{2}{\pi}\int_0^\infty\int_0^\infty \frac{\epsilon_1''(\omega_1)\epsilon_2''(\omega_2)}{\omega_1+\omega_2}\, d\omega_1\, d\omega_2,$$

and the force F is

$$F = \frac{\hbar}{16\pi^3 l^3}\int_0^\infty\int_0^\infty \frac{\epsilon_1''(\omega_1)\epsilon_2''(\omega_2)}{\omega_1+\omega_2}\, d\omega_1\, d\omega_2. \qquad (90.5)$$

The force of interaction between rarefied media may be regarded as the resultant of the interactions between pairs of molecules. Then the force (90.5) corresponds to an interaction of molecules with an energy which depends on the distance R between them:

$$U = -\frac{3\hbar}{8\pi^4 R^6 N^2}\int_0^\infty\int_0^\infty \frac{\epsilon_1''(\omega_1)\epsilon_2''(\omega_2)}{\omega_1+\omega_2}\, d\omega_1\, d\omega_2, \qquad (90.6)$$

where N is the number of atoms per unit volume. Formula (90.5) is obtained from this by integration over the two half-spaces separated by a gap of width l, followed by differentiation of the total energy with respect to l. Formula (90.6) is the same as that derived by F. London by applying the ordinary perturbation theory of quantum mechanics to the dipole interaction between atoms. In making the comparison, it should be borne in mind that $\epsilon''(\omega)$ is related to the spectral density of "oscillator strengths" $f(\omega)$ by (62.13). The oscillator strengths are expressed, in the usual manner, in terms of the squared matrix elements of the dipole moment of the atom. Thus we see that the microscopic formula can be derived from the macroscopic theory.

Let us now consider the opposite limiting case, where the distance l is large compared with the wavelengths λ_0 which are of greatest importance in the absorption spectra of the bodies. The temperature will at first be supposed zero, as before.

In the general formula (90.3) we again introduce as a new variable of integration $x = 2p\xi l/c$, but leave p instead of ξ as the second variable:

$$F = \frac{\hbar c}{32\pi^2 l^4}\int_0^\infty\int_1^\infty \frac{x^3}{p^2}\left\{\left[\frac{(s_1+p)(s_2+p)}{(s_1-p)(s_2-p)}e^x - 1\right]^{-1} + \right.$$

$$\left. + \left[\frac{(s_1+\epsilon_1 p)(s_2+\epsilon_2 p)}{(s_1-\epsilon_1 p)(s_2-\epsilon_2 p)}e^x - 1\right]^{-1}\right\} \mathrm{d}p\,\mathrm{d}x,$$

$$\epsilon = \epsilon(ixc/2pl), \qquad s = \sqrt{[\epsilon(ixc/2pl) - 1 + p^2]}.$$

On account of the factor e^x in the denominators, the important values of x are ~ 1, and, since $p \geqslant 1$, the argument of ϵ is almost zero (for large l) throughout the important range of values of the variables. We can therefore replace ϵ_1 and ϵ_2 by their values for $\omega = 0$, i.e. the electrostatic dielectric permeabilities, which we denote by ϵ_{10} and ϵ_{20}. For metals, the function $\epsilon(\omega)$ tends to infinity as $\omega \to 0$, and so $\epsilon_0 = \infty$.

Thus we have finally

$$F = \frac{\hbar c}{32\pi^2 l^4}\int_0^\infty\int_1^\infty \frac{x^3}{p^2}\left\{\left[\frac{(s_{10}+p)(s_{20}+p)}{(s_{10}-p)(s_{20}-p)}e^x - 1\right]^{-1} + \right.$$

$$\left. + \left[\frac{(s_{10}+\epsilon_{10} p)(s_{20}+\epsilon_{20} p)}{(s_{10}-\epsilon_{10} p)(s_{20}-\epsilon_{20} p)}e^x - 1\right]^{-1}\right\} \mathrm{d}p\,\mathrm{d}x, \tag{90.7}$$

$$s_{10} = \sqrt{(\epsilon_{10} - 1 + p^2)}, \qquad s_{20} = \sqrt{(\epsilon_{20} - 1 + p^2)}.$$

Here the force of attraction is inversely proportional to l^4. It is noteworthy that, in this limiting case, the force depends only on the electrostatic dielectric permeabilities of the two media.

Let us consider some special cases. A particularly simple result is obtained when both media are metals. Putting in (90.7) $\epsilon_{10} = \epsilon_{20} = \infty$, we find

$$F = \frac{\hbar c}{16\pi^2 l^4}\int_0^\infty\int_1^\infty \frac{x^3\,\mathrm{d}p\,\mathrm{d}x}{p^2(e^x - 1)} = \frac{\hbar c}{l^4}\cdot\frac{\pi^2}{240}. \tag{90.8}$$

This force is independent of the kind of metal concerned (a property which ceases to hold at small distances, the interaction then depending on the values of $\epsilon(i\xi)$ for all ξ and not only for $\xi = 0$).†

† Formula (90.8) had previously been derived in another manner by H. B. G. Casimir (1948).

For two media of the same dielectric ($\epsilon_{10} = \epsilon_{20} = \epsilon_0$), numerical integration of (90.7) gives

$$F = \frac{\hbar c}{l^4} \cdot \frac{\pi^2}{240}\left(\frac{\epsilon_0 - 1}{\epsilon_0 + 1}\right)^2 \phi(\epsilon_0), \tag{90.9}$$

where $\phi(\epsilon_0)$ is a function shown graphically in Fig. 44.

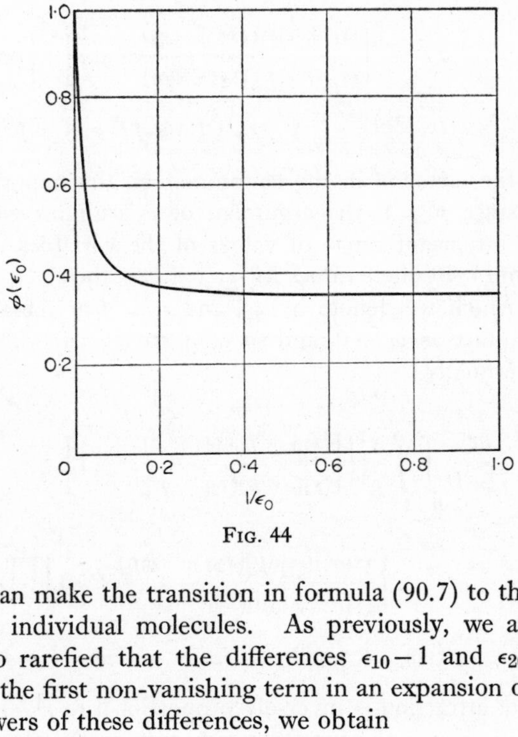

FIG. 44

Finally, we can make the transition in formula (90.7) to the case of interaction between individual molecules. As previously, we assume the two media to be so rarefied that the differences $\epsilon_{10} - 1$ and $\epsilon_{20} - 1$ are small. Retaining only the first non-vanishing term in an expansion of the integrand in (90.7) in powers of these differences, we obtain

$$F = \frac{\hbar c}{32\pi^2 l^4} \int_0^\infty x^3 e^{-x}\, dx \int_1^\infty \frac{1 - 2p^2 + 2p^4}{8p^6} dp (\epsilon_{10} - 1)(\epsilon_{20} - 1)$$

or

$$F = \frac{\hbar c}{l^4} \cdot \frac{23}{640\pi^2} (\epsilon_{10} - 1)(\epsilon_{20} - 1). \tag{90.10}$$

This force corresponds to a molecular interaction with energy

$$U = -\frac{23\hbar c}{64\pi^3 R^7} \frac{(\epsilon_{10} - 1)(\epsilon_{20} - 1)}{N^2} = -\frac{23\hbar c}{4\pi R^7} \alpha_1 \alpha_2, \tag{90.11}$$

where α_1 and α_2 are the static polarisabilities of the two molecules. This formula is the same as that obtained by H. B. G. CASIMIR and D. POLDER

(1948), using quantum methods, for the attraction between two molecules at a large distance apart, when the delay in interaction becomes important.

To obtain formulae which take account of the temperature we return to the initial expression (90.1) and see how the transformation which for $T = 0$ leads to (90.3) must be modified when $T \neq 0$. The function $\coth(\hbar\omega/2T)$ has an infinite number of poles on the imaginary axis, at the points

$$\omega_n = i\xi_n = 2\pi i T n/\hbar, \tag{90.12}$$

where n is any integer. When the path of integration with respect to ω is moved on to the imaginary axis, therefore, it must be indented by semicircles at these poles, and by a quarter-circle at $\omega = 0$ (Fig. 43c). This gives rise to contributions to the real part of the integral, equal to πi ($\frac{1}{2}\pi i$ for $n = 0$) times the residues of the integrand at the poles. The integration along the imaginary axis between the poles gives only imaginary quantities, which do not affect the real part.

Thus we have

$$F = \frac{T}{\pi c^3} \sum_{n=0}^{\infty}{}' \xi_n^3 \int_1^{\infty} p^2 \left\{ \left[\frac{(s_{1n}+p)(s_{2n}+p)}{(s_{1n}-p)(s_{2n}-p)} e^{2p\xi_n l/c} - 1 \right]^{-1} + \right.$$

$$\left. + \left[\frac{(s_{1n}+\epsilon_{1n}p)(s_{2n}+\epsilon_{2n}p)}{(s_{1n}-\epsilon_{1n}p)(s_{2n}-\epsilon_{2n}p)} e^{2p\xi_n l/c} - 1 \right]^{-1} \right\} \mathrm{d}p, \tag{90.13}$$

$$s_n = \sqrt{(\epsilon_n - 1 + p^2)}, \qquad \epsilon_n = \epsilon(i\xi_n).$$

The prime indicates that the term with $n = 0$ is halved. As $T \to 0$, the distances between the poles tend to zero, the summation over n can be replaced by an integration with respect to ξ, and we return to formula (90.3), which does not involve T.

Whereas, in the limiting case of small distances, the temperature can always be taken as zero in determining the interaction force, at large distances the effect of the temperature may be considerable. The characteristic temperature for a distance l is $\hbar c/l$, and the condition for T to be negligible is, roughly, $lT/\hbar c \ll 1$. At sufficiently low temperatures this condition is compatible with $l \gg \lambda_0$, but at high temperatures the two conditions may be contradictory, and the limiting form (90.7) is then never applicable.

Let us consider the limiting case of distances so large that $lT/\hbar c \gg 1$. Then only the first term in the sum in (90.13) need be retained. We cannot at once put $n = 0$, however, because an indeterminacy results: the factor ξ_n^3 is zero, but the integral with respect to p diverges. This difficulty may be circumvented by replacing p by a new variable of integration $x = 2p\xi_n l/c$ (the factor ξ_n^3 being thereby removed). Putting now $n = 0$ we obtain

$$F = \frac{T}{16\pi l^3} \int_0^{\infty} x^2 \left[\frac{(\epsilon_{10}+1)(\epsilon_{20}+1)}{(\epsilon_{10}-1)(\epsilon_{20}-1)} e^x - 1 \right]^{-1} \mathrm{d}x. \tag{90.14}$$

Thus, at sufficiently large distances, the force of interaction decreases less rapidly and returns to the $1/l^3$ law, with a coefficient which depends on the temperature and on the static value of the dielectric permeability. The remaining terms in the sum (90.13) all diminish exponentially when $lT/\hbar c$ is large.

CHAPTER XIV

SCATTERING OF ELECTROMAGNETIC WAVES

§91. The general theory of scattering in isotropic media

IN THE theory of propagation of electromagnetic waves in transparent media discussed in Chapters IX–XI, a phenomenon has been neglected which, though not prominent, is of fundamental importance: *scattering*. Scattering results in the appearance of *scattered waves* of small intensity, whose frequencies and directions are not those of the main wave.

Scattering is ultimately due to the change in the motion of the charges in the medium under the influence of the field of the incident wave, resulting in the emission of the scattered waves. The microscopic mechanism of scattering must be investigated by quantum methods, but this investigation is not needed in developing the macroscopic theory described below. We shall therefore give only some brief remarks on the nature of the processes which cause the change in the wave frequency on scattering.

The basic scattering process consists in the absorption of the original quantum $\hbar\omega$ by the scattering system and the simultaneous emission by that system of another quantum $\hbar\omega'$. The frequency ω' of the scattered quantum may be either less or greater than ω; these two cases are called respectively *Stokes scattering* and *anti-Stokes scattering*. In the former case the system absorbs an amount of energy $\hbar(\omega-\omega')$; in the latter case it emits $\hbar(\omega'-\omega)$ and makes a transition to a state of lower energy. In the simple case of a gas, for example, scattering takes place at individual molecules, and the change in frequency may be due either to a transition of the molecule to another energy level or to a change in the kinetic energy of its motion.

Another kind of process occurs when the primary quantum $\hbar\omega$ remains unchanged but causes the scattering system to emit two quanta: one of energy $\hbar\omega$, with the same frequency and direction, and a "scattered" quantum $\hbar\omega'$. The energy $\hbar(\omega+\omega')$ is obtained from the scattering system. Processes of this type, however, are, under ordinary conditions, very rare in comparison with those of the first type, and are of little importance as regards the phenomenon of scattering.†

Proceeding now to consider the macroscopic theory of scattering, we must first make precise the meaning of the averaging processes performed in that theory. As already mentioned at the beginning of §88, the averaging of quantities in macroscopic electrodynamics can be regarded as comprising

† We shall see in §92 that this *stimulated emission* is unimportant at all temperatures $T \ll \hbar(\omega+\omega')$. It may become significant for radio waves.

two operations, that of averaging over a physically infinitesimal volume with a given position of all the particles in it, followed by that of averaging the result with respect to the motion of the particles. In the theory of scattering, however, this procedure is impossible, because the averaging with respect to the motion of the particles annuls the very phenomenon which is to be discussed. Thus (e.g.) the field and induction of the scattered wave which appear in the theory of scattering must be taken to be those resulting from the first averaging only. The single-frequency components of the fields in the scattered wave, taken in this sense, will be denoted in this section by **E**′, **H**′, **D**′ and **B**′.

The fields in the incident wave will be denoted by the unprimed letters **E**, **H**. In the present chapter we always suppose the incident wave to be of a single frequency ω.

In the propagation of the scattered wave we have the relation $\mathbf{D}' = \epsilon(\omega')\mathbf{E}'$ between the electric induction and field (the scattering medium being assumed isotropic), but this relation does not reveal the phenomenon of scattering, i.e. the formation of the scattered wave from the incident wave. To describe this, additional small terms must be included in the expression for **D**′. In the first approximation, these terms must be linear in the field of the incident wave. The most general form of the relation is then.

$$D'_i = \epsilon' E'_i + \alpha_{ik} E_k + \beta_{ik} E_k^*. \tag{91.1}$$

Here ϵ' denotes $\epsilon(\omega')$; α_{ik} and β_{ik} are tensors which characterise the scattering properties of the medium. In general they are not symmetrical, and their components are functions both of the frequency ω' of the scattered wave and of the primary frequency ω.†

The last term in (91.1) pertains to the part of the scattering which results from processes of stimulated emission. All the terms on the right-hand side of equation (91.1) must correspond to the same frequency ω' as **D** on the left-hand side. Since **E*** has the frequency $-\omega$, the frequency of the quantities β_{ik} must be $\omega + \omega'$ to make the frequency of the products $\beta_{ik}E_k^*$ equal to ω'. But $\omega + \omega'$ is the frequency which characterises processes of stimulated emission. Because this effect is small, as mentioned above, we can neglect the corresponding term in (91.1), and in what follows we shall write

$$D'_i = \epsilon' E'_i + \alpha_{ik} E_k. \tag{91.2}$$

Similar formulae give the relation between **B**′ and **H**′. We shall, however, neglect the magnetic properties of the medium, which are usually of no importance as regards the scattering of light, and therefore put $\mathbf{B}' = \mathbf{H}'$.

Maxwell's equations for the field in the scattered wave are $\mathbf{curl}\,\mathbf{E}' = i\omega'\mathbf{H}'/c$, $\mathbf{curl}\,\mathbf{H}' = -i\omega'\mathbf{D}'/c$. Eliminating **H**′ from these equations, we

† The fact that α and β are tensors does not, of course, contradict the assumed isotropy of the medium. Only the fully averaged properties of the medium are isotropic; the local deviations from the average properties, which include the additional terms in (91.1), need not be isotropic.

find **curl curl** $\mathbf{E}' = \omega'^2\mathbf{D}'/c^2$. Substituting from (91.2) $\mathbf{E}' = \mathbf{D}'/\epsilon' - \boldsymbol{\alpha}\cdot\mathbf{E}/\epsilon'$, where $\boldsymbol{\alpha}\cdot\mathbf{E}$ denotes the vector whose components are $\alpha_{ik}E_k$, and using the equation div $\mathbf{D}' = 0$, we obtain for $\mathbf{D}'$ the equation

$$\triangle\mathbf{D}' + k'^2\mathbf{D}' = -\,\mathbf{curl}\,\mathbf{curl}\,(\boldsymbol{\alpha}\cdot\mathbf{E}), \tag{91.3}$$

where $k' = \omega\sqrt{\epsilon'}/c$ is the wave number of the scattered wave.

For an exact formulation of the conditions under which equation (91.3) is to be solved, we divide the scattering medium into small regions (whose dimensions are still large compared with molecular distances). On account of the molecular nature of the scattering processes, their correlation at different points in the medium (assumed non-crystalline) extends in general only to molecular distances.† Hence the scattered light from the various regions is non-coherent. We can therefore treat scattering from one region as if the light were not scattered at all in the remainder of the medium. In this way we calculate the field of the scattered wave at a large distance from the scattering region. Using a well-known approximation for the retarded potentials at a large distance from the source,‡ we can immediately derive the required solution of equation (91.3):

$$\mathbf{D}' = \frac{1}{4\pi}\mathbf{curl}\,\mathbf{curl}\frac{\exp(ik'R_0)}{R_0}\int\boldsymbol{\alpha}\cdot\mathbf{E}\exp(-ik'\cdot\mathbf{r})\,\mathrm{d}V. \tag{91.4}$$

Here $\mathbf{R}_0$ is the radius vector from some point within the scattering volume (the integration being over that volume) to the point where the field is to be calculated; the vector $\mathbf{k}'$ is in the direction of $\mathbf{R}_0$. The integral in (91.4) is independent of the co-ordinates of the point considered; retaining in the differentiation, as usual, only terms in $1/R_0$, we obtain

$$\mathbf{D}' = -\frac{\exp(ik'R_0)}{4\pi R_0}\mathbf{k}'\times\left[\mathbf{k}'\times\int\boldsymbol{\alpha}\cdot\mathbf{E}\exp(-i\mathbf{k}'\cdot\mathbf{r})\,\mathrm{d}V\right].$$

Since, at the point considered, the medium is regarded as not scattering, the relation between $\mathbf{D}'$ and $\mathbf{E}'$ there is given by $\mathbf{D}' = \epsilon'\mathbf{E}'$ simply. In the field of the incident wave $\mathbf{E}$ we separate a factor periodic in space, putting $\mathbf{E} = \mathbf{E}_0\exp(i\mathbf{k}\cdot\mathbf{r})$. Then, with the notation

$$\mathbf{G} = \int\boldsymbol{\alpha}\cdot\mathbf{E}_0\exp(-i\mathbf{q}\cdot\mathbf{r})\,\mathrm{d}V, \tag{91.5}$$

where $\mathbf{q} = \mathbf{k}'-\mathbf{k}$, we have

$$\mathbf{E}' = -\frac{\exp(ik'R_0)}{4\pi R_0\epsilon'}\mathbf{k}'\times(\mathbf{k}'\times\mathbf{G}). \tag{91.6}$$

† Exceptions may occur for particular cases of scattering, which will be discussed in §94. In such cases the dimensions of the scattering regions must be supposed large in comparison with the wavelength of the light.

‡ See *The Classical Theory of Fields*, §9–2, Addison-Wesley Press, Cambridge (Mass.), 1951; Pergamon Press, London, 1959.

The vector $\mathbf{E}'$ is perpendicular to the direction $\mathbf{k}'$ of the scattered wave, and is given by the component of the vector $\mathbf{G}$ perpendicular to $\mathbf{k}'$.

Having thus determined the non-averaged field in the scattered wave, we can now investigate the intensity and polarisation of the scattered light. To do so, we form the tensor

$$I_{ik} = \overline{E'_i E'_k{}^*}, \tag{91.7}$$

where the bar denotes the final averaging over the motion of the particles, which so far has not been carried out. The averaging of a quadratic expression gives, of course, a result which is not zero. Since $\mathbf{E}'$ is perpendicular to $\mathbf{k}'$, the tensor I_{ik} has non-zero components only in the plane perpendicular to $\mathbf{k}'$. These components form a two-dimensional tensor $I_{\alpha\beta}$ in that plane (Greek suffixes take two values). The tensor $I_{\alpha\beta}$ is, by definition, Hermitian: $I_{\alpha\beta} = I_{\beta\alpha}{}^*$. It can be reduced to "principal axes", and the ratio of its two principal values gives the degree of depolarisation, while their sum is proportional to the total intensity.†

The products $E'_i E'_k{}^*$ involve products of integrals G_i, which must also be averaged. Writing the product as a double integral, we have

$$G_i G_k{}^* = E_{0l} E_{0m}{}^* \int\int \alpha_{il,1}\alpha_{km,2}{}^* \exp[-i\mathbf{q}\cdot(\mathbf{r}_1 - \mathbf{r}_2)]\,dV_1\,dV_2. \tag{91.8}$$

The suffixes 1 and 2 indicate that the values of α are taken at two different points in space.

In averaging the integrand it must be remembered that the correlation between the values of α at different points in the body extends in general only over molecular distances. After averaging, therefore, the integrand will be appreciably different from zero only for $|\mathbf{r}_2 - \mathbf{r}_1| \sim a$, where a is of the order of molecular distances. The exponent is $\sim a/\lambda$, where λ is the wavelength of the scattered wave; but $a/\lambda \ll 1$ if the macroscopic theory is applicable, and so we can replace the exponential factor by unity.‡

Next, the integration with respect to the co-ordinates $\mathbf{r}_1$ and $\mathbf{r}_2$ can be replaced by one with respect to $\frac{1}{2}(\mathbf{r}_1 + \mathbf{r}_2)$ and $\mathbf{r} = \mathbf{r}_1 - \mathbf{r}_2$. Since the integrand depends, after averaging, on $\mathbf{r}$ only, we have

$$\overline{G_i G_k{}^*} = V E_{0l} E_{0m}{}^* \int \overline{\alpha_{il,1}\alpha_{km,2}{}^*}\,dV, \tag{91.9}$$

where V is the volume of the scattering region. It is evident *a priori* that the scattering must be proportional to V. It should be noted that the direction of the wave vector $\mathbf{k}$ in the incident wave appears neither in (91.9) nor, consequently, in the following formulae.

---

† See *Classical Theory of Fields*, §6–7. The reduction of an Hermitian tensor to principal axes means putting it in the form $I_{ik} = \lambda_1 n_{i1} n_{k1}{}^* + \lambda_2 n_{i2} n_{k2}{}^*$, where $\mathbf{n}_1$, $\mathbf{n}_2$ are, in general, perpendicular complex "unit" vectors: $\mathbf{n}_1\cdot\mathbf{n}_1{}^* = 1$, $\mathbf{n}_2\cdot\mathbf{n}_2{}^* = 1$, $\mathbf{n}_1\cdot\mathbf{n}_2{}^* = 0$. The principal values λ_1, λ_2 of an Hermitian tensor are real.

‡ This procedure requires further discussion in the case of Rayleigh scattering (§94).

The integrals in (91.9) form a tensor of rank four, which depends only on the properties of the scattering medium. Since the medium is isotropic, the most general form of this tensor is

$$\int \overline{\alpha_{il,1}\alpha_{km,2}^*}\,\mathrm{d}V = \tfrac{1}{2}(a+c)\delta_{il}\delta_{km} + \tfrac{1}{2}(a-c)\delta_{im}\delta_{kl} + b\delta_{ik}\delta_{lm}, \quad (91.10)$$

where a, b and c are scalar functions of ω and ω'. This tensor is automatically symmetrical with respect to an interchange of the suffixes i, l and k, m; this interchange is equivalent to taking the complex conjugate, since the points 1 and 2 are equivalent; the tensor (91.10) is therefore real, and so are a, b, c.

Substituting (91.10) in (91.9) we obtain

$$\overline{G_iG_k^*} = V\{\tfrac{1}{2}(a+c)E_{0i}E_{0k}^* + \tfrac{1}{2}(a-c)E_{0i}^*E_{0k} + bE_{0l}E_{0l}^*\delta_{ik}\}. \quad (91.11)$$

This expression could have been written down at once, since it is the most general Hermitian tensor of rank two which is quadratic in $\mathbf{E}_0$ and involves no other particular directions. This tensor is, of course, not transverse to $\mathbf{k}'$. The required general form of the tensor $I_{\alpha\beta}$ is obtained by "projecting" the tensor (91.11) on a plane perpendicular to $\mathbf{k}'$; to do this, it is sufficient to take a co-ordinate system with one axis in the direction of $\mathbf{k}'$ and find the components of the tensor along the other two axes.

Let us consider the scattering of a linearly polarised wave. The amplitude of the field $\mathbf{E}_0$ can be defined as a real quantity.† The components of the tensor $I_{\alpha\beta}$ for the scattered light are therefore also real. This means that the scattered light is partially polarised, and can be divided into two independent (non-coherent) waves, each of which is linearly polarised. Since there are only two distinctive directions (those of $\mathbf{E}_0$ and $\mathbf{k}'$) on which the tensor $I_{\alpha\beta}$ can depend, it is evident that one of these waves must be polarised with $\mathbf{E}'$ in the plane of $\mathbf{E}_0$ and $\mathbf{k}'$, and the other with $\mathbf{E}'$ perpendicular to this plane. The intensities of the two scattered-light components will be denoted by I_1 and I_2; they are the principal values of the tensor $I_{\alpha\beta}$.

For real $\mathbf{E}_0$, the expression (91.11) becomes

$$\overline{G_iG_k^*} = V\{aE_{0i}E_{0k} + bE_0^2\delta_{ik}\}. \quad (91.12)$$

We may note first of all that the scattering of linearly polarised light is determined by two, not three, independent constants. To find I_1 and I_2, we take the components of $\mathbf{E}_0$ in the two directions mentioned. The corresponding components of the tensor (91.12) give the result

$$I_1 \sim a\sin^2\theta + b, \qquad I_2 \sim b, \quad (91.13)$$

the coefficients of proportionality being the same; θ is the angle between $\mathbf{E}_0$ and the direction of scattering $\mathbf{k}'$. The intensity of the scattered-light component whose electric field is polarised perpendicular to the plane of $\mathbf{E}_0$ and $\mathbf{k}'$ is independent of the direction of scattering.

---

† See *The Classical Theory of Fields*, §§6–5, 6–7. We shall not consider here the scattering of elliptically polarised light, on account of the complexity of the formulae.

When natural light passes through a medium, the scattered light is partially polarised, and it is evident from symmetry that the two non-coherent components are linearly polarised, with their electric fields parallel and perpendicular to the scattering plane (the plane of **k** and **k**′). Let the intensities of these components be $I_{\parallel}$ and $I_{\perp}$ respectively. To determine these, we average (91.11) over all directions of the vector $\mathbf{E}_0$ in the plane perpendicular to **k**. The averaging of the product $E_{0i}E_{0k}^*$ gives

$$\overline{E_{0i}E_{0k}^*} = \tfrac{1}{2}|\mathbf{E}_0|^2(\delta_{ik} - n_i n_k), \tag{91.14}$$

where **n** is a unit vector in the direction of **k**. This is a tensor of rank two which depends only on the direction of **k**, gives $|\mathbf{E}_0|^2$ on contraction, and satisfies the condition $n_i\overline{E_{0i}E_{0k}^*} = \overline{(\mathbf{n}\cdot\mathbf{E}_0)E_{0k}^*} = 0$. Thus we have, when natural light is scattered,

$$\overline{G_iG_k^*} = V|\mathbf{E}_0|^2\{\tfrac{1}{2}a(\delta_{ik} - n_i n_k) + b\delta_{ik}\}. \tag{91.15}$$

Finally, taking the components of this tensor in the two directions of polarisation, we obtain the required formulae:

$$I_{\parallel} \sim \tfrac{1}{2}a\cos^2\vartheta + b, \qquad I_{\perp} \sim \tfrac{1}{2}a + b, \tag{91.16}$$

where ϑ is the scattering angle (i.e. that between **k** and **k**′).

Let us return to formula (91.10), which relates the scalar quantities a, b and c to the tensor α_{ik}. Like any tensor of rank two, α_{ik} can be written, in general, as a sum of three independent parts:

$$\alpha_{ik} = \tfrac{1}{3}\alpha\delta_{ik} + s_{ik} + a_{ik}, \tag{91.17}$$

where $\alpha = \alpha_{ii}$ is a scalar, s_{ik} a symmetrical tensor whose trace is zero ($s_{ik} = s_{ki}$, $s_{ii} = 0$) and a_{ik} an antisymmetrical tensor. We substitute this in (91.10) and contract with respect to various pairs of suffixes, obtaining the three equations†

$$\left.\begin{aligned}
6a + 3b + 3c &= \int\overline{\alpha_{ii,1}\alpha_{kk,2}^*}\,\mathrm{d}V = \int\overline{\alpha_1\alpha_2^*}\,\mathrm{d}V,\\
3a + 9b &= \int\overline{\alpha_{ik,1}\alpha_{ik,2}^*}\,\mathrm{d}V\\
&= \tfrac{1}{3}\int\overline{\alpha_1\alpha_2^*}\,\mathrm{d}V + \int\overline{s_{ik,1}s_{ik,2}^*}\,\mathrm{d}V + \int\overline{a_{ik,1}a_{ik,2}^*}\,\mathrm{d}V,\\
6a + 3b - 3c &= \int\overline{\alpha_{ik,1}\alpha_{ki,2}^*}\,\mathrm{d}V\\
&= \tfrac{1}{3}\int\overline{\alpha_1\alpha_2^*}\,\mathrm{d}V + \int\overline{s_{ik,1}s_{ik,2}^*}\,\mathrm{d}V - \int\overline{a_{ik,1}a_{ik,2}^*}\,\mathrm{d}V.
\end{aligned}\right\} \tag{91.18}$$

† The integrals on the right-hand sides of these equations are positive, since each can be written as a square by a transformation inverse to that whereby (91.8) becomes (91.9). Expressing the three integrals in terms of a, b, c (i.e. solving equations (91.18) for these integrals) we obtain the inequalities $2a + b + c > 0$, $2b + c - a > 0$, $2b + a - c > 0$. From these, in particular, it follows that $b > 0$.

The right-hand sides of these equations, and therefore their solutions for a, b, c, do not involve cross-products of α, s_{ik} and a_{ik}. This means that scattering can always be regarded as a superposition of three types of process, which may be called *scalar, symmetrical* and *antisymmetrical scattering*. We shall discuss each of these in turn.

Retaining only the first terms on the right of equations (91.18), we have

$$a = c = \frac{1}{9}\int \overline{\alpha_1\alpha_2^*}\,\mathrm{d}V, \qquad b = 0. \tag{91.19}$$

It is seen from (91.13) that, in scalar scattering of polarised light, the scattered light is itself completely polarised, and its angular intensity distribution is given by $I = (3/2)\sin^2\theta$. (Here and henceforward the expressions for I are normalised so as to give unity on averaging over directions.) In scattering of natural light, however, the angular distribution of the total intensity and the degree of depolarisation of the scattered light are given, according to (91.16), by $I = I_\perp + I_\parallel = \frac{3}{4}(1+\cos^2\vartheta)$, $I_\parallel/I_\perp = \cos^2\vartheta$; see the second footnote to §72.

For symmetrical scattering, equations (91.18) give

$$a = \frac{1}{3}b = -\frac{1}{5}c = \frac{1}{30}\int \overline{s_{ik,1}s_{ik,2}^*}\,\mathrm{d}V. \tag{91.20}$$

In scattering of polarised light we have $I = I_1 + I_2 = \frac{3}{20}(6+\sin^2\theta)$, $I_2/I_1 = 3/(3+\sin^2\theta)$, and in scattering of natural light $I = \frac{3}{40}(14-\sin^2\vartheta)$, $I_\parallel/I_\perp = 1-\frac{1}{7}\sin^2\vartheta$.

Finally, for antisymmetrical scattering we obtain

$$b = c = -a = \frac{1}{6}\int \overline{a_{ik,1}a_{ik,2}^*}\,\mathrm{d}V; \tag{91.21}$$

in scattering of polarised light $I = \frac{3}{4}(1+\cos^2\theta)$, $I_1/I_2 = \cos^2\theta$, and in scattering of natural light $I = \frac{3}{8}(2+\sin^2\vartheta)$, $I_\perp/I_\parallel = 1/(1+\sin^2\vartheta)$.

§92. The principle of detailed balancing applied to scattering

The general principle of detailed balancing† can be used to obtain a relation between the intensities in various scattering processes.

Let $\mathrm{d}w_{12}$ be the probability that a quantum $\hbar\omega_1$ is scattered (on a path of unit length) and gives rise to a quantum $\hbar\omega_2$ in the solid angle element $\mathrm{d}o_2$; let $\mathrm{d}w_{21}$ be the probability of the converse process, in which a quantum $\hbar\omega_2$ yields a quantum $\hbar\omega_1$ in the solid angle element $\mathrm{d}o_1$. According to the principle of detailed balancing we have $\mathrm{d}w_{12}/k_2^2\,\mathrm{d}o_2 = \mathrm{d}w_{21}/k_1^2\,\mathrm{d}o_1$, where k_1 and k_2 are the wave numbers of the two quanta. Substituting $k_1^2 = \epsilon_1\omega_1^2/c^2$, $k_2^2 = \epsilon_2\omega_2^2/c^2$ (where $\epsilon_1 = \epsilon(\omega_1)$, $\epsilon_2 = \epsilon(\omega_2)$), we obtain

$$\epsilon_1\omega_1^2\,\mathrm{d}w_{12}/\mathrm{d}o_2 = \epsilon_2\omega_2^2\,\mathrm{d}w_{21}/\mathrm{d}o_1. \tag{92.1}$$

† See *Quantum Mechanics*, §116, Pergamon Press, London, 1958.

Here it is assumed that the initial and final states of the scattering system correspond to discrete energy levels E_1 and E_2, related by $E_1+\hbar\omega_1 = E_2+\hbar\omega_2$. This statement of the problem is not quite true to reality, since the energy levels of a macroscopic body are extremely closely spaced and can be regarded as quasi-continuous.

Instead of the scattering probability dw_{12} with an exactly determined frequency change, we must therefore use the probability of scattering into a frequency range $d\omega_2$, i.e. of the body's entering a state whose energy lies in a range $dE_2 = \hbar d\omega_2$. Denoting this probability (again per unit path length) by dh_{12}, we have $dh_{12} = dw_{12}\, d\Gamma_2 = dw_{12}(d\Gamma_2/dE_2)\hbar\, d\omega_2$, where $d\Gamma_2$ is the number of quantum states of the body in the energy range dE_2. Instead of (92.1), we therefore have

$$\frac{d\Gamma_1}{dE_1}\epsilon_1\omega_1^2\frac{dh_{12}}{do_2\, d\omega_2} = \frac{d\Gamma_2}{dE_2}\epsilon_2\omega_2^2\frac{dh_{21}}{do_1\, d\omega_1}.$$

According to a well-known relation between the statistical weight of a macroscopic state of a body and its entropy $\mathscr{S}$, the derivative $d\Gamma/dE$ is essentially $\exp \mathscr{S}$, so that $(d\Gamma_1/dE_1):(d\Gamma_2/dE_2) = \exp(\mathscr{S}_1-\mathscr{S}_2)$. Since the relative change in the energy of the body resulting from the scattering of one quantum is negligible, the relative change in entropy is also small, and can be taken as $\mathscr{S}_1-\mathscr{S}_2 = (d\mathscr{S}/dE)(E_1-E_2) = (E_1-E_2)/T = \hbar(\omega_2-\omega_1)/T$. Using this result, we can write the final expression of the principle of detailed balancing for scattering in the form

$$e^{-\hbar\omega_1/T}\epsilon_1\omega_1^2\frac{dh_{12}}{do_2\, d\omega_2} = e^{-\hbar\omega_2/T}\epsilon_2\omega_2^2\frac{dh_{21}}{do_1\, d\omega_1}. \qquad (92.2)$$

The quantity dh, whose dimensions are cm^{-1}, is called the *differential extinction coefficient* for scattering of light. It can also be defined as follows: dh is the ratio of the number of quanta scattered in the direction do and the frequency range $d\omega$ per unit time and volume to the incident photon flux density. By integrating dh over all directions and frequencies of the scattered light, we obtain the *total extinction coefficient*, which represents the damping decrement of the photon flux density as the light passes through the scattering medium.

Let $\omega_2 < \omega_1$. The relation (92.2) connects the intensities (extinction coefficients) of Stokes ($1 \to 2$) and anti-Stokes ($2 \to 1$) scattering. We see that the latter is in general less than the former by approximately the factor $e^{-\hbar(\omega_1-\omega_2)/T}$. This is a very general result, and corresponds to the fact that the transfer of energy from the body to the electromagnetic field reduces the probability of the process by a factor $e^{-\Delta E/T}$, where ΔE is the energy transferred. In particular, the stimulated emission, in which the body gives up an energy $\hbar(\omega_1+\omega_2)$ in each scattering process, is therefore usually very weak. The probability of such a process, when $\hbar(\omega_1+\omega_2) \gg T$, contains the small factor $e^{-\hbar(\omega_1+\omega_2)/T}$.

The general relation (92.2) is much simplified in the important case of scattering with a relatively small change in frequency. We shall denote ω_1 by ω simply, and the small difference $\omega_2 - \omega_1$ by $\Delta\omega\,(\ll \omega)$, and put for brevity $dh_{12}/do_2\,d\omega_2 = I(\omega, \Delta\omega)$. In the non-exponential factors $\epsilon\omega^2$ in (92.2) we can neglect the difference $\Delta\omega$; these factors then cancel, leaving

$$I(\omega, \Delta\omega)e^{-\hbar\omega/T} = I(\omega + \Delta\omega, -\Delta\omega)e^{-\hbar(\omega+\Delta\omega)/T}.$$

In the first argument of the function $I(\omega+\Delta\omega, -\Delta\omega)$, which gives the initial frequency of the light, we can neglect $\Delta\omega$, i.e. refer the scattered intensity to a somewhat displaced frequency of the incident light. Then

$$I(\omega, \Delta\omega) = I(\omega, -\Delta\omega)e^{-\hbar\Delta\omega/T}. \tag{92.3}$$

In this approximation I on each side of the equation refers to the same frequency of the incident light. In other words, the relation (92.3) gives a simple relation between Stokes and anti-Stokes scattering of the same light with the same magnitude of the frequency change $\Delta\omega$.

§93. Scattering with small change of frequency

The theory given in §91 is entirely general, and is applicable to all cases of scattering in an isotropic medium, whatever the mechanism of scattering. Such a general discussion, of course, cannot proceed very far, and a further investigation of the phenomenon of scattering requires some restrictive assumptions.

In most practical cases the scattering of light involves only a relatively small change in frequency, $\Delta\omega = \omega' - \omega$. The calculations given below pertain to this case. Besides the condition $\Delta\omega \ll \omega$, we shall suppose that the relative change in the refractive index of the medium over the frequency range $\Delta\omega$ is small. This condition means that the frequency ω must not lie close to a range in which the scattering medium is also absorbing.

If ω is in the optical range, the microscopic mechanism of scattering with small $\Delta\omega$ may involve various kinds of motion of atoms and molecules (as opposed to the purely electronic motions which give rise to optical transitions), including intramolecular vibrations of atoms, rotations or vibrations of molecules, etc.

Let $q = q(t)$ denote the set of co-ordinates describing the motion which causes the scattering.† Since this motion is relatively slow, the macroscopic description of the motion can be regarded from a different standpoint by introducing the dielectric permeability tensor $\epsilon_{ik}(q)$, whose components at any instant depend only on the values of the co-ordinates q at that instant as parameters. This property follows from the assumed smallness of the relative change in ϵ. The dielectric permeability thus defined pertains to the field averaged with respect to the electron motion for a given position of

† For simplicity, we shall give a classical discussion. The results are actually still valid when quantum mechanics is used to describe the motion of the nuclei.

the nuclei. When the averaging of the field with respect to the motion of the nuclei is carried out, the dielectric permeability reduces to the scalar $\epsilon(\omega)$. Let the deviation of ϵ_{ik} from this value be $\delta\epsilon_{ik}$:

$$\epsilon_{ik}(q) = \epsilon\delta_{ik} + \delta\epsilon_{ik}(q). \tag{93.1}$$

The tensor ϵ_{ik} gives the relation between the field and the induction as functions of time. It should be emphasised that the incident wave is still assumed to have a single frequency ω, but the field $\mathbf{E}'$ in the scattered wave is now regarded as a function of time, not resolved into single-frequency components. The total field consists of the field $\mathbf{E}$ in the incident wave and the field $\mathbf{E}'$ in the scattered wave. Thus $D_i + D'_i = \epsilon_{ik}(E_k + E'_k)$. Cancelling $D_i = \epsilon E_i$ and omitting the second-order term $\delta\epsilon_{ik}E'_k$, we obtain

$$D'_i = \epsilon E'_i + \delta\epsilon_{ik}(q)E_k. \tag{93.2}$$

The relation (93.2) is of the same form as (91.2). There is a difference, however, in that with this approach it is clear that the tensor $\alpha_{ik} = \delta\epsilon_{ik}$ is symmetrical. This follows at once from the general theorem concerning the symmetry of the dielectric permeability tensor. Furthermore, since this tensor is real for a transparent medium, the tensor $\delta\epsilon_{ik}$ is also real.

Since the tensor α_{ik} has no antisymmetrical part, there is no antisymmetrical scattering (§91) with small change in frequency.

Let us calculate the total scattered intensity with all frequency changes $\Delta\omega \ll \omega$. This can easily be done as follows. In equation (91.3) for the field in the scattered wave we can replace k' by $k = \omega\sqrt{\epsilon}/c$ (and take the value of α for $\omega' = \omega$); this equation does not then involve ω', i.e. it is the same for every component of the spectral resolution of the field. The equation is therefore valid for the unresolved field in the scattered wave, which we shall denote by the same letter $\mathbf{E}'$. Using the solution (91.6), we obtain

$$\overline{|\mathbf{E}'|^2} = \frac{k^4}{16\pi^2\epsilon^2 R_0^2}\overline{|\mathbf{G}|^2}\sin^2\theta = \frac{\omega^4}{16\pi^2 R_0^2 c^4}\overline{|\mathbf{G}|^2}\sin^2\theta,$$

where θ is the angle between $\mathbf{k}$ and $\mathbf{G}$, and the bar denotes, as in §91, the final average with respect to the motion of the particles (i.e. with respect to the time dependence of q).

We define the extinction coefficient h as the ratio of the total intensity of light scattered in all directions per unit volume of the scattering medium to the incident flux density:†

$$h = \frac{1}{V|\mathbf{E}|^2}\int \overline{|\mathbf{E}'|^2} R_0^2\, do' = \frac{\omega^4}{6\pi c^4 V}\frac{\overline{|\mathbf{G}|^2}}{|\mathbf{E}|^2}.$$

† This definition differs by a factor ω'/ω from the general definition (in terms of the number of scattered quanta) given in §92. In the present case this factor may be taken as unity, and the two definitions are equivalent.

As we have seen in §91, in calculating the mean value $\overline{|\mathbf{G}|^2}$ we can replace the exponential factor in the integrand in **G** by unity, so that

$$\overline{|\mathbf{G}|^2} = E_{0i}E_{0k}^* \overline{\int \delta\epsilon_{li}\, \mathrm{d}V \int \delta\epsilon_{lk}\, \mathrm{d}V}.$$

The expression to be averaged is a tensor of rank two and, since the medium is isotropic, the result of the averaging is

$$\overline{\int \delta\epsilon_{li}\, \mathrm{d}V \int \delta\epsilon_{lk}\, \mathrm{d}V} = \tfrac{1}{3}\delta_{ik}\overline{\left(\int \delta\epsilon_{lm}\, \mathrm{d}V\right)^2}.$$

Thus we have finally

$$h = \frac{\omega^4}{18\pi c^4}\frac{1}{V}\overline{\left(\int \delta\epsilon_{lm}\, \mathrm{d}V\right)^2}, \tag{93.3}$$

or

$$h = (\omega^4/18\pi c^4)V\overline{(\delta\epsilon_{lm})_V{}^2}, \tag{93.4}$$

where the suffix V denotes an averaging over the volume V.

The mean value of the squared integral can be written as the mean value of a double integral, and is found to be proportional to the volume V (cf. §91). Hence the value of the extinction coefficient is independent of the scattering volume, as it should be, and also of the polarisation of the incident light.

Formula (93.4) can be regarded in the following way. We can say formally that scattering would not occur in a completely homogeneous medium (i.e. one whose dielectric permeability is exactly constant). The scattering can be macroscopically described as resulting from inhomogeneities in the medium. The variation of these inhomogeneities with time, when resolved into spectral components, gives the change in frequency of the light when it is scattered.

§94. Rayleigh scattering in gases and liquids

Two types of scattering can be distinguished, depending on the change in frequency of the light: (1) *combination scattering*, which is the *Raman–Landsberg–Mandel'shtam effect* and results in the appearance in the scattered light of lines whose frequency differs from that of the incident light, (2) *Rayleigh scattering*, in which the frequency is essentially unchanged.

Combination scattering in gases results from a change, due to the incident light, in the vibrational, rotational or electronic state of the molecule.† Rayleigh scattering, on the other hand, does not involve a change in the internal state of the molecule. In the limiting case of a rarefied gas, when the mean free path l of the molecules is large compared with the wavelength λ of the light, scattering takes place independently at each molecule, and can be discussed microscopically, using quantum mechanics.

† Under ordinary observational conditions, electronic transitions are unimportant.

Here we shall discuss the opposite limiting case, where $l \ll \lambda$,† and the Rayleigh scattering in gases can be divided into two parts. One part is due to irregularities in the orientation of the molecules (called *fluctuations of anisotropy*). The other part is scattering by fluctuations in the gas density. The orientation of the molecules is entirely changed by a few collisions, i.e. after a time of the order of the mean free time τ. Hence the scattering by fluctuations of anisotropy results in the appearance of a relatively broad line with its peak at $\omega' = \omega$ and width $\sim \hbar/\tau$. The scattering by fluctuations of density gives a much sharper line superposed on the other. As we shall see below, fluctuations of density in volumes $\sim \lambda^3$ are of importance in the scattering of light with wavelength λ. Since these volumes are large, the fluctuations in them occur comparatively slowly, and so the scattered line is narrow. In what follows we shall regard this sharp line as being undisplaced.

The scattering by density fluctuations is scalar scattering (see the end of §91): since the density ρ is a scalar, so is the change in the dielectric permeability $\delta\epsilon$ resulting from a change in ρ. The change in the dielectric permeability in fluctuations of anisotropy, on the other hand, is described by a symmetrical tensor $\delta\epsilon_{ik}$ with zero trace. The latter property follows from the fact that the effect must vanish on averaging over all directions. Thus the scattering by anisotropy fluctuations is symmetrical scattering.

In liquids the situation is less simple. Combination scattering can arise only from a change in the vibrational or electronic state of the molecule; rotational combination lines do not occur for scattering in liquids. The reason is that, because of the strong interaction between molecules in a liquid, they cannot rotate freely so as to acquire discrete rotational energy levels. The rotation of the molecules, therefore, like any motion in which their relative position changes, contributes in a liquid only to the relatively broad scattering line at $\omega' = \omega$, which in this case may be regarded as the effect of Rayleigh scattering. The relaxation time of such motions depends on the viscosity of the liquid.

The possibility of separating from the total Rayleigh scattering in a liquid a part due to thermodynamic fluctuations (of density or temperature) depends on the magnitudes of the various relaxation times. It is necessary that the relaxation times of all processes of establishment of equilibrium in the liquid should be small in comparison with the times characterising the fluctuations concerned. In this case a narrow "undisplaced" line and a broader one are observed. The undisplaced line corresponds to scalar scattering. The broader background, however, does not in general correspond, as it does in gases, to purely symmetrical scattering with no scalar part.

The total intensity of the undisplaced line is easily calculated by means of

† More precisely, the necessary condition is $l \ll \lambda \sin \frac{1}{2}\vartheta$, where ϑ is the scattering angle. This is because the expression (94.4) which gives the scattered intensity involves the frequency only in the expression $q = (2\omega/c) \sin \frac{1}{2}\vartheta$.

the general formula (93.4). For scalar scattering $\delta\epsilon_{ik} = \delta\epsilon\delta_{ik}$, and the extinction coefficient is therefore

$$h = \frac{\omega^4}{6\pi c^4} V\overline{(\delta\epsilon)_V{}^2}. \tag{94.1}$$

If $\delta\rho$ and δT are the changes in density and temperature, then

$$\delta\epsilon = (\partial\epsilon/\partial\rho)_T\delta\rho + (\partial\epsilon/\partial T)_\rho\delta T.$$

The fluctuations of density and temperature are statistically independent† ($\overline{\delta T\delta\rho} = 0$), and their mean squares are

$$\overline{(\delta T)_V{}^2} = T^2/\rho c_v V, \qquad \overline{(\delta\rho)_V{}^2} = (T\rho/V)(\partial\rho/\partial p)_T,$$

where c_v is the specific heat per unit mass. Thus we have finally

$$h = \frac{\omega^4}{6\pi c^4}\left[T\rho\left(\frac{\partial\rho}{\partial p}\right)_T\left(\frac{\partial\epsilon}{\partial\rho}\right)_T^2 + \frac{T^2}{\rho c_v}\left(\frac{\partial\epsilon}{\partial T}\right)_\rho^2\right]. \tag{94.2}$$

This formula was first derived by A. Einstein (1910).

For gases formula (94.2) becomes much simpler. The dielectric permeability of a gas (at optical frequencies) is almost independent of temperature, and hence the second term in the brackets can be neglected. The density dependence is that $\epsilon - 1$ is proportional to ρ, and hence

$$\rho(\partial\epsilon/\partial\rho)_T \approx \epsilon - 1 \approx 2(n-1),$$

where $n = \sqrt{\epsilon}$ is the refractive index. Since, from the equation of state of a perfect gas, $(1/\rho)(\partial\rho/\partial p)_T = 1/NT$, where N is the number of particles in unit volume, we find that

$$h = 2\omega^4(n-1)^2/3\pi c^4 N. \tag{94.3}$$

This formula was first derived by Rayleigh (1881).

Let us now examine the fine structure of the undisplaced line. This requires a consideration of the time variation of the fluctuations. In this respect, thermodynamic fluctuations fall into two classes.‡ Adiabatic fluctuations of pressure in a fluid are propagated as undamped waves with the velocity of sound u; we here neglect the absorption of sound, since it causes only a broadening of the line (see below). Fluctuations of entropy at constant pressure, however, are not propagated relative to the fluid, and are damped only gradually as a result of thermal conduction.

The time variation of the intensity (not averaged with respect to time) is given by the squared modulus of the integral

$$\mathbf{G}(t) = \int \delta\epsilon(t).\exp(-i\mathbf{q}\cdot\mathbf{r})\,dV.\mathbf{E}_0, \tag{94.4}$$

† See *Statistical Physics*, §111, Pergamon Press, London, 1958.
‡ See *Fluid Mechanics*, §79, Pergamon Press, London, 1959.

in which $\delta\epsilon$ is regarded as a function of time. In order to determine the shape of the scattering line, $\mathbf{G}(t)$ must be resolved into spectral components (i.e. $\delta\epsilon(t)$ must be so resolved); the distribution of intensity as a function of $\Delta\omega$ will then be given by the squared modulus of the component $\mathbf{G}_{\Delta\omega}$. However, the factor $\exp(-i\mathbf{q}\cdot\mathbf{r})$ in (94.4) cannot be replaced by unity, as we have done hitherto. The reason is that the quantity $|\mathbf{G}_{\Delta\omega}|^2$ depends markedly on the correlation of the time variation of the fluctuations at different points in space. This is clear when $|\mathbf{G}_{\Delta\omega}|^2$ is written as a double integral

$$\int\int \delta\epsilon(t)\delta\epsilon(t')\exp[-i\mathbf{q}\cdot(\mathbf{r}-\mathbf{r}')]\exp[i\Delta\omega(t-t')]\,\mathrm{d}V\,\mathrm{d}V'\,\mathrm{d}t\,\mathrm{d}t'.$$

On account of the wave propagation of sound disturbances, the time variation of pressure fluctuation is correlated even at great distances. This fact was of no importance in determining the total intensity of the line, which is obtained by averaging the square $|\mathbf{G}(t)|^2$ with respect to time; since, in this case, $\mathbf{G}(t)$ and $\mathbf{G}^*(t)$ are taken at the same instant, it follows that only the correlation between the values of $\delta\epsilon$ at different points at the same instant is of importance, and this correlation extends only over short distances.

Let us first consider the changes $\delta\epsilon$ which result from pressure fluctuations. The quantity (94.4) is the Fourier space component of the fluctuation $\delta\epsilon$ whose wave vector is $\mathbf{q}$; its time dependence is given by $e^{-it\Delta\omega}$, where $\Delta\omega = \pm qu$. Since $\omega \approx \omega'$, we have $q = |\mathbf{k}'-\mathbf{k}| = (2\omega/c)\sin\frac{1}{2}\vartheta$, where ϑ is the angle between $\mathbf{k}$ and $\mathbf{k}'$. If the corresponding value of $\Delta\omega$ is denoted by $\Delta\omega_0$, then

$$\Delta\omega_0 = qu = \pm(2\omega u/c)\sin\tfrac{1}{2}\vartheta. \tag{94.5}$$

Thus the scattering by pressure fluctuations results in the appearance of a doublet (called the *Mandel'shtam–Brillouin doublet*), the distance $2\Delta\omega_0$ between whose components depends on the angle of scattering.

The fluctuations of entropy have zero frequency, as stated above, and so scattering by them gives a central line with $\Delta\omega = 0$.

Let us determine the intensities of the doublet and the central line. The total intensity of the undisplaced line is given by formula (94.2), so that it is sufficient to determine, say, $I_{\text{doublet}}/I_{\text{total}}$ (where I_{doublet} is the combined intensity of the two components of the doublet, i.e. twice the intensity of each component†). Since the doublet lines are due to scattering by adiabatic pressure fluctuations, their intensity is given by the mean square $(\partial\epsilon/\partial p)_S{}^2\overline{(\delta p)_V{}^2}$.

Using the formula for adiabatic pressure fluctuations and a simple transformation by means of the formula for the ratio of adiabatic and isothermal

† The difference between the intensities of the two components is, according to formula (92.3), usually negligible, since $\hbar\Delta\omega_0 \ll T$.

compressibilities, we obtain

$$\left(\frac{\partial\epsilon}{\partial p}\right)_S^2 \overline{(\delta p)_V^2} = \frac{\rho T}{V}\left(\frac{\partial p}{\partial \rho}\right)_S \left(\frac{\partial \epsilon}{\partial p}\right)_S^2$$
$$= \frac{\rho T}{V}\left(\frac{\partial \rho}{\partial p}\right)_S \left(\frac{\partial \epsilon}{\partial \rho}\right)_S^2$$
$$= \frac{\rho T c_v}{V c_p}\left(\frac{\partial \rho}{\partial p}\right)_T \left(\frac{\partial \epsilon}{\partial \rho}\right)_S^2. \quad (94.6)$$

The adiabatic derivative $(\partial\epsilon/\partial\rho)_S$ can be expressed in terms of more convenient quantities by transforming it to the variables ρ and T:

$$(\partial\epsilon/\partial\rho)_S = (\partial\epsilon/\partial\rho)_T + (T/c_v\rho^2)(\partial p/\partial T)_\rho(\partial\epsilon/\partial T)_\rho.$$

The required ratio of intensities is given by the ratio of (94.6) to the mean square total fluctuation (the expression in brackets in (94.2)). We shall not give the cumbersome general formula, but only the simpler form obtained when the temperature dependence of ϵ is neglected:

$$h_{\text{doublet}}/h_{\text{total}} = c_v/c_p \quad (94.7)$$

(L. Landau and G. Placzek, 1933).

To determine the shape of the lines, it is necessary to consider the dissipative processes which result in the "decay" of the fluctuations. These processes cause a damping of the fluctuation amplitude as $e^{-\gamma t}$, where γ is a definite constant. If the "eigenfrequency" of the oscillations is $\Delta\omega_0$, the total time dependence is given by $e^{-t(i\Delta\omega_0+\gamma)}$. The intensity distribution in the line is proportional to the squared moduli of the Fourier components of this factor, i.e.

$$dI = \frac{I_0}{\pi}\frac{\gamma}{(\Delta\omega-\Delta\omega_0)^2+\gamma^2}d\Delta\omega, \quad (94.8)$$

where I_0 is the total intensity of the line. This is called the *dispersion form* of the line. The "width" is γ.

According to formulae derived in the theory of absorption of sound,† the damping coefficient for sound fluctuations with wave vector $\mathbf{q}$ is

$$\gamma = \frac{q^2}{2\rho}\left[\frac{4}{3}\eta + \zeta + \kappa\left(\frac{1}{c_v} - \frac{1}{c_p}\right)\right],$$

where η, ζ are the viscosity coefficients of the fluid and κ its thermal conductivity. Substituting $q^2 = 2(\omega/c)^2(1-\cos\vartheta)$, we obtain the following expression for the width of the doublet components:

$$\gamma = \frac{\omega^2}{\rho c^2}(1-\cos\vartheta)\left[\frac{4}{3}\eta + \zeta + \kappa\left(\frac{1}{c_v} - \frac{1}{c_p}\right)\right]. \quad (94.9)$$

† See *Fluid Mechanics*, §77.

The damping of isobaric fluctuations of entropy (and therefore of temperature) is determined by the heat-conduction equation $\partial T/\partial t = \chi \triangle T$, where χ is the thermometric conductivity. For fluctuations with wave vector $\mathbf{q}$ (i.e. spatial variation as $\exp(i\mathbf{q}\cdot\mathbf{r})$), we therefore have

$$\gamma = \chi q^2 = 2\chi(\omega^2/c^2)(1 - \cos\vartheta). \qquad (94.10)$$

The shape of the central line is given by (94.8) with $\Delta\omega_0 = 0$, the width γ being (94.10).

As already mentioned at the beginning of this section, the above theory is applicable to scattering in a liquid if all the relaxation times in it are small compared with those characterising the fluctuations. It should be borne in mind that, in any liquid, there are relaxation times of various orders of magnitude. The most rapid relaxation process, apparently, is the "decay" of elastic stresses in the liquid. The corresponding *Maxwellian relaxation time* is $\tau_M \sim \eta/G$, where G is the modulus of rigidity.† The reorientation of the molecules, i.e. the "decay" of the anisotropy fluctuations, takes place less rapidly. The corresponding *Debye relaxation time* is $\tau_D \sim \eta a^3/kT$, where a is the dimension of the molecule; the difference between τ_M and τ_D is particularly large in liquids with large molecules. Finally, various other slow relaxation processes leading to the dispersion of sound are also possible (e.g. chemical reactions, slow transfer of energy to vibrational degrees of freedom of the molecule). The important processes as regards scattering are those for which $1/\tau$ is comparable with the frequency of the "sound" disturbances which cause the scattering. There is as yet no complete survey of all the possible cases, and we shall not give one here, but merely mention that, when the viscosity of the liquid is sufficiently high, and so

$$\tau_M \gg 1/qu \sim c/\omega u \sin\tfrac{1}{2}\vartheta,$$

the liquid behaves as an amorphous solid with respect to the scattering of light.

Finally, we may note an unusual type of scattering which occurs at the free surface of a liquid. The fluctuations have the result that this surface is no longer perfectly plane, and the consequent "roughness" causes a partial scattering of the light reflected from it (L. I. Mandel'shtam, 1913).‡

PROBLEM

Light is scattered in a gas whose molecules are linear, with polarisabilities $\alpha_\parallel$ and $\alpha_\perp$ along and across the axis respectively. Determine the intensity resulting from the various types of scattering.

Solution. The total intensity of scattered light (for given vibrational and electronic states of the molecules) includes the Rayleigh scattering and the rotational part of the combination scattering. Since the scattering takes place at the individual molecules of the gas,

† See *Theory of Elasticity*, §31, Pergamon Press, London, 1959.

‡ See L. I. Mandel'shtam, *Annalen der Physik* **41**, 609, 1913, where a calculation is given for light scattered in the plane of incidence.

the total extinction coefficient is most simply obtained from formula (72.3), by multiplying by the number of particles per unit volume N and replacing the squared polarisability by $\frac{1}{3}\alpha_{ik}^2 = \frac{1}{3}(\alpha_{\parallel}^2 + 2\alpha_{\perp}^2)$:

$$h = \frac{8\pi\omega^4 N}{9c^4}(\alpha_{\parallel}^2 + 2\alpha_{\perp}^2). \tag{1}$$

The undisplaced Rayleigh line is due to the scalar part of the polarisability, i.e. it is the same as if the polarisability tensor of the molecule were $\frac{1}{3}\alpha_{ll}\delta_{ik}$. The same formula, (72.3), therefore gives

$$h_{\text{undisp}} = \frac{8\pi\omega^4 N}{27c^4}(\alpha_{\parallel} + 2\alpha_{\perp})^2. \tag{2}$$

The difference $h_{\text{total}} - h_{\text{undisp}}$ includes the "background" (scattering by anisotropy fluctuations) and the rotational combination scattering. In order to separate the former, we must first average the polarisability tensor of the molecule with respect to rotation about some particular axis (perpendicular to the axis of the molecule). The polarisability along the axis of rotation averaged in this way is evidently $\alpha_{\perp}$, and that along any direction in a plane perpendicular to the axis of rotation is $\frac{1}{2}(\alpha_{\perp} + \alpha_{\parallel})$. In other words, a molecule rotating about a given axis is to be regarded as a particle for which the principal values of the polarisability tensor are $\alpha_{\perp}$, $\frac{1}{2}(\alpha_{\perp} + \alpha_{\parallel})$, $\frac{1}{2}(\alpha_{\perp} + \alpha_{\parallel})$. Using these, we calculate the symmetrical tensor $\alpha_{ik} - \frac{1}{3}\alpha_{ll}\delta_{ik}$, whose trace is zero, and then a procedure similar to the derivation of formulae (1) and (2) gives

$$h_{\text{backg}} = \frac{8\pi\omega^4 N}{9c^4}\frac{(\alpha_{\perp} - \alpha_{\parallel})^2}{6}. \tag{3}$$

Finally, the intensity of the rotation combination scattering is obtained by subtracting (2) and (3) from (1):

$$h_{\text{combin}} = \frac{8\pi\omega^4 N}{9c^4}\frac{(\alpha_{\perp} - \alpha_{\parallel})^2}{2}.$$

§95. Critical opalescence

The isothermal compressibility $(\partial\rho/\partial p)_T$ increases without limit as the critical state is approached. The expression (94.2) for the total intensity due to scalar Rayleigh scattering therefore increases also. This indicates a marked increase in scattering near the critical point, called *critical opalescence*.† The formula (94.2) itself is, however, inapplicable, because the expressions for the thermodynamic fluctuations used in its derivation are no longer correct.

The increase in intensity does not take place for all three components of the fine structure of the Rayleigh line, but only for the central component. According to (94.2) and (94.7), the intensity of the doublet is

$$h_{\text{doublet}} \cong \frac{\omega^4}{6\pi c^4}\frac{T\rho c_v}{c_p}\left(\frac{\partial\rho}{\partial p}\right)_T\left(\frac{\partial\epsilon}{\partial\rho}\right)_T^2.$$

The thermodynamic formula

$$c_p - c_v = \frac{T}{\rho^2}\frac{(\partial p/\partial T)_\rho^2}{(\partial p/\partial\rho)_T}$$

† A similar phenomenon occurs for scattering in a solid near the critical point of a second-order phase transition. It has been discussed by V. L. Ginzburg, *Doklady Akademii Nauk SSSR* **105**, 240, 1955.

gives near the critical point

$$h_{\text{doublet}} = \frac{\omega^4}{6\pi c^4} \frac{\rho^3 c_v}{(\partial p/\partial T)_\rho^2} \left(\frac{\partial \epsilon}{\partial \rho}\right)_T^2. \tag{95.1}$$

As we shall see below, the factor $\exp(-i\mathbf{q}\cdot\mathbf{r})$ in (94.4) cannot be replaced by unity near the critical point, even in calculating the total scattered intensity. Let $\mathrm{d}h$ be the differential extinction coefficient, relating to scattering into a given solid angle $\mathrm{d}o$ (corresponding to a given value of $\mathbf{q} = \mathbf{k}-\mathbf{k}'$). Considering, for definiteness, the scattering of unpolarised light, and using the result that the angular dependence (for scalar scattering) is given by the expression $\frac{3}{4}(1+\cos^2\vartheta)$, we have

$$\mathrm{d}h = \frac{\omega^4}{6\pi c^4}\frac{1}{V}\overline{\left|\int \delta\epsilon \exp(-i\mathbf{q}\cdot\mathbf{r})\,\mathrm{d}V\right|^2} \cdot \tfrac{3}{4}(1+\cos^2\vartheta)\frac{\mathrm{d}o'}{4\pi}. \tag{95.2}$$

Near the critical point, the density fluctuations increase but the temperature fluctuations remain finite. It is therefore sufficient to consider $\delta\epsilon = (\partial\epsilon/\partial\rho)_T\delta\rho$, so that

$$\mathrm{d}h = \frac{\omega^4}{6\pi c^4}\left(\frac{\partial\epsilon}{\partial\rho}\right)_T^2 \frac{1}{V}\overline{\left|\int \delta\rho \exp(-i\mathbf{q}\cdot\mathbf{r})\,\mathrm{d}V\right|^2} \cdot \tfrac{3}{4}(1+\cos^2\vartheta)\frac{\mathrm{d}o'}{4\pi}. \tag{95.3}$$

According to the theory of fluctuations, the mean square density fluctuation near the critical point can be expressed in terms of the coefficients a and b in the formula

$$F - \bar{F} = \tfrac{1}{2}a(\delta\rho)^2 + \tfrac{1}{2}b(\mathbf{grad}\,\delta\rho)^2, \tag{95.4}$$

where F is the free energy per unit volume.†

This formula gives the leading terms in an expansion of the change in the free energy in powers of $\delta\rho$ and of its gradient; the latter has to be taken into account because of the amplification of local inhomogeneities in the body near the critical point. The constant a is expressed in terms of the ordinary thermodynamic quantities by‡

$$a = (1/\rho)(\partial p/\partial\rho)_T. \tag{95.5}$$

The mean square in (95.3) can be expressed in terms of a and b by

$$\overline{\left|\int \delta\rho \exp(-i\mathbf{q}\cdot\mathbf{r})\,\mathrm{d}V\right|^2} = VT/(a+bq^2). \tag{95.6}$$

---

† See *Statistical Physics*, §116.

‡ The derivative $(\partial F/\partial\rho)_T$ is the thermodynamic potential per unit mass, and the second derivative is therefore $a = (\partial^2 F/\partial\rho^2)_T = (\partial\Phi/\partial\rho)_T = (1/\rho)(\partial p/\partial\rho)_T$.

Substituting in (95.3), we obtain the final result

$$dh = \frac{\omega^4}{32\pi^2 c^4}\left(\frac{\partial\epsilon}{\partial\rho}\right)_T^2 \frac{1+\cos^2\vartheta}{\dfrac{1}{\rho}\left(\dfrac{\partial p}{\partial\rho}\right)_T + 2\dfrac{\omega^2}{c^2}b(1-\cos\vartheta)}\,do'. \tag{95.7}$$

This formula was first derived by L. S. ORNSTEIN and F. ZERNIKE (1914). When the angle ϑ is not small, the first term in the denominator may be neglected, and

$$dh = \frac{\omega^2}{64\pi^2 c^2 b}\left(\frac{\partial\epsilon}{\partial\rho}\right)_T^2 \frac{1+\cos^2\vartheta}{1-\cos\vartheta}\,do'. \tag{95.8}$$

The total intensity scattered in all directions is obtained by integrating (95.7) with respect to o'. When $(\partial p/\partial\rho)_T = 0$, i.e. at the critical point, the integral is logarithmically divergent for small angles. In reality, the integration should be extended only to angles of the order of the diffraction angle ($\sim \lambda/L$, where L is the dimension of the body). The total intensity therefore depends logarithmically on the dimension of the scattering body.

§96. Scattering in amorphous solids

Rayleigh scattering in amorphous solids differs considerably from that in fluids. In an isotropic solid there are two velocities of propagation of sound, u_l (longitudinal) and u_t (transverse). The fine structure of the Rayleigh line therefore includes not one but two Mandel'shtam–Brillouin doublets. They are due to scattering by transverse and longitudinal "sound waves", and their distances from the centre of the line are respectively $\pm\Delta\omega_l$, $\pm\Delta\omega_t$, where $\Delta\omega_l = qu_l$, $\Delta\omega_t = qu_t$. Since $u_l > u_t$, it follows that $\Delta\omega_l > \Delta\omega_t$. The central component of the line is again due to fluctuations which are not propagated relative to the medium. In this case the main fluctuations of the latter type are those of structure. In an amorphous body, where the atoms are not arranged in an ordered manner, these fluctuations are comparatively large and vary only slowly with time (on account of the extreme slowness of the diffusion processes in a solid). Scattering by these fluctuations leads to a strong line whose width is almost zero. As regards polarisation and angular distribution, this line results from a superposition of scalar and symmetrical scattering.

Next, let us consider the doublet components of the Rayleigh line in amorphous bodies. Here we cannot put $\exp(-i\mathbf{q}\cdot\mathbf{r}) = 1$ in the integral $\mathbf{G}$, as we did for fluids, even in calculating the total intensity (and polarisation) of the scattered light; moreover, the scattering cannot be classified according to dependence on angle as in §91. The reason is that, in a solid, the effect of any deformation (in this case, fluctuations) extends to considerable distances. Hence the fluctuations at different points in the body at the same instant are correlated even at distances large compared with $1/q$.

The field in the scattered wave is

$$\mathbf{E}' = -\frac{\omega^2 \exp(ikR_0)}{4\pi R_0 c^2}\mathbf{n}' \times (\mathbf{n}' \times \mathbf{G}), \tag{96.1}$$

where

$$G_i = \int \delta\epsilon_{ik} \exp(-i\mathbf{q}\cdot\mathbf{r})\, \mathrm{d}V . E_{0k}, \tag{96.2}$$

and $\mathbf{n}'$ is a unit vector in the direction of scattering. The change in the dielectric permeability resulting from the deformation of an isotropic body is

$$\delta\epsilon_{ik} = a_1 u_{ik} + a_2 u_{ll}\delta_{ik}, \tag{96.3}$$

where u_{ik} is the strain tensor (see (81.1)). Since the integral (96.2) isolates from $\delta\epsilon_{ik}$ the Fourier space component with wave vector $\mathbf{q}$, u_{ik} in (96.3) must be taken as the deformation in a sound wave with this wave vector. We therefore write the displacement vector as

$$\mathbf{u} = \mathrm{re}\{\mathbf{u}_0 \exp(i\mathbf{q}\cdot\mathbf{r})\} = \tfrac{1}{2}[\mathbf{u}_0 \exp(i\mathbf{q}\cdot\mathbf{r}) + \mathbf{u}_0^* \exp(-i\mathbf{q}\cdot\mathbf{r})], \tag{96.4}$$

whence the strain tensor is

$$\begin{aligned} u_{ik} &= \frac{1}{2}\left(\frac{\partial u_i}{\partial x_k} + \frac{\partial u_k}{\partial x_i}\right) \\ &= \mathrm{re}\{\tfrac{1}{2}i(u_{0i}q_k + u_{0k}q_i)\exp(i\mathbf{q}\cdot\mathbf{r})\}, \end{aligned}$$

and the volume integral is

$$\int u_{ik} \exp(-i\mathbf{q}\cdot\mathbf{r})\, \mathrm{d}V = \tfrac{1}{4}iV(u_{0i}q_k + u_{0k}q_i). \tag{96.5}$$

Let us first consider scattering by transverse "sound" waves. Since in a transverse wave $\mathbf{u}$ is perpendicular to $\mathbf{q}$, and $u_{ll} = 0$, $\delta\epsilon_{ik} = a_1 u_{ik}$. Using (96.5), we therefore have

$$\mathbf{G} = \tfrac{1}{4}iVa_1\{\mathbf{u}_0(\mathbf{q}\cdot\mathbf{E}_0) + \mathbf{q}(\mathbf{u}_0\cdot\mathbf{E}_0)\}. \tag{96.6}$$

A transverse sound wave can have two independent directions of polarisation: the vector $\mathbf{u}$ may be in the plane of $\mathbf{k}$ and $\mathbf{k}'$, or perpendicular to that plane. Since $\mathbf{E}$ is perpendicular to $\mathbf{k}$, it is easy to see that in the first case the component of $\mathbf{G}$ in the plane perpendicular to $\mathbf{k}'$ is zero. Thus transverse sound waves "polarised" in the plane of $\mathbf{k}$ and $\mathbf{k}'$ do not scatter light.

If the vector $\mathbf{u}$ is perpendicular to the plane of $\mathbf{k}$ and $\mathbf{k}'$, a simple calculation, using (96.1) and (96.6), gives for the field in the scattered wave

$$\begin{aligned} E'_{\parallel} &= \frac{\omega^2 \exp(ikR_0)}{4\pi R_0 c^2} . \tfrac{1}{4}a_1 iVqu_0 \cos\tfrac{1}{2}\vartheta . E_{\perp}, \\ E'_{\perp} &= \frac{\omega^2 \exp(ikR_0)}{4\pi R_0 c^2} . \tfrac{1}{4}a_1 iVqu_0 \cos\tfrac{1}{2}\vartheta . E_{\parallel}. \end{aligned} \tag{96.7}$$

Here ϑ is, as usual, the angle between $\mathbf{k}$ and $\mathbf{k}'$, and the suffixes $\parallel$ and $\perp$ denote components in the plane of scattering and perpendicular to that plane. The coefficient of proportionality in these two formulae involves the same fluctuation u_0. This means that no depolarisation occurs on scattering: linearly polarised light remains so (though it is polarised in a different plane).

Since the coefficients in formulae (96.7) are exactly the same, the extinction coefficient dh does not depend on the state of polarisation of the incident light, and is

$$\mathrm{d}h = \left(\frac{q\omega^2 a_1}{16\pi c^2}\right)^2 V\overline{|u_0|^2}\cos^2\tfrac{1}{2}\vartheta\,\mathrm{d}o. \tag{96.8}$$

It remains to determine the mean square amplitude of the fluctuation u_0.

From the point of view of the general theory of thermodynamic fluctuations, the sound wave (96.4) may be regarded as a combination of two classical oscillators (waves propagated to the right and to the left), each having a mean kinetic energy $\frac{1}{2}T$. Since the frequency of the oscillations is here $\Delta\omega = qu_t$, the mean kinetic energy is $\frac{1}{2}V\rho\overline{\dot{\mathbf{u}}^2} = \frac{1}{4}V\rho(u_t q)^2\overline{|u_0|^2}$. Equating this to $2 \cdot \frac{1}{2}T$, we have

$$\overline{|u_0|^2} = 4T/V\rho u_t^2 q^2. \tag{96.9}$$

Finally, substituting (96.9) in (96.8), we obtain

$$\mathrm{d}h = \frac{a_1^2\omega^4 T}{64\pi^2 c^4 u_t^2 \rho}\cos^2\tfrac{1}{2}\vartheta\,\mathrm{d}o. \tag{96.10}$$

The angular dependence of the scattering is totally different from that which occurs in fluids.

Let us now consider scattering by longitudinal "sound" waves. In these waves $\mathbf{u}$ is parallel to $\mathbf{q}$, and from (96.3) and (96.4) we find

$$\mathbf{G} = \tfrac{1}{2}iVu_0 q\left\{a_1\frac{\mathbf{q}(\mathbf{q}\cdot\mathbf{E}_0)}{q^2} + a_2\mathbf{E}_0\right\}.$$

A simple calculation gives for the field in the scattered wave

$$\begin{aligned} E_\perp &= \frac{\omega^2\exp(ikR_0)}{4\pi R_0 c^2}\cdot\tfrac{1}{2}iVu_0 q a_2 E_\perp, \\ E_\parallel &= \frac{\omega^2\exp(ikR_0)}{4\pi R_0 c^2}\cdot\tfrac{1}{2}iVu_0 q[\tfrac{1}{2}a_1 + (\tfrac{1}{2}a_1 + a_2)\cos\vartheta]E_\parallel. \end{aligned} \tag{96.11}$$

In this case also there is no depolarisation on scattering. The angular distribution and the extinction coefficient, however, depend on the state and direction of the polarisation of the incident light. We shall not pause to write out the relevant formulae, which are somewhat cumbersome. The calculations are wholly similar to those given above, and the expression for $\overline{|u_0|^2}$ differs only in that u_t is replaced by u_l in (96.9).

CHAPTER XV

DIFFRACTION OF X-RAYS IN CRYSTALS

§97. The general theory of X-ray diffraction

THE phenomenon of X-ray diffraction in crystals occupies a special place in the electrodynamics of matter, since the wavelengths concerned are comparable with the distances between atoms. For this reason the usual macroscopic approach to matter as a continuous medium is entirely invalid, and we must begin by considering scattering by individual charged particles, and essentially by electrons; the scattering by nuclei is unimportant, because of their much greater mass.

The frequencies of the motion of electrons in the atom are of order $\omega_0 \sim v/a$, where v is their velocity and a the dimension of the atom. If $\lambda \sim a$, then, since $v \ll c$, these frequencies are small compared with the X-ray frequency $\omega \sim c/\lambda$. This makes it possible to write the equation of motion of an electron in the field of the electromagnetic wave as

$$m\dot{\mathbf{v}}' = e\mathbf{E}, \tag{97.1}$$

i.e. the electrons may be regarded as free (see §59).

From (97.1) we find the additional velocity acquired by the electron under the action of the wave field: $\mathbf{v}' = ie\mathbf{E}/m\omega$.

Let $n(x, y, z)$ be the number density of electrons in a crystal, averaged over the quantum states of the electrons and over the statistical distribution of the thermal motion of the nuclei in the lattice. It should be emphasised that the usual macroscopic averaging over physically infinitesimal volume elements is *not* included, i.e. $n(x, y, z)$ is the actual density of the "electron cloud" in the crystal lattice. The corresponding current density due to the wave field is:

$$\mathbf{j}' = en\mathbf{v}' = ie^2 n\mathbf{E}/m\omega. \tag{97.2}$$

We substitute this current in the microscopic Maxwell's equations:

$$\mathbf{curl}\,\mathbf{E} = i\omega\mathbf{H}/c, \tag{97.3}$$

$$\begin{aligned}\mathbf{curl}\,\mathbf{H} &= -i\omega\mathbf{E}/c + 4\pi\mathbf{j}'/c\\ &= -\frac{i\omega}{c}\left(1 - \frac{4\pi e^2 n}{m\omega^2}\right)\mathbf{E}.\end{aligned} \tag{97.4}$$

We thereby take account of its reciprocal effect on the field, i.e. scattering.

It is, of course, assumed that this effect is small, i.e. that the inequality

$$4\pi e^2 n/m\omega^2 \ll 1 \tag{97.5}$$

holds. Putting $\mathbf{D} = \epsilon\mathbf{E}$, where

$$\epsilon = 1 - \frac{4\pi e^2 n}{m\omega^2}, \tag{97.6}$$

in accordance with the usual definition of the induction, we reduce equation (97.4) to the usual form $\mathbf{curl\, H} = -i\omega\mathbf{D}/c$. Thus, in this sense, the expression (97.6) for the dielectric permeability (cf. (59.1)) can be used even for wavelengths $\lambda \sim a$, though it must of course be remembered that the symbols **E** and **D** no longer retain their previous meanings: they now pertain to the field which has not been averaged over physically infinitesimal volumes, and ϵ is accordingly a function of the co-ordinates.

In the scattering of X-rays by heavy atoms it may happen that the condition $\omega \gg \omega_0$ is fulfilled for the outer electron shells but not for the inner ones, where $\omega \lesssim \omega_0$ and so the inequality $\lambda \gg a$ holds. In this case the dielectric permeability can still be regarded as the coefficient of proportionality between **D** and **E**, but the formula corresponding to (97.6) gives only the contribution of the outer electrons. That of the inner electrons must in principle be calculated by averaging over the volume of their shells. Thus, if we put $\mathbf{D} = \epsilon\mathbf{E}$ with ϵ a function of the co-ordinates, all possible cases are allowed for. In what follows we shall, for definiteness, use the expression (97.6).

In effecting the averaging of the electron density in (97.2) to obtain $n(x, y, z)$ independent of time, we exclude a possible change of frequency on scattering. That is, we consider only strictly coherent scattering, with no change in frequency.

Eliminating **H** from the two equations (97.3) and (97.4), we obtain $\mathbf{curl\,curl\,E} = \omega^2\mathbf{D}/c^2$. Here we substitute $\mathbf{E} = \mathbf{D} + 4\pi e^2 n\mathbf{E}/m\omega^2$ and expand the expression $\mathbf{curl\,curl\,E}$, using the fact that $\operatorname{div}\mathbf{D} = 0$, as follows from (97.4). Then

$$\triangle\mathbf{D} + \omega^2\mathbf{D}/c^2 = \mathbf{curl\,curl}\,(4\pi e^2 n\mathbf{E}/m\omega^2). \tag{97.7}$$

On the right-hand side of this equation, which already contains the small quantity $4\pi e^2 n/m\omega^2$, **E** must be taken as the given field of the incident wave. Let us find the solution of equation (97.7) in the region outside the scattering crystal and at large distances from it.† Since this equation is of the same form as equation (91.3), the required solution is obtained immediately by

† In solving equation (91.3) it was not possible to consider the field outside the body, since the boundary conditions on the surface would have had to be taken into account (the quantity ϵ' on the left-hand side being different inside and outside the body). The left-hand side of equation (97.7), however, is the same in all space.

analogy with (91.4):

$$\mathbf{E} = \frac{e^2}{m\omega^2}\frac{\exp(ikR_0)}{R_0}\mathbf{k}' \times (\mathbf{k}' \times \mathbf{E}_0)\int n\exp(-i\mathbf{q}\cdot\mathbf{r})\,\mathrm{d}V. \tag{97.8}$$

Here R is the distance from the origin, which is within the crystal, to the point considered; $\mathbf{q} = \mathbf{k}'-\mathbf{k}$; $k = k' = \omega/c$; $\mathbf{E}_0$ is the amplitude of the incident wave. We put $\mathbf{E}$ instead of $\mathbf{D}$ on the left-hand side because the two are equal in the vacuum outside the crystal.

To characterise the intensity of X-ray diffraction we use an effective cross-section σ, defined as the ratio of the intensity diffracted into a solid angle $\mathrm{d}o'$ to the energy flux density in the incident wave. By (97.8) we have

$$\mathrm{d}\sigma = \left(\frac{e^2}{mc^2}\right)^2 \sin^2\theta \left|\int n\exp(-i\mathbf{q}\cdot\mathbf{r})\,\mathrm{d}V\right|^2 \mathrm{d}o', \tag{97.9}$$

where θ is the angle between $\mathbf{E}_0$ and $\mathbf{k}'$. If the incident radiation is "natural" (not polarised), the factor $\sin^2\theta$ in this formula becomes $\frac{1}{2}(1+\cos^2\vartheta)$, where ϑ is the angle between $\mathbf{k}$ and $\mathbf{k}'$ (see the second footnote to §72):

$$\mathrm{d}\sigma = \frac{1}{2}\left(\frac{e^2}{mc^2}\right)^2 (1+\cos^2\vartheta)\left|\int n\exp(-i\mathbf{q}\cdot\mathbf{r})\,\mathrm{d}V\right|^2 \mathrm{d}o'. \tag{97.10}$$

In what follows we shall, for definiteness, consider this particular case.

We see that the intensity of radiation diffracted in a given direction is essentially proportional to the squared modulus of the integral

$$\int n\exp(-i\mathbf{q}\cdot\mathbf{r})\,\mathrm{d}V, \tag{97.11}$$

i.e. the Fourier space component (with the appropriate value of $\mathbf{q}$) of the electron density. As $\mathbf{q} \to 0$ this integral becomes simply the electron density $\bar{n}$ averaged over a lattice cell. If n is replaced by $\bar{n}$ in equations (97.3) and (97.4), we obtain the usual macroscopic Maxwell's equations, with dielectric permeability $\epsilon(\omega) = 1-4\pi e^2\bar{n}/m\omega^2$. According to these equations, when X-rays pass through a crystal they are refracted according to the ordinary laws of refraction, with refractive index $\sqrt{\epsilon}$. Thus diffraction through small angles amounts to ordinary refraction, which is of no interest here. In what follows we shall always assume that $\mathbf{q}$ is appreciably different from zero.

The electron density, like any function of position in a crystal lattice, can be expanded as a Fourier series:

$$n = \sum_{\mathbf{b}} n_{\mathbf{b}}\exp(2\pi i\mathbf{b}\cdot\mathbf{r}), \tag{97.12}$$

where the summation is taken over all periods $\mathbf{b}$ of the reciprocal lattice.†

† See *Statistical Physics*, §132, Pergamon Press, London, 1958.

When (97.12) is substituted in (97.11) and the result is integrated over the volume of the crystal, we obtain practically zero except for values of **q** close to some $2\pi\mathbf{b}$. Between these values the intensity is negligible. We can therefore consider each diffraction maximum separately, putting

$$n = n_{\mathbf{b}} \exp(2\pi i \mathbf{b}\cdot\mathbf{r})$$

with the appropriate value of **b**. Substitution in (97.10) gives

$$d\sigma = \frac{1}{2}\left(\frac{e^2}{mc^2}\right)^2 (1+\cos^2\vartheta)|n_{\mathbf{b}}|^2 \times$$
$$\times \left|\int \exp[-i(\mathbf{k}'-\mathbf{k}-2\pi\mathbf{b})\cdot\mathbf{r}]\,dV\right|^2 do'. \qquad (97.13)$$

The strongest maxima occur in directions for which the equation

$$\mathbf{k}'-\mathbf{k} = 2\pi\mathbf{b} \qquad (97.14)$$

(*Laue's equation*) is exactly satisfied, and are called *principal maxima*. For given **b**, however, a principal maximum does not occur for an arbitrary direction and frequency of the incident radiation. If the equation (97.14) is written as $\mathbf{k}' = \mathbf{k}+2\pi\mathbf{b}$ and squared, and we use the fact that $k^2 = k'^2$, we have

$$\mathbf{b}\cdot\mathbf{k} = -\pi b^2. \qquad (97.15)$$

This equation determines the values of the wave vector **k** for which principal maxima occur with the given value of **b**. Geometrically, equation (97.15) represents a plane in **k**-space perpendicular to the vector **b** at a distance πb from the origin. In particular, we see that $k \geqslant \pi b$.

Since $|\mathbf{k}'-\mathbf{k}| = 2k \sin \frac{1}{2}\vartheta$, it follows from (97.14) that

$$k \sin \tfrac{1}{2}\vartheta = \pi b \qquad (97.16)$$

(*Bragg and Vul'f's equation*), which determines the angle of diffraction at the principal maximum.

Any vector **b** of the reciprocal lattice determines a family of crystal planes represented by the equations $\mathbf{r}\cdot\mathbf{b}$ = constant integer. These planes are perpendicular to **b**, and the vectors **k** and **k**$'$ corresponding to the condition (97.14) make equal angles of incidence and reflection with the planes (Fig. 45). For this reason, diffraction at a principal maximum is sometimes spoken of as "reflection" from the corresponding crystal planes.

The total intensity of the diffraction "spot" near a maximum is obtained by integrating (97.13) over a solid angle about the direction of **k**$'$. Let us determine the intensity near a principal maximum. We denote by $\mathbf{k}'_0$ the value of **k**$'$ corresponding to Laue's equation for a given $\mathbf{k}$: $\mathbf{k}'_0 = \mathbf{k}+2\pi\mathbf{b}$, and put also $\boldsymbol{\varkappa} = \mathbf{k}'-\mathbf{k}'_0$. Near the maximum, $\boldsymbol{\varkappa}$ is small; since **k**$'$ and $\mathbf{k}'_0$

differ only in direction, $\boldsymbol{\varkappa}$ is perpendicular to $\mathbf{k}'_0$. The solid angle element can therefore be written

$$do' = d\kappa_x \, d\kappa_y / k'^2 = d\kappa_x \, d\kappa_y / k^2, \tag{97.17}$$

where the z-axis is taken in the direction of $\mathbf{k}'_0$. Thus

$$\sigma = \frac{1}{2k^2}\left(\frac{e^2}{mc^2}\right)^2 (1 + \cos^2 \vartheta)|n_{\mathbf{b}}|^2 \int\int d\kappa_x \, d\kappa_y \left|\int \exp(-i\boldsymbol{\varkappa}\cdot\mathbf{r}) \, dV\right|^2.$$

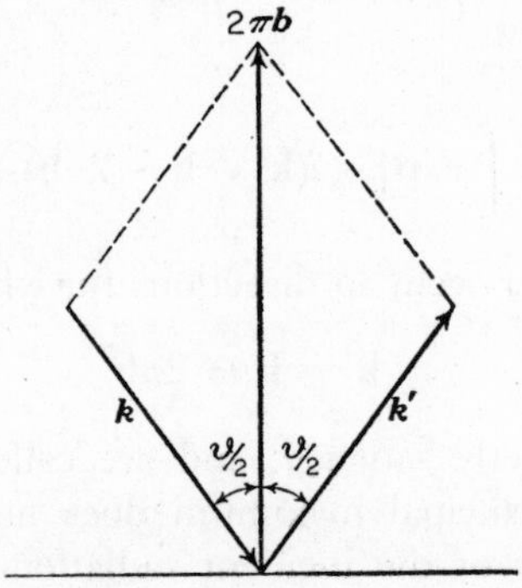

FIG. 45

In the volume integral we can effect the integration with respect to z, since $\exp(-i\boldsymbol{\varkappa}\cdot\mathbf{r})$ is independent of z: $\int \exp(-i\boldsymbol{\varkappa}\cdot\mathbf{r}) \, dV = \int Z \exp(-i\boldsymbol{\varkappa}\cdot\mathbf{r}) \, df$, where $df = dx \, dy$ and $Z = Z(x, y)$ is the length of the body in the direction of $\mathbf{k}'_0$. Finally, using a well-known formula in the theory of Fourier integrals:

$$\int |\phi_\kappa|^2 \, d\kappa_x \, d\kappa_y = \frac{1}{(2\pi)^2} \int \phi^2 \, dx \, dy, \tag{97.18}$$

where

$$\phi_\kappa = \frac{1}{(2\pi)^2} \int \phi(x, y) \exp(-i\boldsymbol{\varkappa}\cdot\mathbf{r}) \, dx \, dy$$

are the two-dimensional Fourier components, we obtain

$$\sigma = \frac{2\pi^2}{k^2}\left(\frac{e^2}{mc^2}\right)^2 (1 + \cos^2 \vartheta)|n_{\mathbf{b}}|^2 \int Z^2 \, df$$

$$= \frac{2}{b^2}\left(\frac{e^2}{mc^2}\right)^2 \sin^2 \tfrac{1}{2}\vartheta (1 + \cos^2 \vartheta)|n_{\mathbf{b}}|^2 \int Z^2 \, df. \tag{97.19}$$

The integral is of the order of L^4, where L is the linear dimension of the body. Thus the total effective cross-section, and therefore the total intensity of the spot, are proportional to $V^{4/3}$, where V is the volume of the body. The maximum intensity, however, follows a different law. For $\mathbf{k}' - \mathbf{k} = 2\pi\mathbf{b}$, the integral in (97.13) is just V, and so $d\sigma$ is proportional to V^2:

$$\left(\frac{d\sigma}{do'}\right)_{\max} = \frac{1}{2}\left(\frac{e^2}{mc^2}\right)^2 (1+\cos^2\vartheta)|n_{\mathbf{b}}|^2 V^2. \qquad (97.20)$$

The sharpness of the maximum is shown by the fact that the maximum intensity is proportional to a higher power of V than the total intensity. The "width" of the peak is evidently proportional to $V^{4/3}/V^2 = V^{-2/3}$.

The theory given above is valid only if the diffraction effect is small. We now see that this requirement imposes a certain condition on the dimension of the crystal: σ must be small compared with the geometrical cross-section of the body ($\sim L^2$), whence

$$\frac{e^2}{mc^2}\frac{L}{k}|n_{\mathbf{b}}| \ll 1. \qquad (97.21)$$

PROBLEMS

PROBLEM 1. Determine the intensity distribution in the diffraction spot round a principal maximum in diffraction by a crystal in the form of a cuboid of sides L_x, L_y, L_z.

SOLUTION. As above, we use the vector $\boldsymbol{\kappa} = \mathbf{k}'-\mathbf{k}'_0$, and take the axes of co-ordinates parallel to the sides of the cuboid, with the origin at its centre.

The integral $\int\exp(-i\boldsymbol{\kappa}\cdot\mathbf{r})\,dV$ becomes a product of three integrals of the form

$$\int_{-\frac{1}{2}L_x}^{\frac{1}{2}L_x} \exp(-i\kappa_x x)\,dx = \frac{2}{\kappa_x}\sin\tfrac{1}{2}\kappa_x L_x.$$

Thus

$$d\sigma = 32\left(\frac{e^2}{mc^2}\right)^2(1+\cos^2\vartheta)|n_{\mathbf{b}}|^2\frac{1}{\kappa_x^2\kappa_y^2\kappa_z^2}\sin^2\tfrac{1}{2}\kappa_x L_x\sin^2\tfrac{1}{2}\kappa_y L_y\sin^2\tfrac{1}{2}\kappa_z L_z\,do'.$$

The components of the vector $\boldsymbol{\kappa}$ are not independent, being related by the condition $\boldsymbol{\kappa}\cdot\mathbf{k}'_0 = 0$.

PROBLEM 2. The same as Problem 1, but for diffraction by a spherical crystal of radius a.

SOLUTION. We again put $\boldsymbol{\kappa} = \mathbf{k}'-\mathbf{k}'_0$, and take the z-axis in the direction of $\boldsymbol{\kappa}$, with the origin at the centre of the sphere. Then

$$\int \exp(-i\kappa z)\,dV = \int_{-a}^{a}\pi(a^2-z^2)\exp(-i\kappa z)\,dz$$

$$= \frac{4\pi}{\kappa^3}(\sin\kappa a-\kappa a\cos\kappa a).$$

Thus

$$d\sigma = 8\pi^2\left(\frac{e^2}{mc^2}\right)^2(1+\cos^2\vartheta)|n_{\mathbf{b}}|^2\frac{1}{\kappa^6}(\sin\kappa a-\kappa a\cos\kappa a)^2\,do'.$$

PROBLEM 3. Determine the total intensity of the diffraction spot round a subsidiary maximum.

SOLUTION. In this case the wave vector $\mathbf{k}$ of the incident wave does not satisfy the condition (97.15). As shown above (97.15) is the equation of a plane perpendicular to the vector $\mathbf{b}$. Let the small displacement of the terminus of the vector $\mathbf{k}$ from this plane be $\eta\mathbf{b}$, where $\eta \ll 1$. That is, we put $\mathbf{k} = \mathbf{k}_0+\eta\mathbf{b}$, where $\mathbf{k}_0$ satisfies equation (97.15) (Fig. 46).

The maximum intensity in the spot occurs for a direction of $\mathbf{k}'$ for which the difference $\mathbf{k}'-(\mathbf{k}+2\pi\mathbf{b})$ has its least magnitude (so that the integral in (97.13) has its maximum value). The magnitude of the difference of two vectors, one of which is arbitrary in direction, has its least value when they are parallel. Hence, since $k' = k$, we have

$$|\mathbf{k}'-\mathbf{k}-2\pi\mathbf{b}|_{\min} = k-|\mathbf{k}+2\pi\mathbf{b}| = \frac{k^2-(\mathbf{k}+2\pi\mathbf{b})^2}{k+|\mathbf{k}+2\pi\mathbf{b}|}.$$

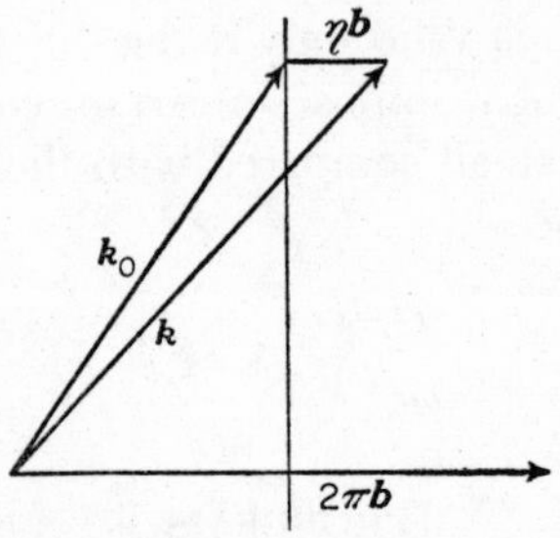

FIG. 46

Since $\mathbf{k}$ is close to $\mathbf{k}_0$ and we are considering the region near the maximum, $\mathbf{k}' \cong \mathbf{k}+2\pi\mathbf{b}$ and the denominator can be replaced by $2k$. In the numerator, we expand the squared parenthesis and obtain

$$-2\mathbf{k}\cdot 2\pi\mathbf{b}-(2\pi\mathbf{b})^2 = [-2\mathbf{k}_0\cdot 2\pi\mathbf{b}-(2\pi\mathbf{b})^2]-2\eta\mathbf{b}\cdot 2\pi\mathbf{b} = -4\pi\eta b^2.$$

Thus $|\mathbf{k}'-\mathbf{k}-2\pi\mathbf{b}|_{\min} \cong -2\pi\eta b^2/k$.

Next, we put

$$\mathbf{k}' = (\mathbf{k}+2\pi\mathbf{b})\left(1-\frac{2\pi\eta b^2}{k}\right)+\boldsymbol{\varkappa},$$

and take the z-axis in the direction of $\mathbf{k}+2\pi\mathbf{b}$. This reduces the problem to the calculation of the integral (cf. the derivation of formula (97.19))

$$\int\int \mathrm{d}\kappa_x\, \mathrm{d}\kappa_y \left|\int \exp\{2\pi i\eta b^2/k-z-i\boldsymbol{\varkappa}\cdot\mathbf{r}\}\, \mathrm{d}V\right|^2 = \int\int \mathrm{d}\kappa_x\, \mathrm{d}\kappa_y \left|\int \exp(-i\boldsymbol{\varkappa}\cdot\mathbf{r})\frac{\sin(\pi\eta b^2 Z/k)}{\pi\eta b^2/k}\, \mathrm{d}f\right|^2.$$

Finally, using formula (97.18), we obtain

$$\sigma = \frac{2\pi^2}{k^2}\left(\frac{e^2}{mc^2}\right)^2(1+\cos^2\vartheta)|n_{\mathbf{b}}|^2 \int \frac{\sin^2(\pi\eta b^2 Z/k)}{(\pi\eta b^2/k)^2}\,\mathrm{d}f.$$

As $\eta \to 0$ this formula becomes (97.19). If $\pi\eta b^2 Z/k \gg 1$ (which is compatible with $\eta \ll 1$), the squared sine can be replaced by its mean value $\frac{1}{2}$, and we have

$$\sigma = \left(\frac{e^2}{mc^2}\right)^2 \frac{1+\cos^2\vartheta}{\eta^2 b^4}|n_{\mathbf{b}}|^2 S,$$

where S is the area of the "shadow", i.e. the projection of the body on the xy-plane.

§98. The integral intensity

The formulae derived in §97 give the diffracted intensity when a plane wave of a single frequency is incident on a crystal. Let us now consider some cases where these conditions are not fulfilled.

First, let the incident wave be plane but not of a single frequency,† its spectral resolution including waves with wave vectors $\mathbf{k}$ whose directions are the same but whose magnitudes $k = \omega/c$ are not. Let $\rho(k)$ be the frequency distribution of the incident radiation intensity, normalised by the condition $\int \rho(k)\, dk = 1$.

The total intensity of the diffraction spot is determined by the effective cross-section, which is obtained by multiplying the expression (97.13) by $\rho(k)$ and integrating with respect to o' and k:

$$\sigma = \frac{1}{2}\left(\frac{e^2}{mc^2}\right)^2 |n_{\mathbf{b}}|^2 \int \int \left| \int \exp[-i(\mathbf{k}' - \mathbf{k} - 2\pi\mathbf{b})\cdot\mathbf{r}]\, dV \right|^2 \times$$
$$\times (1 + \cos^2 \vartheta)\rho(k)\, do'\, dk. \qquad (98.1)$$

We put temporarily $\mathbf{K} = \mathbf{k}' - \mathbf{k} - 2\pi\mathbf{b}$ and write the squared modulus as a double integral:

$$|\int \exp(-i\mathbf{K}\cdot\mathbf{r})\, dV|^2 = \int \int \exp[i\mathbf{K}\cdot(\mathbf{r}_2 - \mathbf{r}_1)]\, dV_1\, dV_2.$$

Using instead of $\mathbf{r}_1$ and $\mathbf{r}_2$ the variables $\frac{1}{2}(\mathbf{r}_1 + \mathbf{r}_2)$ and $\mathbf{r} = \mathbf{r}_2 - \mathbf{r}_1$ and integrating with respect to the first gives $|\int \exp(i\mathbf{K}\cdot\mathbf{r})\, dV|^2 = V \int \exp(i\mathbf{K}\cdot\mathbf{r})\, dV$. In the remaining integral we can effect the integration over all space,‡ and the result is

$$|\int \exp(i\mathbf{K}\cdot\mathbf{r})\, dV|^2 = (2\pi)^3 V \delta(\mathbf{K}). \qquad (98.2)$$

Substituting this result in (98.1), we obtain

$$\sigma = 4\pi^3 \left(\frac{e^2}{mc^2}\right)^2 |n_{\mathbf{b}}|^2 V(1 + \cos^2 \vartheta_0) \times$$
$$\times \int \int \delta(\mathbf{k}' - \mathbf{k} - 2\pi\mathbf{b})\rho(k)\, do'\, dk; \qquad (98.3)$$

on account of the presence of the delta function, the factor $1 + \cos^2 \vartheta$ in the integrand can be replaced by its value at $\vartheta = \vartheta_0$, where ϑ_0 is the angle between the $\mathbf{k}$ and $\mathbf{k}'$ which satisfy Laue's condition (denoted by $\mathbf{k}_0$ and $\mathbf{k}'_0 = \mathbf{k}_0 + 2\pi\mathbf{b}$).

The integration with respect to o' can be carried out by noticing that it is equivalent to an integration with respect to

$$d\mathbf{k}' = k'^2\, dk'\, do' = \tfrac{1}{2} k'\, d(k'^2)\, do',$$

† Corresponding to *Laue's method* in the X-ray analysis of crystals.

‡ This is possible because we require only the total intensity of the diffraction spot, and not its width.

if an additional factor $(2/k)\delta(k'^2-k^2)$ is included in the integrand. Thus the integral in (98.3) becomes

$$\int\int \frac{2}{k}\delta(\mathbf{k}'-\mathbf{k}-2\pi\mathbf{b})\delta(k'^2-k^2)\rho(k)\,d\mathbf{k}'\,dk.$$

Effecting the integration with respect to $\mathbf{k}'$ by means of the first delta function, we can replace k'^2 by $(\mathbf{k}+2\pi\mathbf{b})^2$ in the second delta function, and the result is

$$\int \frac{2}{k}\delta(4\pi^2b^2+4\pi\mathbf{b}\cdot\mathbf{k})\rho(k)\,dk = \int \frac{1}{2\pi k}\delta(\mathbf{b}\cdot\mathbf{k}+\pi b^2)\rho(k)\,dk,$$

so that

$$\sigma = 2\pi^2\left(\frac{e^2}{mc^2}\right)^2|n_{\mathbf{b}}|^2V(1+\cos^2\vartheta_0)\int\frac{1}{k}\delta(\mathbf{b}\cdot\mathbf{k}+\pi b^2)\rho(k)\,dk. \tag{98.4}$$

Finally, we have to carry out the integration over k (the direction $\mathbf{n}=\mathbf{k}/k$ being given). The argument of the delta function is zero for $k=k_0$, and the integral is $\rho(k_0)/k_0|\mathbf{b}\cdot\mathbf{n}| = \rho(k_0)/|\mathbf{b}\cdot\mathbf{k}_0| = \rho(k_0)/\pi b^2$. Thus

$$\sigma = 2\pi\left(\frac{e^2}{mc^2}\right)^2|n_{\mathbf{b}}|^2V(1+\cos^2\vartheta_0)\rho(k_0)/b^2. \tag{98.5}$$

Let us now consider another case, where the incident wave is of a single frequency but its components have varying directions of $\mathbf{k}$ which differ by rotation about some axis;† let $\mathbf{l}$ be a unit vector along that axis, and ψ the angle of rotation about it. Let $\rho(\psi)$ be the angular distribution of the incident radiation intensity, normalised by the condition

$$\int_0^{2\pi}\rho(\psi)\,d\psi = 1.$$

The calculations leading to formula (98.4) are valid in this case also, except that the integration with $\rho(k)\,dk$ must be replaced by one with $\rho(\psi)\,d\psi$:

$$\sigma = 2\pi^2\left(\frac{e^2}{mc^2}\right)^2|n_{\mathbf{b}}|^2V(1+\cos^2\vartheta_0)\int\frac{1}{k}\delta(\mathbf{b}\cdot\mathbf{k}+\pi b^2)\rho(\psi)\,d\psi. \tag{98.6}$$

We again denote by $\mathbf{k}_0$ the value of $\mathbf{k}$ for which the argument of the delta function is zero, and measure ψ from the plane of $\mathbf{l}$ and $\mathbf{k}_0$. For small ψ, $\mathbf{k}=\mathbf{k}_0+(\mathbf{l}\times\mathbf{k}_0)\psi$. Then the integral in (98.6) becomes

$$\begin{aligned}\int\frac{1}{k}\delta(\mathbf{b}\cdot\mathbf{l}\times\mathbf{k}_0\psi)\rho(\psi)\,d\psi &= \rho(0)/k|\mathbf{b}\cdot\mathbf{l}\times\mathbf{k}_0|\\ &= \rho(0)/k^2|\mathbf{b}\cdot\mathbf{l}\times\mathbf{n}_0|\\ &= \rho(0)\sin^2(\tfrac{1}{2}\vartheta_0)/\pi^2b^2|\mathbf{b}\cdot\mathbf{l}\times\mathbf{n}_0|.\end{aligned}$$

† Corresponding to *Bragg's method* (the *rotation method*) in X-ray analysis. The rotation referred to is that of the crystal about $\mathbf{l}$, not that of the direction of $\mathbf{k}$.

Thus

$$\sigma = \frac{2}{b^2}\left(\frac{e^2}{mc^2}\right)^2 \sin^2\tfrac{1}{2}\vartheta_0(1+\cos^2\vartheta_0)|n_{\mathbf{b}}|^2 V \frac{\rho(0)}{|\mathbf{b}\cdot\mathbf{l}\times\mathbf{n}_0|}. \tag{98.7}$$

Finally, let us consider the diffraction of a plane wave, of a single frequency, from a body consisting of crystallites arranged at random.†

Let $\mathbf{k}'_0$ and $\mathbf{b}_0$ be values of $\mathbf{k}'$ and $\mathbf{b}$ such that Laue's condition $\mathbf{k}'_0 = \mathbf{k}+2\pi\mathbf{b}_0$ is satisfied. The directions of $\mathbf{k}'_0$ and $\mathbf{b}_0$ are not uniquely determined, since Laue's condition is, of course, still fulfilled when the triangle $\mathbf{k}$, $2\pi\mathbf{b}_0$, $\mathbf{k}'_0$ is rotated about the direction of $\mathbf{k}$. Thus the principal maximum corresponds to directions of $\mathbf{k}'$ occupying a conical surface of vertical angle $2\vartheta_0$. Instead of a diffraction "spot" we now have a "ring".

The required total effective cross-section is determined by a formula which differs from (98.4) only in that the integration with $\rho(k)\,dk$ is replaced by an averaging over the directions of $\mathbf{b}$:

$$\sigma = 2\pi^2 V\left(\frac{e^2}{mc^2}\right)^2 |n_{\mathbf{b}}|^2(1+\cos^2\vartheta_0) \int \frac{1}{k}\delta(\mathbf{b}\cdot\mathbf{k}+\pi b^2)\frac{do_{\mathbf{b}}}{4\pi}, \tag{98.8}$$

where $do_{\mathbf{b}}$ is an element of solid angle about the direction of $\mathbf{b}$. Denoting by α the angle between $\mathbf{k}$ and $\mathbf{b}$, we can write the integral in (98.8) as

$$\int \frac{1}{k}\delta(bk\cos\alpha+\pi b^2)\frac{2\pi d\cos\alpha}{4\pi} = \frac{1}{2bk^2} = \frac{1}{2b^3\pi^2}\sin^2\tfrac{1}{2}\vartheta_0.$$

Each of the three cases considered in this section corresponds to a particular method of averaging the diffraction pattern. The dependence of the total averaged diffraction intensity on the volume of the body reduces, as we should expect, to a simple proportionality. In the pattern which is not averaged, the intensity and its distribution over the spot depend more markedly on the volume.

§99. Diffuse thermal scattering of X-rays

In §§97 and 98 we have taken $n(x, y, z)$ to be the time average electron density in the crystal: various density oscillations were thereby excluded, and consequently so was the corresponding (non-coherent) scattering of X-rays. One cause of non-coherent scattering is the thermal fluctuations of density. This scattering is "diffusely" distributed in all directions, but it is characterised by a relatively high intensity near directions corresponding to the sharp lines of the "structural" scattering described in the preceding sections. Here we shall discuss these maxima of the thermal scattering (W. H. Zachariasen, 1940).

The thermal oscillations of the crystal lattice can be represented as combinations of "sound" waves. As we shall see, the maxima of the thermal scattering arise from wavelengths large compared with the lattice constant.

† Corresponding to *Debye and Scherrer's method* (the *powder method*) in X-ray analysis.

The change in the electron density due to such a wave can be regarded, at any point, as due to a simple displacement of the lattice by an amount equal to the local value of the displacement vector $\mathbf{u}$ in the wave. Thus the change in the density (*not* averaged with respect to time) when a given sound wave passes can be expressed in terms of the mean density by

$$\delta n = n(\mathbf{r}-\mathbf{u})-n(\mathbf{r}) \cong -\mathbf{u}\cdot\partial n/\partial\mathbf{r}.$$

In considering diffuse scattering near a given line, we must replace n by $n_{\mathbf{b}}\exp(2\pi i\mathbf{b}\cdot\mathbf{r})$ with the appropriate $\mathbf{b}$, so that

$$\delta n = -2\pi i\mathbf{b}\cdot\mathbf{u}n_{\mathbf{b}}\exp(2\pi i\mathbf{b}\cdot\mathbf{r}). \tag{99.1}$$

The scattering by density fluctuations is, of course, not coherent with that by the mean density, and the two therefore do not interfere. Hence the effective cross-section for diffuse scattering can be obtained from (97.10), substituting δn for n and then carrying out the statistical averaging over fluctuations:

$$d\sigma = 2\pi^2\left(\frac{e^2}{mc^2}\right)^2|n_{\mathbf{b}}|^2(1+\cos^2\vartheta)\times$$

$$\times\overline{\left|\int \mathbf{b}\cdot\mathbf{u}\exp(-i\mathbf{K}\cdot\mathbf{r})dV\right|^2}\,do', \tag{99.2}$$

where $\mathbf{K} = \mathbf{k}'-\mathbf{k}-2\pi\mathbf{b}$. The scattered intensity is large for directions where $K \ll 2\pi b$.

The integral $\int \mathbf{u}\exp(-i\mathbf{K}\cdot\mathbf{r})\,dV$ gives the Fourier space component of $\mathbf{u}$ whose wave vector is $\mathbf{K}$, and we can therefore take $\mathbf{u}$ to be simply the displacement vector in a sound wave having this wave vector. The inequality $K \ll 2\pi b$ therefore implies that the wavelength of the scattering sound wave is large compared with the dimension of the crystal lattice cell.

Thus we can put

$$\mathbf{u} = \tfrac{1}{2}[\mathbf{u}_0\exp(i\mathbf{K}\cdot\mathbf{r})+\mathbf{u}_0^*\exp(-i\mathbf{K}\cdot\mathbf{r})], \tag{99.3}$$

so that $\int(\mathbf{b}\cdot\mathbf{u})\exp(-i\mathbf{K}\cdot\mathbf{r})\,dV = \frac{1}{2}V\mathbf{b}\cdot\mathbf{u}_0$ and the effective cross-section is

$$d\sigma = \frac{\pi^2}{2}\left(\frac{e^2}{mc^2}\right)^2|n_{\mathbf{b}}|^2(1+\cos^2\vartheta)b_ib_k\overline{u_{0i}u_{0k}}V^2\,do'. \tag{99.4}$$

The products of the components of $\mathbf{u}_0$ are averaged as in §96 for a sound wave in an isotropic medium. The elastic energy per unit volume of a deformed crystal is $\frac{1}{2}\lambda_{iklm}u_{ik}u_{lm}$, where u_{ik} is the strain tensor and λ_{iklm} the elastic modulus tensor.† Hence the mean elastic energy of the whole crystal is $\frac{1}{2}V\lambda_{iklm}\overline{u_{ik}u_{lm}}$. We substitute

$$u_{ik} = \frac{1}{2}\left(\frac{\partial u_i}{\partial x_k}+\frac{\partial u_k}{\partial x_i}\right)$$
$$= \tfrac{1}{2}\mathrm{re}\{(iK_ku_{0i}+iK_iu_{0k})\exp(i\mathbf{K}\cdot\mathbf{r})\}.$$

† See *Theory of Elasticity*, §10, Pergamon Press, London, 1959.

The terms containing $\exp(\pm 2i\mathbf{K}\cdot\mathbf{r})$ give zero on averaging. Using also the symmetry of the tensor λ_{iklm} with respect to interchange of i, k, or l, m, or i, k and l, m, we obtain $\frac{1}{4}V\lambda_{iklm}K_kK_m\overline{u_{0i}u_{0l}^*}$ or $\frac{1}{4}Vg_{ik}\overline{u_{0i}u_{0k}^*}$, where

$$g_{ik} = \lambda_{ilkm}K_lK_m. \tag{99.5}$$

According to the general theory of thermodynamic fluctuations, we can at once write down the required mean values:†

$$\overline{u_{0i}u_{0k}^*} = (4T/V)g^{-1}{}_{ik}, \tag{99.6}$$

where $g^{-1}{}_{ik}$ is the tensor inverse to g_{ik}, and the effective scattering cross-section is

$$d\sigma = 2\pi^2\left(\frac{e^2}{mc^2}\right)^2 TV|n_{\mathbf{b}}|^2(1+\cos^2\vartheta)b_ib_kg^{-1}{}_{ik}\,do'. \tag{99.7}$$

Thus the diffusely scattered intensity is, as we should expect, proportional to the volume of the crystal. A characteristic feature of this scattering is the way in which its intensity is distributed over the area of the spot. Apart from the factor $1+\cos^2\vartheta$, which is almost constant for a given spot, the intensity is given by the expression $g^{-1}{}_{ik}b_ib_k$. This expression is the product of $1/K^2$ and a fairly involved function of the direction of the vector $\mathbf{K}$ with respect to the crystal axes. For scattering near a principal maximum the diffusely scattered intensity is itself a maximum where $\mathbf{K} = 0$ (the expression (99.7) becomes infinite for $\mathbf{K} = 0$ and is, of course, invalid). If the condition (97.15) $\mathbf{b}\cdot\mathbf{k} = -\pi b^2$ is not satisfied, however, $\mathbf{K}$ cannot be zero, and the maximum of the diffusely scattered intensity lies at some $\mathbf{K}$ different from zero, which in general does not coincide with the maximum of the structural scattering. In either case the diffuse scattering forms a background whose intensity falls off essentially as $1/K^2$, that is, considerably more slowly than the intensity in the sharp structural-scattering line superposed upon it.

† See *Statistical Physics*, §110. If the probability distribution for fluctuating quantities $x_1, x_2, \ldots$ is of the form $\exp(-\frac{1}{2}\lambda_{ik}x_ix_k)$, then $\overline{x_ix_k} = \lambda^{-1}{}_{ik}$. A factor 2 in (99.6) appears because each of the complex u_{0i} involves two independent quantities.

APPENDIX

CURVILINEAR CO-ORDINATES

WE give below, for reference, certain formulae relating to vector operations in curvilinear co-ordinates, both general and particular.

In an arbitrary system of orthogonal curvilinear co-ordinates u_1, u_2, u_3, the squared element of length is $dl^2 = h_1^2\,du_1^2 + h_2^2\,du_2^2 + h_3^2\,du_3^2$, where the h_i are functions of the co-ordinates. The element of volume is

$$dV = h_1 h_2 h_3\,du_1\,du_2\,du_3.$$

The various vector operations can be expressed in terms of the functions h_i as follows. For vector operations on a scalar:

$$(\mathbf{grad}\,f)_i = \frac{1}{h_i}\frac{\partial f}{\partial u_i},$$

$$\triangle f = \frac{1}{h_1 h_2 h_3}\sum \frac{\partial}{\partial u_1}\left(\frac{h_2 h_3}{h_1}\frac{\partial f}{\partial u_1}\right),$$

where the summation is over cyclic interchanges of the suffixes 1, 2, 3. For vector operations on a vector:

$$\operatorname{div}\mathbf{A} = \frac{1}{h_1 h_2 h_3}\sum \frac{\partial}{\partial u_1}(h_2 h_3 A_1),$$

$$(\mathbf{curl}\,\mathbf{A})_1 = \frac{1}{h_2 h_3}\left[\frac{\partial}{\partial u_2}(h_3 A_3) - \frac{\partial}{\partial u_3}(h_2 A_2)\right].$$

The remaining components of **curl A** are obtained by cyclic interchanges of the suffixes.

Cylindrical co-ordinates r, ϕ, z.

Element of length: $dl^2 = dr^2 + r^2\,d\phi^2 + dz^2$;

$$h_r = 1, \qquad h_\phi = r, \qquad h_z = 1.$$

Vector operations:

$$\triangle f = \frac{1}{r}\frac{\partial}{\partial r}\left(r\frac{\partial f}{\partial r}\right) + \frac{1}{r^2}\frac{\partial^2 f}{\partial \phi^2} + \frac{\partial^2 f}{\partial z^2},$$

$$\operatorname{div}\mathbf{A} = \frac{1}{r}\frac{\partial}{\partial r}(rA_r) + \frac{1}{r}\frac{\partial A_\phi}{\partial \phi} + \frac{\partial A_z}{\partial z},$$

$$(\mathbf{curl\,A})_r = \frac{1}{r}\frac{\partial A_z}{\partial \phi} - \frac{\partial A_\phi}{\partial z},$$

$$(\mathbf{curl\,A})_\phi = \frac{\partial A_r}{\partial z} - \frac{\partial A_z}{\partial r},$$

$$(\mathbf{curl\,A})_z = \frac{1}{r}\frac{\partial}{\partial r}(rA_\phi) - \frac{1}{r}\frac{\partial A_r}{\partial \phi},$$

$$(\triangle\mathbf{A})_r = \triangle A_r - \frac{A_r}{r^2} - \frac{2}{r^2}\frac{\partial A_\phi}{\partial \phi},$$

$$(\triangle\mathbf{A})_\phi = \triangle A_\phi - \frac{A_\phi}{r^2} + \frac{2}{r^2}\frac{\partial A_r}{\partial \phi},$$

$$(\triangle\mathbf{A})_z = \triangle A_z.$$

In the expressions for the components of $\triangle\mathbf{A}$, $\triangle A_i$ signifies the result of the operator $\triangle$ acting on A_i regarded as a scalar.

Spherical co-ordinates r, θ, ϕ.

Element of length: $dl^2 = dr^2 + r^2\,d\theta^2 + r^2\sin^2\theta\,d\phi^2$;

$$h_r = 1, \qquad h_\theta = r, \qquad h_\phi = r\sin\theta.$$

Vector operations:

$$\triangle f = \frac{1}{r^2}\frac{\partial}{\partial r}\left(r^2\frac{\partial f}{\partial r}\right) + \frac{1}{r^2\sin\theta}\frac{\partial}{\partial \theta}\left(\sin\theta\frac{\partial f}{\partial \theta}\right) + \frac{1}{r^2\sin^2\theta}\frac{\partial^2 f}{\partial \phi^2},$$

$$\operatorname{div}\mathbf{A} = \frac{1}{r^2}\frac{\partial}{\partial r}(r^2A_r) + \frac{1}{r\sin\theta}\frac{\partial}{\partial \theta}(A_\theta\sin\theta) + \frac{1}{r\sin\theta}\frac{\partial A_\phi}{\partial \phi}$$

$$(\mathbf{curl\,A})_r = \frac{1}{r\sin\theta}\left[\frac{\partial}{\partial \theta}(A_\phi\sin\theta) - \frac{\partial A_\theta}{\partial \phi}\right],$$

$$(\mathbf{curl\,A})_\theta = \frac{1}{r\sin\theta}\frac{\partial A_r}{\partial \phi} - \frac{1}{r}\frac{\partial}{\partial r}(rA_\phi),$$

$$(\mathbf{curl\,A})_\phi = \frac{1}{r}\left[\frac{\partial}{\partial r}(rA_\theta) - \frac{\partial A_r}{\partial \theta}\right],$$

$$(\triangle\mathbf{A})_r = \triangle A_r - \frac{2}{r^2}\left[A_r + \frac{1}{\sin\theta}\frac{\partial}{\partial \theta}(A_\theta\sin\theta) + \frac{1}{\sin\theta}\frac{\partial A_\phi}{\partial \phi}\right],$$

$$(\triangle\mathbf{A})_\theta = \triangle A_\theta + \frac{2}{r^2}\left[\frac{\partial A_r}{\partial \theta} - \frac{A_\theta}{2\sin^2\theta} - \frac{\cos\theta}{\sin^2\theta}\frac{\partial A_\phi}{\partial \phi}\right],$$

$$(\triangle\mathbf{A})_\phi = \triangle A_\phi + \frac{2}{r^2\sin\theta}\left[\frac{\partial A_r}{\partial \phi} + \cot\theta\frac{\partial A_\theta}{\partial \phi} - \frac{A_\phi}{2\sin\theta}\right].$$

INDEX